The Nature of the Cairngorms

Diversity in a changing environment

Edited by Philip Shaw and Des B.A. Thompson

Assisted by David Bale, Eleanor Charman, Keith Duncan, Murray Ferguson, Debbie Greene, Jo Newman, Andy Rockall, Neale Taylor and Kirsten Thompson

SCOTTISH
NATURAL
HERITAGE

Front cover image: Abernethy Forest at dawn in mid-summer. Abernethy is remarkably rich in the many rare and threatened species for which the Cairngorms are nationally and internationally important.
Photo: *N. Benvie*

Back cover images: Loch Gamhna and Loch an Eilein, Strathspey.
Photo: *L. Gill*

Natural regeneration of native pinewoods should benefit the many forest species for which the Cairngorms are nationally important.
Photo: *N. Benvie*

The Cairngorms hold a substantial proportion of Britain's Dotterel population.
Photo: *L. Campbell*

First published in the UK in 2006 by The Stationery Office Limited,
71 Lothian Road, Edinburgh, EH3 9AZ

© Scottish Natural Heritage, 2006
Reprinted 2006

Applications for reproduction should be made to Scottish Natural Heritage
www.snh.gov.uk

A copy of the British Library Cataloguing in Publication Data is available on request from the British Library

The maps contained in this book are based upon Ordnance Survey material with the permission of Ordnance Survey on behalf of the Controller of Her Majesty's Stationery Office © Crown copyright 2005. Any unauthorised reproduction infringes Crown copyright and may lead to prosecution or civil proceedings. © Scottish Natural Heritage 100017908 (2005).

ISBN 0 114 97326 1
Printed in the UK

This book was printed in the UK on fineblade smooth, a paper made from wood fibre supplied from pulp mills using wood from managed plantations where the trees are regularly harvested and replanted.

Editorial note
Website addresses cited in chapters have been checked. However, as a matter of principle such addresses are given for information only, and are not viewed as formal sources of published information. Many chapters have cross-references to other chapters in the book, and are not cited in the References.

'Each chapter of The Nature of the Cairngorms has been written by an expert... the whole is topped and tailed by a well-written introduction and a fascinating account of 'patterns of species diversity' by the editors...Top marks to them for bringing it all together in an accessible form.'
Peter Marren in *British Wildlife*

'...one of the delights of the book – you can delve deeply or just dip in it...Habitat associations are discussed, the richest areas identified and the importance of continued monitoring of all species found in the Park stressed. I have immensely enjoyed reading this book, knowing that having visited the area, I can then come back to find out more from the book before the next visit.'
Janet Crummy in *Scottish Bird News*

'...a true landmark...beautifully illustrated, elegantly designed.'
Kenny Taylor in *BBC Wildlife*

'This is an outstandingly good book about an exceptional important area...'
Thomas Huxley in *Biological Recording in Scotland Recorder News*

PREFACE

This is a book about a unique part of the world, which is arguably the most important in Britain for nature conservation. Here, there are magnificent native forests, rich expanses of moorland and hill country dissected by glens, and some of Britain's highest mountains, with great corries, plateaux, rivers, Arctic-alpine heaths and fell-fields. The diversity of wildlife and habitats is exceptional, and many people visiting the Cairngorms see for their first time special birds, plants, habitats and landforms. Ask visitors where they saw their first Osprey, Crested Tit, Capercaillie, Reindeer Moss (or indeed Reindeer), Creeping Lady's-tresses or Trailing Azalea, and many will reply "in the Cairngorms". But being in the Cairngorms is about much more than ticking off birds or plants; it is about experiencing a remarkable ecosystem as rich in sights, sounds and scents as in the diversity of its species and features. It is a special area, which acts as a magnet for thousands of skiers and walkers each year. Yet still you can spend a day in the area wandering through a relatively natural, boreal landscape, seeing hardly a soul.

This book draws together the results of more than 20 years of field research and survey in the Cairngorms, much of it by people working for or with Scottish Natural Heritage and its predecessors, the Nature Conservancy Council and the Countryside Commission for Scotland. It builds on a rich legacy of research. Desmond Nethersole-Thompson and Adam Watson (1981) provided the definitive work on the natural history and nature conservation importance of the Cairngorms; their book is a wonderfully readable and comprehensive exposition on the research of naturalists in the area, with especially detailed accounts of the vegetation and bird interests. More recently, Charles Gimingham (2002) edited an important overview of the ecology, land-use and conservation of the area, which highlighted the need for integrated management of the many land-use influences. Several other publications have described the nature conservation importance of the area (e.g. Ratcliffe, 1977; Curry-Lindahl *et al.*, 1982; Conroy *et al.*, 1990; Scottish Natural Heritage, 2002), its recreational opportunities (e.g. Watson, 1992) and the nature of change (Cairngorms Working Party, 1992; Watson, 1992; McConnell & Conroy, 1995; Scottish Natural Heritage, 2002).

In writing this book we have not wished to repeat assessments of the international importance of the Cairngorms (e.g. Ratcliffe, 1977, 1981; Ratcliffe & Thompson, 1988; Thompson *et al.*, 1994) or background geographical and ecological accounts of the area (e.g. Nethersole-Thompson & Watson, 1981; Watson, 1992; Brown & Clapperton, 2002; Davidson *et al.*, 2002; Scottish Natural Heritage, 2002). Instead, our team of writers has sought to describe the nature and recreation opportunities for which the Cairngorms area is so important, and the complex range of factors influencing these. The table overleaf highlights some of the key publications and events concerned with its conservation and management, and advances in our knowledge of the area.

A chronicle of events in relation to the conservation and management of nature in the Cairngorms (with acknowledgement to Nethersole-Thompson & Watson, 1981; Watson, 1992; Scottish Natural Heritage, 2002; Matthew, 2002; and contributors to this book).

Year	Event
1618	Publication of *The Pennyless Pilgrimage of John Taylor, the King's Majesty's Water Poet*, giving one of the earliest descriptions of the Cairngorms.
1654	Publication of Blaeu's *Atlas Novus*, giving maps and descriptions of the Cairngorms.
1750	Evidence of major tree felling in the Cairngorms, though some major clearances happened much earlier
1804	Publication of *Sporting Tour*, giving details of Colonel T. Thornton's 18th century visit to Strath Spey, and making the first published reference to the 'Cairngorms'.
1810	George Don describes many botanical discoveries in the Cairngorms, in *Herbarium Britannicum*.
1811	Earliest scientific description of the Cairngorms by Reverend G.S. Keith in *General View of the Agriculture in Aberdeenshire*.
1831	Publication of the first guidebook to the Cairngorms, *The Guide to the Highlands of Deeside*.
1855	Publication of W.H. MacGillivray's *The Natural History of Dee Side and Braemar*.
1907	Scottish Ski Club founded.
1923	Publication of *The Cairngorms* by the Scottish Mountaineering Club, 6th edition published in 1992.
1925	Publication of *The Cairngorm Hills of Scotland* by Seton Gordon.
1931	The Addison Committee propose the Cairngorms area for National Park status, and call for new measures to protect the countryside.
1943	Start of an on-going population study of Ptarmigan in the Cairngorms, by Adam Watson; longest study of a grouse population in the UK.
1944	Start of an on-going population study of Golden Eagles in Deeside, by Adam Watson; longest study of a raptor population in the UK.
1946	Planners propose that much of the high ground of the Cairngorms should become a National Park.
1947	The Scottish National Parks Committee appointed by Government. The committee confirmed that five areas, including the Cairngorms, should be made a National Park. It listed 51 areas recommended for conservation, including the high ground above 2,500 feet in the central Cairngorms. Four sites were recommended as Nature Conservation Areas: Valley of the Quoich, Muir of Dinnet, Dinnet Oakwood, and Glen Doll and Coire Fee.
1948	Glen More Forest Park created. The high ground was made available to the Cairngorms Winter Sports Development Board for skiing.
1951	Publication of *The Greenshank* by Desmond Nethersole-Thompson, one of the first bird species monographs, based largely on research in the Cairngorms. Later monographs, also based mainly on research in the Cairngorms, include *The Snow Bunting* (1966), *The Dotterel* (1973) and *Pine Crossbills* (1975).
1952	Pony trekking (from Balavil Arms Hotel, Newtonmore) initiated as a pursuit under the auspices of the Scottish Council of Physical Recreation.
1954	Cairngorms National Nature Reserve declared (16,068 ha – the largest NNR in Britain). Most of the reserve was established by Nature Reserve Agreements (the first of its type negotiated by the NC) and private owners of Rothiemurchus, Mar and Inshriach estates; the NC purchased Invereshie (2,157 ha) from the Forestry Commission.
1954	First confirmed breeding of Ospreys in Scotland, in Speyside, having been exterminated by 1917, through human persecution (although pairs may have bred sporadically in Strathspey during the 1930s and 1940s).
1954	Cairngorms Site of Special Scientific Interest designated.
1956	Beginning of a major population study of Red Grouse, led by David Jenkins and Adam Watson, and sponsored by V.C. Wynne-Edwards.
1959	Publication of *The Native Pinewoods of Scotland*, by H.M. Steven and A. Carlisle, describing the old forests of Scotland. The Nature Conservancy completed the first Management Plan for the Cairngorms NNR.
1961	Construction of chairlifts, large car parks, and a café on Cairn Gorm began (the Cairnwell chairlift construction began in 1962; Lecht development started in 1978).
1962	Publication of *The Plant Communities of the Scottish Highlands*, by Donald McVean and Derek Ratcliffe, including important details on the vegetation of the Cairngorms, and building on earlier classic studies by Alex Watt and colleagues.
1963	Publication of *The North-East of Scotland* by the British Association, providing the first general systematic account of rocks, soils, flora and fauna.
1965	On 1 April major series of aerial photographs taken to indicate snow lie, with a view to investigating potential for skiing development.
1966	Adam Watson began his studies of the human impacts of downhill ski developments on soils, vegetation and birds.

Year	Event
1967	Publication of the Scottish Office Technical Planning Group's report *Cairngorm Area*, proposing various tourism and skiing developments.
1971	Six children die at Feith Buidhe, after their school party failed to find a refuge hut built in the 1960s. Subsequently, two such refuge huts were removed; others were removed later. Cairngorm Estate transferred by Forestry Commission to Highlands and Islands Development Board.
1973	First record of successful breeding by Shorelark, by Adam Watson Sen.
1974	Publication of *The Cairngorms: Their Natural History and Scenery*, by Desmond Nethersole-Thompson and Adam Watson; a landmark study of the region's natural history (reprinted 1975; updated 1981).
1977	Publication of the two-volume *A Nature Conservation Review*, edited by Derek Ratcliffe, which afforded the Cairngorms its premier position in Great Britain from a nature conservation perspective. Publication of 'Wildlife potential in the Cairngorms region' by Adam Watson, in *Scottish Birds*.
1980	World Conservation Strategy identified Scottish Highlands in need of improved measures of protection.
1981	Two National Scenic Areas identified in the Cairngorms: the main Cairngorms massif, and upper Deeside and Lochnagar. Five of the Cairngorms lochs designated as Ramsar sites (wetlands of international importance). IUCN General Assembly called on British Government to 'take all practical steps to secure for the Cairngorm Mountains protection appropriate to their international significance'.
1982	Abernethy Forest declared a National Nature Reserve. Publication of *The Future of The Cairngorms*.
1983	The John Muir Trust is established to protect wilderness.
1984	Creag Meagaidh SSSI purchased by the Nature Conservancy Council to protect it from afforestation. National Planning Guidelines for ski development published.
1985	Scottish Affairs Committee (Westminster Parliament) report recommended there should be no ski development within the Northern Corries SSSI; Government did not accept this. Highland Regional Council convened a working group to review the future of skiing on Cairn Gorm and options for development; with the exception of NCC the group concluded that the westward expansion of development into Lurcher's Gully was feasible without significant damage to visual amenity or nature conservation. Save the Cairngorms Campaign formed.
1986	World Wilderness Conference called on the British Government to propose the Cairngorms to IUCN as a World Heritage Area (call repeated in 1987). Creag Meagaidh declared a National Nature Reserve. Dell Wood at Abernethy purchased by NCC.
1988	Abernethy Forest Lodge Estate purchased by the Royal Society for the Protection of Birds (the largest of a series of land acquisitions by the RSPB at Abernethy, commencing in 1975).
1989	The Countryside Commission for Scotland called for National Parks to be established, naming the Cairngorms as one of four candidates.
1990	First EC Special Protection Area (Abernethy Forest) classified in the Cairngorms. Kai Curry-Lindahl called for improved protection of the Cairngorms, published in '*Caring For The High Mountains: conservation of the Cairngorms*'. CCS publish *The Mountain Areas of Scotland* and *Conservation and Management*, recommending the Cairngorms and three other areas as National Parks.
1991	Secretary of State rejected skiing development proposals at Lurcher's Gully, and established Cairngorms Working Party, which recognised the outstanding nature of the area, and made recommendations for protection and enhancement.
1992	Publication of *Common Sense and Sustainability,* by the Cairngorms Working Party (chaired by Magnus Magnusson).
1993	Publication of the Geological Conservation Review *Quaternary of Scotland*, by the Nature Conservancy Council.
1994	Glen Feshie purchased by Will Woodlands. Cairngorms Chairlift Company submitted planning application for construction of 2 km funicular railway. Scottish Natural Heritage submits proposals to government for National Parks in Scotland (including The Cairngorms). The Cairngorms Partnership is formed to advise on the conservation and management of the Cairngorms.
1995	First candidate Special Areas of Conservation in the Cairngorms submitted to the EC (Creag nan Gamhainn, Morrone Birkwood, Tulach Hill and Glen Fender Meadows). Mar Lodge Estate purchased by the National Trust for Scotland.
1996	Publication of *The Cairngorms Assets,* by the Cairngorms Partnership. Deer (Scotland) Act made provisions for control of deer to prevent damage to the natural heritage.
1997	Publication of Management Strategy by the Cairngorms Partnership after extensive consultation. Planning permission for the Cairn Gorm funicular granted in May. Glen Feshie bought by Klaus Helveson, beating a joint bid from SNH, FC, Highland Council, Highlands and Islands Enterprise, John Muir Trust and NTS.
1999	Publication of *Biodiversity of the Cairngorms: an assessment of priority habitats and species,* by the Cairngorms Partnership.
2000	The National Parks (Scotland) Act 2000 passed into law.
2002	Publication of *The Ecology, Landuse and Conservation of The Cairngorms*, edited by Charles Gimingham.
2003	Cairngorms National Park established.

References

Brown, I.M. & Clapperton, C.M. (2002). The physical geography. In: Gimingham, C.H. (ed.) *The Ecology, Landuse and Conservation of The Cairngorms*. Packard: Chichester. pp. 8-22.

Cairngorms Working Party (1992). *Common Sense and Sustainability; a partnership for the Cairngorms*. HMSO: Edinburgh

Conroy, J.W.H., Watson, A. & Gunson, A.R. (eds.) (1990). *Caring for The High Mountains: conservation of the Cairngorms*. NERC and Aberdeen University Centre for Scottish Studies: Aberdeen.

Curry-Lindahl, K., Watson, A. & Watson, R.D. (eds) (1982). *The Future of The Cairngorms*. North East Mountain Trust: Aberdeen.

Davidson, M.B., Owen, R.P. & Mackay, D.W. (2002). The ecology of aquatic and sub-aquatic habitats. In: Gimingham, C.H. (ed.) *The Ecology, Landuse and Conservation of The Cairngorms*. Packard: Chichester. pp. 67-84.

Gimingham, C.H. (ed.) (2002). *The Ecology, Landuse and Conservation of The Cairngorms*. Packard: Chichester.

McConnell, J. & Conroy, J (eds.) (1996). The Environmental History of The Cairngorms. *Botanical Journal of Scotland* 48(1). Special issue.

Nethersole-Thompson, D. & Watson, A. (1981). *The Cairngorms: Their Natural History and Scenery*. Melven Press: Perth. (First published 1974 by Collins, London).

Ratcliffe, D.A. (ed.) (1977). *A Nature Conservation Review*. Vols. 1 and 2. Cambridge University Press: Cambridge.

Ratcliffe, D.A. (ed.) (1981). The vegetation. In: Nethersole-Thompson, D. & Watson, A. *The Cairngorms: Their Natural History and Scenery*. Collins: London. pp. 42-76.

Ratcliffe, D.A. & Thompson, D.B.A. (1988). The British Uplands: their ecological character and international significance. In: Usher, M.B. & Thompson, D.B.A. (eds.), *Ecological Change in the Uplands*. Blackwell Scientific Publications: Oxford. pp. 9-36.

Scottish Natural Heritage (2002). *Natural Heritage Futures: Cairngorms Massif*. SNH: Perth.

Thompson, D.B.A., Horsfield, D., Gordon, J.E. & Brown, A. (1994). The environmental importance of the Cairngorms massif. In: Watson, A. & Conroy, A. (ed.) *The Cairngorms: planning ahead*. Kincardine and Deeside District Council: Stonehaven. pp. 15-24.

Watson, A. (1977). Wildlife potential in the Cairngorms region. *Scottish Birds* 9(5): 245-262.

Watson, A. (1992). *The Cairngorms*. The Scottish Mountaineering Trust: Edinburgh. 6th edition (First edition published 1928).

Acknowledgements

The preparation of this book has involved a substantial team effort. On behalf of the authors we are grateful to scores of people who have contributed information, advice, comments or practical assistance during its development. In particular, we would like to thank the following for their comments on an earlier draft of all or parts of the book: Hamish Anderson, Brian Coppins, Roy Dennis, Colin Galbraith, Charles Gimingham, Georg Grabherr, Dave Horsfield, Martin Kirkbride, David Long, Murdo MacDonald, Ed Mackey, Peter Marren, Roger Owen, Torstein Solhøy, Nigel Trewin, Roy Watling, Adam Watson, Mark Young and the late Derek Ratcliffe.

In addition, the following individuals are thanked for providing information for one or more chapters: Zeshan Akhter, Alison Averis, Ben Averis, Andrew Bachell, David Barbour, Stuart Benn, Duncan Blake, Nigel Buchan, John Burlison, Kenna Chisholm, Peter Cosgrove, Alwyn Coupe, Humphrey Crick, Bob Davidson, Susan Davies, Richard Davison, Carolyn Dunnet, Siobhan Egan, Anne Elliott, Brian Etheridge, Lynne Farrell, Ian Francis, Derek Fraser, Ross Gardiner, Phil Gaskell, Martin Gaywood, Jan Gebbie, Nick Halfhide, Jon Hardey, Susan Haysom, Roger Hayward, Richard Hearn, Mark Hennessy, George Hogg, Julian Holbrook, Adrian Hudson, Sarah Hutcheon, Carol John, Andrew King, Paul Kirkland, Kenny Kortland, Bob Laughton, Alan Leitch, Ron MacDonald, Geraldine MacGowan, Iain MacGowan, Ed Mackey, Peter Maitland, Mick Marquiss, Wendy Mattingley, Iain McLaren, Julian McLean, David McLeod, Carl Mitchell, Kenny Monteith, Robert Moss, Stuart Newson, Mike Nicoll, Steve North, Bob Palmer, Mark Parsons, Tom Prescott, Kevin Redgewell, Lachlan Renwick, Helen Riley, Paul Robertson, Innes Sim, Patrick Stirling-Aird, Rik Smith, Colin Stewart, David Summers, Ron Summers, Stewart Taylor, Athayde Tonhasca, Hamish Trench, Phil Whitfield and Iain Young.

During the preparation of the book, we have also had substantial help and support from the following, for which we are extremely grateful: David Bale, Eleanor Charman, Keith Duncan, Murray Ferguson, Debbie Greene, Jo Newman, Andy Rockall, Neale Taylor and Kirsten Thompson.

Many photographers and researchers have provided us with stunning images; we thank: Andy Amphlett, Ted Benton, Niall Benvie, Peter Cairns, Laurie Campbell, Brian Coppins, Ern Emmet, Alan Fryday, Lorne Gill, John Gordon, Mark Hamblin, Elizabeth Holden, Dave Horsfield, Roger Key, Patricia MacDonald, Iain MacGowan, Derek McGinn, Neil McIntyre, John McPherson, Gordon Rothero, Sue Scott, Ron Summers, Terry Whittaker and Rachel Wignall. We also thank Betty Common and Lorne Gill for procuring and scanning the images used.

We are grateful for the enthusiastic advice, technical support and skills of Jane McNair and her colleagues at TSO Scotland throughout the publication process. We would particularly like to thank Lucy Boyd, whose creative skills have contributed so much to the design and appearance of the book.

Finally, we hope that this book will stimulate further interest and research in the Cairngorms. We have timed its publication to coincide with the formal public consultation on the draft Park Plan, prepared by the Cairngorms National Park Authority. The Park Plan sets out priorities for the management of the area. The Cairngorms deserve the very best efforts to ensure that the richness, and some would say magic, of the area is safeguarded for future generations.

Phil Shaw and Des Thompson
Scottish Natural Heritage
March 2006

CONTENTS

Part Two: The Nature of Change

Part Three: An Overview

LIST OF CONTRIBUTORS

Andy Amphlett, The RSPB, Forest Lodge, Nethybridge, Inverness-shire, PH25 3EF

Carol Anderson, 12B Boswall Road, Edinburgh, EH5 3RH

Colin Bean, SNH, Clydebank, Caspian House, 2 Mariner Court, 8 South Avenue, Clydebank Business Park, Clydebank, G81 2NR

Frank Bowles, 37 Albany Terrace, Dundee, DD3 6HS

Patricia M.C. Bruneau, SNH, 2 Anderson Place, Edinburgh, EH6 5NP

Jenny Bryce, SNH, 10 Henderson Road, Inverness, IV1 1AU

Nigel Buxton, SNH, Achantoul, Aviemore, PH22 1QD

Laura Campbell, SNH, 16/17 Rubislaw Terrace, Aberdeen, AB10 1XE

Mairi Cole, SNH, 2 Anderson Place, Edinburgh, EH6 5NP

Keith Duncan, SNH, Achantoul, Aviemore, PH22 1QD

Noranne Ellis, SNH, 2 Anderson Place, Edinburgh, EH6 5NP

Alan Fryday, 1309 East Oakland Avenue, Lansing, MI 48906, USA

John Gordon, SNH, 2 Anderson Place, Edinburgh, EH6 5NP

Jeanette Hall, SNH, Clydebank, Caspian House, 2 Mariner Court, 8 South Avenue, Clydebank Business Park, Clydebank, G81 2NR

Elizabeth M. Holden, Allanaquoich, Mar Lodge Estate, Braemar, Ballater, AB35 5YJ

David Horsfield, SNH, 2 Anderson Place, Edinburgh, EH6 5NP

Alex Mackay, SNH, 12 Hope Terrace, Edinburgh, EH9 2AS

Edward C. Mackey, SNH, 2 Anderson Place, Edinburgh, EH6 5NP

Geraldine McGowan, Northern Ecological Services, Aboyne Castle Business Centre, Aboyne, AB34 5JP

John McKinnell, SNH, Carmont House, The Crichton, Bankend Road, Dumfries, DG1 4ZF

Laszlo Nagy, McConnell Associates Ecological Research Consultancy, 41 Eildon Street, Edinburgh, EH3 5JX

Graham Neville, SNH, 10 Henderson Road, Inverness, IV1 1AU

Philip R. Ratcliffe Lochan Wood, Sandbank Road, Dunoon, Argyll, PA23 8QR

Robert Raynor, SNH, 16/17 Rubislaw Terrace, Aberdeen, AB10 1XE

Graeme E. Rotheray, 4 Gillespie Crescent, Edinburgh, EH10 4HT

Gordon Rothero, Stronlonag, Glenmassan, Dunoon, Argyll, PA23 8RA

Claudia Rowse, SNH, 2 Anderson Place, Edinburgh, EH6 5NP

Ro Scott, SNH, 10 Henderson Road, Inverness, IV1 1AU

Philip Shaw, SNH, Battleby, Redgorton, Perth, PH1 3EW

Michael Shewry, SNH, Battleby, Redgorton, Perth, PH1 3EW

Chris Sydes, SNH, 2 Anderson Place, Edinburgh, EH6 5NP

Des B.A. Thompson, SNH, 2 Anderson Place, Edinburgh, EH6 5NP

John Thomson, SNH, Achantoul, Aviemore, PH22 1QD

Colin Wells, 7 The Marshes, Hope, Hope Valley, Derbyshire, S33 6RL

Rachel Wignall, SNH, 2 Anderson Place, Edinburgh, EH6 5NP

1. INTRODUCTION: A SENSE OF BEING IN THE CAIRNGORMS

Des B.A. Thompson, Philip Shaw and John Gordon

"The idea of the Cairngorms as a wilderness, as a place one visits to recharge the batteries and obtain a sense of a world apart from our own, is potent."

From: *Nature Conservation. A Review of the Conservation of Wildlife in Britain 1950-2001.* By Peter Marren, published by HarperCollins (2002)

The ancient pine forests of Abernethy, Rothiemurchus and Mar provide a glimpse of life as it once was throughout much of the Scottish Highlands. These great forests have a timeless feel, their eccentric pines standing in silent disorder amidst the foothills of the Cairngorms. For the casual visitor this is an uncomplicated forest of pine, birch and Juniper, its open character allowing occasional views of the high tops. But for those who know it well the forest has a hidden complexity, and is still capable of revealing species long overlooked, and new to Britain or to science. At Abernethy Forest such species include a wolf spider, new to Britain in 2005; a *Cladonia* lichen missed for almost 20 years; and those crossbills chipping high overhead are more likely to be Parrot than Scottish, as was once assumed.

Leaving the forest, you come upon richly textured expanses of moorland, at first peppered with aspiring young pines. Further on, a Short-eared Owl gets up from tall, leggy heather, its shallow wing-beats silently patting the air, as if testing a hot stove. Eventually the heather thins out, and you come to the high ground; to towering corries, great boulder fields and plateaux graced with tors, crags and rock, in places barely vegetated. These high, open places are exposed to the raw elements of nature – wind, mist, rain, frost, sleet and snow – often in gusting, blizzard or torrential conditions. It may be impossible to stand upright on some days, yet on others the tranquillity, the clarity of the air, and the silence can be overwhelming.

In *The Living Mountain* (1977), Nan Shepherd wrote, "Mankind is sated with noise; but up here, this naked, this elemental savagery, this infinitesimal cross-section of sound from the energies that have been at work for aeons in the universe, exhilarates rather than destroys. Each of the senses is a way into what the mountain has to give". In this Introduction we try to give a personal flavour of the elements of nature which appeal to us in the Cairngorms, and we quote liberally from some writers who have enhanced our enjoyment of the area.

The 'Cairngorms' is a term used to describe the great massif lying between Aviemore and Glen Feshie in the west, and Braemar and Geal Charn in the east – roughly 30 km across by 20 km north to south. Within this remarkable area are half of Scotland's ten highest peaks - Braeriach (1,296 m), Cairn Toul (1,291 m), Ben Macdui (1,309 m), Cairn Gorm (1,245 m) and, to the east, Beinn a' Bhuird (1,196 m). This tableland is the most extensive area of high mountain terrain in Britain.

As Adam Watson (1992) reminds us, the term 'the Cairngorms' is a nickname for the massif named after its best-known hill, Cairn Gorm. Strictly speaking, the range should be referred to as the Am Monadh Ruadh (the red hill-range), with the corresponding Am Monadh Liath (the grey hill-range) west of the River Spey. Like others, including Desmond Nethersole-Thompson and Adam Watson (1981), and Charles Gimingham (2002a), we have adopted a much wider geographical boundary to encompass the interests of the area. Moving clockwise, we have included the Hills of Cromdale, Ben Rinnes, the Ladder Hills, Dinnet, Glen Tanar, the Forest of Birse, the Angus Glens, Glen Shee, Ben Vrackie, the Drumochter Hills, Dalwhinnie, and the River Spey and its strath, stretching north-eastwards to Lochindorb, north of Grantown-on-Spey. Throughout this book we refer to this as **'the Cairngorms area'**, or occasionally as **'the wider Cairngorms'**, as distinct from Cairngorms National Park. Their respective boundaries are shown in Figure 1.1.

The Cairngorms area, spanning 6,516 km², is arguably the most important for nature conservation in Britain, and ranks as one of the best in Europe. Offering great enjoyment to mountaineers, hill-walkers, skiers and naturalists, many

Carn Fiaclach, leading up onto South Top, Beinn a' Bhuird. The 'feel' of much of the high tops of the Cairngorms is Arctic in character.
Photo: *L. Gill*

Thompson, D.B.A., Shaw, P. & Gordon, J. (2006). Introduction: A sense of being in the Cairngorms. In: Shaw, P. & Thompson, D.B.A. (eds.). *The Nature of the Cairngorms: Diversity in a changing environment.* The Stationery Office. pp. 1-11.

visitors and residents alike enthuse over its natural attractions. In 2003, almost 60% of the Cairngorms area was designated as Scotland's second National Park, making it the largest National Park in the UK. Substantial parts of the Cairngorms have also been designated as Special Protection Areas, Special Areas of Conservation[1] (Figure 1.2) and as Sites of Special Scientific Interest[2] (Figure 1.3), the latter accounting for 20% of the Cairngorms area.

Foundations of the landscape

The Cairngorms are truly a landscape fashioned by geology, with a remarkable story that can be traced today in the rocks, landforms and soils that lie under our feet and in the shapes of the mountains. The hallmark granite was forged deep in the Earth's crust over 400 million years ago as a firey mass of molten rock moving up from even greater depths cooled and solidified. This was a time of unimaginable geological upheaval, when movements of the tectonic plates thrust up over millions of years a mountain range of Himalayan proportions across the land that is now Scotland. Battered by the forces of nature, these mountains were reduced over aeons to their very roots, revealing the red granite that lies at the heart of the present landscape. Weathering and erosion under climates warmer than today's then shaped the broad outlines of the granite mass, forming the distinctive plateau surfaces and their dome-shaped summits. Later, during the Ice Age, the harsh, incisive regime of frost and ice chiselled the granite and surrounding rocks into their now distinctive shapes, excavated the corries, deepened the glens and exhumed the tors. As the last glaciers melted, they released their load of ground-up rock debris and formed a mosaic of mounds, flatter areas and wet hollows in the glens and straths, laying the foundations for the soils and precious habitats of the area.

The 'massive grandeur and repose', so aptly described by Henry Alexander (1928) as the distinguishing feature of the mountains today, reflect the form and characteristics of the granite mass and the processes which have shaped the landscape through geological time. Through this close link between geology and landscape, the Cairngorms have a special 'feel' of vastness and space, quite different from the mountains of western Scotland. Again quoting from Henry Alexander, "one realises the immensity of the scale upon which the scene is set, and the greatness and dignity and calm of the Cairngorms cast their spell over the spirit". In a similar vein, an uplifting sense of essence or purity emerging from the great turmoil of the geological past is most eloquently expressed by Nan Shepherd (1934) in her poem, *The Hill Burns*:

"Out of these mountains,
Out of the defiant torment of Plutonic rock,
Out of fire, terror, blackness and upheaval,
Leap the clear burns,
Living water,
Like some pure essence of being,
Invisible in itself,
Seen only by its movement."

Another outstanding characteristic of the Cairngorms is the remarkable arrangement of ancient plateau surfaces, tors and rotted rock, which have survived from before the last glaciation and in some cases before the Ice Age, alongside landforms which are clearly glacial. It is as if the glaciers have incised through the landscape with knife-edge precision, selectively carving the Lairig Ghru, Glen Avon and Gleann Einich out of the pre-existing plateaux (Sugden, 1968). Similarly, those iconic landmarks of the Ice Age, the corries, have been hewn with equal clarity, forming amphitheatres along the northern and eastern margins of the plateaux. The high plateau surfaces, exposed to the full force of the elements and with their wastes of frost-shattered rock and sparsely vegetated gravel, convey the appearance of an Arctic wilderness. This is still a dynamic landscape, but not only on the high tops. The slopes of the glens are scarred by recent debris flows produced during intense summer rainstorms, while periodic floods and changing river channels shift large amounts of gravel, and are a reminder of the powerful forces still at work today.

The diversity and patterns of rocks, landforms and soils also provide the foundations for the special habitats and species of the Cairngorms area, from the forest and wetlands on the glacial deposits in the glens and straths, through the moorland of the intermediate slopes to the exposed montane habitats of the corries and high tops. This interplay is clearly apparent as you walk up from Glen Quoich to Beinn a' Bhuird or Ben Avon, or from Rothiemurchus to Braeriach, and enhances the sense of the integrity of the mountain environment. This sense of integrity between the geological past and the present landscape, between the natural processes and the plants and animals, was wonderfully conveyed by Nan Shepherd (1977) in *The Living Mountain*: "So there I lie on the plateau, under me the central core of fire from which was thrust this grumbling grinding mass of plutonic rock, over me blue air, and between me the fire of the rock and the fire of the sun, scree, soil and water, moss, grass, flower and tree, insect, bird and beast, wind, rain and snow - the total mountain".

[1] Under the EC Birds Directive (79/409/EEC) and EC Habitats Directive (92/43/EEC), respectively.
[2] Under UK nature conservation legislation (The Wildlife & Countryside Act 1981).

Figure 1.1   The boundaries and main features of the Cairngorms area and of Cairngorms National Park.

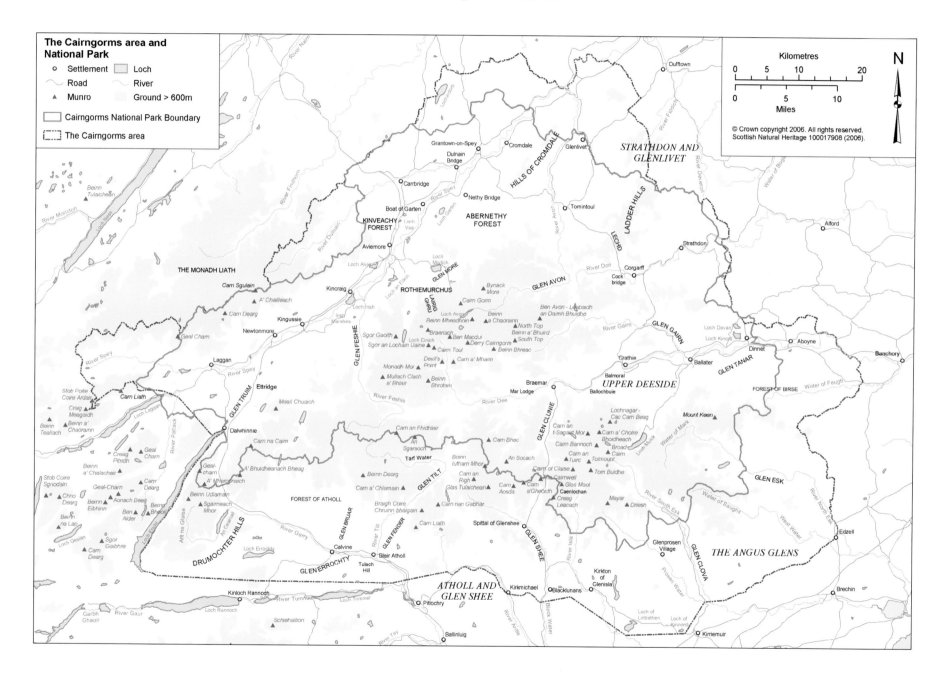

In the forest

The pinewoods of the Cairngorms are developed on a variety of glacial deposits, particularly the better-drained sands and gravels, and include the largest continuous tract of native woodland in Britain. Dominated mainly by Scots Pine and birch, and boreal in character, these woods rise into open heaths dominated by Heather, and bordered in a few areas by some of the last remaining upper treelines in Britain. "To stand in them is to feel the past", is how Steven and Carlisle (1959) described the glory of being in the pine forest.

In Strathspey, they range from the depths of Glen Feshie in the west, arcing clockwise through Invereshie, Inshriach, Rothiemurchus, Glenmore, Kinveachy, and the huge forest of Abernethy. On the other side of the massif, in Deeside, there are ancient forest remnants in the glens of the Quoich, Lui and Derry, and, further east, at Ballochbuie and Glen Tanar. As Derek Ratcliffe (1977a) put it, "Wander into the pinewoods and you can soon be lost to the outside world. They are large enough for one to capture, for a moment, the sense of solitude of the vast northern forests of the Boreal regions. The fine pinewoods of Rothiemurchus, Abernethy, Inshriach, Invereshie and Glen Feshie are amongst our national treasures".

Special birds found here include the Capercaillie, Scottish and Parrot Crossbill, and the Crested Tit, whose distinctive chittering call is so evocative of Strathspey pinewoods, often breaking the silence of a chill winter's afternoon. If you hear a great crashing noise, it may be a cock 'Caper' launching himself from a nearby pine. Displaying males can be aggressive, and have been known to attack people. Seton Gordon mentions in *The Cairngorm Hills of Scotland* (1925): "So bold was a capercaillie cock in Rothiemurchus Forest that it attacked any person venturing into that part of the wood which it frequented. Children lived in terror of it, and it attacked with fury a lady with white stockings, pecking at her offending legs as she fled round the trees. But it went a little too far when it flew on to the driver of a dogcart, biting his ear severely. After this misdeed it was caught and banished from the district in disgrace." Some have suggested that the source of the bird's name is derived from the Gaelic *gabhar coillie*, which translates into 'goat of the woods', or from *Capull-choille*; the 'horse of the woods'.

Plant life in the forests is particularly rich, and includes pinewood specialist Creeping Lady's-tresses, with its cream-coloured florets, and the One-flowered Wintergreen, with its large, downward-facing flowers. Where grazing pressure is light, the woodland floor is carpeted with Blaeberry, Cowberry and Heather.

In places, Juniper forms an under-scrub, adding to the natural feel of the wood. In contrast, the birchwoods are light, airy and delicate, and tend to occur on soils formed on Dalradian rather than granite rocks. On the Morrone hillside above Braemar, the Downy Birch woodland is rich in plants, and is the nearest equivalent, in Britain, to the sub-alpine birch forests of Scandinavia.

Many of the trees have stood for more than 200 years, and some may be almost 350 years old. They can reach 30 m, but most are around 15-20 m tall, and sometimes have huge girths, especially in the Forest of Mar. The range of growth forms is astonishing, especially where the trees are well spaced. Thomas Pennant wrote in 1771 that "here are the finest natural pines in Europe, both in respect to the size of the trees and the quality of the timber: they were from 80-90 feet high, without a lateral branch, and 4½ feet in diameter at the lower end … Some of the pines that I measured were 10, 11 and even 12 feet in circumference. These trees are of a great age, having, it is supposed, seen two centuries" (see Gordon, 1925).

Seton Gordon gives fascinating details of forest fires that have heavily influenced the character of the forest. In 1920 a large fire burned in Abernethy, and days later many trees were destroyed in Rothiemurchus and Glenmore. Five years on, Gordon (1925) observed that "acres of blackened trees show the course of the great conflagration … The Forest of Mar escaped these fires of 1920, so old trees remain and are full of life, except where, here and there, a veteran, rotten in the heart-wood, has been uprooted by some wild winter's storm". Some of these fires would have started naturally, but many spread from heather burning. In 1693 two men were accused of heather burning in Abernethy. Seton Gordon quotes from the time that "They are ordained to be taken to the gallows of the moor of the Belintomb and their lugs nailed to the said gallows".

At Creag Fhiaclach stunted, wind-beaten trees mark the former upper treeline; at around 600-640 m it is arguably the best example of a natural treeline in Britain. Here, on a rocky north-west slope, pine grows at altitudes of up to 648 m. The gnarled pines, mixed with Juniper, give way to heather in a way that much of the central Highland pinewoods must have done in the past.

The wetlands

In the forest bogs, such as at Abernethy, you may hear or see Greenshank. This wader nests in forest marsh in other parts of Europe, but in Scotland does so only in the Cairngorms, albeit increasingly rarely. If you are lucky you may also hear Wood Sandpipers, and there is a good chance you will see Goldeneye. Around Loch Garten you should see Ospreys, and many other woodland and wetland birds and plants. The mantle of bog moss (*Sphagnum*) is striking, often mixed with other mosses and lichens. On some of the drier areas, Reindeer Moss can provide a fresh white appearance. The shallow bogs often have stunted pines, hinting at the former boreal forest bogs which would have been present.

Most of the wetlands, ranging from forest bogs and lochs to fens and swamps, lie within straths of the Spey, Dee and Avon. The largest of these is at Insh Marshes, a great swamp-like fen stretching out along each side of the Spey for about five kilometres. Here there is a richness of plants, including Marsh-marigold, Water Horsetail, Skullcap, String Sedge and Marsh Cinquefoil in the wetter ground, and Red Rattle, Cotton Grass and Ragged Robin just above the water table. Willow is widespread here, notably Goat and Eared Willow, and there are Alder woodlands. These wetlands also represent valuable environmental archives. Pollen and other plant and insect remains preserved in the sediments on their boggy floors record the environmental changes and human impacts on the landscape since the end of the Ice Age.

The rivers are exciting places to watch birds, and at the upper reaches you come upon dynamic channels and river beds, changing course subtly year-on-year and sometimes dramatically after flash floods.

Onto the moor

Most visitors to the Cairngorms travel first to Strathspey, approaching from the south, through Drumochter. As the road and railway rise above Pitlochry, through the Forest of Atholl, a broad sweep of rounded, heathery hills appears. At Dalnaspidal, with the Sow of Atholl, and then the Boar of Badenoch to the north, the heathery flanks are prominent as you turn to head north, then east, passing through an open expanse of heath, which reaches high onto the Drumochter plateaux. To the north, the vista is of open heather moorland, forming a mottled patchwork of different aged stands, burned in rotation to boost Red Grouse numbers. Some parts have much more Bell Heather and Bearberry, although Heather tends to become dominant many years after a fire.

Heather predominates, especially in the northern and eastern Cairngorms and Grampian mountains, and on the slopes of many of the major glens and straths.

Walk into the forest and stand beside a great old pine. Look at it; marvel at its hulking form; touch it; and feel the richly textured bark. And listen, as woody sinews creak and groan; do you hear the sibilant noise of the wind in its upper limbs? What has this great tree witnessed? Ancestors of the tree would have harboured Wolf, Lynx and Brown Bear. No wonder Seton Gordon commented: "It is remarkable that each of these ancient firs is the offspring of parents with a like history. And so their ancestors must have flourished on the same ground in the days when Diarmid was killed by a bear on Beinn Ghielleinn and when the wolf and the wild boar and even the elk roamed through the wild Caledonian Forest". These great trees are some of our oldest and most precious life forms, and deserve respect.

Photographer: *L. Gill*

Figure 1.2 Sites protected under UK legislation. Site names are listed on page 8.

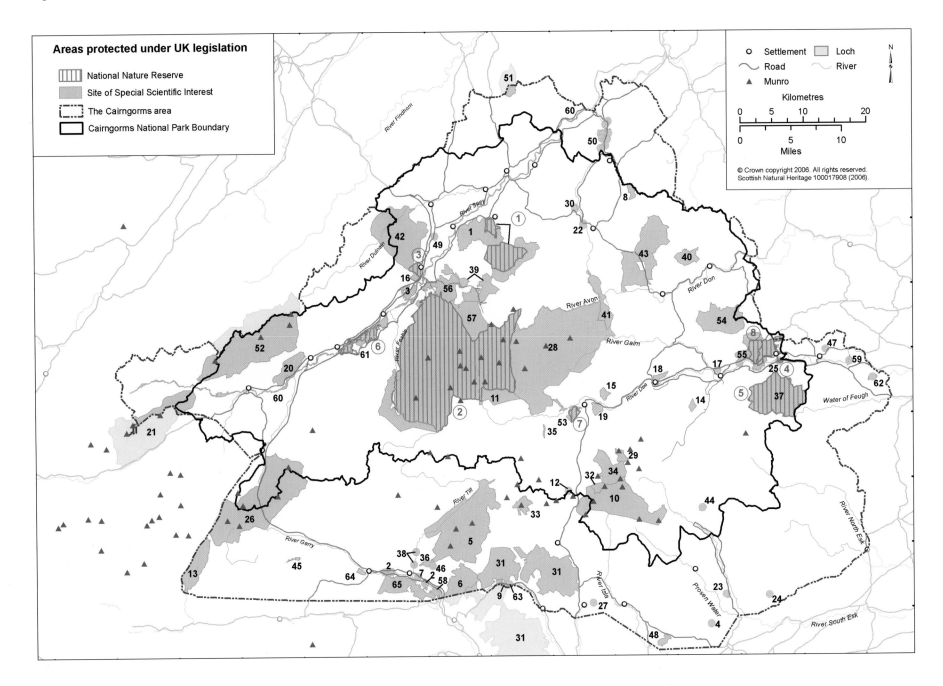

Figure 1.3   Sites protected under international legislation or agreements: the EC Birds Directive, EC Habitats Directive, and the Ramsar Convention. Site names are listed overleaf.

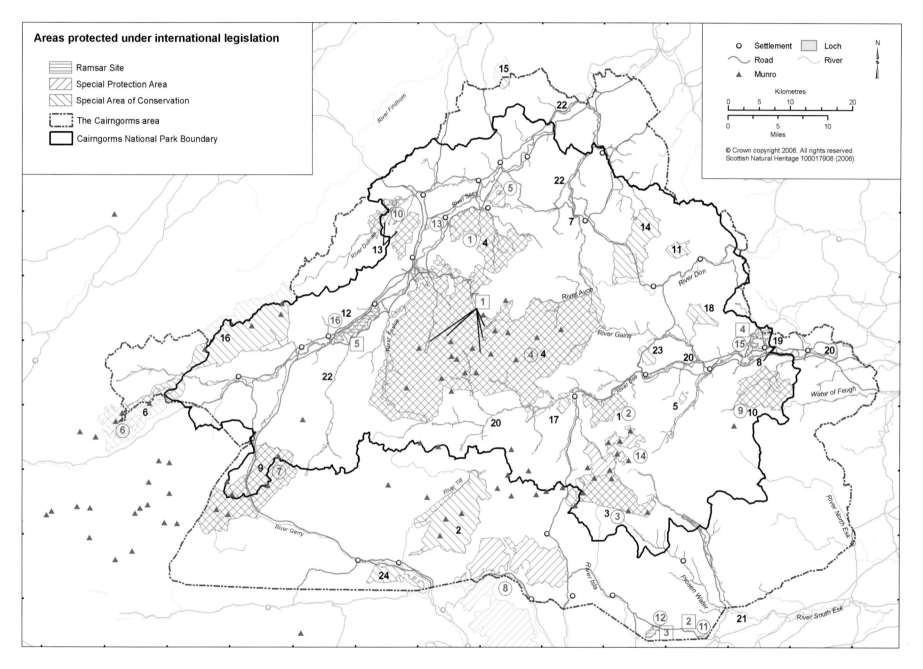

Key to Figures 1.2 and 1.3

Figure 1.2: UK designations

Sites of Special Scientific Interest **(numbered in black font)**

1.	Abernethy Forest	34.	Glen Callater
2.	Aldclune and Invervack Meadows	35.	Glen Ey Gorge
3.	Alvie	36.	Glen Fender Meadows
4.	Balloch Moss	37.	Glen Tanar
5.	Beinn a' Ghlo	38.	Glen Tilt Woods
6.	Ben Vrackie	39.	Glenmore Forest
7.	Blair Atholl Meadow	40.	Green Hill of Strathdon
8.	Bochel Wood	41.	Inchrory
9.	Brerachan Meadows	42.	Kinveachy Forest
10.	Caenlochan	43.	Ladder Hills
11.	Cairngorms	44.	Loch Brandy
12.	Cairnwell	45.	Loch Con
13.	Coire Bhachdaidh	46.	Loch Moraig
14.	Coyles of Muick	47.	Loch of Aboyne
15.	Craig Leek	48.	Loch of Lintrathen
16.	Craigellachie	49.	Loch Vaa
17.	Craigendarroch	50.	Lower Strathavon Woods
18.	Crathie Wood	51.	Moidach More
19.	Creag Clunie and the Lion's Face	52.	Monadhliath
20.	Creag Dhubh	53.	Morrone Birkwood
21.	Creag Meagaidh	54.	Morven and Mullachdubh
22.	Creag nan Gamhainn	55.	Muir of Dinnet
23.	Crossbog Pinewood	56.	North Rothiemurchus Pinewood
24.	Den of Ogil	57.	Northern Corries, Cairngorms
25.	Dinnet Oakwood	58.	Pass of Killiecrankie
26.	Drumochter Hills	59.	Quithel Wood
27.	Drumore Loch	60.	River Spey
28.	Eastern Cairngorms	61.	River Spey Insh Marshes
29.	Fafernie	62.	Shannel
30.	Fodderletter	63.	Straloch Moraines
31.	Forest of Clunie	64.	Struan Wood
32.	Garbh Choire	65.	Tulach Hill
33.	Glas Tulaichean		

National Nature Reserves **(numbered in green font, circled)**

1.	Abernethy Forest	5.	Glen Tanar
2.	Cairngorms	6.	Insh Marshes
3.	Craigellachie	7.	Morrone Birkwood
4.	Dinnet Oakwood	8.	Muir of Dinnet

Figure 1.3: International designations

Special Protection Areas **(numbered in purple font, circled)**

1.	Abernethy Forest	9.	Glen Tanar
2.	Ballochbuie	10.	Kinveachy Forest
3.	Caenlochan	11.	Loch of Kinnordy
4.	Cairngorms	12.	Loch of Lintrathen
5.	Craigmore Wood	13.	Loch Vaa
6.	Creag Meagaidh	14.	Lochnagar
7.	Drumochter Hills	15.	Muir of Dinnet
8.	Forest of Clunie	16.	River Spey - Insh Marshes

Special Areas of Conservation **(numbered in black font)**

1.	Ballochbuie	13.	Kinveachy Forest
2.	Beinn A Ghlo	14.	Ladder Hills
3.	Caenlochan	15.	Moidach More
4.	Cairngorms	16.	Monadhliath
5.	Coyles of Muick	17.	Morrone Birkwood
6.	Creag Meagaidh	18.	Morven and Mullachdubh
7.	Creag nam Gamhainn	19.	Muir of Dinnet
8.	Dinnet Oakwood	20.	River Dee
9.	Drumochter Hills	21.	River South Esk
10.	Glen Tanar	22.	River Spey
11.	Green Hill of Strathdon	23.	The Maim
12.	Insh Marshes	24.	Tulach Hill and Glen Fender Meadows

Ramsar Sites **(numbered in green font, boxed)**

1.	Cairngorms Lochs	4.	Muir of Dinnet
2.	Loch of Kinnordy	5.	River Spey - Insh Marshes
3.	Loch of Lintrathen		

Often interspersed with Bell Heather, it dominates the heather-Blaeberry heath community (Gimingham, 2002b). There is great variety in form across the moor. In places the heather is leggy, where there has been no burning for many years. Where it has died the resulting gaps may be dominated by crustose lichens or by young heather seedlings. One of the most attractive types of heath, so characteristic of the Cairngorms, is that dominated by Heather and Bearberry. This may have Bell Heather, Cowberry, Crowberry, and herbs such as Bitter-vetch, St John's-wort, Petty Whin and Mountain Everlasting, as well as lichens and mosses. There are also 'oceanic' heaths, more characteristic of western Scotland, but with an eastern outpost in the Cairngorms. In these, Green-ribbed Sedge and Bell Heather are prevalent. Heather-Blaeberry heaths are found more in the northern British uplands, and have species such as Chickweed Wintergreen, Lesser Twayblade, Blaeberry, Cowberry and Crowberry.

These are areas notable for high densities of Red Grouse, Golden Plover, and for birds of prey such as Merlin, Peregrine, Hen Harrier and Golden Eagle. Great sweeps of heathery moor give way to the high ground dominated by rock. In August and early September the blaze of purple and pink draws you up into the beauty of the high mountain landscape.

On the high tops

High above forest and moor we come upon wind-swept spurs and ridges, many bordered by crags, and giving way to bare plains, dominated by late-lying snow, rock fields and distinctly patterned vegetation. On a boulder-strewn ridge, cloaked in heavy cloud, you may hear croaking Ptarmigan and the tinkling song of a Snow Bunting. As the mist clears a great snowy vista unfolds, reminiscent of an Arctic landscape. For most people this is as close as they will get to experiencing Arctic tundra. Between Cairn Gorm and Ben Macdui you will see some of the finest mountain views in Europe, and unrivalled landforms, plants and bird life. To the east, the views across the great trough of Glen Avon to the tor-capped summit of Beinn Mheadhoin reveal the remarkable selectivity of glacial erosion in these mountains; to the west, beyond the Lairig Ghru, the glacial cliffs of a line of corries, dominated by the great amphitheatre of An Garbh Coire, fill a wide expanse between Braeriach and Cairn Toul.

Much of the high ground resembles mountain tundra or fell-field found in the Arctic. Here, wind, frost and solifluction continue to shape the mosaic of landform and vegetation. Ascending, you notice the impact of wind and late snow-lie on the vegetation. On exposed areas, the heather becomes stunted and flat, reaching the record British elevation of just under 1,100 m on Beinn a' Bhuird (Ratcliffe, 1981). On the windier terraces, Crowberry and Bearberry occur, the Bearberry extending even higher, growing alongside the beautiful pink-flowered shrub Trailing Azalea. Garlands of solifluction sheets and lobes, sometimes boulder-fronted, cover the slopes. On the most exposed reaches much of the ground is bare, although there can be a rich covering of lichens, including Reindeer Moss. Clumps of Three-leaved Rush and Woolly Fringe-moss, interspersed with Rigid Sedge and lichen patches, give the land a mottled appearance. Here and there, Viviparous Sheep's-fescue, Least Willow and Moss Campion grow alongside a diversity of lichens and mosses.

In sheltered areas, snow-lie has a significant influence on the vegetation. Mat-grass communities, often with Deer Sedge, replace heather where snow lies late. Here, mosses and liverworts become more prevalent, and we find Dwarf Willow, Alpine Lady's-mantle, Dwarf Cudweed and Starry Saxifrage (Ratcliffe, 1981). Each landform, be it a hollow, ridge, gully, boulder field, scree slope, snow-bed depression, stream bed or rock face has a different assortment of plants, with much of this variety determined by snow-lie, wind exposure and temperature. The rock types are also important. Base-rich rocks at high altitudes, mainly calcareous schists and limestones in the southern and eastern fringes of the Cairngorms, support a distinctive range of plants, notably Mountain Avens, Rock Sedge, Alpine Bistort and Yellow Saxifrage (Gimingham, 2002b).

The 'feel' of much of this land is Arctic, enhanced in spring and summer by the presence of nesting Ptarmigan, Snow Bunting and Dotterel. At a distance, on the hill flanks, the stripes, lobes and terraces of dwarf shrub heath look stunning at dawn and dusk. Detailed studies have shown that the shrubs in these areas grow slowly along the leeward edge, and die away along the windward edge, with the overall pattern of movement influenced by wind action, frost heave and slope angle.

Nethersole-Thompson (1966) wrote about his family's research on the Snow Bunting in the Cairngorms. In 1934, aged 26, he made his first visit to the high tops, and describes his first night thus, "Well after midnight we pitched the small tent beside a snowfield about 3000 feet above sea-level. There was now a high wind. Wisps of wet mist came smoking down the burn. Soon we were shouting against the storm. All was now tumult in the clinging greyness. We struggled to unravel the tent, fumbling with poles and pegs and strings. The canvas flapped and strings slipped from numb fingers, and we became wetter, colder, and still more miserable". This was an inauspicious start, but that year their tent stood for 66 nights on the high ground, and Nethersole-Thompson went on to make a detailed study of the Snow Bunting and Dotterel, two specialist birds of the high mountains.

Importance of the area

The past 10-20 years have seen an upsurge in research and survey work in the Cairngorms, resolving a few of their mysteries and setting their great value on a national and international scale. Perhaps four over-arching aspects make the Cairngorms so special. First, the rocks and landforms provide an exceptional record of the processes of landscape evolution in a mid-latitude area on the continental margin of western Europe. In particular, the Cairngorms form an outstanding example of a landscape of selective glacial erosion, but also contain a remarkable diversity of features in a relatively compact area. Second, there is still a large expanse, albeit fragmented, of native, near-natural habitat in the area. Its forest and mountain habitats are especially important in this regard. Third, no other part of Britain has so much high mountain terrain within such a comparatively small area. The Arctic-alpine landforms, habitats, invertebrates and soil complexes are outstanding in terms of their range and biodiversity, and are of special interest in being located at the western edge of Europe. Finally, the mixture and close proximity of so many features is special. In other parts of Europe one has to travel far greater distances to experience comparable woodland, open heath and alpine habitats and their associated landforms. In the Cairngorms you can pass through these in a matter of hours on foot. Many experts and specialists who come to the Cairngorms are left with the abiding impression that wild nature is rich and accessible here; something we should never take for granted.

In this Introduction we have tried to give a flavour of the nature of the Cairngorms. The chapters which follow delve into the detail of this. In our view, the richness of landforms, habitats, species, landscapes and soils is exceptional in its own right; that all of this occurs in one area is remarkable.

Acknowledgements

We are grateful for the writings of Charles Gimingham, Seton Gordon, Peter Marren, Desmond Nethersole-Thompson, Derek Ratcliffe, Nan Shepherd and Adam Watson for reminding us how special the Cairngorms are.

References

Alexander, H. (1928). *The Cairngorms*. The Scottish Mountaineering Club: Edinburgh. 1st edition.

Gimingham, C.H. (ed.) (2002a). *The Ecology, Landuse and Conservation of the Cairngorms*. Packard: Chichester.

Gimingham, C.H. (2002b). Vegetation. In: Gimingham, C.H. (ed.), *The Ecology, Landuse and Conservation of the Cairngorms*. Packard: Chichester. pp. 23-42.

Gordon, S. (1925). *The Cairngorm Hills of Scotland*. Cassell: London.

Marren, P. (2002). *Nature Conservation. A Review of The Conservation of Wildlife in Britain 1950-2001*. HarperCollins: London.

Nethersole-Thompson, D. (1966). *The Snow Bunting*. Oliver & Boyd: Edinburgh.

Nethersole-Thompson, D. & Watson, A. (1981). *The Cairngorms: Their Natural History and Scenery*. Melven Press: Perth. (First published 1974 by Collins, London).

Ratcliffe, D.A. (1977a). *Highland Flora*. Highlands and Islands Development Board: Inverness.

Ratcliffe, D.A. (ed.) (1981). The vegetation. In: Nethersole-Thompson, D. & Watson, A. *The Cairngorms: Their Natural History and Scenery*. Melven Press: Perth. (First published 1974 by Collins, London). pp. 42-76.

Shepherd, N. (1934). *In the Cairngorms*. The Moray Press: Edinburgh.

Shepherd, N. (1977). *The Living Mountain. A celebration of the Cairngorm mountains of Scotland*. Aberdeen University Press: Aberdeen.

Steven, H.M. & Carlisle, A. (1959). *The Native Pinewoods of Scotland*. Oliver & Boyd: Edinburgh.

Sugden, D.E. (1968). The selectivity of glacial erosion in the Cairngorm Mountains, Scotland. *Transactions of the Institute of British Geographers* 45: 79-92.

Watson, A. (1992). *The Cairngorms*. The Scottish Mountaineering Trust: Edinburgh. 6th edition (First edition published 1928).

Further reading

Brown, I.M. & Clapperton, C.M. (2002). The physical geography. In: C.H. Gimingham (ed.), *The Ecology, Landuse and Conservation of the Cairngorms*. Packard: Chichester. pp. 8-22.

Cairngorms Working Party (1992). *Common Sense and Sustainability; a partnership for the Cairngorms*. HMSO: Edinburgh

Conroy, J.W.H., Watson, A. & Gunson, A.R. (eds.) (1990). *Caring for The High Mountains: conservation of the Cairngorms*. NERC and Aberdeen University Centre for Scottish Studies: Aberdeen.

Curry-Lindahl, K., Watson, A. & Watson, R.D. (eds.) (1982). *The Future of The Cairngorms*. North East Mountain Trust: Aberdeen.

Davidson, M.B., Owen, R.P. & Mackay, D.W. (2002). The ecology of aquatic and sub-aquatic habitats. In: C.H. Gimingham (ed.), *The Ecology, Landuse and Conservation of the Cairngorms*. Packard: Chichester. pp. 67-84.

Gordon, J.E. & Sutherland, D.G. (1993). *Quaternary of Scotland*. Geological Conservation Review Series No. 6. Chapman & Hall: London.

Gordon, J.E., Wignall, R.M.L., Brazier, V. & Bruneau, P.M.C. (2006). *Cairngorms. A Landscape Fashioned by Geology*. Scottish Natural Heritage: Perth.

Hall, A.M. (2006). *Cairngorm Landscapes*. http://www.fettes.com/Cairngorms/

McConnell, J. & Conroy, J (eds.) (1996). The Environmental History of The Cairngorms. *Botanical Journal of Scotland* 48(1). Special issue.

Ratcliffe, D.A. (ed.) (1977b). *A Nature Conservation Review*. Vols. 1 & 2. Cambridge University Press: Cambridge.

Ratcliffe, D.A. & Thompson, D.B.A. (1988). The British Uplands: their ecological character and international significance. In: Usher, M.B. & Thompson, D.B.A. (eds.), *Ecological change in the Uplands*. Blackwell Scientific Publications: Oxford. pp. 9-36.

Scottish Natural Heritage (2002). *Natural Heritage Futures: Cairngorms Massif*. SNH: Perth.

Thompson, D.B.A., Horsfield, D., Gordon, J.E. & Brown, A. (1994). The environmental importance of the Cairngorms massif. In: Watson, A. & Conroy, A. (eds.), *The Cairngorms: planning ahead*. Kincardine & Deeside District Council: Stonehaven. pp. 15-24.

2. GEODIVERSITY: GEOLOGY AND LANDFORMS

John Gordon and Rachel Wignall

Here are the largest areas of lofty ground in these islands, where the forces of nature – frost and heat, snow and rain, wind and tempest – work with a power and a violence undreamed at lower heights.

Sir Henry Alexander, 1928. *The Cairngorms.* Scottish Mountaineering Club.

Introduction

The Cairngorms include the largest continuous areas of high ground above 1,000 m in Britain and most of the highest summits in Scotland. With their distinctive plateau surfaces and glacially sculpted features, the Cairngorms lie at the heart of an extensive tract of mountains and glens in the Central Highlands. The variety of the rocks and landforms present provides a record of the fascinating and turbulent Earth history of Scotland, stretching back some 700 million years. This ranges from global-scale events, involving ancient continental collisions, mountain building, volcanic activity and glaciation, to the local formation of postglacial soils, plant colonisation and the powerful 'forces of nature' still at work today (Table 2.1). Not only does this geodiversity[1] offer a rare insight into long-term processes of mountain landscape evolution and environmental change on the continental margin of western Europe, it also forms the foundation for the highly valued habitats and biodiversity of the area. Thus, there are close links between the habitats and the geology, soils, geomorphological processes and topography, and their interactions with the climate. This can be seen, for example, both in the large-scale habitat variations across the area and in the local mosaics of vegetation communities (e.g. Gordon *et al.*, 1998).

The most outstanding Earth heritage interest in the Cairngorms area is the *internationally* important landscape of the central Cairngorms massif – a largely granite landscape formed under warmer conditions before the Ice Age,

Coire an Lochain, Braeriach.

Photo: *J. Gordon*

but later modified to varying degrees by the glaciers and freezing cold of the Ice Age. Carved and moulded by glaciers into corries and steep-sided glens, the Cairngorms massif also bears the marks of large glacial meltwater rivers, ancient lakes dammed by the ice, and the more subtle signs of a landscape subjected to a harsh, freezing climate when the glaciers were less extensive. The international importance of the geodiversity of this area is recognised by its inclusion in the UK Tentative List of World Heritage sites (Department for Culture, Media and Sport, 1999).

Many features of *national* importance for geodiversity also occur, both in the central Cairngorms massif and in the wider Cairngorms area. They include examples of river landforms and processes, occurrences of rare minerals and sites with valuable records of vegetation and climate history. There are also nationally important sites for metamorphosed sedimentary rocks (former sea-floor sediments that have been heated and compressed) and igneous intrusions or 'plutons' (formerly molten rock now cooled and solidified).

The Geological Conservation Review: important features and sites

In a detailed and systematic survey conducted between 1977 and 1990, the Geological Conservation Review (GCR) identified key sites for geology and geomorphology in Britain (Ellis *et al.*, 1996). These localities, known as GCR sites, make up a series representing all of the key features of Britain's Earth heritage, and include over 800 sites in Scotland. The GCR site network provides the basis for statutory Earth heritage conservation in Britain and is being periodically updated in the light of new research and discoveries. The majority of these sites are now protected through designation as Sites of Special Scientific Interest (SSSIs). Within the GCR series, each site is regarded as

Gordon, J. & Wignall, R. (2006). Geodiversity: Geology and landforms. In: Shaw, P. & Thompson, D.B.A. (eds.). *The Nature of the Cairngorms: Diversity in a changing environment.* The Stationery Office. pp. 13-41.

[1] Geodiversity is the variety of rocks, minerals, fossils, landforms, sediments and soils, together with the natural processes which form and alter them.

being of national or international importance, either on its own, or as part of a network of closely related sites.

There are 44 GCR sites in the Cairngorms area, representing key aspects of several Earth science site networks. Of these, 30 lie within Cairngorms National Park (Table 2.2; Figure 2.1). Since GCR sites are defined as single interest localities, an area with multiple interests may have several overlapping GCR sites. Scientific accounts of these sites are published in individual GCR volumes (Gordon & Sutherland 1993; Werritty & McEwen,1997; Stephenson *et al.*, 1999, in press; Barclay *et al.*, 2005; Smith & Livingstone, in prep.). Many aspects of the geology of the area and its wider context within Scotland are discussed in Trewin (2002).

Geology: foundations of the landscape

The ancient history of the Cairngorms area is recorded in its rocks and minerals. The rocks predominantly comprise metamorphosed sedimentary

Dalradian rocks exposed in the gorge below the road bridge at Linn of Dee.
Photo: *L. Gill*

rocks, which form part of what is known as the 'Dalradian Supergroup', and 'igneous intrusions' (Figure 2.2). The former are sea-floor sediments that have been heated and compressed; the latter are rocks, such as granite, which were once molten and, as molten rock, were pushed into the metamorphosed sedimentary rocks where they cooled and solidified. The following sections provide a summary of the key features of geological interest in the area. More technical information is available in Stephenson and Gould (1995) and in the British Geological Survey Memoirs for the Aviemore (Highton, 1999), Ballater (Smith *et al.*, 2002), Aboyne (Gould, 2001) and Glen Shee (Crane *et al.*, 2002) areas. An overview of the area and its wider context is provided by Strachan *et al.* (2002).

Dalradian rocks – deposition

The rocks of the 'Dalradian Supergroup' underlie most of the area between the Great Glen Fault (which defines the line of the Great Glen) and the Highland Boundary Fault (which runs across mainland Scotland from Stonehaven to Helensburgh). These Dalradian rocks are the oldest in the Cairngorms area. They formed from sediments deposited on the floor of an ancient ocean, called the Iapetus Ocean, around 700 million years ago. The Dalradian rocks are named after the Dalradians who ruled the ancient Celtic west coast kingdom of Dalriada. The Iapetus Ocean was created when the immense Earth forces that cause continental drift broke apart a huge ancient continent, known as a 'supercontinent'. The Iapetus Ocean formed between fragments of this broken supercontinent. Present-day Scotland, North America and Greenland were part of one of these fragments, on a continent known as 'Laurentia', which lay on one edge of the Iapetus Ocean.

Sediment eroded from Laurentia over millions of years was deposited on the floor of the Iapetus Ocean. However, movement on geological faults, which occurred while the sediment was being deposited, caused the repeated formation of deep underwater depressions or 'basins'. These then filled with sediment, causing the water depth to become shallower. The sediments, laid down under these varying water depths, and which eventually formed the Dalradian rocks, are consequently a mix of fine-grained, deep-water sediments such as mud and clay, and shallow-water sediments such as coarse-grained coastal sand and calcium carbonate (lime) chemically deposited in lagoons. The resulting Dalradian sedimentary rocks therefore include gritstones, sandstones and quartzite from various sands; siltstones, mudstones, slate and shales from finer silts, muds and clays; and limestones from chemically precipitated lime.

Table 2.1. The Cairngorms through time.

Geological period	Main events in the Cairngorms
QUATERNARY (THE ICE AGE) 2.6 million years ago to present	**11,500 years ago to the present day.** The climate warmed rapidly at the start of the present interglacial (the Holocene). Soils stabilised and pioneer vegetation was followed by the spread of pine forest about 10,000 years ago. River terraces formed and river channels changed positions during floods. Human activity resulted in significant clearance of the natural woodland during the last 6,000 years. Today, periglacial processes continue to modify the higher slopes and summits, and debris flows and floods periodically alter the slopes and floors of the glens. **12,900 to 11,500 years ago.** The climate became intensely cold again at the time of the Loch Lomond Readvance; small mountain glaciers re-formed in some corries and glens and produced moraines; slopes were extensively modified by solifluction and rockfalls. **15,000 to 12,900 years ago.** The climate warmed rapidly, with summer temperatures similar to those of today; most if not all of the remaining glaciers melted. Pioneer plants colonised the glacial deposits and the soil stabilised; arctic shrub tundra developed, with Dwarf Birch *Betula nana* and Crowberry *Empetrum nigrum*. **18,000 to 15,000 years ago.** Retreat and local readvances of the last ice sheet resulted in the formation of moraines, meltwater channels, kame terraces, eskers, kettle holes, ice-dammed lakes and deltas. **30,000 to 18,000 years ago.** The last (Late Devensian) ice sheet expanded, reaching its maximum extent about 22,000 years ago or slightly earlier; the glaciers further enlarged the major features of glacial erosion. **2.6 million years to 30,000 years ago.** Onset of the Ice Age occurred about 2.6 million years ago. There were many glacial (cold) and interglacial (warmer) episodes with repeated growth and decay of glaciers - mainly mountain (including corrie) glaciers before about 750,000 years ago and thereafter a succession of large ice sheets. Major features of glacial erosion were formed, including glacial troughs, breached watersheds and corries. Further, shallower, weathering of the bedrock took place, with stripping of the weathered rock and exhumation of the present tors.
NEOGENE 23 to 2.6 million years ago	Weathering continued under warm, temperate conditions. Further uplift of the area and erosion of the glens continued. Cooling of the climate intensified after about 3 million years ago.
PALAEOGENE 66 to 23 million years ago	Chemical weathering of the granite took place under humid, sub-tropical conditions. Periods of uplift and erosion of the glens and straths occurred, and the plateau surfaces were formed. The Cairngorms were re-established as an upland area. The North Atlantic Ocean opened to the west of Scotland.
CRETACEOUS 145 to 66 million years ago	Warm, shallow seas covered most of Scotland. The Cairngorms were probably a low area rising above sea level.
JURASSIC 200 to 145 million years ago	The Cairngorms remained an upland area, with rivers draining to deltas in the North Sea basin.
TRIASSIC 251 to 200 million years ago	The Cairngorms remained an upland area, but with reduced relief, surrounded by arid continental plains. Scotland lay 20-30° north of the Equator at this time.
PERMIAN 299 to 251 million years ago	The Cairngorms remained an upland area and desert sands accumulated along the present-day margins of Scotland.
CARBONIFEROUS 359 to 299 million years ago	Scotland drifted north into equatorial latitudes. Deposits of coal formed in low-lying coastal swamps in the Midland Valley, but the Cairngorms remained an upland area. Rivers continued to erode the main lines of weakness in the granite.
DEVONIAN 416 to 359 million years ago	Intensive erosion of the Caledonian mountains produced vast thicknesses of sand and gravel which were deposited by rivers in semi-arid basins within the mountains and in adjacent areas of the Midland Valley. After the Cairngorm granite was exposed at the ground surface, rivers selectively eroded the main lines of weakness in the granite, forming the precursors of the present glens. Scotland at this time lay about 10° south of the Equator.
SILURIAN 444 to 416 million years ago	The continents of Baltica (Scandinavian Europe) and Eastern Avalonia (containing England) collided with Laurentia as the Iapetus Ocean closed completely. The Cairngorm granite rose as a molten mass from deep in the Earth's crust to within several kilometres of the surface. By 427 million years ago, the Cairngorm granite had cooled and solidified.
ORDOVICIAN 488 to 444 million years ago	Formation of the Caledonian mountains as the Iapetus Ocean closed and a chain of volcanic islands collided with Laurentia, the continent on which Scotland was then located. The collision was accompanied by metamorphism and folding of the Dalradian sediments.
CAMBRIAN 542 to 488 million years ago	Dalradian sediments continued to be deposited in the Early Cambrian. In Late Cambrian times, the Iapetus Ocean began to close.
PRECAMBRIAN Before 542 million years ago	**After 800 million years ago.** Dalradian sediments began to be deposited in shallow seas and later on the edge of the widening Iapetus Ocean. **4000 million years ago.** Formation of the oldest known rocks on Earth. **4500 million years ago.** Formation of the Earth.

Table 2.2. Geological Conservation Review sites in the Cairngorms area. Sites in Cairngorms National Park are shown in bold.

GCR Block	No. of GCR sites		GCR site names	Principal interests	GCR volumes
	Cairngorms Area	National Park			
Dalradian	17	9	A9 & River Garry; **An Suidhe, Kincraig**; Balnacraig; Ben Vuirich; **Blargie Craig**; **Bridge of Avon**; **Bridge of Brown**; **Cairn Leuchan**; Garva Bridge; Gilbert's Bridge, Glen Tilt; Glen Esk; **Glen Ey Gorge**; **Kinlochlaggan Road**; **Kymah Burn**; Meall Dail-chealach; Meall Reamhar (part); **Muckle Fergie Burn**	Representative sections of the Dalradian Supergroup – a sequence of sedimentary rocks, originally sandy and muddy sediments on the floor of an ancient ocean basin around 700 million years ago. The Dalradian Supergroup underlies most of the area between the Great Glen Fault (line of the Great Glen) and the Highland Boundary Fault (line from Stonehaven to Helensburgh).	Dalradian Rocks of Scotland (Stephenson et al., in press)
Caledonian Igneous	2	1	**Red Craig**; Forest Lodge	Igneous rocks formed as a result of the Caledonian Orogeny – a mountain building event which resulted from continental collisions around 480-425 million years ago. These rocks are important in understanding magmatic processes – the processes by which molten rock forms, moves and cools.	Caledonian Igneous Rocks of Great Britain (Stephenson et al., 1999)
Non-Marine Devonian	1	0	North Esk River	Sites representing key features of the Devonian time period (416-359 million years ago). In Scotland, most Devonian deposits are river or fresh water lake sediments and many sites contain information important for palaeogeography and palaeoenvironment reconstruction.	The Old Red Sandstone of Great Britain (Barclay et al., 2005)
Mineralogy of Scotland	5	5	**Creag nam Ban**; **Gairnshiel Bridge**; **Lecht Mine**; **Loch Avon**; **Loch Kander**	The occurrence of rare and unusual minerals.	Mineralogy of Scotland (Smith & Livingstone, in preparation)
Quaternary of Scotland	11	9	**Abernethy Forest**; **Cairngorms**; **Coire Fee**; **Glen Feshie**; **Loch Etteridge**; **Lochnagar**; **Morrone**; **Muir of Dinnet**; North Esk and Westwater; Parallel Roads of Lochaber (part); **Tomintoul**	Nationally and internationally important sites for glacial geomorphology and mountain landscape evolution; Late-glacial and Holocene (post-glacial) vegetation history and history of arctic/alpine species recorded in peat, loch and tufa deposits.	Quaternary of Scotland (Gordon & Sutherland, 1993)
Fluvial Geomorphology of Scotland	8	6	Allt Dubhaig; **Allt Mór**; **Derry Burn**; **Dorback Burn**; **Glen Feshie**; **Luibeg Burn**; North Esk and Westwater; **Quoich Water Fan**	Sites representing the major features of upland rivers, including mountain torrents, alluvial fans, wandering gravel-bed rivers, meanders and channel changes.	Fluvial Geomorphology of Great Britain (Werritty & McEwen, 1997)

Excellent examples of both deep- and shallow-water Dalradian sediments are found in the Cairngorms National Park and in the wider Cairngorms area. There are also important examples of contacts between rocks formed during different periods of sedimentation, some of which are used to divide the Dalradian rocks conveniently into 'groups'. These occur at *Bridge of Avon* and *Bridge of Brown* near Tomintoul, and *Glen Ey Gorge* above Inverey, where the Dalradian rocks are exposed in the dramatic gorge of The Colonel's Bed. Contacts between the Dalradian sediments and the rocks thought to underlie them can be seen at *An Suidhe, Kincraig* and *Blargie Craig*, Laggan. The underlying rocks are known as the 'Dava and Glen Banchor successions' and appear to resemble the Moine rocks found to the north of the Great Glen, rather than the overlying Dalradian rocks. However, there is still considerable scientific debate about this. In the wider

Cairngorms, sites in the *A9 and River Garry* area, at *Garva Bridge*, Laggan, and *Gilbert's Bridge, Glen Tilt*, contain further important sections within the Dalradian rock sequence. Within the National Park, at *Muckle Fergie Burn*, Tomintoul, and *Kinlochlaggan Road*, unusual boulders within the rocks are interpreted as debris floated out to sea on icebergs. This could only have occurred if the Earth was experiencing a glaciation, or Ice Age, at the time. Because two different layers of these boulders are found, it is believed that glaciation occurred at least twice during the accumulation of the Dalradian sediments.

Dalradian rocks - deformation
For around 200 million years after it first formed, the Iapetus Ocean grew wider and wider, then it began to close again due to the forces of continental

Figure 2.1. Geological Conservation Review sites. Note that since GCR sites are defined as single interest localities, an area with multiple interests may have several overlapping GCR sites.

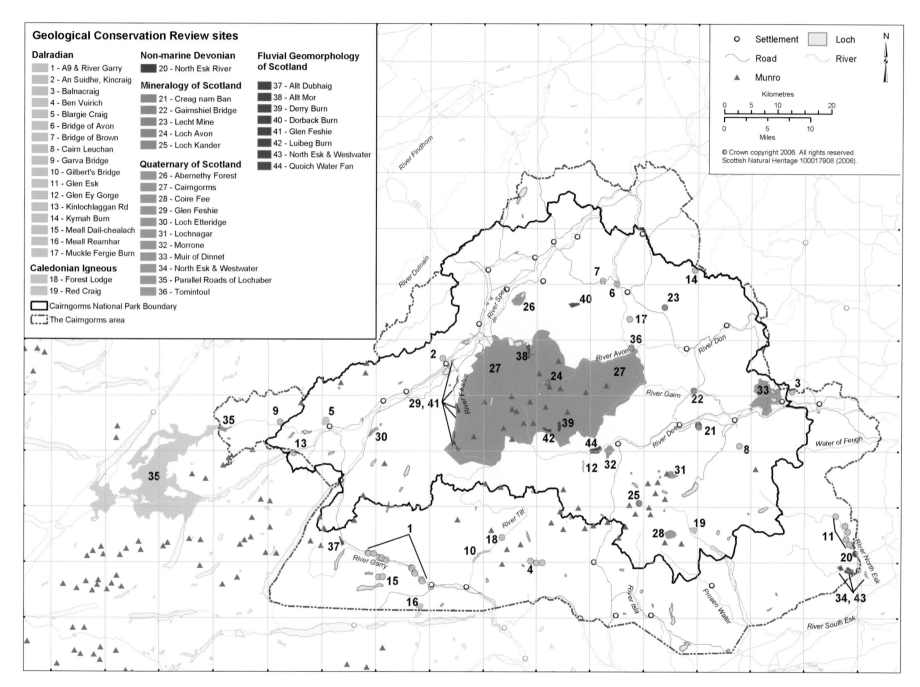

drift. Over a period of around 100 million years the ocean grew narrower, until around 425 million years ago, when it closed completely. As the ocean closed, first a chain of volcanic islands, and then two continents, Baltica (Scandinavian Europe) and Eastern Avalonia (containing England), collided with Laurentia. These massive continental collisions, which had begun by 480 million years ago, resulted in the Dalradian sediments being squeezed, crumpled and deformed. The sediments were buried deeply, compressed and heated, turning them into 'metamorphic' or 'metamorphosed' rocks. The metamorphic Dalradian rocks in the Cairngorms area are mainly schists, which are metamorphosed mudstones and shales, but also include metamorphosed limestone, slate and quartzite. As the rocks were deformed, they were also raised upwards into a huge mountain chain of Himalayan proportions, known as the Caledonian mountain belt. This has now been almost completely eroded away, but its roots include the Scandinavian mountains and the Appalachian Mountains in North America, as well as the Grampian Highlands of Scotland.

Important examples of the deformation of the Dalradian rocks are found within Cairngorms National Park at **Blargie Craig**, Laggan, **Bridge of Avon** near Tomintoul, **Cairn Leuchan**, Ballater, **Glen Ey Gorge** above Inverey, and **Kymah Burn**, Glen Livet; and elsewhere in the Cairngorms area, at **Balnacraig**, Dinnet, **Glen Esk**, **Meall Dail-chealach**, **Meall Reamhar** in Glen Errochty, and in the **A9 and River Garry** area.

Igneous intrusions

The continental collisions 480-425 million years ago not only crumpled the Dalradian rocks into a huge mountain chain, but also caused rock deep down in the Earth's crust to melt. This molten rock welled upwards, pushing its way into the metamorphosed Dalradian sediments. Much of the molten rock never reached the surface. Instead, it cooled and solidified several kilometres below the surface, forming igneous intrusions or plutons which are abundant today in parts of the Cairngorms area where they have been exposed by subsequent erosion. The hot molten rock also affected the Dalradian rocks nearby, effectively 'cooking' them in an extra burst of heating.

The igneous intrusions in the Cairngorms area can be divided roughly into four groups: 'granitic' intrusions formed during deformation of the Dalradian rocks; 'basic' intrusions also formed during deformation; 'granitoid' intrusions formed during the late stages of deformation; and 'granitoid' intrusions formed after deformation had ceased. The last of these are known as 'post-tectonic' intrusions. The terms 'basic', 'granitoid' and 'granitic' describe the composition

The eastern corries of Beinn a' Bhuird form a spectacular granite landscape.
Photo: *J. Gordon*

of the rock. 'Basic' means that the rocks have a very low silica content. 'Granitic' means they have a very high silica content, but also that the rock is 'coarse-grained', with individual crystals being large and easily seen with the naked eye. 'Granitoid' is a term that includes granitic rocks but also some other coarse-grained rocks with a slightly lower silica content; hence the intrusions referred to as granitoid may have a variety of compositions.

Post-tectonic intrusions are the most abundant intrusions in the Cairngorms area, but examples of all four groups are present. Small intrusions of early granites occur in the National Park in Glen Clova, and elsewhere in the Cairngorms at **Ben Vuirich** and Meall Gruaim. The former is particularly important because dating of the granite there has been used to help date deformation events in the Dalradian rocks. Basic intrusions are found in the eastern part of the Cairngorms. These include the Coyles of Muick intrusion and the large Morven-Cabrach intrusion, which extends some 10 km on either side of the A944 north of Ballater. 'Granitoid' intrusions from the late stages of deformation occur in Glen Clova, and also at Grantown-on-Spey (Grantown intrusion) and near Dalwhinnie (Strathspey intrusion) at the western edge of the National Park.

Post-tectonic granitoid intrusions occur throughout the Cairngorms, ranging from the Glen Shee and Glen Tilt intrusions in the south to the Monadhliath granite and Corrieyairack intrusion in the west, the Ben Rinnes granite in the north, and the large Mount Battock granite in the east. The densest cluster of these intrusions, however, is along the line of an ancient fault, called the 'Deeside Lineament', followed today by the Dee valley. This fault is thought to be associated with the opening of the Iapetus Ocean, and provided a zone of weakness exploited by the rising magma. The largest intrusions in the Dee valley cluster are the Cairngorm granite, which underlies the bulk of the Cairngorms massif; the Mount Battock granite, which underlies much of the ground to the south of the A93 between Ballater and Banchory; the Lochnagar granite centred on Lochnagar and underlying much of the Balmoral Estate; the Glen Gairn granite in the area around Tom Breac and The Ca on either side of the River Gairn; and the Ballater granite in the Ballater to Culblean Hill area.

The Cairngorm granite

The Cairngorm granite is of great significance because it forms the bedrock of the central Cairngorms massif. The properties of the granite have strongly affected the form of the internationally important landscape produced by pre-glacial weathering and erosion and by the action of glaciers and frost during the Ice Age. This is Britain's second largest single area of granite, after Dartmoor. It underlies all of the high ground of the Cairngorms massif, except for the Mòine Mhór in the south-west, and extends over an irregularly shaped area from Glen Feshie to Glen Builg, and from the Northern Corries to upper Glen Dee and the south slopes of Beinn a' Bhuird. The granite is poorly exposed over much of the Cairngorm plateau; however, where fresh rock is exposed, it is mostly pink to red in colour, and has a variable texture. The latter is due to variations in the average crystal size of the constituent minerals and the presence or absence of unusually large crystals or fragments of Dalradian rock caught up in the intrusion. These variations in texture suggest that the Cairngorm granite may have formed from a number of distinct 'pulses' of molten rock, each rising to the surface separately, but in relatively quick succession. Each pulse of magma would have had a slightly different composition and risen along a slightly different pathway through the Earth's crust, or cooled at a slightly different rate, giving rise to variations in the appearance of the rock.

Although the Cairngorm granite is now exposed at ground level, and some has clearly been removed by erosion, it is believed that the amount eroded away is relatively small; hence the present-day land surface is not very far below the original 'roof' of the intrusion. During the final stages of cooling of the granite, water which was super-heated by the magma and rich in dissolved minerals circulated through cracks and altered the hard granite on either side to a much softer and more crumbly rock. This 'hydrothermal alteration' has been an important influence on the development of the present-day landscape. Once the Dalradian rocks, originally overlying the granite, had been worn away, the granite itself was exposed to erosion. The weaker, hydrothermally altered zones eroded more rapidly, forming valleys which were excavated still further by the Ice Age glaciers. Gleann Einich, the Lairig Ghru, Glen Avon, Glen Derry and the Lairig an Laoigh are all thought to follow the lines of hydrothermal alteration zones exploited by erosion.

The cracks or 'joints' in the Cairngorm granite have also contributed to the form of the landscape today. Some poorly jointed areas remain standing as massive tors, over 25 m high, which were left spectacularly isolated when the more heavily jointed areas around them were eroded away. As today's rock climbers in the Cairngorms know well, there are both vertical and horizontal joints in the granite. The vertical joints were formed by shrinking and cracking of the granite as it cooled. The horizontal joints were formed much later, and result from the release of pressure which occurred as the rock above the granite was eroded away. As the weight of rock above was removed, the granite

Figure 2.2. Geological map of the Cairngorms area.

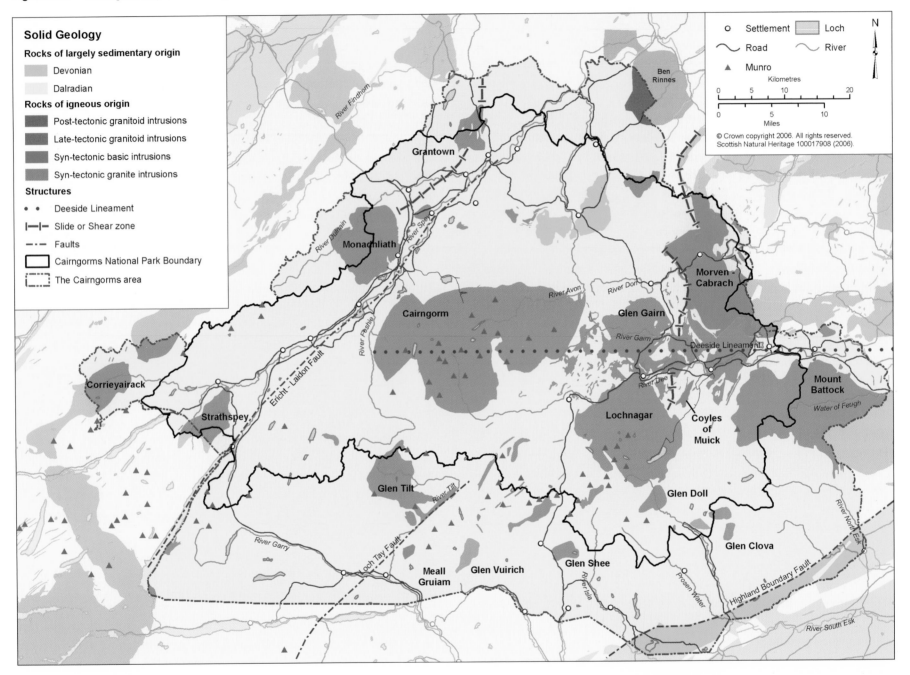

Solid Geology

Rocks of largely sedimentary origin
- Devonian
- Dalradian

Rocks of igneous origin
- Post-tectonic granitoid intrusions
- Late-tectonic granitoid intrusions
- Syn-tectonic basic intrusions
- Syn-tectonic granite intrusions

Structures
- • • Deeside Lineament
- ⊢•⊣ Slide or Shear zone
- —·—·— Faults
- Cairngorms National Park Boundary
- The Cairngorms area

Settlement   Loch
Road   River
Munro

Kilometres
0   5   10   20

Miles
0   5   10

© Crown copyright 2006. All rights reserved.
Scottish Natural Heritage 100017908 (2006).

Ben Rinnes

River Findhorn

Grantown

River Dulnain

River Spey

Monadhliath

River Avon   River Don

Morven - Cabrach

Cairngorm   Glen Gairn

River Gairn

River Feshie

Deeside Lineament

Corrieyairack

Ericht - Laidon Fault

River Dee

Mount Battock

Water of Feugh

Strathspey

Lochnagar   Coyles of Muick

Glen Tilt

River Tilt

Glen Doll

River Garry

Glen Clova

Loch Tay Fault

Meall Gruiam   Glen Vuirich   Glen Shee

River Isla

Prosen Water

Highland Boundary Fault

River North Esk

River South Esk

expanded upwards, with cracks forming parallel to the upward-expanding surface. The 'horizontal' joints are, in fact, not all truly horizontal but follow the gentle contours of the pre-glacial land surface and are truncated by later glacial erosion.

Glen Doll and Glen Tilt intrusions

In addition to the Cairngorm granite, there are two other particularly important sites relating to the igneous intrusions. **Red Craig**, at the head of Glen Clova and within the National Park, contains part of the post-tectonic Glen Doll igneous intrusion made up of a particularly unusual mixture of rock types. It illustrates well the interaction between the Dalradian rocks and the up-welling molten rock, indicating that Dalradian rocks were melted and combined with the original molten intrusion to give the mix of rocks now observed.

The **Forest Lodge section** in Glen Tilt, which lies outside the National Park, contains a section of the post-tectonic Glen Tilt igneous intrusion. It was here, in 1785, that the eminent Scottish geologist, James Hutton, first showed that igneous intrusions originated as molten rock. He demonstrated that this was the only way to explain the relationships between the Glen Tilt igneous intrusion and the surrounding Dalradian rocks. This was a crucial development in geological science, and therefore on historical grounds this site is of international importance.

Devonian 'Old Red Sandstone' sediments

After the continental collisions 425 million years ago, weathering and erosion wore away at the landscape for millions of years. Many of the igneous intrusions, which were originally buried deep underground, became exposed, and the landscape began to take on a form similar to that of the present day. During the Devonian period (416–359 million years ago), Scotland lay just south of the Equator and had a semi-arid, sub-tropical climate. Rock debris eroded from the high mountains was carried away by large rivers, and much of it was dumped in low-lying areas and lakes both in the mountains and beyond. The rocks formed from these river and lake sediments include conglomerates from pebbles, cobbles and boulders; sandstones from sand; and finer-grained shales and silts from mud. These sediments are often called 'Old Red Sandstone' sediments because of their reddish colour, and the sandstone itself forms a good building stone.

Little Devonian sediment is likely to have been deposited in areas such as the Cairngorms massif, which formed high eroding mountains in Devonian times. Devonian sediment would have been deposited in depressions within

Hutton's classic section in Glen Tilt.
Photo: R. Wignall

Fragments of dark grey Dalradian rock incorporated in the pink coloured granite of the Glen Tilt intrusion.
Photo: R. Wignall

the mountain belt and around the mountain margins; however, since the Devonian, much of this sediment has itself been eroded away. Consequently, relatively little Devonian sediment is found in the Cairngorms area today.

In the National Park, early Devonian sediments are found around Tomintoul, filling a depression in the underlying Dalradian rock basement. These sediments include conglomerates and sandstones deposited by rivers flowing from the area which is now dominated by the granite of the Cairngorms massif. However, the pebbles and boulders in the early Devonian rocks do not include any granite, indicating that the Cairngorm granite was still buried and hence not yet exposed to erosion during the early Devonian.

Along the **North Esk River**, at the eastern edge of the Cairngorms area, there are important outcrops of Devonian sediments. This site lies to the south of the Highland Boundary Fault which was active in Devonian times. The rocks here contain important information about the erosion of the Dalradian rocks and the transport of the resulting sediment across the active fault to form Devonian rocks in the Midland Valley to the south.

Mineral sites

A number of rare and unusual minerals occur in the Cairngorms. Thin veins of granite melt, which forced their way through the Cairngorm granite during the last stages of its formation, have been the main source of the semi-precious smoky quartz known as 'Cairngorm Crystal' or 'Cairngorm Stone'. Large and decorative samples of Cairngorm Crystal have been found in a number of areas, including at Loch Avon. The **Loch Avon** area is also a nationally important locality for the occurrence of blue topaz and rare minor minerals within the granite, including the beryllium-aluminium mineral, chrysoberyl, and columbite, an iron-rich oxide containing niobium and tantalum.

At **Gairnshiel Bridge**, in the Dee Valley, late hydrothermal fluids in the Glen Gairn granite have produced rare tungsten-molybdenum mineralisation and the only UK occurrence of the lithium-bearing mineral, zinnwaldite. To the south, at **Loch Kander**, near Braemar, circulation of hydrothermal fluids during deposition of the Dalradian sediments has produced barium, sulphur, zinc, lead and silver minerals, including the first recorded occurrence of the barium- and calcium-bearing mineral, armentite.

An artist's impression of how the landscape around Tomintoul may have looked during the Devonian time period.
Illustration: *Clare Hewitt*

Devonian rocks form the steep sides of the Ailnack Gorge, south of Tomintoul.
Photo: *L. Gill*

A rare occurrence of the magnesium-rich silicate mineral, cummingtonite, in Dalradian rocks at **Creag nam Ban**, Ballater, is thought to result from volcanic ash in the Dalradian rock sequence being heated and compressed during deformation. This is one of the earliest signs of volcanic activity during the deposition of the Dalradian Supergroup.

At the **Lecht Mine**, a former commercial iron mine south-east of Tomintoul, unusual zinc-manganese and lithium-manganese minerals occur alongside more common iron and manganese oxide minerals. These minerals are believed to be part of a 'bog iron ore' which is a deposit of low-grade iron ore formed within an ancient soil. In this case the soil formed from iron- and manganese-rich Dalradian rock when it was deeply weathered in the tropical climate before the Ice Age. Iron ore was commercially extracted from the Lecht Mine for a decade commencing in 1730, and the ore was taken by pack horse to Nethy Bridge for smelting. In 1841, the Lecht Mine was reopened for six years to produce manganese ore, which was sent to Newcastle for use in the bleach trade. At the height of its activity, the Lecht Mine provided employment for over 60 people.

Iron and manganese ores were extracted at the Lecht mine during the 18th and 19th centuries.
Photo: *L. Gill*

Faults

There are many geological faults (fractures in the Earth's crust) in the Cairngorms area, although few, if any, are active today. The oldest faults are related to the formation of the Iapetus Ocean and the deposition of the Dalradian sediments. Later faults are associated with the compression and deformation of the Dalradian rocks when the Iapetus Ocean closed. These later faults range from 'slides' and 'shear zones' (where deeply buried, hot, ductile rock, stretched to breaking point, was sheared and pushed over adjacent rock layers), to brittle faults (formed in cold, surface rock in the later stages of deformation).

In many cases, older faults appear to have become reactivated during later phases of movement. Faults pre-dating the igneous intrusions are thought likely to have acted as zones of weakness, channelling the up-welling molten rock. The Deeside Lineament is the largest structure believed to be an ancient fault associated with the opening of the Iapetus Ocean. It runs roughly along the line of the Dee valley from the coast to the west side of the Cairngorms massif. As mentioned above, this line of weakness may explain the abundance of granite intrusions along the Dee valley.

There are two prominent 'slides' or 'shears' in the Cairngorms area. Both run roughly north-south. One roughly parallels the line of Strathspey to the west of Grantown-on-Spey, and the other cuts the Dee valley between Braemar and Ballater. Sites of importance for studying this latter slide occur at **Glen Ey Gorge** above Inverey, and **Bridge of Brown** near Tomintoul. The orientations of these slides or shears, and the geometry of the folding and deformation in the Dalradian rocks, indicates compression from the east and south. This provides evidence that continental collisions were from the south and east as the Iapetus Ocean closed.

The structurally important Highland Boundary Fault cuts across the far south-east of the Cairngorms area and separates the Dalradian terrain to the north from the younger rocks of the Midland Valley to the south. The history of the Midland Valley prior to Devonian times is not well known as few rocks of pre-Devonian age occur within it. It may originally have been part of the volcanic island chain which collided with Laurentia as the Iapetus Ocean closed. The area which is now the Midland Valley was initially some distance south-west of the Dalradian rocks currently adjacent to it; however, the two converged through sideways movement along the Highland Boundary Fault, before the Devonian.

Of the numerous, smaller, late brittle faults in the area, many trend from south-west to north-east, sub-parallel to the Great Glen and Highland Boundary faults. The largest of these is the Ericht-Laidon Fault, which runs along Strathspey and Loch Ericht. The weakened rock of this fault line, exploited by erosion to form Loch Ericht and a large section of Strathspey, has significantly influenced landscape development and transport routes in the Cairngorms area.

Landforms: shaping the landscape

Evolution of the landscape

The broad outlines of the Cairngorms massif began to emerge when the Cairngorm granite was exposed by erosion during the Devonian (Table 2.1). Weathering and erosion of the high Caledonian mountain belt, uplifted during the continental collisions that closed the Iapetus Ocean, continued during Devonian times and on through the subsequent 200 million years. This weathering and erosion selectively exploited the weaker rocks, such as the hydrothermally altered areas and the fractured rock along geological faults, to form the precursors of the present straths and glens. Similar processes shaped the landscape of the wider area. By Cretaceous times (142 to 65 million years ago), the Caledonian mountain belt had been reduced to a landscape of low relief near sea level. During the early Palaeogene, however, beginning around 65 million years ago, the area was rapidly uplifted. This uplift was associated with the massive crustal movements which opened the North Atlantic Ocean to the west of the Hebrides. Different parts of the Highlands were uplifted by different amounts, some by as much as 1 km. Intermittent uplift and erosion of the landscape continued during the Neogene (24 to ~2.6 million years ago).

Global warming during the Early Palaeogene peaked around 52 million years ago and was accompanied by a hot and humid climate in Scotland, like the tropics or subtropics in parts of West Africa today. This produced ideal conditions for deep chemical weathering of the bedrock and accelerated erosion of weaker areas of granite as the land was uplifted. The climate then cooled during the later part of the Palaeogene and throughout the Neogene, and weathering of the bedrock continued at a slower pace. The uplift, weathering and erosion of the landscape produced a series of tilted plateau surfaces rising in steps inland from the coast of north-east Scotland and culminating in the high plateaux and gently rolling summit hills of the Cairngorms massif. They include the Eastern Grampian plateau south of the River Dee, the Gaick plateau and the Monadhliath plateau. Hence, the broad outlines of the landscape were essentially in place before the start of the Quaternary, or Ice Age, period about 2.6 million years ago.

The Ice Age played a significant role in shaping the finer detail of the landforms and landscapes of the Cairngorms area. It consisted of many long cold periods known as 'glacials' or 'glacial periods', when permanent snow cover in the mountains led to the formation of glaciers and ice sheets. Between the glacial periods there were shorter, warmer periods called 'interglacials', when temperatures rose to similar or slightly higher levels than those of today. During the Ice Age, local mountain glaciers would frequently have been present in the Cairngorms area. During the more intensely cold episodes, large ice sheets probably covered the entire landscape.

The last ice sheet expanded some time after about 30,000 years ago and reached its maximum extent about 22,000 years ago or earlier, when it covered all of Scotland and extended southwards to the Midlands of England. Glaciers extended out from the Cairngorms and merged with external ice flowing around the massif from the south-west along Strathspey and into Glenmore and upper Deeside. By 15,000 years ago, the climate was warming rapidly and the ice was in retreat, producing dramatic landscape changes. This warming, however, was interrupted by a further short, cold episode between about 12,900 and 11,500 years ago, when small glaciers and icefields again formed in the Cairngorms area during a period of glacier growth known as the Loch Lomond Readvance. Thereafter, the climate warmed rapidly at the start of the present interglacial, which is known as the Holocene.

Most of the recent studies on the landscape evolution of Cairngorms National Park and the wider Cairngorms have focused on the Cairngorms massif, an area which is internationally important for its gemorphology or landforms. Overviews of the landforms and landscape history are provided by Gordon (1993), Brazier et al. (1996a), Glasser and Bennett (1996), Brown and Clapperton (2002) and Brazier and Gordon (2006). The geomorphology of the central Grampian Highlands, including the Gaick and Drumochter areas, is reviewed by the contributors in Lukas et al. (2004); that of the Lochnagar area, by Hall (in press). The main river landforms in the sites selected for the GCR are described by Werritty and McEwen (1997). The postglacial vegetation and environmental history of the landscape, including sites selected for the GCR, is summarised in Gordon and Sutherland (1993). Bennett (1996a,b) also reviewed the vegetation history of the Cairngorms, including the history of the native Scots Pine woodland (Bennett, 1995).

The landscape and landforms of the Cairngorms massif

The core mountain area, which forms the Quaternary of Scotland **Cairngorms** GCR site (Figure 2.1), is internationally important for its different types of landforms, or landform assemblages, which represent the long-term evolution of a mountain landscape from before the Ice Age to the present day (Table 2.3). Relict features which originated before the last glaciation include plateau surfaces, tors and weathered bedrock. They form a marked contrast to adjacent glacially modified corries and glens. Together they are an outstanding example of a 'landscape of selective glacial erosion', where some parts of the landscape have been significantly modified by the glaciers while others have been affected relatively little. In addition, there are other outstanding features: examples of glacial and periglacial landforms, the latter produced by freezing and thawing of the soil and rocks; landforms associated with upland rivers, including mountain torrents, alluvial fans and wandering gravel-bed rivers; and detailed records of climate and vegetation changes preserved in peat bogs and loch sediments, including the history of the pine forest and rare arctic/alpine plant species. The presence of such a range of features in a relatively small area is quite exceptional.

Because successive glaciations removed much of the evidence, the geological record of events pre-dating the last glaciation is far from complete in Scotland. Traces of the pre-glacial landscape survive only in areas where glacial erosion was very limited. The Cairngorms, however, are exceptional for the degree of preservation of earlier features in a glaciated mountain landscape. Pre-glacial landform remnants include the broad, sweeping plateaux which epitomise the Cairngorms, the dome-shaped summits which rise from the plateaux and are sometimes capped with tors, and the shallow river valleys such as Coire Domhain and the valley of the Feith Buidhe between Cairn Gorm and Ben Macdui. There are also local pockets of weathered bedrock which have survived glacial erosion. One of these occurs in Coire Raibert, between Cairn Gorm and Cairn Lochan, where the decomposed granite can be crumbled in the hand.

The Cairngorms tors are an important feature of the landscape and are the finest in Scotland. The best examples occur on Beinn Mheadhoin, Ben Avon and Bynack More, where the Barns of Bynack reach a height of over 20 m. The classic explanation for the formation of the tors is that they developed under the warm, humid climate in pre-glacial times. Areas of densely jointed granite were decomposed by deep, sub-surface, chemical weathering, leaving intervening areas of less densely jointed rock more intact. The weaker rotted rock was later eroded away, with the sound rock remaining as tors. However, recent research suggests that the present tors are unlikely to be truly pre-glacial

remnants and that the oldest surviving features today were first exhumed around a million years ago. Probably shallower chemical weathering of the granite during milder phases early in the Ice Age, followed by repeated removal of the weathered material, played a significant part in their development.

The survival of spectacular tors, particularly on the more easterly plateaux of the Cairngorms, suggests that in these areas the glaciers did not modify the landscape greatly. The contrast between the preservation of the rolling plateau landscape, with tors and pockets of weathered granite, and the deeply eroded, steep-sided glens and corries is quite remarkable and is explained by the characteristics of the glaciers. Those on the plateaux were generally thin, often frozen to the underlying bedrock and slow-moving; movement of the ice occurred through deformation within the ice mass, rather than by sliding over the ground. These glaciers were therefore incapable of much erosion, enabling the unexpected survival of relict features in a glaciated landscape.

Relatively fast-flowing glaciers sliding down the valleys were much more efficient agents of erosion during the numerous episodes of glaciation that occurred during

The Barns of Bynack: Granite tors on Bynack More.
Photo: *R. Wignall*

Table 2.3.   Landform assemblages and landforms in the Cairngorms

Landform assemblage	Examples of landforms/features of interest
Relict features (pre-dating the last glaciation and in some cases, the Ice Age)	plateau surfaces with shallow (fluvial-shaped) valleys tors areas of deeply rotted bedrock ancient sheet jointing in the granite
Landforms of glacial and glacifluvial erosion	glacial troughs breached watersheds glacial diversion of drainage corries ice-scoured bedrock roches moutonnées truncated spurs meltwater channels
Landforms of glacial and glacifluvial deposition	drift mantles erratics lateral and recessional moraines boulder moraines and hummocky moraines eskers kame terraces ice-dammed lake deposits outwash fans and terraces kettle holes
Periglacial landforms	blockfields deflation surfaces large-scale patterned ground gelifluction (solifluction) lobes talus slopes and related features (rock glaciers and protalus ramparts)

Postglacial and contemporary geomorphological features	a) slope processes
	    rock slope failures
	    solifluction
	    debris flows
	    debris cones
	    snow avalanche features
	
	b) periglacial processes
	    deflation surfaces and wind-patterned vegetation
	    small-scale patterned ground
	    nivation
	
	c) dynamic river channel and valley floor changes
	    braided and wandering gravel-bed rivers
	    alluvial fans
	    river channel changes
	    palaeochannels
	    river terraces

Peat bogs and loch sediments	microfossils (e.g. pollen, diatoms, chironomids and testate amoebae) macrofossils (e.g. pine stumps, other plant remains and charcoal) sediment physical properties and geochemistry

the Ice Age. These glaciers produced a series of deeply eroded glens and troughs, with steep cliffs that cut through the gently rolling pre-glacial plateau surfaces. Glen Avon and Gleann Einich are particularly striking examples. In places, the glaciers also carved through pre-existing watersheds. This caused the headwaters of the River Feshie and the River Avon to be diverted from their pre-glacial to their present courses, and formed spectacular glacial breaches such as the Lairig Ghru, Pass of Ryvoan, upper Glen Feshie, Inchrory and the Lairig an Laoigh.

There are also other features of glacial erosion for which the central Cairngorm massif is particularly noted. Truncated spurs, such as the Devil's Point, occur where pre-glacial valleys were straightened by the glaciers. Corries are steep mountain basins formed by small glaciers during episodes of less extensive glaciation. Their locations on north- and east-facing slopes reflect the influence of wind-blown snow and shading on the development of mountain glaciers. 'Roches moutonnées' are asymmetric bedrock forms, smooth and streamlined on their up-glacier sides but steep and rough on their down-glacier sides, where weakened rock was plucked away by the ice. Roches moutonnées can vary in size from small rocky knolls to hills hundreds of metres high.

The Cairngorms massif is a classic landscape of selective glacial erosion. The extensive plateau surfaces have generally been little modified by glacial erosion and contrast markedly with the deeply incised glacial troughs, such as that of Loch Avon.

Photo: *J. Gordon*

The Cairngorm glens and straths support an equally diverse assemblage of glacial deposits and other landforms produced by the melting glaciers, all of which are important aspects of the geomorphology. Moraines are mounds of glacial debris deposited at the margins of glaciers. They may mark the maximum extent of a glacier advance or the positions where the front of a retreating glacier temporarily halted. On the northern flanks of the Cairngorms, for example north of Loch Einich, there is evidence of a readvance or stillstand of the last ice sheet, while several corries contain excellent examples of moraines left by the corrie glaciers of the Loch Lomond Readvance.

Meltwater channels were eroded by glacial meltwater as it flowed from the glaciers and also underneath them; dramatic examples include the rough bouldery gaps below Creag a' Chalamain and Airgiod-meall in upper Glenmore, and the channel of Clais Fhearnaig, which links Glen Lui and Glen Quoich in the upper Dee Valley. Eskers are formed of sand and gravel which was deposited in rivers flowing underneath the ice, and then left as steep-sided ridges when the surrounding ice melted. Kames are mounds of sediment left by the melting of stagnant ice. Kettle holes are deep hollows where buried ice blocks melted leaving a void into which sediment collapsed. Good examples of all of these features occur in an area from lower Glen Feshie through Glenmore to the Braes of Abernethy.

Kame terraces formed where the meltwater rivers flowed along the edges of the glaciers; there are good examples at the north end of Strath Nethy. River terraces also occur, for example in Strathspey and the Dee Valley. They are the remains of glen floors filled with sediment from meltwater rivers, their terraced appearance being the result of later, smaller rivers cutting into the original valley floor flood-plain.

Landforms associated with ice-dammed lakes also form an important part of the special interest of the Cairngorms. Lakes formed in Glen Quoich, Glen Derry, Gleann Einich and the north end of the Lairig Ghru where the huge glaciers in the Dee Valley and Strathspey blocked the flow of meltwater from local mountain glaciers. The deltas formed by glacial meltwater rivers flowing into some of these lakes remain as distinctive accumulations of sediments in these glens. They also contain evidence that the lakes periodically drained and re-filled, probably due to fluctuations in the thickness of the glacial ice which dammed them.

Periglacial landforms are produced by seasonal freezing and thawing in the loose rock and soil, known as regolith, particularly under conditions of extreme

Hummocky moraine is particularly well developed in the Pass of Drumochter.
Photo: *J. Gordon*

Meltwater channel near Creag a' Chalamain, northern Cairngorms.
Photo: *L. Gill*

cold beyond the margins of glacial ice where the snow cover is seasonal. In the Cairngorms massif, periglacial landforms are extensively developed on the higher slopes and plateau surfaces. Downslope movement of the regolith has resulted in the widespread development of solifluction sheets, terraces and lobes, where frost-weathered debris has 'flowed' downhill by soil creep under water saturated conditions. The larger solifluction features, such as boulder lobes, are now inactive and probably date from the time of the Loch Lomond Readvance or earlier, while smaller-scale features have probably been active throughout the Holocene and are still continuing to form.

On some of the summits, including Ben Macdui and Derry Cairngorm, frost shattering of the bedrock has produced areas of broken rock or 'blockfields'. Patterned ground features, such as large sorted circles and stripes, were formed in the past by freeze-thaw processes, and smaller features are still active today. Wind-patterned vegetation and deflation scars and surfaces, caused by wind erosion, are presently active on exposed spurs and slopes. Rock slopes eroded by the glaciers were left steep and unstable when the ice melted. In a few cases, these slopes subsequently failed catastrophically and several large rock slope failures are

Blockfield on Derry Cairngorm produced by frost weathering of the bedrock.
Photo: *L. Gill*

present in the Cairngorms massif, notably in Strath Nethy and at the northern end of the Lairig Ghru. Some of these have been linked with the formation of rock glaciers (tongues or lobes of rock debris and ice) at the time of the Loch Lomond Readvance, but this remains questionable. Elsewhere, talus (scree) slopes are common below the glacially steepened cliffs and have been extensively modified by debris flows which continue to be active today, triggered by intense rainstorms. Good examples occur in Glen Feshie and the Lairig Ghru.

The patterns of climate change and vegetation development during the last 15,000 years are recorded in the sediments, plant remains and pollen grains preserved in numerous loch basins and peat bogs within the Cairngorms massif and in the wider Cairngorms area. These allow detailed reconstructions of palaeoenvironmental conditions and permit a wider historical perspective on present environmental changes. Such palaeoenvironmental records document the pattern of expansion and decline of the native pine forest, the spread of blanket bog and the increasing human impacts on the landscape since the middle Holocene. At the Tomintoul GCR site near **Inchrory**, in Glen Avon, a tufa deposit has yielded a valuable record of environmental change during the last 11,500 years. Human impacts are evident from palaeolimnological studies which show that the high corrie lochs are contaminated by fly-ash particles and trace metals, and that some have undergone significant acidification from atmospheric pollution over the last 100 years.

Within the Cairngorms massif, there are also several key sites for river geomorphology. **Glen Feshie** is internationally famous, comprising one of the most active braided river sections in Britain in its upper reaches, a wandering gravel-bed river in its middle reaches, and a highly dynamic confluence fan at its junction with the Spey. Each section is important in a national context, but together the suite of different river patterns, which demonstrate downstream change in river behaviour, add up to be the most important fluvial geomorphology site in Scotland. The Feshie fan has been subject to river engineering in the recent past, and flood mitigation proposals were the subject of a Public Inquiry in 1992. However, the high rates of fluvial activity particularly during flood conditions allow the river to restore its planform to a more natural state.

The north-flowing **Allt Mór** (River Druie) drains the northern corries of Cairn Gorm. It is an excellent example of a mountain torrent with coarse-grained bed material. The river is relatively stable for most of the year, but can generate significant channel change during periods of intense localised rainfall over the northern Cairngorms.

The **Derry Burn** occupies an alluvial basin (itself situated within a wider glacial trough), which has developed due to the local base level control exerted by the presence of an outcrop of resistant bedrock. The river is important for the tortuous, rectangular meander bends, the presence of cut-offs and former channels of varying age on the valley floor, and features such as meander scrolls.

The neighbouring catchment, the **Luibeg Burn**, has a much steeper gradient, and the river provides a good example of a coarse-grained mountain torrent. Of added interest is the persistence of features relating to floods in 1829 and 1956. The Quoich Water Fan at the confluence of the **Quoich Water** and the River Dee provides an excellent example of a large, active, low-angle alluvial fan. The Quoich debouches from a rock-controlled reach shortly upstream of the confluence, making a rapid downstream transition which, unfortunately, has been subject to engineering. The drains in the area surrounding the Quoich Water have recently been blocked in an attempt to create a wetland environment (see Chapter 10).

Landforms of the wider Cairngorms area

As well as the internationally and nationally important features of the central Cairngorms massif, there are other, nationally important interests within the Cairngorms National Park and in the wider Cairngorms area.

Three GCR sites have been selected for their glacial features. **Lochnagar**, underlain by the Lochnagar granite, is noted for its spectacular solifluction lobes, corrie landforms and moraines. The floors of the glens are infilled with till and glacifluvial deposits (eskers, kames and kettle holes), as in Strathspey (notably at **Loch Etteridge**) and along the Dee Valley (notably at **Muir of Dinnet**), where there are fine examples of meltwater channels, eskers and kettleholes. Loch Etteridge is also important for the radiocarbon dates on its basal organic sediments, which provide a time constraint on the deglaciation of Strathspey around 15,000 years ago.

Two sites are important for their river landforms. The **Allt Dubhaig**, a small tributary of the River Garry, is one of the most intensively studied rivers in Britain, and has been likened to an outdoor laboratory for fluvial studies. The controls on river planform change downstream, generating a river system which shows a downstream progression in channel pattern over a distance of around 3 km. **Dorback Burn**, a tributary of the River Nethy, is an excellent example of a wandering gravel-bed river. It is notable for the rapidity and extent of channel changes since the mid 20th century.

Meanders on the River Dee in Glen Geusachan.
Photo: *J. Gordon*

The vegetation and environmental history of the National Park and the wider area are also represented in a number of key GCR sites. These are *Abernethy Forest*, *Morrone*, *Coire Fee*, *Loch Etteridge* and Loch Kinord at *Muir of Dinnet*. During the middle Holocene, a woodland cover of pine and birch predominated. In some areas (Coire Fee and Morrone), certain arctic-alpine species have survived throughout the Holocene in favourable habitats (see Chapter 14).

The Cairngorms National Park and wider area include additional, non-GCR geomorphological features. To the south-west of the central Cairngorms massif, the Gaick area is noted for the occurrence of substantial thicknesses of deeply weathered bedrock. Glacial erosion is localised along major drainage lines, watershed breaches (e.g. Glen Tilt, Gaick and the Pass of Drumochter) and in shallow corries. Excellent examples of large roches moutonnées occur along the Dee Valley between Braemar and Ballater, and in Strathspey at Dulnain Bridge and south of Aviemore at Ord Ban and Farleitter Crag (Creag Far-leitire). Glacial and glacifluvial deposits add significantly to the topographic detail in many of the glens and straths, such as Glen Truim, Glen Garry, Glen Tromie, Strathspey, the Dulnain Valley, Glen Clova, Glen Esk and Glen Callater. These deposits are often reworked to form river terraces.

In the glens of the Gaick Forest between Drumochter, the Tilt and the Feshie/Geldie, melting glaciers produced many small-scale meltwater channels and extensive deposits of hummocky moraine. Similar features also occur in the West Drumochter Hills, and hummocky moraine is particularly well developed in the Pass of Drumochter. The hills west of Drumochter are also noted for their fine assemblage of periglacial landforms, including solifluction features and ploughing boulders. The latter are boulders that have moved downslope under solifluction and freeze-thaw conditions, 'ploughing up' the ground in front of them and leaving a furrow behind. Postglacial slope modification is particularly well demonstrated at the Pass of Drumochter, where debris flows continue to be active. A number of larger-scale rock slope failures occur in the glacial breaches of the Gaick; and in Glen Clova, above Loch Brandy, there is a spectacular rock slope failure.

In the Monadhliath, extensive remnants of pre-glacial erosion surfaces dominate the landscape, although glacial erosion has formed a number of corries and valley heads, for example around Carn Dearg and adjacent uplands. Glacial deposits in some of the corries and valley heads of the Monadhliath provide a potentially important source of evidence for interpreting the deglaciation of the area.

The Cairngorms area contains the headwaters of many of the main rivers of eastern and north-east Scotland, such as the Spey, Dee and Don and their tributaries. It also contains the headwaters of the south-east flowing rivers such as the Clova, Prosen Water and West Water. The headwater tributaries feeding the main rivers are generally short, steep mountain torrents with coarse bed material and alluvial fans where they join the main glens. The main rivers downstream typically display alternating stable and unstable reaches with rock-controlled sections separating alluvial basins in flat-bottomed glens. The alluvial reaches are sinuous and gently meandering, and have the characteristics of wandering gravel-bed rivers. In some cases they are confined by older river terraces and by 19th and 20th century flood embankments. Sites of note include the Conglass Water, which has a sequence of irregular tortuous meanders in an upland setting, and the River Dulnain, which is an active gravel-bed river with a generally braided upper reach and an irregularly meandering middle reach.

The wider Cairngorms area also contains tributaries of the River Tay, including the River Tilt and the River Garry. The River Garry has been captured for hydro-electricity and has an extremely low base flow for much of the year. The

The postglacial environmental history of the Cairngorms area is recorded in its blanket peat and peat bogs.
Photo: *J. Gordon*

upper Spey has also been adjusting to the effects of impoundment downstream of the Spey Dam.

Recent research and survey findings

Recent research findings are reviewed here from an arbitrary start date of 1990. These findings are summarised below under a number of themes.

Origins, evolution and context of the Dalradian Supergroup

The following summary of research findings is based on the review of Strachan *et al.* (2002).

The rocks underlying the Dalradian Supergroup, the Dava and Glen Banchor successions, were affected by an important compression and heating event around 800 million years ago, probably related to mountain-building. This event also affected the Moine Supergroup rocks, the main rock-type north of the Great Glen Fault. This supports the proposed correlation between the Moine Supergroup and the rocks underlying the Dalradian Supergroup.

Detailed mapping by the British Geological Survey in the Central Highlands appears to confirm that the Dava and Glen Banchor successions are part of the old 'basement' rock on which the Dalradian sediments were deposited. The Dalradian sediments, however, were not affected by the compression and heating event 800 million years ago, which affected the Dava and Glen Banchor successions, implying that the Dalradian sediments were deposited after this event.

Further work on the Dalradian sediments confirms that they were laid down where a continent was rifting to form a new ocean. This was an environment where sediment was being deposited and was characterised by individual 'basins' (depressions in which sediments accumulate) separated by active faults. Variations in sediment layer thicknesses and the architecture of local basins in which the Dalradian sediments were deposited are now better understood.

Fauna (i.e. fossil animal remains) distinctive to the ancient continent of Laurentia have been found in sedimentary rocks which lie above the youngest Dalradian rocks, but are part of the same continuous episode of sedimentation. This confirms that the Dalradian rocks were always part of the continent of Laurentia (not, for example, part of another continent which later became attached to Laurentia through movement along the Great Glen Fault).

The major heating and compression event which affected the Dalradian rocks, known as the 'Grampian orogeny', occurred around 475–460 million years ago and was apparently the result of volcanic islands colliding with Laurentia, rather than, for example, the later major collision with Eastern Avalonia. The massive mountains which were formed during the Grampian orogeny, therefore, had been eroding for 50 million years or so when the post-tectonic Cairngorm granite was intruded approximately 427 million years ago.

The 'crustal blocks' on either side of the Great Glen Fault (Dalradian Supergroup 'block' and Moine Supergroup 'block') both appear to have been parts of the continent of Laurentia. However, the Moine Supergroup rocks to the north of the Great Glen Fault were affected by the collision between Laurentia and Baltica, while the Dalradian rocks and underlying Dava and Glen Banchor successions to the south of the Great Glen were not. This suggests that the two 'crustal blocks' were at least 500 km apart. It is thought that the 'blocks' later moved together to their present positions through sideways, or 'strike-slip', movement along the Great Glen Fault; but movement along this fault of 500 km or more is larger than has previously been supposed.

Magma and hydrothermal history of the Cairngorm granite

A research survey co-funded by SNH and the British Geological Survey on the geology, structure and landscape of the Cairngorm Mountains (Thomas *et al.*, 2004) brought together the results of new field observations and published studies to produce the following interpretation of the magma and hydrothermal history of the Cairngorm granite.

The magma which cooled to form the Cairngorm granite originally began to form around 427 million years ago during the late stages of deformation which resulted from the closure of the Iapetus Ocean. Melting to produce the magma probably occurred in the 'upper mantle' or 'lower crust', which are specific parts of the Earth's internal structure, in this case indicating a depth between 20 and 40 km below the Earth's surface.

The composition of the early magma would have been modified considerably as it rose upwards, due to the rocks through which it passed being fractured, melted and incorporated within the rising magma. This melting and incorporation would also have caused an increase in magma volume. Crystals formed within the magma and sank downwards, effectively being lost from the rising magma. This would have altered the magma composition, increasing the concentration of certain elements and decreasing that of others. The overall effect of these compositional changes was to evolve the magma towards a granite composition.

It is not known whether the 'frozen' magma chamber represented by the presently exposed granite continues to significantly deeper levels, or whether it is a relatively thin structure, perhaps connected by 'feeder channels' to a deeper chamber. In either scenario, rising magma would have mixed, partly crystallised and may have formed texturally discrete units prior to final emplacement in its present-day position. The presently exposed surface through the granite mass (or pluton) was approximately 6–8 km below the Earth's surface when it solidified.

The emplaced magma solidified to form several grain-size and texture variants and a detailed, but a tentative sequence for the emplacement of these has been constructed. Magma units interpreted to have been emplaced early in the sequence probably take the form of large, irregular masses. Much of the granite with a relatively small crystal size, known as 'fine granite', may take the form of a large gently inclined sheet, or perhaps a steeply inclined sheet that spreads laterally at the present level of the high plateaux. Patches and sheets of granite with a very small crystal size, known as 'microgranite', are widespread and take many forms, with extensive gently dipping sheets being prominent in the central part of the granite.

The magma may have incorporated numerous fragments of the surrounding rocks, known as 'xenoliths', during its ascent and emplacement. If so, the great majority of these probably descended to levels below the presently exposed surface. Granite with a very large crystal size, known as 'coarse' granite, is found around Glen Avon, and appears to have trapped a greater number of descending xenoliths than other areas of granite. This may have been because this magma was more viscous and therefore the falling xenoliths were 'stalled' within it.

Landscape evolution

The long-term landscape evolution of the Cairngorms area in the wider context of the Scottish Highlands has been reviewed by Hall (1991) and Hall & Bishop (2002). The study by SNH and the British Geological Survey also produced some significant findings on landscape evolution of the Cairngorms massif (Thomas et al., 2004). In particular, the geology of the massif has significantly affected the development of the landscape. Zones of weakened granite were developed by hot fluids penetrating and chemically altering the rock along steeply inclined joints (linear cracks). This happened soon after the granite magma had been intruded and had largely solidified. Detailed survey of the ubiquitous, steeply inclined joints that cut the Cairngorm granite showed that they have no strongly preferred orientation. However, only certain of these joints, running predominantly NNE, were open to the passage of the hot fluids which altered and weakened the rock.

Once the granite was exposed in the Devonian (416–359 million years ago), weathering and erosion focused on these chemically altered zones of weakened rock. Thus, it is suggested that much of the basic landscape began to be established about 390 million years ago. Since then, weathering and erosion have modified the *gross* landscape *relatively* little. It is also suggested that no new major valleys have developed since the granite was first exposed above ground and significantly eroded. On the medium- to small scale, 'kernels' of massive, poorly jointed granite surrounded by more strongly and densely jointed granite form the tors that are such a conspicuous feature of Ben Avon, Beinn Mheadhoin and Bynack More.

A detailed reconstruction of the pre-glacial relief by Thomas et al. (2004) also allowed an assessment to be made of the patterns of glacial erosion. Glaciations through the Quaternary significantly modified the shape of the existing valleys, deepening them, steepening their sides and altering their profiles. Glaciation was also responsible for excavating the corries. However, the high plateaux suffered *relatively* little modification during the Quaternary and much of the large-scale form of the landscape in these upland areas is broadly as it would have appeared prior to glaciation.

Other recent studies have examined the ages of rock surfaces and the patterns of glacial erosion. Geomorphological mapping and surface exposure dating of rock surfaces using cosmogenic radionuclides has revealed the variability of glacial erosion on the Cairngorm plateaux (Hall & Glasser, 2003; Hall & Phillips, in press a,b). This variability has been shown to be linked to reconstructed basal ice sheet temperatures (Glasser, 1995; Glasser & Hall, 1997; Hall & Glasser, 2003). Geomorphological evidence and cosmogenic radionuclide surface exposure dating also indicate that the tors are younger than previously believed and that it is unlikely that the present rock surfaces pre-date the Quaternary (Phillips et al., 2006; Hall & Phillips, in press a,b). In the central Grampian Highlands, Hall and Jarman (2004) investigated patterns of glacial erosion and rock slope failure, and demonstrated the role of watershed breaching in landscape evolution.

Glacial history

Several studies have demonstrated that the last ice sheet decayed actively, and that its recession was interrupted by a significant stillstand or readvance, in which lakes were dammed in a number of glens, at a time when a local ice cap was centred on the Cairngorms massif (Brown, 1992, 1993; Brazier *et al.*, 1996a,b, 1998; Golledge, 2002, 2003; Everest, 2003; Everest & Kubik, 2006). The application of new surface exposure dating methods using cosmogenic radionuclides has provided confirmation of the stillstand/readvance and suggested links with a significant regional climate event (Everest, 2003; Everest & Kubik, 2006). It has also confirmed the relatively limited extent of Loch Lomond Readvance glaciers in the Cairngorms massif.

Further radiocarbon dating of the basal sediments at Loch Etteridge has confirmed the relatively early deglaciation of Strathspey, around 15,000 years ago (Everest, 2003; Everest & Golledge, 2004).

The central Grampian Highlands, including the Gaick area, Drumochter Pass and the West Drumochter Hills, have been the focus of recent research and debate on deglaciation history and the extent of the Loch Lomond Readvance glaciers (Lukas, 2002, 2003; Lukas *et al.*, 2004 and contributions therein; Benn & Ballantyne, 2005). Benn & Ballantyne (2005) used geomorphological evidence to reconstruct a Loch Lomond Readvance icefield in the West Drumochter Hills and the contemporary palaeoclimatic conditions.

River processes and changes

Studies of the sensitivity of upland rivers to environmental change over the last 250 years showed that rivers have extensively reworked their valley floors, through rapid rates of lateral movement during 'flood-rich' periods, but have otherwise not undergone significant changes in behaviour in response to natural processes (Leys, 1997; Brasington *et al.*, 2000; Rumsby *et al.*, 2001; Werritty & Leys, 2001).

The Allt Dubhaig has been the focus of a number of major studies of river processes and sediment transport (Ferguson & Ashworth, 1991; Drew, 1992; Hoey & Ferguson, 1994; Sambrook-Smith & Ferguson, 1995; Wathen, 1995; Ferguson *et al.*, 1996, 1999; Leys, 1997; Wathen & Hoey, 1998).

A series of studies have addressed the hydrology, geomorphology and management of the River Spey between the Insh Marshes and the River Spey-Feshie confluence and the River Feshie alluvial fan in relation to flood mitigation works (Petts *et al.*, 1990, 1991; Johnson *et al.*, 1991; Johnson, 1992, 1993; Werritty & Brazier, 1991b; Gilvear, 1994; Werritty *et al.*, 1999; Gilvear *et al.*, 2000). A wider survey of the geomorphology of the River Spey floodplain was completed by Rowan *et al.* (1994).

A study of the impoundment of the upper Spey showed that parts of the channel downstream are still adjusting 60 years later, and that the channel has narrowed, reducing its capacity to evacuate large floods (Gilvear, 2004).

A review of trends in river channels and processes, including sites throughout the Cairngorms area, concluded that rivers are characterised by episodic change that is variable from place to place, and that changes may reflect management activities more strongly than natural factors (Werritty & Hoey, 2003).

A case study of landscape response in the Edendon valley in the central Grampian Highlands concluded that onset of floodplain incision occurred after 2,700 years ago, following climatic deterioration and that episodic deposition of an alluvial fan was related to extreme rainstorm events (Ballantyne & Whittington, 1999).

Slope processes

Several studies have investigated the chronology and frequency of hillslope failure and underlying mechanisms and triggers, including reduction in shear strength of slopes due to progressive pedogenesis, the role of rainstorm variations and snow avalanches (Brooks, 1991; Luckman, 1992; Brooks *et al.*, 1993; Brooks & Richards, 1994; Curry, 1998, 2000). A wider review of trends in debris flows, including sites within the Cairngorms area, concluded that debris flows have occurred intermittently over the last 7,000 years but that there was evidence for more frequent and extensive hillslope flow activity within the last few centuries (Ballantyne, 2002a,b).

Periglacial processes in the Cairngorms massif have been reviewed by Ballantyne (1996) and vegetation links by Haynes *et al.* (1998a).

Environmental history

The environmental history of the area during the last 15,000 years is recorded in the sediments and plant and insect remains preserved in loch basins, peat bogs and blanket peat. Such records have allowed interpretations of the expansion and decline of the native pine forest and the spread of blanket peat (Bennett, 1995, 1996a,b), tree-line dynamics (McConnell, 1996; Binney, 1997), the history of arctic-alpine species (Huntley, 1994), past floristic diversity (Allen

& Huntley, 1999) and climate change (Barber *et al.*, 1999, 2000; Battarbee *et al.*, 2001; Langdon & Barber, 2004; Blundell & Barber, 2005).

Human impacts are clearly evident from palaeolimnological studies (Jones *et al.*, 1993; Battarbee *et al.*, 1996; Dalton *et al.*, 2005), which show that the high corrie lochs are contaminated by fly-ash particles and trace metals, and that some have undergone significant acidification from atmospheric pollution over the last 100 years. At Lochnagar, catchment-driven changes during the Holocene have had a stronger influence on the loch biota than climate changes (Dalton *et al.*, 2005).

Application of new methods (Birks, 1996), including analyses of chironomid midges preserved in loch sediments (Brooks, 1996), sediment geochemistry (Jones *et al.*, 1993), stable isotopes in tree rings (Loader & Switsur, 1996) and plant macrofossil, testate amoebae and humification records in peat bogs (Langdon & Barber, 2004; Blundell & Barber, 2005) is leading to greater resolution of the patterns of Holocene environmental changes, particularly when combined in multi-proxy approaches (Battarbee *et al.*, 2001; Dalton *et al.*, 2005; Langdon & Barber, 2005). For example, results from the peat studies

Erosion is a natural process in the uplands, as seen on the right of the photograph, but is locally accelerated by human trampling

Photo: *J. Gordon*

show cyclic patterns of climate change on a millennial timescale that appear to correspond with marine and ice-core records, suggesting that the bogs are responding to the same forcing mechanism (Langdon & Barber, 2005). In addition, the discovery of several tephra horizons in the sediments at Loch Etteridge should enhance palaeoenvironmental interpretations and dating of the environmental changes represented there (Everest, 2003).

Geomorphological inventory, landscape sensitivity and monitoring geomorphological change

An inventory of the geomorphology of the central Cairngorms massif has been completed from field and air photography mapping, and compiled in a GIS (Brazier & Gordon, 2006).

Several studies have addressed the issue of terrain sensitivity from a geo-ecological perspective, examining the links between soils, geomorphology and vegetation. Using examples from the Cairngorms, these have examined the interdependencies between geomorphology and the montane ecosystem (Haynes *et al.*, 1998a; Gordon *et al.*, 1998), the links between geomorphological sensitivity and landscape sensitivity (Haynes *et al.*, 2001; Thompson *et al.*, 2001; Gordon *et al.*, 2001, 2002a,b; Jonasson *et al.*, 2005) and quantitative assessment of vegetation and regolith properties (Morrocco, 2006). The geomorphological sensitivity of key landforms and landform assemblages in relation to specific activities is assessed by Brazier and Gordon (2006), building on earlier work on river systems, notably the River Feshie (Werritty & Brazier, 1991a, 1994; Brazier & Werritty, 1994).

Several baseline studies for monitoring geomorphological sensitivity and change have been undertaken on Cairn Gorm as part of the Visitor Management Plan for the funicular railway (see Chapter 22) and elsewhere in the Cairngorms massif, to provide a wider context for any observed changes (Haynes *et al.*, 1998a,b; Haynes & Grieve, 2000; Haynes, 2001). These have developed a monitoring framework and indicators, and baseline sites have been established on Cairn Gorm/Ben Macdui, Ben a' Bhuird/Ben Avon and Braeriach/Einich Cairn.

Trends

There is little systematic information on current trends in the geology and landforms of the Cairngorms. Baseline information on the geology and geomorphology of individual GCR sites is available from Earth Science Site Documentation Reports compiled by SNH between 1991 and 2001, although the level of detail provided in these reports was not intended for monitoring trends and may be unsuitable for doing so, particularly on larger sites. The first round of Site Condition Monitoring (SCM), initiated in 1999, highlights changes in a few areas, but the short time lapse between publication of the baseline Earth Science Site Documentation Reports and establishment of the SCM programme means that any medium- to long-term changes have not been recorded. As noted above and in Chapter 22, baseline surveys for geomorphology have been conducted as part of the Visitor Management Plan for the funicular railway on Cairn Gorm.

A number of the Dalradian, Caledonian Igneous, Non-Marine Devonian and Mineralogy of Scotland GCR sites in the Cairngorms area have been monitored as part of SNH's SCM Programme. At the Loch Avon mineral site no examples of the important mineral blue topaz were found. All other Dalradian, Caledonian Igneous, Non-Marine Devonian and Mineralogy of Scotland GCR sites monitored so far, however, have been found to be in favourable condition, with minerals and rock outcrops undamaged and appropriately visible for study and research purposes.

A number of the Quaternary of Scotland and Fluvial Geomorphology of Scotland GCR sites in the Cairngorms area have also been monitored as part of SNH's SCM Programme. The majority of Earth science features on sites monitored to date have been found to be in favourable condition, with deposits, landforms and river channels undamaged and sufficiently visible for study and research purposes, and with natural river processes unimpeded to an acceptable degree. However, the River Feshie was found to be in unfavourable condition when assessed (in January 2003), as a result of damage caused by unconsented river works and gravel removal. Other damaging factors noted on monitored sites include dredging of river gravels (date unknown), small borrow pits, erosion of footpaths, off-track vehicle use and natural tree regeneration obscuring features of interest.

Over the last 250 years, river channel changes do not show clear trends, but rather are episodic in nature. Changes in gravel-bed rivers have been rapid during floods, and the rivers have extensively reworked their valley floors through rapid rates of lateral movement. However, they have otherwise not undergone significant changes in behaviour in response to natural processes.

Debris flows have occurred at susceptible sites in the Highlands, including the Cairngorms, over much or all of the past 7,000 years, but there is geomorphological evidence for more frequent and more extensive hillslope activity within the past few centuries.

Conservation issues

Mineral extraction and after-use of quarries and gravel pits. Mineral extraction on a small scale, including re-opening of small disued quarries, may be beneficial in providing fresh exposures in bedrock or glacial deposits. Conversely, large-scale mineral extraction can be highly damaging to geological sites and landforms. Large-scale sand and gravel quarrying may destroy glacial landforms which cannot be replaced. Landfill and restoration of quarries usually excludes access to exposures, unless conservation sections are incorporated early in the planning process. Gravel extraction from rivers disrupts the natural processes and damages the landforms and habitats they support.

Mineral collecting. Local damage from mineral collecting has been noted, although the extent and timing of this are unknown. A few sites may be vulnerable to any large-scale collecting of rare mineral specimens.

Afforestation and natural tree regeneration. Afforestation and natural tree regeneration may impact on landforms through direct damage, or by obscuring views of the features of interest. In Glenmore, lower Glen Feshie and Glen Clova, commercial afforestation has obscured the landforms. Natural tree regeneration, being encouraged in a number of locations in the Cairngorms area, may also obscure in the future some geological and geomorphological features.

Soil erosion, footpath erosion and overgrazing. Soil erosion is a natural process, but is locally enhanced through grazing and recreational pressure. The impacts are likely to be greatest on small-scale periglacial features. Overgrazing is locally affecting slope stability and erosion in Glen Feshie. Footpath erosion has had localised impacts on periglacial features on the higher slopes and plateaux of the Cairngorms. Well-constructed and maintained paths are the most realistic solution to minimising the areas affected by such erosion. A number of such paths have been constructed in recent years on the lower slopes and up towards the plateaux.

Off-track vehicle use. An increase in off-track vehicle use is a potential problem, as this may damage glacial and periglacial features. Only minor surface damage has been noted to date.

Commercial, industrial and infrastructure developments. Road and track cuttings can damage landforms. However, they are also a potential source of geological exposures, and where this is the case their value will be diminished by grading or hydroseeding.

Rivers and river engineering. River engineering for flood control or fisheries management may result in damage to river landforms, disruption of natural processes and adverse effects downstream, particularly where solid structures are emplaced in the river or along the banks. A range of alternative, low impact methods is now available. In the Cairngorms area, river engineering for flood protection, fisheries management and local gravel extraction continues gradually to impede the natural evolution of rivers (e.g. the Allt Mór, the Feshie-Spey confluence, the Quoich Water Fan, and the Spey and its tributaries) and has altered discharges through impoundment (Garry and upper Spey). Some of this work is required to maintain stability of public roads and bridges, but it is important to keep a clear view of how the cumulative effects of numerous small works are affecting the inherent value of the rivers as natural systems. Other changes in land use and management may also impact on river processes, through changes to discharge and sediment inputs.

Artificially modified channel at the apex of the River Feshie fan.
Photo: *J. Gordon*

Drainage of peat bogs and peat erosion. These activities are likely to lead to the loss of palaeoenvironmental records.

Climate change. Impacts of climate change on montane landforms may occur directly, through changes in processes (e.g. increased erosion from greater frequency of intense rainstorms), or indirectly through changes in vegetation (e.g. increased or decreased cover). Similarly, changes in river processes and landform may occur through changes in flood magnitude and frequency.

Awareness and education. Much more could be done to raise wider awareness of the nationally and internationally important geodiversity interests in the Cairngorms area, amongst local people, landowners, land managers and visitors. Issues include raising awareness of geodiversity *per se*, as well as the links between geodiversity and other elements of the landscape and land use. The diversity of Earth heritage interests also offers potential opportunities for local involvement in income-generating tourism (geotourism) based on the area's geodiversity.

Geodiversity Audit and Local Geodiversity Action Plan. Preparation of a geodiversity audit and Local Geodiversity Action Plan for the National Park and the wider Cairngorms would help to promote awareness and understanding and guide the management of the area's outstanding geodiversity. It would also help to inform work on SEA, EIA, LBAPs and geotourism-based activities, and lead to better appreciation of the links between geodiversity and landscape character.

Knowledge gaps. There are still significant gaps in information about the geology and geomorphology of the Cairngorms area, both in terms of inventory and monitoring of changes. In particular, there is no systematic inventory of regionally or locally important sites, and there is a lack of information about the landforms and deposits outwith the central Cairngorms massif based on systematic mapping comparable to that available for the geology and soils. Also, there is no systematic monitoring, other than on SSSIs, of the state of geological and geomorphological features and of any changes arising as a result of natural processes and human activities, nor of how the landscape is changing (e.g. through river and slope processes and soil erosion).

References

Allen, J.R.M. & Huntley, B. (1999). Estimating past floristic diversity in montane regions from macrofossil assemblages. *Journal of Biogeography* 26: 55–73.

Ballantyne, C.K. (1996). Periglacial landforms in the Cairngorm Mountains. In: Glasser, N.F. & Bennett, M.R. (eds.), *The Quaternary of the Cairngorms. Field Guide.* Quaternary Research Association, London: pp. 70–103.

Ballantyne, C.K. (2002a). *Geomorphological changes and trends in Scotland: debris flows.* Scottish Natural Heritage Commissioned Report F00AC107A. SNH: Perth.

Ballantyne, C.K. (2002b). Debris flow activity in the Scottish Highlands: temporal trends and wider implications for dating. *Studia Geomorphologica Carpatho-Balcanica* 36: 7–27.

Ballantyne, C.K. & Whittington, G. (1999). Late Holocene floodplain incision and alluvial fan formation in the central Grampian Highlands, Scotland: chronology, environment and implications. *Journal of Quaternary Science* 14: 651–671.

Barber, K.E., Battarbee, R.W., Brooks, S.J., Eglington, G., Haworth, E.Y., Oldfield, F., Stevenson, A.C., Thompson, R., Appleby, P.G., Austin, W.E.N., Cameron, N.G., Ficken, K.J., Golding, P., Harkness, D.D., Holmes, J.A., Hutchinson, R., Lishman, J.P., Maddy, D., Pinder, L.C.V., Rose, N.L. & Stoneman, R.E. (1999). Proxy records of climate change in the UK over the last two millennia: documented change and sedimentary records from lakes and bogs. *Journal of the Geological Society* 156: 369–380.

Barber, K.E., Maddy, D., Rose, N., Stevenson, A.C., Stoneman, R. & Thompson, R. (2000). Replicated proxy-climate signals over the last 2000 yr from two distant UK peat bogs: new evidence for regional palaeoclimate teleconnections. *Quaternary Science Reviews* 19: 481–487.

Barclay, W.J., Browne, M.A.E., McMillan, A.A., Pickett, E.A., Stone, P. & Wilby, P.R. (2005). *The Old Red Sandstone of Great Britain.* Geological Conservation Review Series No. 31. JNCC: Peterborough.

Battarbee, R.W., Jones, V.J., Flower, R.J., Appleby, P.G., Rose, N.L. & Rippey, B. (1996). Palaeolimnological evidence for the atmospheric contamination and acidification of high Cairngorm lochs, with special reference to Lochnagar. *Botanical Journal of Scotland* 48: 79–87.

Battarbee, R.W., Cameron, N.G., Golding, P., Brooks, S.J., Switsur, R., Harkness, D.D., Appleby, P., Oldfield, F., Thompson, R., Monteith, D. & McGovern, A. (2001). Evidence for Holocene climate variability from the sediments of a Scottish remote mountain lake. *Journal of Quaternary Science* 16: 339–346.

Benn, D.I. & Ballantyne, C.K. (2005). Palaeoclimatic reconstruction from Loch Lomond Readvance glaciers in the West Drumochter Hills, Scotland. *Journal of Quaternary Science* 20: 577–592.

Bennett, K.D. (1995). Post-glacial dynamics of pine (*Pinus sylvestris* L.) and pinewoods in Scotland. In: Aldous, J.R. (ed.), *Our Pinewood Heritage.* Forestry Commission/RSPB/SNH: Farnham. pp. 23–39.

Bennett, K.D. (1996a). Late-Quaternary vegetation dynamics of the Cairngorms. *Botanical Journal of Scotland* 48: 51–63.

Bennett, K.D. (1996b). Late Quaternary vegetation history of the Cairngorm Mountains. In: Glasser, N.F. & Bennett, M.R. (eds.), *The Quaternary of the Cairngorms. Field Guide.* Quaternary Research Association: London. pp. 114–125.

Binney, H.A. (1997). *Holocene environmental change in the Scottish Highlands: multi-proxy evidence from blanket peats.* Unpublished PhD thesis, London Guildhall University.

Blundell, A.C. (2002). *Late Holocene multi-proxy climate records for northern Britain and Ireland derived from raised peat stratigraphy.* Unpublished PhD thesis, University of Southampton.

Blundell, A. & Barber, K. (2005). A 2800-year palaeoclimatic record from Tore Hill Moss, Strathspey, Scotland: the need for a multi-proxy approach to peat-based climate reconstructions. *Quaternary Science Reviews* 24: 1261–1277.

Birks, H.J.B. (1996). Palaeoecological studies in the Cairngorms – summary and future research needs. *Botanical Journal of Scotland* 48: 117–126.

Brasington, J., Rumsby, B.T. & McVey, R.A. (2000). Monitoring and modelling morphological change in a braided gravel-bed river using high resolution GPS-based survey. *Earth Surface Processes and Landforms* 25: 973–990.

Brazier, V. & Gordon, J.E. (2006). *The geomorphological heritage of the Cairngorm Mountains.* Scottish Natural Heritage Commissioned Report F00AC104. SNH: Perth.

Brazier, V., Gordon, J.E., Hubbard, A. & Sugden, D.E. (1996a). The geomorphological evolution of a dynamic landscape: the Cairngorm Mountains, Scotland. *Botanical Journal of Scotland* 48: 13–30.

Brazier, V., Gordon, J.E., Kirkbride, M.P. & Sugden, D.E. (1996b). The Late Devensian ice sheet and glaciers in the Cairngorm Mountains. In: Glasser, N.F. & Bennett, M.R. (eds.), *The Quaternary of the Cairngorms. Field Guide.* Quaternary Research Association: London. pp. 28–53.

Brazier, V., Kirkbride, M.P. & Gordon, J.E. (1998). Active ice-sheet deglaciation and ice-dammed lakes in the northern Cairngorm Mountains, Scotland. *Boreas* 27: 297–310.

Brazier, V. & Werritty, A. (1994). Conservation management of dynamic rivers: the case of the River Feshie. In: O'Halloran, D. Green, C., Harley, M. Stanley, M. and Knill, J. (eds.) *Geological and Landscape Conservation.* The Geological Society: London. pp.147–152.

Brooks, S.J. (1996). Three thousand years of environmental history in a Cairngorms lochan revealed by analysis of non-biting midges (Insecta: Diptera: Chironomidae). *Botanical Journal of Scotland* 48: 89–98.

Brooks, S.M. (1991). *Modelling slope development through mass movement: the interaction of pedogenesis and hillslope hydrology.* Unpublished PhD thesis, University of Cambridge.

Brooks, S.M. & Richards, K.S. (1994). The significance of rainstorm variations to shallow translational hillslope failure. *Earth Surface Processes and Landforms* 19: 85–94.

Brooks, S.M., Richards, K.S. & Anderson, M.G. (1993). Shallow failure mechanisms during the Holocene: utilisation of a coupled slope hydrology – slope stabilty model. In: Thomas, D.S.G. & Allison, R.J. (eds.), *Landscape Sensitivity*. John Wiley & Sons, Chichester. pp. 149–175.

Brown, I.M. (1992). *Deglaciation of the Dee valley, NE Scotland*. Unpublished PhD thesis, University of Aberdeen.

Brown, I.M. (1993). Pattern of deglaciation of the last (Late Devensian) Scottish ice sheet: evidence from ice-marginal deposits in the Dee valley, northeast Scotland. *Journal of Quaternary Science* 8: 235–250.

Brown, I.M. & Clapperton, C.M. (2002). The physical geography. In: Gimingham, C.H. (ed.), *The Ecology, Land Use and Conservation of the Cairngorms*. Packard Publishing Ltd: Chichester. pp. 8–22.

Crane, A., Goodman, S., Krabbendam, M., Leslie, A.C., Paterson, I.B., Robertson, S. & Rollin, K.E. (2002). Geology of the Glen Shee district. *Memoir of the British Geological Survey*, Sheet 56W with parts of sheets 55E, 65W and 64E (Scotland).

Curry, A.M. (1998). *Paraglacial modification of drift-mantled hillslopes*. Unpublished PhD thesis, University of St Andrews.

Curry, A.M. (2000). Holocene reworking of drift-mantled hillslopes in the Scottish Highlands. *Journal of Quaternary Science* 15: 529–541.

Dalton, C., Birks, H.J.B., Brooks, S.J., Cameron, N.G., Evershed, R.P., Peglar, S.M., Scott, J.A. & Thompson, R. (2005). A multi-proxy study of lake-development in response to catchment changes during the Holocene at Lochnagar, north-east Scotland. *Palaeogeography, Palaeoclimatology, Palaeoecology* 221: 175–201.

Department for Culture, Media and Sport (1999). *World Heritage Sites. The Tentative List of the United Kingdom of Great Britain and Northern Ireland*. Department for Culture, Media and Sport: London.

Drew, I.D. (1992). *Bedload transport, vertical exchange and sediment storage in two Scottish Highland gravel-bed streams*. Unpublished PhD thesis, University of St Andrews.

Ellis, N.V., Bowen, D.Q., Campbell, S., Knill, J.L., McKirdy, A.P., Prosser, C.D., Vincent, M.A. & Wilson, R.C.L. (1996). *An Introduction to the Geological Conservation Review*. JNCC: Peterborough.

Everest, J.D. (2003). *The Late Devensian deglaciation in the Cairngorm Mountains, Scotland*. Unpublished PhD thesis, University of Edinburgh.

Everest, J.D. & Golledge, N.R. (2004). Dating deglaciation in Strath Spey and the Cairngorm Mountains. In: S. Lukas, J.W. Merritt & W.A. Mitchell (eds.), *The Quaternary of the Central Grampian Highlands. Field Guide*. Quaternary Research Association: London. pp. 50–57.

Everest, J.D. & Kubik, P.W. (2006). The deglaciation of eastern Scotland: cosmogenic [10]Be evidence for a Lateglacial stillstand. *Journal of Quaternary Science* 20: 95-104.

Ferguson, R.I. & Ashworth, P. (1991). Slope-induced changes in channel character along a gravel-bed stream: the Allt Dubhaig, Scotland. *Earth Surface Processes and Landforms* 16: 65–82.

Ferguson, R.I., Hoey, T.B., Wathen, S.J. & Werritty, A. (1996). Field evidence for rapid downstream fining of river gravels through selective transport. *Geology* 24: 179–182.

Ferguson, R.I., Hoey, T.B., Wathen, S.J., Werritty, A., Hardwick, R.I. & Sambrook Smith, G.H. (1999). Downstream fining of river gravels: integrated field, laboratory and modeling study. In: Klingeman, P.C., Beschta, R.L., Komar, P.D. & Bradley, J.B. (eds.), *Gravel-Bed Rivers in the Environment*. Water Resources Press: Colorado. pp. 85–114.

Gilvear, D.J. (1994). *Hydrological survey of the Insh Marshes*. Unpublished Report to the RSPB.

Gilvear, D.J., Cecil, J. & Parsons, H. (2000). Channel change and vegetation diversity on a low-angle alluvial fan, River Feshie, Scotland. *Aquatic Conservation: Marine and Freshwater Ecosystems* 10: 53–71.

Gilvear, D.J. (2004). Patterns of channel adjustment to impoundment of the upper River Spey, Scotland (1942–2000). *River Research and Applications* 20: 151–165.

Glasser, N.F. (1995). Modelling the effect of topography on ice sheet erosion, Scotland. *Geografiska Annaler* 77A: 67–82.

Glasser, N.F. & Bennett, M.R. (eds.) (1996). *The Quaternary of the Cairngorms. Field Guide*. Quaternary Research Association: London.

Glasser, N.F. & Hall, A.M. (1997). Calculating Quaternary glacial erosion rates in northeast Scotland. *Geomorphology* 20: 29–48.

Golledge, N. (2002). Glaci-tectonic deformation of proglacial lake sediments in the Cairngorm Mountains. *Scottish Journal of Geology* 38: 127–136.

Golledge, N. (2003). A former ice-dammed lake in Glen Luibeg, Cairngorm Mountains, Scotland. *Quaternary Newsletter* 101: 13–24.

Gordon, J.E. & Sutherland, D.G. (1993). *Quaternary of Scotland*. Geological Conservation Review Series No. 6. Chapman & Hall: London.

Gordon, J.E., Thompson, D.B.A., Haynes, V.M., Brazier V. & MacDonald, R. (1998). Environmental sensitivity and conservation management in the Cairngorm Mountains, Scotland. *Ambio* 27: 335–344.

Gordon, J.E., Brazier, V., Thompson, D.B.A. & Horsfield, D. (2001). Geo-ecology and the conservation management of sensitive upland landscapes in Scotland. *Catena* 42: 323–332.

Gordon, J.E., Brazier, V., Haynes, V.M. & Grieve, I.C. (2002a) Geomorphological heritage and sensitivity in the uplands: a case study from the Cairngorm Mountains, Scotland. In: Burt, T.P., Thompson, D.B.A. & Warburton, J. (eds.), *The British Uplands: Dynamics of Change*. JNCC Report No. 319. JNCC: Peterborough. pp. 67–77.

Gordon, J.E., Dvorák, I.J., Jonasson, C., Josefsson, M., Kociánová, M. & Thompson, D.B.A. (2002b). Geo-ecology and management of sensitive montane landscapes. *Geografiska Annaler* 84A: 193–203.

Gould, D. (2001). Geology of the Aboyne district. *Memoir of the British Geological Survey.* Sheet 66W (Scotland).

Gregory, K.J. (1997). *Fluvial Geomorphology of Great Britain.* Geological Conservation Review Series No. 13. Chapman & Hall: London.

Hall, A.M. (1991). Pre-Quaternary landscape evolution in the Scottish Highlands. *Transactions of the Royal Society of Edinburgh: Earth Sciences* 82: 1–26.

Hall, A.M. (in press). The shaping of Lochnagar: pre-glacial, glacial and post-glacial processes. In: Rose, N.L. (ed.), *Lochnagar: the Natural History of a Mountain Lake.* Developments in Paleoenvironmental Research. Vol 12. Springer: Dordrecht.

Hall, A.M. & Bishop, P. (2002). Scotland's denudational history: an integrated view of erosion and sedimentation at an uplifted passive Margin. In: Doré, A.G., Cartwright, J.A., Stoker, M.S., Turner, J.P & White, N. (eds.), *Exhumation of the North Atlantic margin: Timing, Mechanisms and Implications for Petroleum Exploration.* Geological Society, London, Special Publications, 196: 271–290.

Hall, A.M. & Glasser, N.F. (2003). Reconstructing the basal thermal regime of an ice stream in a landscape of selective linear erosion: Glen Avon, Cairngorm Mountains, Scotland. *Boreas* 32: 191–207.

Hall, A.M. & Jarman, D. (2004). Quaternary landscape evolution – plateau dissection by glacial breaching. In: Lukas, S., Merritt, J.W. & Mitchell, W.A. (eds), *The Quaternary of the Central Grampian Highlands. Field Guide.* Quaternary Research Association: London. pp. 26–40.

Hall, A.M. & Phillips, W.M. (in press a). Glacial modification of granite tors, Cairngorm Mountains, Scotland. *Journal of Quaternary Science.*

Hall, A.M. & Phillips, W.M. (in press b). Weathering pits as indicators of the relative age of granite surfaces in the Cairngorm Mountains, Scotland. *Geografiska Annaler.*

Haynes, V.M. (2001). *Monitoring geomorphological changes on the Cairn Gorm/Ben Macdui plateau and the Northern Corries: baseline survey.* Unpublished report to Cairngorm Chairlift Company.

Haynes, V.M. & Grieve, I.C. (2000). *Baseline survey for monitoring geomorphological and soil changes on the Braeriach/Einich Cairn Plateau.* Scottish Natural Heritage Commissioned Report F97AC105. SNH: Perth.

Haynes, V.M., Grieve, I.C., Price-Thomas, P. & Salt, K. (1998a). *The geomorphological sensitivity of the Cairngorm high plateaux.* Scottish Natural Heritage Research, Survey and Monitoring Report No. 66. SNH: Perth.

Haynes, V.M., Grieve, I.C. & Simpson, I. (1998b). *Monitoring geomorphological changes on the Cairngorm/Ben Macdui plateau and in the Northern Corries, associated with changes in visitor access patterns following the development of a funicular railway.* Scottish Natural Heritage Commissioned Report F97AC103. SNH: Perth.

Haynes, V.M., Grieve, I.C., Gordon, J.E., Price-Thomas, P. & Salt, K. (2001). Assessing geomorphological sensitivity of the Cairngorm high plateaux for conservation purposes. In: Gordon, J.E. & Leys, K.F. (eds.), *Earth Science and the Natural Heritage: Interactions and Integrated Management.* The Stationery Office: Edinburgh. pp. 120–123.

Highton, A.J. (1999). Geology of the Aviemore District. *Memoir of the British Geological Survey*, Sheet 74E (Scotland).

Hoey, T.B. & Ferguson, R.I. (1994). Numerical simulation of downstream fining by selective transport in gravel-bed rivers: model development and illustration. *Water Resources Research* 30: 2251–2260.

Huntley, B. (1994). Late Devensian and Holocene palaeoecology and palaeoenvironments of the Morrone Birkwoods, Aberdeenshire, Scotland. *Journal of Quaternary Science* 9: 311–336.

Johnson, R.C. (1992). *Impact assessment of the proposed River Spey regrading on sediment deposits.* Unpublished Report by the Institute of Hydrology to Scottish Natural Heritage.

Johnson, R.C. (1993). *Flood alleviation in upper Strathspey: modelling and environment report.* Unpublished Supplementary Report by the Institute of Hydrology to Scottish Natural Heritage.

Johnson, R.C., Piper, B.S., Acreman, M.C. & Gilman, K. (1991). *Flood alleviation in upper Strathspey: modelling and environment study.* Unpublished Report by the Institute of Hydrology to the Nature Conservancy Council for Scotland, Vol. I.

Jonasson, C., Gordon, J.E., Kociánová, M., Josefsson, M., Dvorák, I.J. & Thompson, D.B.A. (2005). Links between geodiversity and biodiversity in European mountains: case studies from Sweden, Scotland and the Czech Republic. In: Thompson, D.B.A., Price, M. & Galbraith, C.A. (eds.), *The Mountains of Northern Europe: Conservation, Management, People and Nature.* TSO Scotland: Edinburgh. pp. 57–70.

Jones, V.J., Flower, R.J., Appleby, P.G., Natkanski, J., Richardson, N., Rippey, B., Stevenson, A.C. & Battarbee, R.W. (1993). Palaeolimnological evidence for the acidification and atmospheric contamination of lochs in the Cairngorm and Lochnagar areas of Scotland. *Journal of Ecology* 81: 3–24.

Langdon, P.G. (1999). *Reconstructing Holocene climate change in Scotland utilising peat stratigraphy and tephrochronology.* Unpublished PhD thesis, University of Southampton.

Langdon, P.G. & Barber, K.E. (2004). Snapshots in time: precise correlations of peat-based proxy climate records in Scotland using mid-Holocene tephras. *The Holocene* 14: 21–33.

Langdon, P.G. & Barber, K.E. (2005). The climate of Scotland over the last 5000 years inferred from multiproxy peatland records: inter-site correlations and regional variability. *Journal of Quaternary Science* 20: 549–566.

Leys, K.F. (1997). *The geomorphological sensitivity of selected gravel-bed rivers in Scotland over the last 150 years.* Unpublished PhD thesis, University of Dundee.

Loader, N.J. & Switsur, V.R. (1996). Reconstructing past environmental change using stable isotopes in tree-rings. *Botanical Journal of Scotland* 48: 65–78.

Luckman, B.H. (1992). Debris flows and snow avalanche landforms in the Lairig Ghru, Cairngorm Mountains, Scotland. *Geografiska Annaler* 74A: 109–121.

Lukas, S. (2002). *Geomorphological evidence for the pattern of deglaciation around the Drumochter Pass, central Grampian Highlands, Scotland.* Unpublished MSc thesis, Geographisches Institut, Ruhr-Universität, Bochum.

Lukas, S. (2003). The moraines around the Pass of Drumochter. *Scottish Geographical Journal* 119: 383–393.

Lukas, S., Merritt, J.W. & Mitchell, W.A. (2004). *The Quaternary of the Central Grampian Highlands. Field Guide.* Quaternary Research Association: London.

Morrocco, S. (2006). *Terrain sensitivity on high plateaux in the Scottish Highlands.* Unpublished PhD thesis, University of St Andrews.

McConnell, J. (1996). *The history of the* Pinus sylvestris *tree-line at Creag Fhiaclach, Inverness-shire.* Unpublished PhD thesis, University of Edinburgh.

Petts, G.E., Gilvear, G.J. & Large, A.R.G. (1990). *Water level variations along the River Spey between Loch Insh and the Feshie confluence.* Unpublished Report to the Nature Conservancy Council.

Petts, G.E., Large, A.R.G. & Wilby, R. (1991). *Hydrological-ecological interactions: the Insh Marshes.* Unpublished Report to the Nature Conservancy Council for Scotland and the Institute of Hydrology.

Phillips, W.M., Hall, A.M., Mottram, R., Fifield, L.K. & Sugden, D.E. (2006). Cosmogenic ^{10}Be and ^{26}Al exposure ages of tors and erratics, Cairngorm Mountains, Scotland: timescales for the development of a classic landscape of selective linear glacial erosion. *Geomorphology* 73: 222–245.

Rowan, J.S., Werritty, A. & Berry, W.G. (1994). *A geomorphological survey of the River Spey floodplain.* Unpublished Report to Scottish Natural Heritage.

Rumsby, B., McVey, R. & Brasington, J. (2001). The potential for high resolution fluvial archives in braided rivers: quantifying historic reach-scale channel and floodplain development in the River Feshie, Scotland. In: Maddy, D., Macklin, M.G. & Woodward, J. (eds.), *River Basin Sediment Systems: Archives of Environmental Change.* Balkema: Rotterdam. pp. 445–467.

Sambrook-Smith, G. & Ferguson, R.I. (1995). The gravel-sand transition along alluvial channels. *Journal of Sedimentary Research* A65: 423–430.

Smith, C.G., Goodman, S. & Robertson, S. (2002). Geology of the Ballater district. *Memoir of the British Geological Survey*, Sheet 65E (Scotland).

Smith, G. & Livingstone, A. (in prep.). *Mineralogy of Scotland.* Geological Conservation Review Series. JNCC: Peterborough.

Stephenson, D. & Gould, D. (1995). *British Regional Geology: The Grampian Highlands of Scotland* (fourth edition). British Geological Survey. HMSO: London.

Stephenson, D., Bevins, R.E., Millward, D. Highton, A.J., Parson, I., Stone, P. & Wadsworth, W.J. (1999). *Caledonian Igneous Rocks of Great Britain.* Geological Conservation Review Series No. 17. JNCC: Peterborough.

Stephenson, D., Leslie, A.G., Tanner, P.W.G. & Treagus, J.E. (in press). *The Dalradian Rocks of Scotland.* Geological Conservation Review Series No. 17. JNCC: Peterborough.

Strachan, R.A., Smith, M., Harris, A.L. & Fettes, D.J. (2002). The Northern Highland and Grampian terranes. In: Trewin, N.H. (ed.), *The Geology of Scotland.* 4th edition. The Geological Society: London. pp. 81–147.

Thomas, C.W., Gillespie, M.R., Jordan, C. & Hall, A.M. (2004). *Geological structure and landscape of the Cairngorm Mountains.* Scottish Natural Heritage Commissioned Report F00AC103. SNH: Perth.

Thompson, D.B.A., Gordon, J.E. & Horsfield, D. (2001). Montane landscapes in Scotland: are these natural, artefacts or complex relics? In: Gordon, J.E. & Leys, K.F. (eds.), *Earth Science and the Natural Heritage: Interactions and Integrated Management.* The Stationery Office: Edinburgh. pp. 105–119.

Trewin, N.H. (ed.) (2002). *The Geology of Scotland.* 4th edition. The Geological Society, London.

Wathen, S.J. (1995). *The effect of storage upon sediment transfer processes in a small Scottish gravel-bed river.* Unpublished PhD thesis, University of St Andrews.

Wathen, S.J. & Hoey, T.B. (1998). Morphological controls on the downstream passage of a sediment wave in a gravel-bed stream. *Earth Surface Processes and Landforms* 23: 715–730.

Werritty, A. & Brazier, V. (1991a). *The Geomorphology, Conservation and Management of the River Feshie SSSI.* Report for the Nature Conservancy Council, Peterborough, England.

Werritty, A. & Brazier, V. (1991b). Geomorphological aspects of the proposed Strathspey flood alleviation scheme. In: Johnson, R.C., Piper, B.S., Acreman, M.C. & Gilman, K. (eds.), *Flood alleviation in upper Strathspey: modelling and environment study.* Unpublished Supplementary Reports by the Institute of Hydrology to the Nature Conservancy Council for Scotland, Vol. II.

Werritty, A. & Brazier, V. (1994). Geomorphic sensitivity and the conservation of fluvial geomorphology SSSIs. In: Stevens, C., Gordon, J.E., Green C.P & Macklin, M. (eds.), *Conserving our Landscape: Evolving Landforms and Ice-age Heritage.* Proceedings of the Conference on Conserving Our Landscape: Evolving Landforms and Ice-Age Heritage, Crewe 1992: 100–109.

Werritty, A. & Hoey, T.B. (2003). *Geomorphological changes and trends in Scotland: river channels and processes.* Scottish Natural Heritage Commissioned Report F00AC107B. SNH: Perth.

Werritty, A. & Leys, K.F. (2001). The sensitivity of Scottish rivers and upland valley floors to recent environmental change. *Catena* 42: 251–273.

Werritty, A. & McEwen, L.J. (1997). Fluvial geomorphology of Scotland. In: Gregory, K.J. (ed.), *Fluvial Geomorphology of Great Britain.* Geological Conservation Review Series No. 13. JNCC: Peterborough. pp. 19–114.

Werritty, A., Hoey, T.B. & Black, A. (1999). *Geomorphological and hydrological changes at the River Feshie/Spey confluence and Insh Marshes SSSI.* Scottish Natural Heritage Commissioned Report F98AC101. SNH: Perth.

Maps
British Geological Survey Maps: 1:50,000 sheets 63, 64, 65, 74, 75, 76, 85, 86, 95.

3. GEODIVERSITY: SOILS

Patricia M.C. Bruneau

Introduction

Soil functions and properties are an important component of the geodiversity of the Cairngorms area. In conjunction with other factors such as climate, this geodiversity exerts a powerful influence on natural systems, land use, biodiversity, industry and infrastructure. In turn, these diverse influences impact profoundly upon the social, economic and cultural development of the area.

Many soil properties in the Cairngorms area are derived from the nature of the superficial deposits and the underlying solid geology. Glacial drift is widespread, being thickest in the glens and straths and becoming thinner with increasing altitude. Sand and gravel deposits, in the form of glaciofluvial outwash terraces and river terraces, are present in most glens and straths. In general, the hills are covered by a relatively thin, stony, locally-derived mountain-top detritus, which is often soliflucted and, in certain localities, overlies weathered granite or schist. Where this detritus is sufficiently thick, various types of montane soils have developed. Elsewhere, only screes and ranker soils (soils less than 10 cm deep) are present.

Other natural soil-forming factors in the Cairngorms area have favoured the dominance of three principal soil groups – podzols[1], peat and montane soils – with many associated soil sub-groups. Throughout much of the area, where precipitation levels exceed evapotranspiration, soils are prone to leaching, which leads to the development of pozdols. At high altitudes, where temperatures are lower and dryer conditions prevail, montane soils are extensive. Peat formation is widespread where conditions are wetter, the ground is poorly drained and there is a slow rate of decomposition of dead vegetation. Where the soil drainage is impeded, either by the presence of compacted subsoil or by a less permeable geological substrate, gleyed soils also occur.

Compared with other parts of Scotland, where anthropogenic activities have left a more significant impact on the landscape, the Cairngorms area is exceptional for its unusually large extent of rare, undisturbed soils. Many of these soils are of national and international importance; they have evolved from a unique combination of geological, topographical and climatic diversity. Soils of particular note are those associated with the native Caledonian pine forest at Abernethy (iron podzols) and the montane soils (alpine podzols) within snow-bed areas on the Cairngorm plateaux. Other soils of national importance are isolated tabular areas of peat, surrounded by montane soils in the Ladder Hills, and the brown magnesian soils developed on magnesium-rich 'ultrabasic' rocks at Coyles of Muick, near Ballater.

Soils and designated sites

In contrast to the other earth heritage features, soils are not explicitly protected through statutory site designations. However, most soil types occur within existing designated sites (Gauld & Bell, 1997) and, through their role in supporting rare habitats, are offered indirect protection. The soils of the Cairngorms area and their key features are described here in the context of SNH's Cairngorms Massif Natural Heritage Futures Area (Gauld & Bell, 1997; Gauld *et al.*, 2000, 2003).

There has been no systematic national assessment of soils against established criteria, although Gauld *et al.* (2000) identified soils of national and international importance in individual Natural Heritage Futures Areas, based on informed judgement and the experience of soil surveyors (Table 3.1). Soils of international significance are those that are either associated with internationally rare habitats or species, or those that are rare in an international context. Soils of national significance include particularly extensive examples

---

Solifluction lobes in Lurcher's Gully. The seasonal freezing and thawing of soils in the Cairngorms massif has a marked effect on their structure

Photo: *P. & A. Macdonald*

[1] From the Russian pod (under) and zola (ash).

Bruneau, P. (2006). Geodiversity: Soils. In: Shaw, P. & Thompson, D.B.A. (eds.). *The Nature of the Cairngorms: Diversity in a changing environment.* The Stationery Office. pp. 43-51.

Humus – iron podzol profile.
Photo: *MLURI*

Table 3.1. Soils of particular importance in the Cairngorms Massif Natural Heritage Futures Area (from Gauld *et al.*, 2000).

Significance	Soil type
International significance	• Iron podzols under Caledonian pine forest at Abernethy. • Alpine podzols (montane soils) within snow-bed areas on Cairngorm plateau.
National significance	• Peat with isolated tabular areas surrounded by montane soils in the Ladder Hills. • Brown magnesian soils on ultrabasic rocks at Coyles of Muick, near Ballater.
Local significance	• Brown forest soils developed on parent materials derived from calc-silicate rocks in the area between Tomintoul and Blair Atholl, and in Glen Tilt. • Brown forest soils developed on gabbros, norites and other basic igneous rocks in the Cabrach. • Alpine podzols on Beinn Dearg, at the head of Glen Bruar. • Shallow brown earths and brown calcareous soils with limestone community of Rock Rose-fescue grassland, Glen Avon and Glen Tilt. • Podzols (humus-iron, iron and humus) under Caledonian pine forest at Glen Tanar and Ballochbuie.

of well-preserved soil types. Those of local interest are often related to a local context or linked with the presence of native species.

Similar criteria were used to assess the importance of soil types in Cairngorms National Park and in the wider Cairngorms area. A total of 44 SSSIs lie at least partly within the National Park, and 74 within the Cairngorms area as a whole (Chapter 1). Eight SSSIs in the National Park and a further three elsewhere within the Cairngorms area are considered to have soils of international importance. Similarly, 12 SSSIs in the National Park have soils of national significance, as have a further 10 elsewhere in the Cairngorms area. Outside of the National Park, SSSIs tend to be more fragmented and smaller in size, making them less likely to be of high soil conservation value.

The other distinctive feature of the Cairngorms area is the high proportion of undisturbed soils. Indeed, within the National Park, only about 2% of the land area is presently cultivated, with a further 4% of the land area under improved grassland. In the wider Cairngorms area arable land is more widespread, covering almost 7% of the area, with a slightly smaller extent under improved grassland (Macaulay Land Use Research Institute, 1993). Table 3.2 presents the percentage of major soil subgroups in both areas. The distribution of the major soil subgroups is shown in Figure 3.1.

Soil groups

Podzols

Given both the dominance of largely acidic coarse-textured and well-drained soil parent material, and the prevailing climate, with high precipitation, podzolisation is the dominant soil-forming process in the Cairngorms area. True podzols cover 50% of Cairngorms National Park and are characterised by the presence of a largely organic peaty layer at the surface, overlying an ash-coloured mineral soil layer, from which most of the nutrients have been leached. Some of the leached components accumulate in the layer beneath, forming a darker layer of variable thickness, high in organic matter. This usually overlies a reddish-coloured layer enriched in iron and aluminium components, with most of the colour resulting from other forms of leached organic matter.

Although the sequence of horizons within the alpine and sub-alpine zone is less well-defined than at lower altitudes, the principal soil-forming process is podzolisation, which accounts for about 66% of the soils of the Cairngorms area and of the National Park. Of the podzol sub-groups, peaty podzols with a peat layer up to 50 cm thick at the surface are the most widespread (covering 28% and 30% of the Cairngorms area and the National Park, respectively), followed by humus podzols, iron podzols and humus-iron podzols, which show differences in the nature and thickness of their surface accumulation layers (covering 22% and 19%, respectively). Subalpine podzols account for about 11% of the Cairngorms area, and are much shallower overall.

There is a distinct altitudinal zonation for the podzol subgroups, with iron and humus-iron podzols found at lower elevations. Humus-iron podzols are widespread throughout the foothills and lower slopes of the drier areas. Iron podzols are much rarer, usually confined to areas of ancient Caledonian pinewood, such as Abernethy Forest, or long-established coniferous woodland. Peaty podzols and peaty gleyed podzols occur further upslope, at around 600 m. Both of these types have an iron pan, with the latter subgroup gleyed above the pan, due to waterlogging and the concave shape of receiving sites.

Table 3.2. Soils of Cairngorms National Park and the Cairngorms area.

Major Soil Groups	National Park		Cairngorms area	
	Area (km²)	Percentage of National Park	Area (km²)	Percentage of Cairngorms area
Lithosols	17	0.5	21	<0.5
Alluvial soils	67	2	75	1
Rankers	330	9	388	6
Magnesian soils	6	<0.5	7	<0.5
Brown earths	155	4	293	4
Podzols	1,891	50	3,269	50
Montane soils	684	18	1,042	16
Surface-water gleys	164	4	512	8
Ground-water gleys	2	<0.5	2	<0.1
Peats	483	13	850	13
Lochs	17	0.5	30	0.5
Total area mapped (km²)	3,816		6,490	

A common feature of both humus-iron podzols and peaty podzols is the cementation of the subsoil at or below an iron pan (an iron-rich seam at the base of the organic-rich mineral soil layers), supposedly due to the compression effect of overlying ice during the last Ice Age. This cementation can prevent the downward penetration of roots, but seldom reduces downward water movement, or gleying, in the surface horizons, which remain well defined. The change from peaty podzol to subalpine podzol morphology is associated with a gradual disappearance of the thin iron pan, which, at first, becomes weakly expressed and easily penetrated by plant roots, and then disappears as a recognisable feature.

Alpine and subalpine soils

Alpine and subalpine soils occur above about 550 m in the Cairngorms and account for 18% of the National Park and 16% of the Cairngorms area as a whole. These soils are usually very shallow, with only a very thin organic layer over a barely altered parent material. The Cairngorm plateaux form the largest single area of such soils in Scotland.

On the summit plateaux of the Cairngorms and on the Gaick plateau, alpine soils are widespread on the frost-shattered and weathered mountain-top

Humus podzol profile.
Photo: *MLURI*

detritus. Plant growth is usually very slow, with a scarcity of dead vegetation at the surface, so that organic matter in these soils takes many years to accumulate. Such soils are therefore fragile and especially sensitive to damage. On steep slopes, soil erosion can be a problem if the surface vegetation is disturbed or removed. Roots and vegetation anchor the soil on steep slopes and protect the subsoil, which has a coarse texture, is very friable, and so is easily removed by run-off or trampling.

On the high plateaux there are close relationships between soils, geomorphology and plant habitats, for example, in relation to drainage, exposure and snow-lie patterns. The best examples of podzol morphology within the true alpine zone are confined to areas of late snow-melt, where complete and distinctive plant communities are present. Alpine podzols located in areas of snow-bed vegetation show better-developed profiles.

Peat
In poorly-drained areas, such as in sheltered areas of exposed summits and local basins, or in areas of high rainfall, and where the decay of dead plant material by soil organisms is slowed down, organic matter accumulates at the surface, leading to peat formation. A notable location in the Cairngorms massif is the extensive montane blanket mires on the Mòine Mhór.

Peat develops to a depth of 2–3 m on slopes of less than 10°, but on cols and in local basins it may exceed 6 m in depth. Peat accounts for 13% of the soils of both the National Park and the Cairngorms area. Peat is extensively developed on the plateau surfaces north of Glen Clova. Of particular interest, outwith the plant communities dominated by northern blanket bog or upland blanket bog, is the occasional presence of gully erosion.

Also of natural heritage value are isolated tabular areas of peat, usually about 1 m thick, on the severely exposed summit areas of the Ladder Hills, where the hilltops emerge above the surrounding blanket peat. Such areas are seldom more than 10–20 m wide and are completely surrounded by relatively large expanses of subalpine or alpine soils, depending upon the elevation. The Monadhliath Mountains also have extensive areas of severely eroded blanket peat.

Gley soils
Gley soils are formed when the downward movement of water is restricted, for example on till and other drift deposits where the subsoil is compacted. These conditions often arise on concave lower slopes, where there is

Figure 3.1. The distribution of major soil sub-groups in the Cairngorms.

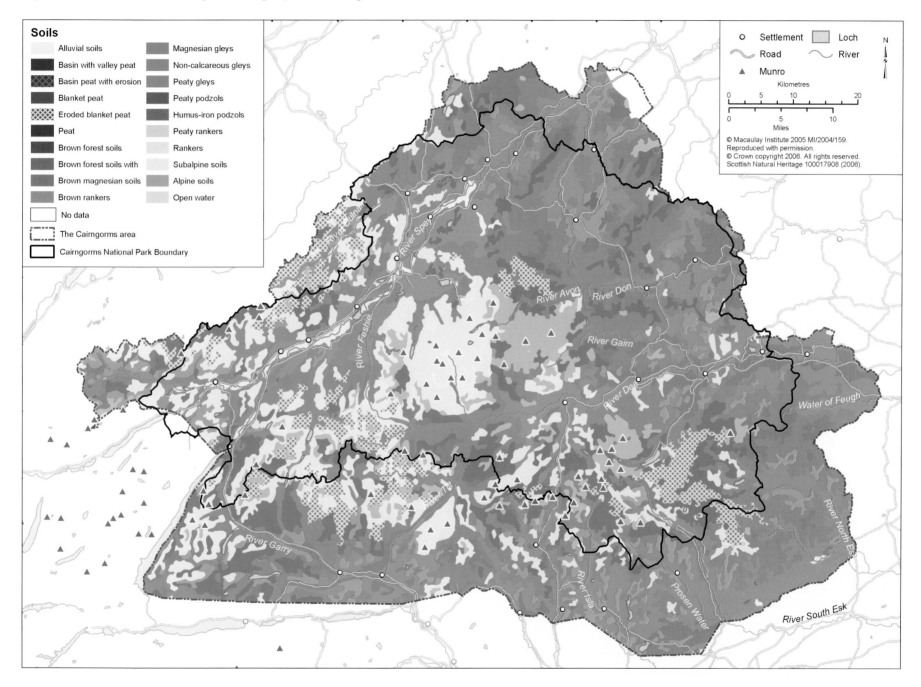

concretion of subsoils by fine silt, or where bedrock impedes drainage. Gley soils have permanent or temporary waterlogged horizons which become deprived of oxygen. This affects soil organisms, which must find other sources of energy (e.g. sulphur, which accounts for the 'rotten eggs' smell of these soils) and also impacts on chemical reactions of soil minerals. Iron, which is naturally present in the soil, giving it its rusty colour, may change its chemical status, turning the soil a grey/bluish colour. This usually happens only in patches, leading to a mottling of the subsoil, reflecting variations in the local oxygenation level.

Gley soils are more common in the wider Cairngorms (8% of the area) than in the National Park (4%). Local differences in drainage and temperature lead to different subgroups of gley soils in the Cairngorms area. At high altitude, on acidic substrates, peaty gleys are the most widespread form of gley soil, while non-calcareous gleys and humic gleys are locally more widespread at lower elevations.

Peat erosion in the Ladder Hills.
Photo: *J. Gordon*

Other soil groups

Brown earths and magnesian soils are both freely-drained soils with leached profiles, and are uncommon in the Cairngorms (Table 3.2). These soils are often deep and fertile and have greater potential for agriculture. They have a dark, well-structured upper horizon (reflecting their high organic content), becoming lighter in colour with depth. Rendzinas and calcareous soils are non-leached soils characterised by the presence of free lime, and differentiated only by depth of profile, the former being shallower. Rankers, regosols and lithosols are more immature soils, and are shallow, with weakly developed horizons.

The more diverse soil types also reflect the complexity of the underlying geology. For example, brown forest and base-rich (rendzina and calcareous) soils are developed on limestones and basic igneous rocks; brown magnesian soils and magnesian gleys are developed on ultrabasic igneous rocks, such as serpentinites.

Brown earths cover only 4% of the Cairngorms area. Improved grassland, smooth grassland and various woodland categories dominate the land cover on these brown forest soils, although it is notable that a high proportion of these soils also support heather moorland. Brown forest soils are also developed on Dalradian limestone, with scattered occurrences extending southwards from Tomintoul and upper Deeside into Glen Tilt in Perthshire.

Where the soil reaction is less acidic, brown calcareous soils have developed, but these, along with rendzinas and rankers, are rare (<0.5% of the wider Cairngorms area) and do not occur within designated areas. Rendzinas and brown rankers represent soils with a high natural heritage value on account of their rarity and the presence of important plant communities. Species-rich communities have been recorded on all of the free-draining soils, with Rock Rose-fescue grassland (the *Polygono-Helictotrichetum pratensis* community) and herb-rich, bent-fescue grassland (part of *Achilleo-Festucetum tenuifoliae*) being typical examples. Calcareous gleys are generally restricted to concave slopes and to other flushed slopes.

In contrast, although limited in extent, accounting for less than 0.5% of the Cairngorms area, almost all of the brown magnesian soils lie within protected areas. Brown magnesian soils occupy less than 10 km² of the Cairngorms area, all of it within statutory sites. Restricted to the Corriebreck and Leslie Associations within upper Nochtyside, near Strathdon, on stony drift derived from basic and ultrabasic rocks, these soils can be freely and imperfectly drained, with some gleys in lower concave slopes. Surface horizons are often organic, and horizon differentiation is weak on account of the dark colours in both the topsoil and subsoil. The soils are often relatively shallow and rest on shattered rock. Plant communities include herb-rich, bent-fescue grassland (part of *Achilleo-Festucetum tenuifoliae*), herb-rich boreal heather moor (part of *Vaccinio-Ericetum cinereae*) and boreal Juniper scrub (*Trientali-Juniperus communis*); sedge mires occur on the gleyed soils.

Recent research and survey findings

A general description of the soils of the Cairngorms is provided in the *Handbook of the Soil Survey of Scotland 1:250,000 Sheet No. 5, Eastern Scotland*. There have been no detailed publications describing the soils of the Cairngorms. The last soil surveys of the area by the (then) Soil Survey of Scotland ended in the 1970s, and many parts are only covered as provisional black and white maps. However, the importance of soils in nature conservation is becoming more widely recognised and their role in supporting ecological services, landscape values, habitat restoration and recreation value is now attracting increasing attention. The following summary is based on research and survey work dating from 1990.

- The Cairngorms area has been included in studies of soils and nature conservation, investigating the distribution of the national soil resource with particular reference to semi-natural soils and their links to habitats (Gauld *et al.*, 2000, 2003). Ongoing work is addressing the links between soil protection and habitat preservation, in relation to the role of soil functions in supporting special habitats and species often under pressure from human activities or natural changes (Towers *et al.*, 2005).

- A baseline study of soils on the Cairngorm/Ben Macdui plateau was undertaken as part of the environmental assessment for the funicular railway (Anderson *et al.*, 1997). This found evidence over the past decades of increased acidification and a decline in fertility, loss of organic matter and increased compaction. Signs of atmospheric deposition (nitrate-N) were shown to have occurred, but it was difficult to differentiate the effects of diffuse pollution from local human impacts at the scale observed.

- Aspects of soils have also been investigated as part of broader geomorphological studies in the Cairngorms, particularly in relation to the links between geomorphological sensitivity and visitor access patterns (Haynes *et al.*, 1998a,b; Grieve, 2000). Textural change in surface horizons (both erosion and thickening in areas adjacent to eroded areas) and the risk of increased compaction and reduced infiltration were identified for footpaths and areas of diffuse trampling. A series of baseline sites has been established for monitoring the possible impacts of the funicular railway development on small-scale geomorphological features and soils (Haynes *et al.*, 1998b; Haynes & Grieve, 2000).

- Soil quality and the changes associated with the transition from moorland to forest habitats have been studied in the RSPB's Abernethy Forest Reserve to investigate whether the environment is acidifying as a result of woodland expansion (Wilson, 1998; Wilson & Puri, 2001), and whether there have been significant effects on soil organic matter following the change in land use (Chapman & Campbell, 1999). Although levels of soil acidification were found to be only minor or moderate where woodland expansion occurred at the expense of moorland, significant changes in the total amount and quality of the organic matter were identified.

- A detailed study of the organic matter and microbial characteristics of the alpine podzols on the Cairngorm plateau was undertaken to improve understanding of the biological diversity of these soils, and to identify indicators of change (Smith, 2001). This study showed that the microbial biomass of the alpine podzol of the Cairngorms is similar to that of soils at lower altitudes. It shows an active, functional and diverse microbial community in these soils mainly concentrated in the upper organic layer.

- In a national study of upland soil erosion, the greatest areas of severe peat erosion were found in eastern Scotland, in the Monadliath and eastern Grampians (Grieve *et al.*, 1994, 1995). These are also areas where there is a high inherent risk of erosion of organic soils by overland flow (Lilly *et al.*, 2002, 2005).

Trends

There is little systematic information on current trends in the soils of the Cairngorms. As noted above and in Chapter 2, baseline surveys of geomorphology and soils have been conducted as part of the Visitor Management Plan for the funicular railway on Cairn Gorm.

Some known changes (as opposed to trends) that have affected the soils of the Cairngorms over recent years are summarised below.

Commercial afforestation and natural tree regeneration are being encouraged in a number of locations in the Cairngorms and are likely to impact on soil drainage patterns, organic matter decomposition, and therefore soil development and properties.

Erosion is a key issue for the fragile upland environment. Soil damage has been associated with footpath erosion on the higher slopes and plateaux of the Cairngorms. Well-constructed and maintained paths are the best realistic solution to minimising the areas affected by such erosion. A number of such paths have been constructed in recent years on the lower slopes and up towards the plateaux. Any increase in off-track vehicle use is also a potential problem, as this will damage soils. Overgrazing is locally affecting slope stability and soil erosion in Glen Feshie. There is anecdotal evidence of links between grazing pressure and erosion but it is unclear whether this relates to the initiation or maintenance of erosion features. Truncation of alpine podzol profiles on the high plateau provides evidence of soil erosion but it is unclear to what extent this reflects current processes or processes in the recent or historical past. Peat erosion is extensive across parts of the area and may be linked to increased dissolved organic matter content in streams. Carbon loss from peat soils is assumed to contribute significantly to greenhouse gas emissions and hence to climate change.

Climate change and ***atmospheric pollution*** have potential effects on soils, both through direct changes in physical processes controlling soil formation and erosion (e.g. frost, wind, water and snow cover), chemical and biochemical processes (nutrient and contaminant deposition, soil microbial activities) and through possible changes in vegetation cover.

Conservation issues

A number of potential pressures may impact on the soils of the Cairngorms area.

Changes in land use and management. Activities such as afforestation and construction of tracks may impact on soils through direct damage to the soil profile (e.g. disturbance of soil surface layers and compaction, leading to erosion) or by indirect impacts on soil biodiversity and functions (e.g. drainage,

nutrient enrichment). The semi-natural or undisturbed nature of many soils in the Cairngorms is of key conservation value. Activities that disturb the upper soil horizons will irreversibly damage this value. Montane and organic soils are also sensitive to physical damage from trampling (through human activities or grazing animals) and a subsequent increased risk of erosion, which may be irreversible in montane soils.

Climate change. Impacts of climate change on montane soils may occur directly, through changes in processes (e.g. increased erosion from greater frequency of intense rainstorms), or indirectly through changes in vegetation (e.g. increased or decreased cover). Soil formation in the Cairngorms reflects a balance between substrate, landforms, climate and vegetation. Changes in the amount and nature of precipitation and changes in temperature will modify the soil-forming processes. Most at risk are the highly organic soils, where there may be significant loss of carbon from greenhouse gas emissions through oxidation of peat, and an increase in dissolved organic carbon in streams through surface water erosion.

Drainage of peat bogs and peat extraction. These activities are likely to lead to the loss of palaeoenvironmental records. They may also result in increased sensitivity to erosion, leading to the partial or total destruction of peat soils.

Soil erosion. Soil erosion is a natural process, but is locally enhanced through grazing and recreational pressures. Peat erosion is an issue of particular concern. Peat soils are important carbon stores. Scottish soils contain 71% of the UK's terrestrial carbon reserves. Many areas of peat are undergoing severe erosion in the Grampian Highlands and Monadliaths. As a source of greenhouse gases, this is a cause for concern. There are also concerns over the impact of soil erosion on water quality from increasing concentrations of dissolved organic carbon in freshwater bodies.

Atmospheric pollution. Atmospheric deposition of contaminants is not concentrated around the source of pollution. In semi-natural habitats, air pollutants can pose a threat to habitats and soils through the acidification of susceptible soils (such as montane soils) by sulphur and nitrogen acidifying compounds or excessive nutrient enrichment (nitrogen deposition). Soils and their functions are at risk as changes in vegetation will affect soil formation and organic matter turnover.

Awareness and education. Much more could be done to raise wider awareness of the nationally and internationally important geodiversity interests in the

Cairngorms amongst local people, landowners, land managers and visitors to the area. Issues include raising awareness of soil *per se*, as well as the wider value of soil functions in supporting habitats, land use and sustainable management.

Knowledge gaps. There are still significant gaps in our knowledge of the soils of the Cairngorms area, both in terms of inventory and monitoring of changes. Soils of upland Scotland have been surveyed as part of the *Soil Survey of Scotland*, but only at a scale of 1:250,000, compared to lowland and agricultural areas which were surveyed at 1:50,000. Also, there is no systematic monitoring of any changes in soil quality.

References

Anderson, H.A., Gauld, J.H. & Stewart, M. (1997). *Pilot study of soils within the Cairngorm Ski area*. Scottish Natural Heritage Commissioned Report F97AC101. SNH: Perth.

Chapman, S.J. & Campbell, C.D. (1999). *Effects of native woodland expansion on soil carbon balance, Abernethy Forest*. Scottish Natural Heritage Commissioned Report F98AC103. SNH: Perth.

Gauld, J.H. & Bell, J.S. (1997). Soils and nature conservation in Scotland. *Scottish Natural Heritage Review*, No. 62. SNH: Perth.

Gauld, J.H., Malcolm, A. & Puri, G. (2000). *Soils and natural heritage zones*. Scottish Natural Heritage Commissioned Report F98AC112. SNH: Perth.

Gauld, J.H., Bell, J.S., McKeen, M.M. & Bruneau, P.M.C. (2003). *Soils and nature conservation: an inventory of selected Natural Heritage Futures areas*. Scottish Natural Heritage Commissioned Report No. 019. (ROAME No. F00AC101). SNH: Perth.

Grieve, I.C. (2000). Effects of human disturbance and cryoturbation on soil iron and organic matter distributions and on carbon storage at high elevations in the Cairngorm Mountains, Scotland. *Geoderma* 95: 1–14.

Grieve, I.C., Davidson, D.A. & Gordon, J.E. (1995). Nature, extent and severity of soil erosion in upland Scotland. *Land Degradation and Rehabilitation* 6: 41–55.

Grieve, I.C., Hipkin, J.A. & Davidson, D.A. (1994). *Soil erosion sensitivity in upland Scotland*. Scottish Natural Heritage Research, Survey and Monitoring Report No. 24. SNH: Perth.

Haynes, V.M. & Grieve, I.C. (2000). *Baseline survey for monitoring geomorphological and soil changes on the Braeriach/Einich Cairn Plateau*. Scottish Natural Heritage Commissioned Report F97AC105. SNH: Perth.

Haynes, V.M., Grieve, I.C., Price-Thomas, P. & Salt, K. (1998a). *The geomorphological sensitivity of the Cairngorm high plateaux*. Scottish Natural Heritage Research, Survey and Monitoring Report No. 66. SNH: Perth.

Haynes, V.M., Grieve, I.C. & Simpson, I. (1998b). *Monitoring geomorphological changes on the Cairngorm/ Ben Macdui plateau and in the Northern Corries, associated with changes in visitor access patterns following the development of a funicular railway*. Scottish Natural Heritage Commissioned Report F97AC103. SNH: Perth.

Lilly, A., Hudson, G., Birnie, R.V. & Horne, P.L. (2002). *The inherent geomorphological risk of soil erosion by overland flow in Scotland*. Scottish Natural Heritage Research, Survey and Monitoring Report No. 183. SNH: Perth.

Lilly, A., Gordon, J.E., Petri, M. & Horne, P. (2005). Mapping the ingherent erosion risk due to overland flow: a tool to guide land management in the Scottish uplands. In: Thompson, D.B.A., Price, M.F. & Galbraith, C.A. (eds.), *Mountains of Northern Europe: Conservation, Management, People and Nature*. The Stationary Office, Scotland: Edinburgh. pp. 191-196.

Macaulay Land Use Research Institute (1993). *Land cover of Scotland*. Macaulay Land Use Research Institute: Aberdeen.

Smith, P. (2001). *Evaluation of organic matter and microbial characteristics of alpine podzols on the Cairngorms plateau*. Unpublished MSc thesis, University of Stirling and Scottish Natural Heritage Commissioned Report F98AC105.

Towers, W., Malcolm, A. & Bruneau, P.M.C. (2005). *Assessing the nature conservation value of soil and its relation with designated features*. Scottish Natural Heritage Commissioned Report No. 111 (ROAME No. F03ACLI04). SNH: Perth.

Wilson, B. (1998). *Pinewood soils in the RSPB Abernethy Forest Reserve*. Scottish Natural Heritage Commissioned Report F97AC102. SNH: Perth.

Wilson, B & Puri, G. (2001). A comparison of pinewood and moorland soils in the Abernethy Forest Reserve, Scotland. *Global Ecology & Biogeography*. 10: 291-303.

Maps

Soil Survey of Scotland Maps: 1:250,000 sheet 5, 1:63,360 sheets 84, 85, 75, 76, 66, 56, 57 and uncoloured 1:50,000 sheets 36, 43 and 44. MLURI, Aberdeen.

4. LANDSCAPE CHARACTER

Laura Campbell and Carol Anderson

Introduction

The distinctive geology and landforms of the Cairngorms have created a scenically diverse landscape. The high massif of the Cairngorm mountains forms the core of the area, which is surrounded by extensive lower hill ranges and dissected by the broad straths of the Dee and the Spey. It is a landscape of many contrasts; while the influence of humans is clearly evident in the settled and farmed straths and glens, natural processes are dominant on the high massif, where the landscape has a strong wild land character. The rich diversity of lochs, woodlands, rivers and montane habitats, together with human influences on the landscape, such as policy woodland, farmland and buildings, give the Cairngorms its distinctive character and make this landscape unlike any other in Britain.

The landscape character of the Cairngorms

Turnbull Jeffrey Partnership (1996a) and Land Use Consultants (1999) have identified landscape character types within the Cairngorms area. These are summarised below.

The Cairngorms plateaux. The summit plateaux of the Cairngorm mountains comprise the largest tracts of high ground in Britain and form the basis of a landscape which is little modified by humans. They are distinctive in their large scale and bare, smooth, flattened tops, broken only by distinctive blocky weathered granite tors, trough-like sheer-sided glens and scooped corries. The lack of settlement, huge scale and high altitude of the Cairngorms plateaux contribute to their wild land quality, which is heightened by unpredictable and often extreme weather conditions.

Uplands and glens. The uplands surrounding the central Cairngorms plateaux form an expansive, remote tract of heather-clad hills, blanket bog and grassland, the last being more extensive in the south. They comprise seemingly endless successive ridges of rounded summits, dissected by a series of wide open glens, such as the Angus Glens in the south. Many of these glens link with passes over the hills, often ancient drove routes. Settlement within this landscape is sparse and largely confined to the glens. This gives the uplands and glens a remote character, which is emphasised by the large scale of the uplands.

Straths. The straths are associated with the major rivers of the Spey and Dee, and the smaller Don and Avon. The main communications and settlements of the Cairngorms are accommodated within this character type. The strath formed by the Spey is diverse, containing a number of landscape character areas. These include the broad farmed floodplain to the north, the wetlands and lochs at Insh, and the rougher grazing, forestry and shooting estates in the headlands of the Spey to the south-west. The Dee is more enclosed and homogenous in character, with extensive coniferous woodlands. Many large estate houses, castles and their associated policies contribute much to its celebrated landscape character. The straths of the Don, Avon and Livet are also defined as separate landscape character areas by virtue of their distinct settlement and land-use patterns.

Important landscape features

While the unique mountain plateaux of the Cairngorms form the dominant feature of the area, a number of other important landscape features occur throughout, and in combination result in a highly diverse landscape. These are as follows.

The Dee at Balmoral. The mature conifers, designed landscapes and policies of many of the estates in upper Deeside have a strong influence on the area's landscape character.
Photo: *J. MacPherson*

Campbell, L. & Anderson, C. (2006). Landscape character. In: Shaw, P. & Thompson, D.B.A. (eds.). *The Nature of the Cairngorms: Diversity in a changing environment.* The Stationery Office. pp. 53-59.

Geology and landform. The central Cairngorm massif forms the largest homogenous granite mass in Britain. This gives rise to rounded, smooth landforms with extensive boulder fields and occasional tors, which are particularly prevalent throughout the Cairngorms plateaux and Lochnagar area. Metamorphosed rocks give characteristically 'knobbly' landforms on the eastern edge of the Monadliath and Ardverikie areas. Glaciation has had its greatest impact on the surrounding glens and straths, producing a series of deeply eroded glens. The glaciers also carved deep corries, predominantly on northern faces of the mountain massif. Selective glacial erosion, meltwater action and deposition have formed a landscape of considerable geomorphological interest (see Chapter 2) including, for example, the distinct, hummocky landforms and terraces found in Strathspey and elsewhere.

Woodlands. The Cairngorms area has a relatively high proportion of woodland cover (Chapter 7), which greatly contributes to the diversity of the landscape. The extensive native pine forests in Rothiemurchus and Abernethy, with their open character and diverse ground cover, are the most striking of these woodlands and form a distinctive landscape character area in their own right.

The wide strath formed by the River Spey encompasses a diversity of landscape features, including the broad, farmed floodplain to the north, the wetlands and lochs at Insh, and the rougher grazing, forestry and shooting estates of the south-west.

Photo: *P. Macdonald*

The birch woodlands along the River Dulnain, at Craigellachie and Dinnet are light and airy in character, contrasting with the nearby dark coniferous woodlands. Larch, spruce and other non-native species are common in areas such as Strathdon and, in Deeside, form a prominent component of the designed landscapes and policies associated with the many estates of the area. Nonetheless, Scots Pine accounts for over 80% of the forest on Deeside, and over half is semi-natural woodland (Callander & MacKenzie, 1991).

Moorland and montane land cover. Of the range of upland vegetation types present, heather moorland is the most prominent and extensive, and represents one of the largest areas of moorland in Britain (Chapter 5). It is particularly striking during the late summer, when huge expanses of purple-pink colour the hills. The sub-arctic vegetation cover of the mountain plateaux is also a distinctive feature. Its low profile and general sparseness accentuates the stark sculptural landform of the Cairngorms and, when viewed closely, creates a surprisingly colourful and intricate pattern of diverse ground-cover plants.

Rivers. The shingle-edged meandering Spey, with its distinctive broad floodplain, and the more enclosed Dee, are the principal rivers of the study area. Smaller rivers such as the Don and Avon have much variety throughout their course, changing from fast mountain burns to rivers winding through small-scale pastures and woodlands or, in the case of the Water of Ailnack, forming deep limestone gorges. Many of the mountain burns and rivers form key visual features which dissect the expansive north-east and southern hill ranges including, for example, the boulder-strewn Tilt and Feshie Rivers.

Lochs and wetlands. Elongated lochs, such as Loch Avon, fill some of the deep trough-like glens found high within the Cairngorms plateaux, while rounded basin lochs are found in Strathspey and Deeside. Bog pool complexes occur throughout the forests of Rothiemurchus and Abernethy, and in parts of the Ladder Hills. The Insh Marshes in Strathspey are particularly important, having a diverse flora and avifauna. Wetland areas such as this, and those associated with the Muir of Dinnet on Deeside, form an important part of the character of the landscape.

Agricultural landscapes. The geometry of open fields and concentration of settlement patterns of the agricultural landscapes within the straths provide a strong visual contrast with the uplands and mountains where semi-natural characteristics are more dominant. The broad strath of the Spey is a highly distinctive landscape feature, in which flat, open pastures with few field boundaries contrast with the woodlands and forestry edging the flood plain on lower sides of the strath. Agricultural practices remain more traditional in the smaller straths and on the lower foothills of the hill and mountain ranges. Here, smaller irregular fields of semi-improved and unimproved pasture lie on lower slopes, bounded by stone dykes and woodlands with farmsteads characteristically located on the edge of farmland at the base of the strath sides.

Designed landscapes. The greatest concentration of estate policies lies in Strathdon, Deeside and at Blair Atholl. These include the extensive and outstanding 18th and 19th century 'improvement' landscapes of Balmoral, Invercauld and Glen Tanar in Deeside, and the smaller estates of Tillypronie, Candacraig House and Kildrummy Castle in Strathdon. These and other designed landscapes make a significant contribution to the landscape character of the Cairngorms, providing a diverse pattern of native and non-native woodlands, parkland and ornamental gardens.

Archaeological features. Human activity has touched even the most remote areas of the Cairngorms. While there is little evidence of human impact on the high mountain plateaux, remains of shieling-huts are found extensively in upland areas to over 800 m. The ruins of pre-improvement townships, such as those in Glen Lui on the Mar Lodge Estate, provide a poignant reminder of past settlement patterns in the upland glens. Extensive areas of moorland and rough grazing have helped preserve their remains in upland areas. The fertile straths have experienced greater change, and 18th and 19th century features largely dominate these areas. A number of historic built features form imposing visual foci and include Ruthven Barracks in Strathspey, and the castles at Corgarff on the headwaters of the River Don and at Loch an Eilein.

Rural built features. The built heritage of estate architecture, vernacular buildings, bridges and monuments makes a valuable contribution to the landscape character of the Cairngorms area. The distinctive 18th and 19th century estate houses, cottages, farms and gatehouses are particularly evident in the major straths of the Spey and Dee and are a consequence of the growing popularity of sporting estates during this period. More modern recreational facilities, including ski developments and visitor centres, are also characteristic of much of the area.

Settlements. Many of the settlements in the area are planned villages laid out by improving landowners in the 18th century. These include Ballater, created to accommodate visitors to the spa at Pannanich, and Tomintoul and Grantown-on-Spey, planned to encourage industrial enterprise in the area.

National Scenic Areas

There are two National Scenic Areas (NSAs) in the Cairngorms area: the Cairngorm Mountains and Deeside & Lochnagar. These form a contiguous area of over 100,000 ha, which includes the core mountain massifs and parts of the main straths and glens. Within these areas, development proposals are subject to stricter planning controls than elsewhere.

Recent research and survey findings

The landscape character assessments (LCAs) that cover the Cairngorms area have identified three broad character types: Mountain Plateaux, Uplands, and Glens & Straths. They have also identified 21 more detailed landscape character areas (Turnbull Jeffrey Partnership, 1996a; Land Use Consultants, 1999). The Cairngorms LCA was undertaken at a broader scale than was used in LCAs elsewhere, due to the large size of the study area, and because the character areas defined are geographically distinct rather than representative

Bog pool complexes and lochans occur throughout the forests of Abernethy and Rothiemurchus, as here at Uath Lochan, Inshriach. These wetland areas form an important part of the character of the landscape.

Photo: *L. Gill*

of a generic type. In addition, similar forces for change were considered likely to act within each character area, so that a smaller division of the study area would not necessarily have been more useful.

A more detailed LCA was carried out within the Cairngorms for Mar Lodge Estate in 1997. This was to provide landscape guidance for a range of issues related to future management changes to the estate, in order to meet the objectives of the then new owner, the National Trust for Scotland (Turnbull Jeffrey Partnership, 1996b). These included the restructuring of the existing forestry, natural regeneration of native woodlands, rationalisation of footpaths, built features in the mountain areas and improvements to the designed landscape associated with Mar Lodge. This LCA was also intended to provide a detailed record of baseline landscape conditions against which future changes can be monitored.

The Royal Commission on the Ancient and Historical Monuments of Scotland (RCAHMS) and Historic Scotland (HS) have undertaken an historic land-use assessment (HLA) of the Cairngorms. The HLA identifies general patterns in the historic components of the landscape, the character of which has been significantly influenced by the nature of land use over the last 200 years. These patterns are important in understanding human influences on the landscape of the Cairngorms area and in considering its cultural heritage. They help to clarify the relationship between land-use change and the distribution of archaeological monuments, and enable an outline to be drawn of the history of settlement in the area from the earliest times to the present.

Several current monitoring programmes in the Cairngorms area have a landscape dimension. Examples of relevant research projects include the following.

- At the University of London a PhD study has been undertaken on the relationship between local people and the natural environment, describing conflicts between livelihood, recreation and conservation interests in the Cairngorms (Vandsteeg, 2000).

- An evaluation has been undertaken of the ways in which new media artists respond to the Scottish Highlands (Nedkova, 2003).

- *BioScene,* a three-year EU research project, began in 2003 with the aim of evaluating threats and opportunities for wildlife conservation resulting from declining agriculture. This project seeks ways of reconciling biodiversity conservation with changing human activities in mountainous regions of Europe, and uses the Cairngorms as a case study (Anon., 2003).

- *Crossplan* was a participatory landscape planning exercise, co-sponsored by the Forestry Commission, the Cairngorms Partnership and European Regional Development Fund, developed during 1998–2001. Strathdon was the Scottish pilot case study, with other case studies in Norway, Finland, and Sweden. The purpose of this project was to find ways of involving local people in planning forestry and moorland initiatives in their own area. An evaluation of the project showed that it was probably successful in its attempts to increase environmental awareness of participants and strengthen cooperation, and that it had a positive impact on the environment (Wickenhagen, 2002). However, this evaluation also suggested that the success of the project was questionable, in that it failed to produce long-term improvements for the local population in *Crossplan* study areas.

Trends

Examples of recent trends in landscape research include an apparent tendency towards greater public, or at least 'stakeholder', involvement (e.g. the *Crossplan* project), and perhaps a greater reliance on qualitative methods (e.g. Vandsteeg, 2000). In the Cairngorms, the scope of recent landscape studies has also tended to widen, to include aspects of anthropology, philosophy and art, as well as geography and planning (e.g. the new media artists study; Nedkova, 2003).

The status of the Cairngorms as a national park and as an icon of the British landscape contributes towards the intensity of debates on its management. Investigations into the background behind environmental debates often use examples from the Cairngorms, such as the funicular railway. This trend is likely to continue as the national park becomes established, and as plans for the area are devised and debated.

Key issues

The following issues seem likely to continue to be important in terms of landscape change and landscape research in the Cairngorms.

Built development pressure. New housing is likely to continue to account for the greatest number of development proposals in the area. This is mostly through the expansion of existing villages and towns throughout the area, but there has also been discussion about a potential new settlement in Strathspey. There is likely to be continuing pressure to build individual houses in the countryside and this might increase following the creation of the National Park. While nothing as prominent as the funicular railway is envisaged, there have been recent proposals for both large- and small-scale developments to cater for the sporting, retail and accommodation requirements of visitors to the area. All of these can have an impact on the landscape, and the cumulative impacts of individual developments may become a significant issue.

Visitor pressure. Recreational facilities such as footpaths, cycle routes, car parks and lavatories can contribute to the gradual alteration of the landscape character and should be considered carefully in terms of need, siting and design. An increase in visitor numbers may have a significant impact in terms of footpath erosion and other damage, and can affect the wild land character that many visitors to the Cairngorms plateaux seek.

Infrastructure upgrading. An increase in housing provision requires the development of infrastructure such as water, electricity, waste water treatment, and transport. These elements all have an impact on the landscape, whether in remote areas where there are potential impacts on wild land character, or near population centres, where visual impacts tend to be greater. Road upgrading also has the potential for large-scale impacts.

Renewable energy developments. The Cairngorms is one of the most highly designated areas in Britain (Chapter 1). This has inevitably deterred developers of windfarms, hydro schemes and other renewable energy technologies. The increasing pressure to reduce our dependence on fossil fuels is likely to mean that adjacent areas will be developed instead, with consequent impacts on the Cairngorms. Windfarm developments, for example, may begin to encircle the national park.

Woodland and forestry. The forests and woodlands of the Cairngorms are a highly characteristic feature of the area. Changes such as clear-felling, forest redesign or expansion are likely to have noticeable impacts on the area. Fencing or tracks, often associated with woodland establishment or management, can add to these impacts. The Cairngorms woodland and forest framework

(Chapter 7) should help ensure that changes to the woodland resource of the area are appropriate to the landscape character.

Moorland. Heather moorland is an important, perhaps almost iconic, component of Cairngorms landscapes. Changes in management, which could be triggered by a variety of pressures, may result in a reduction in the extent of this important feature.

Track reinstatement. Several attempts to ameliorate the negative impacts of bulldozed tracks are evident within the Cairngorms. Work on the track on Beinn a' Bhuird spanned several years, and is now complete, greatly mitigating its landscape and visual impacts. Experience of track reinstatement gained at these altitudes can be applied usefully in similar and less demanding environments.

Plans and policies. Both statutory and non-statutory plans will have a key role to play in the future development of the Cairngorms. The National Park Plan, and the process involved in its production, will be particularly important in ensuring that landscape issues are fully considered in all future decisions

Large- and small-scale developments to meet housing, recreational, communications and other requirements can impact on the quality of the landscape.
Photo: *L. Gill*

affecting the area. There is potential for a range of best practice guidance to flow from this plan, such as that concerning the siting and design of built development in the National Park. The National Scenic Area review, and lessons learned from the development of NSA management plans elsewhere, may also contribute to the Park Plan.

Monitoring. Monitoring of landscape change is underway on the Mar Lodge Estate and in Environmentally Sensitive Areas, and will be a feature of the Rural Stewardship Scheme. Given the importance of the whole area, development of a programme with wider geographical coverage may be justified. This could address geomorphological, historical and archaeological aspects of the landscape, as well as the practical effects of planning policies.

Public attitudes and perceptions of the landscape. There is an increasing awareness that policies and other measures that affect the landscape should be based on more robust assumptions about human preferences than they are at present. Recent studies have attempted to gauge attitudes to the landscape (e.g. Vandesteeg, 2000; University of Newcastle, 2002) but it is unlikely that a common methodology will emerge from these, given their widely differing aims. A more general or structured approach to assessing landscape perception in the area may be helpful.

References

Anonymous (2003). *All Change for Europe's Mountains: New Research to Guide the Future. BioScene* press release. Imperial College at Wye: London.

Callander R.F. & MacKenzie, N.A. (1991). *The Native Pine Woodlands of Highland Deeside.* NCC Report. SNH: Perth.

Land Use Consultants (1999). *Tayside Landscape Character Assessment.* Scottish Natural Heritage Review Series No. 122. SNH: Perth.

Nedkova, I. (ed.) (2003). *Remote: Scottish and international new media artists respond to the Scottish Highlands.* New Media Scotland: Edinburgh.

Turnbull Jeffrey Partnership (1996a). *Cairngorms Landscape Assessment.* Scottish Natural Heritage Review Series No. 75. SNH: Perth.

Turnbull Jeffrey Partnership (1996b). *Mar Lodge Estate: Landscape Assessment.* Scottish Natural Heritage Review Series No. 79. SNH: Perth.

University of Newcastle (2002). *Public and Professional Attitudes to Landscape: Scoping Study.* SNH Commissioned Report FO1AA303. SNH: Perth.

Vandesteeg, B. (2000). *Senses of Place and the Struggle for the Cairngorms.* PhD Thesis, University of London.

Wickenhagen, A. (2002). *Innovative Rural Development Initiatives. Case Study 4: Crossplan International Institute for Applied Systems Analysis (IIASA).* IIASA: Laxenburg, Austria.

Additional reading

Cairngorms Working Party (1992). *Public Consultation Paper.* Scottish Executive Environment Department: Edinburgh.

Department of the Environment, Transport and the Regions (1998). *Environmental Geology in Land Use Planning. Case Study No. 9. Integrated Land Use Planning and Land Management in the Cairngorms.* DETR: London.

Forestry Commission (1999). *Cairngorms Forest and Woodland Framework.* FC: Edinburgh.

Highland Council (1999). *Structure Plan.* Highland Council: Inverness.

Scottish Natural Heritage (2002). *Natural Heritage Futures: Cairngorms Massif.* SNH: Perth.

Scottish Natural Heritage (2002). *Natural Heritage Futures: North East Glens.* SNH: Perth.

Scottish Office Development Department (1999). *National Planning Policy Guideline NPPG 14 Natural Heritage.* Scottish Office: Edinburgh.

5. LAND COVER CHANGE

Edward C. Mackey and Michael Shewry

Introduction

The vegetation cover among the straths and lower slopes of the Cairngorms area has been greatly influenced by human activity. In contrast, descendants of the late glacial flora among the fell-field and tundra-like communities of the high plateaux are almost undisturbed (Gimingham, 2002a). The much-reduced native pine-birch forest, which had remained more-or-less intact until around 1600, represents some of the finest and most extensive remnants in Britain (MacKenzie, 2002) (Chapter 7). Elsewhere, the management of land for grazing and field sports from the 18th century onwards has suppressed woodland regeneration and given rise to extensive tracts of heath and moor (Shucksmith, 2002).

According to the Land Cover Map 2000 (LCM2000), which was derived from satellite imagery (Fuller et al., 2002) some 44% of the Cairngorms area is characterised by heath or bog (Table 5.1). Montane habitats, which comprise prostrate dwarf heath, sedge and rush, moss heaths and snow bed communities, accounted for a further 25% of the area. In practice, however, the montane zone was taken to be all land above the 600 m contour. Three grassland types accounted for 12% of the area, as did the two woodland types. The coniferous woodland category, representing three-quarters of the wooded area, included plantation forest. Altogether, woodland was thought to account for 12% of the Cairngorms area; rather less than the 17% estimated by the Scottish Semi-Natural Woodland Inventory in 1988 (see Chapter 7)[1]. Enclosed farmland, which may be taken as arable and horticulture, together with improved grassland, covered 5% of the area. Built-up land and other minor features accounted for the remaining 2%. The land cover map is illustrated in Figure 5.1.

Trends

An interpretation of aerial photography between 1946 and 1988 has shown that woodland cover in a selected area of the Cairngorms expanded from 11% cover in 1946 to 17% in 1988, while heather moorland declined from 42% cover to 36% (Government Statistics Service, 1992). Hester et al. (1996) found that conifer planting showed the greatest net increase within parts of Strathspey and the central Cairngorms during 1946–88, expanding by 200%.

At a higher resolution, land cover change has been estimated by the National Countryside Monitoring Scheme (NCMS), a sample survey of aerial photography captured around 1947, 1973 and 1988 (Peltenburg et al., 2003). Due to the distribution of sample squares, change estimates were found to be more reliable for the area enclosed by the National Park boundary than for the wider Cairngorms area. Consequently, change estimates presented here are those for the National Park. Note, however, that both sets of results reflect the sort of changes reported for Highland Region as a whole (Mackey et al., 1998). Differences in method, definition and boundary mean that estimates in Tables 5.1 and 5.2 are not directly comparable, and should not be used to imply change during the intervening time.

Of the 467 NCMS sample squares for Scotland, 21 fell within the National Park boundary. Statistically significant changes were evident for 12 habitats. These were ranked by magnitude of change (from the largest increases, through no significant change, to the largest decreases) in Table 5.2. With reference also to schematic illustrations in Figures 5.2 and 5.3, the key changes are as follows.

During the 1940s to 1980s the area of semi-natural coniferous woodland in the Cairngorms declined, while plantations expanded, often at the expense of heather moorland.

Photo: *P. & A. Macdonald*

Mackey, E.C. & Shewry, M. (2006). Land cover change. In: Shaw, P. & Thompson, D.B.A. (eds.). *The Nature of the Cairngorms: Diversity in a changing environment.* The Stationery Office. pp. 61-69.

[1] This disparity reflects differences in the classification system, scale and methods used in preparing the Land Cover Map 2000, and those used in the Scottish Semi-natural Woodland Inventory and elsewhere. Disparities in woodland cover estimates will be addressed in the next land cover map survey: LCM2007.

Increases

- An estimated 80% increase occurred in the area of rough grassland, due mainly to heather moorland becoming grass-dominant. Mire drainage (for tree planting) also contributed to the expansion of rough grassland (since mire or bog, when drained, was re-classified according to its dominant vegetation).

- Plantation forest expanded by around 90%, mainly on heather moorland and mire, and to a lesser extent on rough grassland. A 48% increase in ditch length reflects mire drainage for afforestation.

- An apparent increase in bracken should be viewed with caution, as it may partly reflect improved clarity of photography, and therefore improved detectability, between the 1940s and 1980s.

- Wet ground, for example denoted by the presence of rush *Juncus* spp., encroached on a variety of habitats.

- Scattered trees may have increased as a result of woodland thinning, degeneration or regeneration.

- Built land and transport corridor increased in extent, as did bare ground.

Decreases

- Blanket mire was reduced by around 15%, through drainage for forestry (and thereby converted to heather moorland or rough grassland) and tree planting.

- Heather moorland was reduced by 11%, through conversion to rough grassland and afforestation.

- Managed grassland was reduced by 22%, mainly due to its conversion to arable. The length of hedgerow, a feature of livestock and mixed farming systems, was reduced by 72%.

- Semi-natural coniferous and broadleaved woodland were both reduced. Typically, they would have been replaced by conifer plantation forest.

Sample squares from the NCMS can be used also to examine change on the ground. Three examples are summarised in Figure 5.4. In each example, the change sequence, in a clockwise direction, is given by a) the first edition Ordnance Survey map dating from the 1860s or 1870s; b) the NCMS interpretation for the 1940s; c) the NCMS interpretation for the 1980s; and d) current Ordnance Survey map 2000. Shown also are a key to the NCMS maps and a location map for the sample square in the Cairngorms area.

Figure 4a, west of Laggan, shows an open landscape of mire and moor in the 1872 map. With the River Spey in the north and Loch Crunachdan in the south-east, the catchment drains to the east. Changes on the ground, which are illustrative of results for the Cairngorms as a whole (above), include the following.

Table 5.1. Broad Habitat extent within the Cairngorms area, estimated from the Land Cover Map 2000 (Fuller *et al.*, 2002).

Group	Broad habitat	Extent (km²)	%
Forest and woodland	Broadleaf woodland	170	3
	Coniferous woodland	622	10
	Total	**792**	**12**
Enclosed farmland	Arable and horticulture	98	1
	Improved grassland	255	4
	Total	**352**	**5**
Semi-natural/rough grass and bracken	Neutral grassland	232	4
	Calcareous grassland	21	0
	Acid grassland	513	8
	Bracken	1	0
	Total	**767**	**12**
Mountain, heath and bog	Dwarf shrub heath	1,443	22
	Open dwarf shrub heath	1,295	20
	Bog	118	2
	Montane habitats	1,655	25
	Inland rock	51	1
	Total	**4,563**	**70**
Built-up land	Built up areas, gardens	9	0
	Continuous urban	1	0
	Total	**10**	**0**
Standing water	Standing water	31	0
	Total extent	**6,515**	**100**

Note: Being based on reflectance, the Land Cover Map 2000 cannot distinguish Broad Habitats that are defined by floristic composition in the field survey. Confusion in the LCM2000 classification is notable among the grassland types, and between dwarf shrub heath and bog. Results in the table should therefore be viewed with caution.

Figure 5.1. Land cover in the Cairngorms in 2000, based on the classification of satellite imagery (from Fuller *et al.*, 2002).

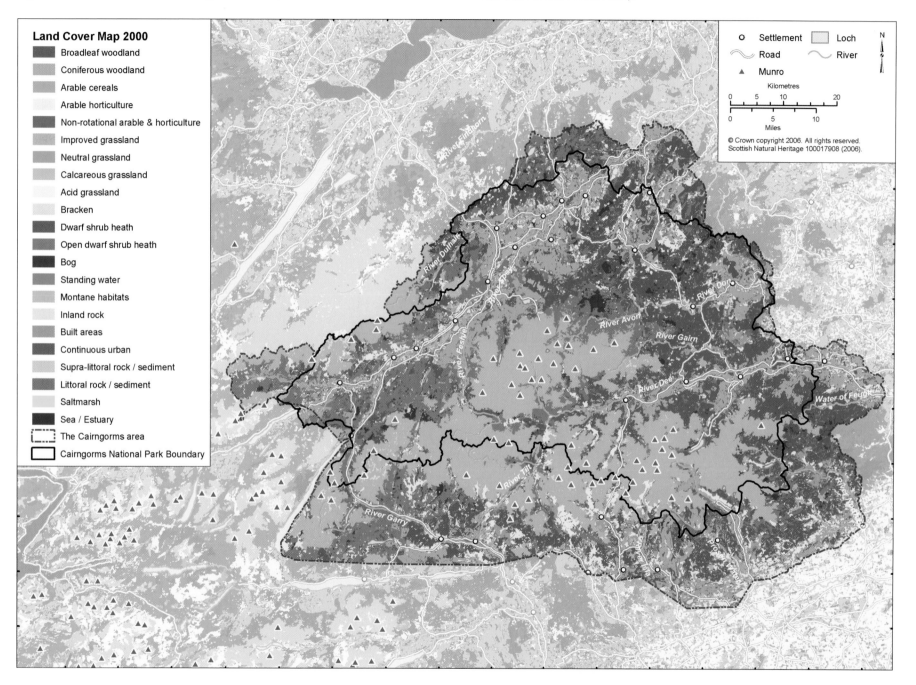

Table 5.2. Land cover change (in km²) during *c.* 1947 to *c.* 1988, within the area now enclosed by the Cairngorms National Park boundary. Estimates, derived from NCMS data (Mackey *et al.*, 1998), are shown in order of magnitude of change, where statistical significance is given at the 5% level.

Feature	1940s extent	1980s extent	lower[1]	change	upper[1]	% change
Areal features						
Significant increases						
Rough grassland	249	449	107	200	292	80
Plantation forest	196	372	63	176	288	90
Bracken	3	29	3	27	51	1,017
Wet ground	12	26	4	14	24	113
Scattered trees	1	11	3	11	18	2,143
Built+transport corridor	25	36	4	10	17	40
Bare ground	1	5	1	4	6	266
Non-significant changes						
Arable	98	121	-8	23	54	24
Reservoirs	0	12	-10	12	34	6,997
Tall scrub	3	6	0	3	6	93
Rivers	13	14	-1	1	2	5
Canals	1	1	-1	0	1	17
Recreational land	0	0	-	0	-	-
Quarry	0	0	-	0	-	-
Marginal inundation	3	2	-2	-1	0	-30
Rock	15	13	-5	-2	0	-16
Low scrub	17	9	-19	-8	4	-46
Lowland mire	18	9	-25	-9	8	-48
Lochs	24	15	-33	-10	14	-40
Significant decreases						
Coniferous woodland	55	30	-49	-25	-2	-46
Broadleaved woodland	92	63	-58	-29	0	-32
Managed grassland	238	187	-100	-52	-3	-22
Heather moorland	1,493	1,331	-304	-162	-20	-11
Blanket mire	1,257	1,074	-295	-182	-70	-15
Linear features						
Significant increases						
Ditches	1,617	2,400	344	783	1,222	48
Non-significant changes						
Lines of trees	388	415	-114	27	168	7
Tracks	1,703	1,574	-821	-130	561	-8
Streams	6,218	5,938	-712	-280	151	-5
Significant decreases						
Hedgerows	314	89	-423	-225	-27	-72

[1] The lower and upper limits define a range of values that contains the true area or length, with 95% confidence

Figure 5.2. Land cover change in Cairngorms National Park, *c.* 1947–*c.* 1988. Statistically significant changes and their 95% confidence intervals are shown.

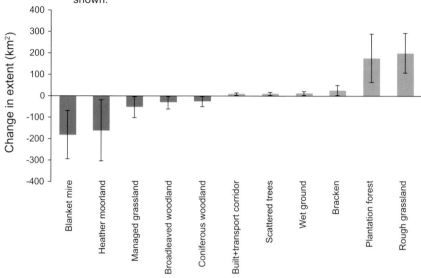

Figure 5.3. Dynamics of change in Cairngorms National Park, *c.* 1947 to *c.* 1988. Change is multi-directional. Net change in Table 5.2 is the sum of gains and losses. The arrow width is proportional to the amount of interchange between features.

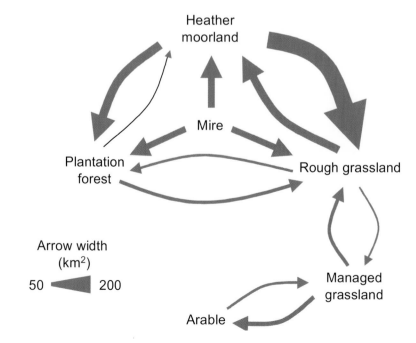

Figure 5.4. Examples of land cover change, *c.* 1947 to *c.* 1988. a. West of Laggan.

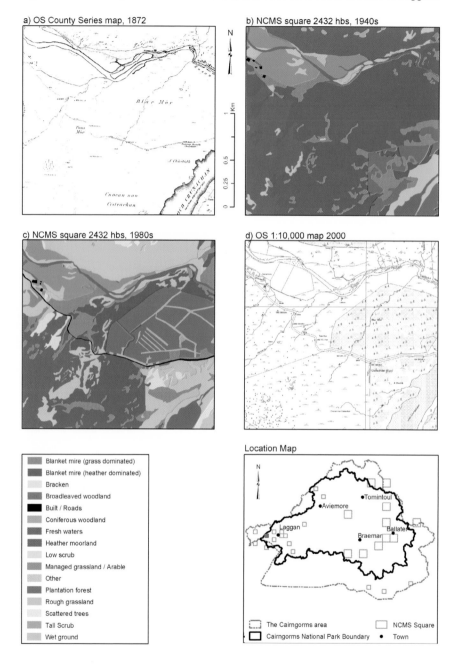

Figure 5.4b. North of Aviemore.

Figure 5.4c. Glen Gairn, north-west of Ballater.

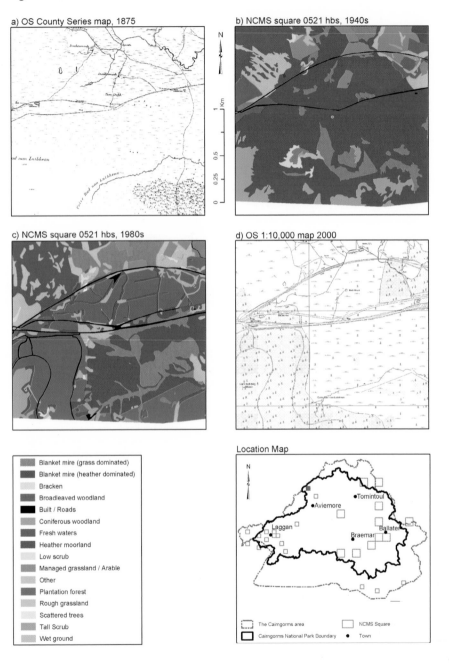

a) OS County Series map, 1875

b) NCMS square 0521 hbs, 1940s

c) NCMS square 0521 hbs, 1980s

d) OS 1:10,000 map 2000

Blanket mire (grass dominated)
Blanket mire (heather dominated)
Bracken
Broadleaved woodland
Built / Roads
Coniferous woodland
Fresh waters
Heather moorland
Low scrub
Managed grassland / Arable
Other
Plantation forest
Rough grassland
Scattered trees
Tall Scrub
Wet ground

Location Map

The Cairngorms area
Cairngorms National Park Boundary
NCMS Square
Town

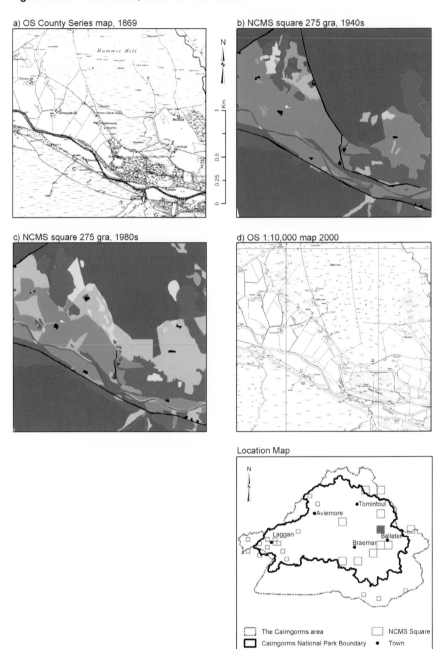

a) OS County Series map, 1869

b) NCMS square 275 gra, 1940s

c) NCMS square 275 gra, 1980s

d) OS 1:10,000 map 2000

Location Map

The Cairngorms area
Cairngorms National Park Boundary
NCMS Square
Town

- Plantation forest, which was of limited extent in the 1940s, had by the 1980s become prominent within the area of heather-dominated blanket mire.

- In the north, heather moorland in the 1940s had turned to rough grass by the 1980s. Some patches had become bracken dominant.

Figure 4b, north of Aviemore, is bisected by transport features. The open mire plain of 1875 shows the railway close to The Slocht summit. The railway and the A9 trunk road to its north, which share a route through the Grampian and Monadhliath Mountains, provide visual reference points in the 1940s scene. Changes between the 1940s and the 1980s include the following.

- A considerable expanse of heather-dominated mire was planted as conifer forest between the 1940s and the 1980s. Some patches of semi-natural coniferous woodland were replaced by forest and some were retained.

- The current route of the A9, immediately south of the railway, can be seen in the 1980s map. The old road, new road and railway come together at its western edge.

Figure 4c shows Glen Gairn, north-west of Ballater, with remnants of semi-natural pine-birch woodland and more extensive broadleaved woodland within a swathe of grass- or arable-land defining the more sheltered and fertile places. Characteristic features can be traced through the 1869, 1940s, 1980s and 2000 maps. Ascending within the Grampian Mountains towards The Lecht ski area in the north, the dominant and mainly unaltered feature is that of extensive tracts of heather moorland.

Conservation issues

Cairngorms National Park is recognised nationally and internationally for its natural heritage importance, in terms of the outstanding scenic quality of its landscapes, its assemblages of land forms, and for the plants and animals that are to be found among them. As a mountain recreation area, it is unsurpassed in Scotland. However, ecological damage has been attributed to a) aspects of land management that have led to the loss of habitat diversity or potential, and b) pressures resulting from the rapid increase in popularity of the area to visitors, tourists and participants in various forms of outdoor recreation (Gimingham, 2002b).

A historical perspective and ecological interpretation of results in Table 2 are provided by Gimingham (2002b). The former mixture of rather open pine-birch woodland, interspersed with glades and clearings occupied by heath and bog and patches of Juniper *Juniperus communis* – birch scrub has been replaced by extensive, relatively uniform, heather moorland and species-poor acidic grassland. Heather has often been damaged by intensive grazing (heather moorland was reduced by 11%), resulting in its replacement by coarse grasses (rough grassland increased by 80%). Such trends, Gimingham notes, represent ecological deterioration, since they have led to great reductions in plant and animal populations, reduced soil productivity and an expansion of bog conditions. Trends towards intensification and specialisation of farming methods on the one hand (hedgerow length decreased by 72%), or the abandonment of farms on the other (e.g. amalgamated or going to afforestation), do not serve the wider interests of conservation. Afforestation within Cairngorms National Park boundary (90% increase) is lower than the national average (Chapter 7), but large, uniform plantations of exotic tree species are especially inappropriate in the core area and do little to restore lost biodiversity or to improve the soil.

The sample from the latest Countryside Survey (Haines-Young *et al.*, 2000; McGowan *et al.*, 2002) is too small to be applied at the scale of the Cairngorms. However, across Scotland as a whole, broadleaved woodland expanded between 1990 and 1998. After decades of decline, this reversal reflects new planting, regeneration and forest restructuring during the 1990s. Evidence from other semi-natural features, however, suggests that long-term declines elsewhere have not been arrested.

The analysis of land cover change provides factual corroboration of, and a valuable degree of quantification for, the observations of ecologists. However, the existing stock of change data is inadequate for today's needs. The advent of high-resolution digital aerial photography makes it possible to create a map-registered backdrop for landscape-scale and site-specific visualisation. In combination with context information from, for example, vegetation surveys and past change studies, it would provide a powerful new capability for land cover interpretation and planning.

References

Fuller, R.M, Smith, G.M., Sanderson, R.A., Hill, R.A., Thomson. A.G., Cox, R., Brown, N.J., Clarke, R.T., Rothery, P. & Gerard, F.F. (2002). *Land Cover Map 2000. Final Report.* Centre for Ecology and Hydrology: Monks Wood. (see also www.cs2000.org.uk).

Gimingham, C.H. (2002a). Introduction. In: Gimingham, C.H. (ed.), *The Ecology, Land Use and Conservation of the Cairngorms.* Packard Publishing Limited: Chichester.

Gimingham, C.H. (2002b). Towards an Integrated Management Strategy. In: Gimingham, C.H. (ed.), *The Ecology, Land Use and Conservation of the Cairngorms.* Packard Publishing Limited, Chichester.

Government Statistics Service (1992). *The Scottish Environment – Statistics.* The Scottish Office: Edinburgh.

Haines-Young, R.H., Barr, C.J., Black, H.I.J., Briggs, D.J., Bunce, R.G.H., Clarke, R.T., Cooper, A., Dawson, F.H., Firbank, L.G., Fuller, R.M., Furse, M.T., Gillespie, M.K., Hill, R., Hornung, M., Howard, D.C., McCann, T., Morecroft, M.D., Petit, S., Sier, A.R.J., Smart, S.M., Smith, G.M., Stott, A.P., Stuart, R.C. & Watkins, J.W. (2000). *Accounting for Nature: Assessing Habitats in the UK Countryside.* DETR: London. (see also www.cs2000.org.uk).

Hester, A.J., Miller, D.R. & Towers, W. (1996). Landscape-scale vegetation change in the Cairngorms, Scotland, 1946–1988: Implications of land management. *Biological Conservation* 77: 41–51.

MacKenzie, N.A. (2002). The Native Woodlands – History, Decline and Present Status. In: Gimingham, C.H. (ed.), *The Ecology, Land Use and Conservation of the Cairngorms.* Packard Publishing Limited: Chichester.

Mackey, E.C., Shewry, M.C. & Tudor, G.J. (1998). *Land Cover Change: Scotland from the 1940s to the 1980s.* The Stationery Office: Edinburgh. (see also www.snh.org.uk/trends/landcover).

McGowan, G.M., Palmer, S.C.F., French, D.D., Barr, C.J., Howard, D.C., Smart, S.M. Mackey, E.C. & Shewry, M.C. (2002). *Trends in Broad Habitats: Scotland 1990–1998.* Scottish Natural Heritage Commissioned Report F00NB03. (available from www.snh.org.uk/trends/landcover).

Peltenburg, J., Shewry, M.C., Orr, J.L. & Mackey, E.C. (2003). *The National Countryside Monitoring Scheme Visualisation and Analysis System.* SNH: Perth.

Shucksmith, D.M. (2002). Land Use Change in the Cairngorms. In: Gimingham, C.H. (ed.), *The Ecology, Land Use and Conservation of the Cairngorms.* Packard Publishing Limited: Chichester.

6. UPLAND PLANT COMMUNITIES

David Horsfield

Introduction

The Cairngorms have the largest area of high ground and the most extensive tracts of montane (or alpine) plant communities in the UK above 900 m. These include rush, sedge and lichen-rich heaths, snow-bed communities and bryophyte springs associated with snow melt. Blanket bog also extends into the montane zone, supporting the largest and highest tracts of montane bog in the UK. The Cairngorms area also includes the largest areas of upland forms of wet heath in the UK which, exceptionally, extend up into the montane zone.

The steepness of the terrain, together with large tracts of acid rocks (chiefly granite and schists), giving rise to poor, infertile soils, has encouraged low intensity land-use in the Cairngorms. This, along with the relatively harsh climate of the eastern Highlands, has favoured the development of extensive tracts of tall dwarf-shrub heath, dominated by Heather *Calluna vulgaris*, from around 250 to 900 m. These include special types of eastern, boreal dwarf-shrub heath. On wind-swept ridges and summits, prostrate *Calluna* heaths provide some of the best examples of lichen-rich vegetation in the UK (see Chapter 12).

High altitude exposures of acidic rock form one of the most important areas in the UK for montane plant communities of rock habitats, including rock outcrops and crevice (chasmophytic) vegetation and scree. This is the richest area for acid montane flora, and has some of the most important outcrops of base-rich rock for upland flora and plant communities in the UK. They include occurrences of base-rich rock at some of the highest altitudes found in the UK, and a wide range of base-rich plant communities, including montane willow scrub, grasslands, dwarf-herb communities and base-rich flushes and springs. These also include nationally rare plant communities and species.

Cairngorms National Park is one of only three areas in Scotland containing a cluster of sites on serpentine rock, the others being Lendalfoot in Ayrshire and the Shetland Isles. Of these three areas, the Cairngorms have a more continental, rather than oceanic, climate. Serpentine vegetation (Calaminarian grassland) is developed at a range of altitudes and the Cairngorms area includes the highest development of serpentine vegetation in the UK. It also contains the UK's best development of regenerating submontane scrub, with Juniper *Juniperus communis* (ssp. *communis*) and Scots Pine *Pinus sylvestris*, as well as the most extensive stands of Juniper scrub which, uniquely, extend into the montane zone.

Important plant communities

Upland plant communities in the Cairngorms occur in four vegetation zones. Table 6.1 lists these, and breaks down each zone into broad kinds of vegetation, habitats and key plant communities, together with their relevant National Vegetation Classification (NVC) types (Rodwell 1991a,b, 1992, 1994, 2000). Areas mapped using the NVC scheme currently account for about 31% of the Cairngorms area and 49% of the National Park (Figure 6.1). Upland NVC codes and names are listed in Annex 6.1.

Plant communities for which the Cairngorms are important in a national or international context are defined here as: those that have more than 10% of their UK range within the Cairngorms area; or those that form a part of a priority habitat under the UK Biodiversity Action Plan, or of a habitat listed in Annex I of the EC Habitats Directive (Table 6.1).

High montane zone
The Cairngorms holds the largest area of ground above 900 m in the UK. This high montane zone is dominated by montane grasses, sedges, rushes,

---

Where pressure from grazing and burning allows, diverse upland plant communities may develop, dominated by dwarf-shrub heath, montane willow scrub, mosses and herbs.
Photo: *L. Gill*

Horsfield, D. (2006). Upland plant communities. In: Shaw, P. & Thompson, D.B.A. (eds.). *The Nature of the Cairngorms: Diversity in a changing environment.* The Stationery Office. pp. 71-89.

mosses and lichens, and is concentrated in the core area, encompassing the summits of extensive high plateaux, including Cairn Gorm (1,245 m), Ben Macdui (1,309 m), Braeriach (1,235 m), Cairn Toul (1,291 m), Beinn a' Bhuird (1,196 m) and Ben Avon (1,171 m). Other high plateaux with significant areas of ground above 900 m include the summits of Lochnagar (1,150 m), Fafernie (1,000 m), Glas Maol (1,068 m) and Beinn a' Ghlo (1,121 m). High plateaux and summits like these are of limited extent outside of the Cairngorms. Those of the Cairngorms support a number of key high montane plant communities, listed in Table 6.1.

Low montane

The low montane zone is the vegetation zone which lies between the high montane zone and the upper limit of the natural tree-line, and is dominated by dwarf-shrub heaths and moss-heaths. This zone takes in the lower plateaux, summits, ridges and corries, at around 650–900 m. An exceptionally wide range of montane plant communities occur here. Lichen-rich montane dwarf-shrub heaths on windswept ridges are superlatively developed, especially on the core Cairngorms Mountains and on Drumochter. The Cairngorms holds the best and most extensive examples in Britain of blanket mire occurring at high altitude.

Submontane

The submontane zone lies below the upper limit of the natural tree-line but above the forest zone. The natural tree-line has largely disappeared from the Cairngorms, but the potential tree-line limit is estimated to be around 650 m (see Chapter 7). This is the lowest upland zone and is limited downwards by improved agricultural land and by the forest edge. The Cairngorms area is one of the few upland areas with extensive woods, concentrated on Strathspey and Deeside. The highest woodland edge is around 550 m, except at Creag Fhiaclach where there is a natural tree-line extending to over 600 m. The key plant communities of the submontane zone include extensive dwarf-shrub heaths, dominated by heather moorland, Juniper scrub, wet heath and semi-natural dry grasslands.

Forest zone

This zone includes plant communities developed in open areas within and around forests and woods, and includes essentially the same range of plant communities as occurs in the submontane zone.

A colourful bryophyte spring wih Philonotis fontana *and* Scapania undulata, *on the high plateau of the Cairngorm mountains.*
Photo: *L. Gill*

International importance

Twenty upland habitats listed under Annex I of the EC Habitats Directive qualify within Special Areas of Conservation (SACs) in the Cairngorms (Annex 6.2). The Cairngorms are important for European dry heaths, primarily for the large extent and best representation of north-eastern subtypes (NVC H12, H16; see Annex 6.1). While H16 is local outside of the Cairngorms, H12 is widespread in the British uplands, but is proportionally most extensive in the Cairngorms. This is one of the best areas in the UK, and also in the EU, for landscapes dominated by European dry heaths.

The Cairngorms area is one of the most important in the UK for Alpine and boreal heaths. The eastern lichen-rich forms of Alpine and boreal heath are best developed here, with either prostrate heather – a growth form virtually restricted to the UK (represented by extensive H13) – or Blaeberry *Vaccinium myrtillus* and Crowberry *Empetrum nigrum* dominant (H19). Montane forms of heaths with Cloudberry *Rubus chamaemorus* (H22) are also superlatively well-developed and occur in larger stands than anywhere else in the UK.

Some of the most important stands of sub-Arctic willow *Salix* spp. scrub (W20) – a rare relict community in the UK – occur in the Cairngorms. Even here, however, stands are tiny, consisting mostly of clumps of only a few bushes. The largest single stand (about 0.5 ha) in the UK occurs in the Cairngorms and other stands, while tiny, are among the best developed (see Chapter 7). The main willow species is Downy Willow *S. lapponum*, but the rare Woolly Willow *S. lanata* occurs in some of its largest populations in the UK, while Whortle-leaved Willow *S. mysinites* is rare (see Chapter 7, Figure 7.3).

In the Cairngorms area all UK subtypes of Siliceous alpine and boreal grasslands are represented and are well-developed. They are: grass-heath (U7), sedge heath (U8), Three-leaved Rush-heath (U9), moss-heath (U10), late-lie snow-beds (U11/U12) and dwarf-herb community (U14). Oceanic moss-heaths and rush-heaths with Woolly-fringe Moss *Racomitrium lanuginosum* (represented by U9, U10) are among the best developed in the UK. The Cairngorms is superlative for Three-leaved Rush-heath (U9) and sedge-heath (U8), and, although it has some of the best moss-heath (U10) and some of the largest and most floristically important late-lie snow-beds (U11/U12) in the UK, the latter are relatively small in an international context.

Figure 6.1. Areas mapped using the National Vegetation Classification (NVC) scheme.

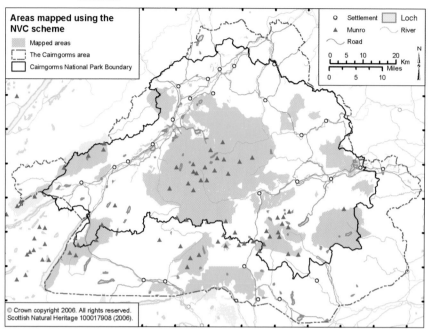

The Cairngorms have some of the largest and most floristically important late-lie snow-beds in the UK.
Photo: *L. Gill*

Semi-natural dry grasslands and scrubland facies on calcareous substrates (*Festuco-Brometalia*) occur at, or near, their northern limit in the UK. The Cairngorms is the most important area for these grasslands in Scotland. Similarly, some of the most extensive stands in Scotland of *Juniperus communis* formations on heaths or calcareous grasslands (as defined in the EC Habitats Directive; Annex 6.2) occur in the Cairngorms, mainly on heaths. This is the most important upland area for this habitat in the UK, although even here the habitat is rarely extensive. It occurs on acidic and base-rich soils derived both from limestone and, unusually, from serpentine. There is a wide altitudinal range, and the habitat shows natural altitudinal sequences, from the submontane to the low montane zone, occurring up to and above the limit of tree growth. Contrasting species-poor and species-rich stands occur on acidic and base-rich soils respectively. An outstanding boreal flora occurs, with its headquarters in the Cairngorms.

The Cairngorms is one of only two main areas in the UK in which pockets of natural serpentine debris are developed with Calaminarian grasslands of the *Violetalia calaminariae*. Stands are floristically varied, with many nationally rare plants represented, and occur at up to 883 m at Meikle Kilrannoch, on Caenlochan.

Some of the UK's best and highest-altitude stands of Hydrophilous tall herb fringe communities of plains and of montane to alpine levels (Annex 6.2) occur in the Cairngorms. These are especially rich in Arctic-alpine plants, and include many national rarities.

Blanket bog reaches its most extensive development in the EU in Britain and Ireland. The Cairngorms are important because this is the best place for high altitude blanket bog rich in montane plants and Reindeer lichens (*Cladonia* spp.). In these high altitude blanket bogs heather is replaced by Crowberry, Cowberry *Vaccinium vitis-idaea* and by other montane dwarf-shrubs.

In the UK, the Cairngorms area is also outstanding for:

- upland examples of Alkaline fens, which have a high representation of northern and Arctic-alpine species, and a full range of upland subtypes;

- Alpine pioneer formations of *Caricion bicoloris-atrofuscae*, with some exceptional examples of rare Arctic-alpines;

- sites for Calcareous rocky slopes with chasmophytic vegetation, including one of the two floristically richest sites for this habitat; and

- Arctic-alpines of Siliceous rocky slopes with chasmophytic vegetation. There are several outstanding examples of this habitat, which include the richest site in Britain.

Important species associated with upland plant communities in the Cairngorms are described in Chapters 11–19.

Important areas

Important areas for upland plant communities in the Cairngorms are listed in Table 6.2. They are defined as statutory sites (SACs and Sites of Special Scientific Interest; SSSIs) holding examples of key upland plant communities. The NVC communities corresponding to key plant communities on sites are

A base-rich flush with Yellow Saxifrage Saxifraga aizoides.
Photo: *L. Gill*

Table 6.1. Upland plant communities of national or international importance. The proportion of each plant community's UK range occurring within the Cairngorms is shown for the Cairngorms area (CA) and for the National Park (NP) separately.

Percentage of UK range: The percentage of the plant community's range (in 10-km squares) occurring in the Cairngorms area or Cairngorms National Park: *** 75–100%; ** 25–75%; * 10–24%; '-' <10%.

Nationally rare: NVC types recorded in fewer than 40 10-km squares in the UK.

Habitats Directive Codes: See Annex 6.2 for habitat names.

Vegetation Zone	Broad vegetation type	Key plant communities	NVC type(s)	Nationally rare	Habitats Directive Annex I Codes	BAP Priority Habitat	Percentage of UK range in: CA	NP
High Montane	Montane Moss-heath and associated vegetation	Three-leaved Rush – Woolly-Fringe Moss heath	U9	Y	H6150		**	**
	Snow-bed	Late-lie moss-dominated snow-beds	U11 U12	Y	H6150		**	*
		Alpine Lady's Mantle – *Sibbaldia* dwarf-herb community	U14	Y	H6150		*	*
		Stiff-sedge – *Polytrichum* heaths	U8		H6150		**	*
	Montane flushes	Yellow Sedge – Yellow Mountain Saxifrage mire	M11	Y	H7240	Fens	*	*
		Russet Sedge mire	M12	Y	H7240	Fens	-	-
		Anthelia – Bog Moss spring	M31			Fens	*	*
		Philonotis-Starry Saxifrage spring	M32			Fens	*	-
		Pohlia wahlenbergii var. *glacialis* spring	M33	Y		Fens	**	*
	Siliceous scree	Parsley Fern – Alpine Lady-fern snow-bed community	U18		H8110		*	*
Low Montane	Montane Moss-heaths and associated vegetation	Woolly-fringe Moss – Stiff Sedge moss-heath	U10		H6150		*	-
		Matgrass – Stiff Sedge grass-heath	U7		H6150		*	-
		Tufted Hair-grass – Heath Bedstraw grassland	U13				*	-
	Montane heaths	Prostrate heather – lichen heath	H13		H4060		**	*
		Blaeberry – lichen heath	H19		H4060		**	*
		Blaeberry – Woolly-fringe Moss heath	H20		H4060		*	*
		Blaeberry – Cloudberry heath	H22		H4060		*	*
	Mountain Willow scrub	Downy Willow – Great Wood-Rush scrub	W20	Y	H4080		**	*
	Moorland Juniper scrub		W19		H5130		**	**
	Submontane wet dwarf-shrub heath	Cross-leaved heath – Bog Moss wet heath	M16		H4010	Upland heathland	-	-
	Blanket bog	Montane dwarf-shrub rich and lichen-rich blanket bog	M19		H7130	Blanket bog	*	*
	Montane calcareous grassland	Mountain Avens – Moss Campion ledge community	CG14	Y	H6170	Calcareous grassland	*	*
	Yellow Mountain Saxifrage banks		U15				*	*
	Montane flushes	White Sedge – Bog Moss mire	M7	Y		Fens	*	*
		Bottle Sedge – *Sphagnum warnstorfii* mire	M8	Y		Fens	**	*
		Yellow Sedge – Yellow Mountain Saxifrage mire	M11		H7240	Fens	*	*
	Petrifying springs	*Cratoneuron* – Common Sedge spring	M38	Y	H7220	Fens	**	*
	Tall-herb ledge	Great Wood-Rush – Water Avens tall-herb community	U17		H6430		*	-

Vegetation Zone	Broad vegetation type	Key plant communities	NVC type(s)	Nationally rare	Habitats Directive Annex I Codes	BAP Priority Habitat	Percentage of UK range in:	
							CA	NP
Low Montane	Calaminarian grassland & serpentine heath	Calaminarian grassland			H6130		-	-
	Rocky slopes	Calcareous rock-crevice communities / Green Spleenwort – Brittle Bladder-fern community	U40		H8210		-	-
		Siliceous rock-crevice communities			H8220		-	-
	Calcareous scree	Calcareous scree communities			H8120		-	-
	Siliceous scree	Siliceous scree communities			H8110		*	*
Submontane	Submontane wet dwarf-shrub heath	Deer-Grass – Cross-leaved Heath wet heath	M15		H4010	Upland heathland	-	-
		Cross-leaved Heath – Bog Moss wet heath	M16				-	-
	Submontane dry dwarf-shrub heath	Heather – Bell Heather heath / Heather – Blaeberry heath	H10 / H12		H4030	Upland heathland	- / *	- / -
		Heather – Bearberry heath	H16		H4030	Upland heathland	**	**
	Moorland Juniper scrub		W19		H5130	Upland heathland	**	**
	Submontane calcareous grassland	Semi-natural dry grasslands (Sheep's Fescue-Bent-Thyme grassland)	CG10		H6210	Upland calcareous grassland	-	-
		Species-rich Matgrass grasslands (Sheep's Fescue-Bent-Thyme grassland, Sheep's Fescue-Bent-Alpine Lady's Mantle grassland)	CG10 CG11		H6230	Upland calcareous grassland	*	*
	Blanket bog	Heather – Cotton-grass blanket mire / Cross-leaved Heath – Bog Moss blanket mire	M18 / M19		H7130	Blanket bog	- / -	- / -
	Submontane flushes	Dioecious Sedge – Butterwort mire	M10		H7230	Fens	-	-
		Cratoneuron – Common Sedge spring	M37		H7220	Fens	*	*
	Calaminarian grassland and serpentine heath	Calaminarian grassland			H6130		-	-
	Limestone pavement				H8240	Limestone pavements	-	-
Forest zone	Dwarf-shrub heath (lowland)	Cross-leaved Heath – Bog Moss wet heath	M16		H4010	Upland heathland	-	-
		Heather – Blaeberry heath	H12		H4030	Upland heathland	*	-
		Heather – Bearberry heath	H16		H4030	Upland heathland	**	**
	Moorland juniper scrub		W19		H5130	Upland heathland	**	**
	Blanket bog	Cross-leaved Heath – *Sphagnum papillosum* blanket mire	M18		H7130	Blanket bog	-	-
	Springs (including flushes)	*Cratoneuron* – Common Sedge spring	M37		H7220	Fens	*	*

given, together with important rock communities (Calaminarian grassland, rock crevice and scree communities) not dealt with by the NVC.

Table 6.2 includes 15 SACs (*c.* 103,000 ha) and 31 SSSIs (*c.* 115,000 ha) – the two designations largely overlapping. It also lists all upland qualifying habitats for SACs. Examples of non-statutory areas in which key plant communities are represented are given in the following area accounts. These are not intended to be comprehensive, but rather concentrate on those areas holding the best examples of key plant communities in the UK, or that are unique in the UK or EU.

Cairngorms SAC (Table 6.2), incorporating the Cairngorms, Eastern Cairngorms, Inchrory, Northern Corries, North Rothiemurchus Pinewood, Glenmore Forest and Abernethy Forest SSSIs, is the single-most important site for upland plant communities in the UK. The most extensive representation (on SSSIs) of montane grassland types occurs on the Cairngorms, including grass-heath (U7), Three-leaved Rush-heath (U9), moss-heath (U10), late-lie snow-beds (U11/U12) and dwarf-herb community (U14). Together, these constitute the largest extent of Siliceous alpine and boreal grassland (a qualifying habitat on SACs) in the UK.

The Cairngorms SAC contains the most extensive, or best examples in the UK of:

• two montane dwarf-shrub heaths (H13, H19, H20 and H22), which, together form the best example of eastern lichen-rich montane heath;

• M16 wet heath, which constitutes the best boreal example rich in lichens;

• two montane springs (M31, M33); and

• high altitude siliceous rock-crevice communities of high crags, supporting outstanding acidic Arctic-alpine flora.

The montane dwarf-shrub heath, especially H13, is widely developed on gently sloping ridges in 'waves' of heath separated by strips of bare ground (Bayfield, 1984). The Cairngorms SAC is the best place internationally for this 'wave' form of prostrate *Calluna* heath.

The most extensive examples of sub-montane dwarf-shrub heaths (H12, H16) in the UK occur on the SSSIs of the Cairngorms SAC. The second largest area

of H16 in the UK occurs on *The Maim* on Deeside, while the *Muir of Dinnet* supports the best examples of species-rich types of H16 in the UK.

Caenlochan is the most important site in the UK for montane willow scrub (W20) and tall-herb community (U17). The largest single fragmentary stand of W20 in the UK occurs on Caenlochan, which is also the best site in the UK for Sub-Arctic *Salix* spp. scrub, listed in Annex 1 of the Habitats Directive. The largest area of sedge-heath (U8) on SSSIs in the UK occurs on Caenlochan, which is also one of the best sites in the UK for calcareous rock-crevice communities (OV40), perhaps being surpassed only by Ben Lawers in the Breadalbanes. At Caenlochan, Calaminarian grassland reaches its highest altitude in UK, and this habitat is one of only two UK locations for the nationally rare Alpine Catchfly *Lychnis alpina* (Chapter 14).

Beinn a' Ghlo is the most important northern outlier for the Annex I habitat Semi-natural dry grasslands and scrubland facies: on calcareous substrates (Festuco-Brometalia) which occurs on limestone and base-enriched schist. *Inchrory*, *Tulach Hill* and *Morrone Birkwood* are also important for this habitat. The largest example of species-rich *Nardus* grassland (CG11) in the Eastern Highlands occurs on Beinn a' Ghlo. In the UK, this is second only to Trotternish Ridge on Skye in terms of area.

Drumochter Hills is one of the best sites for montane willow scrub (W20) in the UK, perhaps second only to Caenlochan, having a large number of stands, albeit tiny fragments, developed in a variety of situations, such as on crags, by gorges and in scree. In the Pass of Drumochter there is the most extensive easterly example of western blanket mire (M17).

Morrone Birkwood is a key site that has probably changed little since the end of the last glaciation. It provides one of the best examples of a relatively unmodified landscape, with a mix of woodland and scrub grading to a wide range of open plant communities on both acid and base-rich soils. It has an extensive mixed woodland of birch and Juniper, with a species-rich ground flora. This extends into the upper sub-montane (or sub-alpine zone), forming the only example of sub-montane birch-juniper wood in the Cairngorms, and is virtually unique in the UK.

Tulach Hill and *Glen Fender Meadows* hold some of the best upland and northern examples in the UK of the Annex I habitat Alkaline fens

(M9, M10, M11), while the **Monadhliath** has the largest extent in the UK of well-developed high altitude blanket bog (M19), with a high lichen cover and montane dwarf-shrubs. **Morven and Mullachdubh** support the largest example in the UK of Juniper scrub (W19), occurring up to high altitude.

Cairnwell supports floristically unusual stands of the nationally rare Mountain Avens *Dryas octopetala* ledge community (CG14), although these are fragmentary and tiny. *Dryas* occurs with Mountain Crowberry *Empetrum nigrum* ssp. *hermaphroditum*, forming a sub-type not known elsewhere in the UK.

In areas of the Cairngorms outside of the SSSI and SAC series there are large tracts of BAP Priority habitats, and of habitats listed on Annex I of the Habitats Directive. The BAP Priority habitat 'Upland heathland' and the Annex I habitat 'European dry heaths' are extensive in most upland areas. The extensive NVC dwarf-shrub heath is H12. Areas where it predominates include the **Hills of Cromdale**, **Balmoral Forest**, **Angus Glens**, **Glen Clunie** and **Forest of Atholl**.

Blanket bog is a BAP Priority and Annex I habitat, and is extensive on flat ground and gentle slopes, generally from 450 m to as high as 900 m. Ground occupied includes glens, lower plateaux, summits and shelves. The most notable development of blanket bog in the Cairngorms occurs in high altitude tracts, as on the high plateaux (at 600–900 m), north of **Glen Avon**, east of **Glen Clova**, in the Forest of Atholl and the Monadhliath. The predominant NVC type is M19.

Many montane plant communities are protected through the EC Habitats Directive. They are generally developed on ground above *c.* 750 m, which occurs widely outside of statutory sites. The most outstanding montane plant communities to occur outwith the statutory sites correspond with the Annex I habitat Alpine and boreal heath, which predominates, for example, on the summits of **Geal-charn Mòr**, **Brown Cow Hill**, **An Socach** and **Beinn Dearg**. NVC communities represented include H13, H19 and H22. Another montane Annex I habitat – Siliceous alpine and boreal grassland – is more localized, being confined to hills exceeding 900 m in altitude. Significant stands with representation of the rarer communities occur on **Mount Keen**, **Bynack More**, **Cairn Gorm** and **An Sgarsoch**. NVC communities represented include grass-heath U7, sedge-heath U8, Three-leaved Rush-heath U9, moss-heath U10

and late-lie snow-beds U11/U12. On the north-east ridge of Cairn Gorm there is the outstanding late-lie snow bed of **Ciste Mhearaid**; one of the most important snow-beds in the UK.

Recent research and survey findings

The foundation for research and surveys of plant communities in the Cairngorms was laid by the work of Watt and Jones (1948), Metcalfe (1950), Burgess (1951) and Ingram (1958). Watt and Jones (1948) examined the relationship between the environment and the altitudinal zonation of the vegetation. The other three authors investigated the ecology of the montane zone, the *Empetrum-Vaccinium* zone, and the mountain Callunetum and *Juncus trifidus* communities, respectively.

Building on this work, Poore and McVean (1957) related the ecology of mountain vegetation in the Cairngorms to other parts of Scotland and to Scandinavia, providing a basis for deciding what is important about Scottish

On exposed, gently sloping ridges prostrate Calluna *heath sometimes occurs in 'waves', separated by strips of bare ground. This wave pattern is exceptionally well-developed in the central Cairngorms.*
Photo: *L. Gill*

Table 6.2. Important areas for upland plant communities and habitats in the Cairngorms. Sites are listed in descending order of the number (*n*) of internationally important habitats that qualify under Annex I of the EC Habitats Directive, or the number of nationally important plant communities.

SAC/SSSI site name	Key plant communities[1]	SAC qualifying habitats[2]	*n*
1. Cairngorms[3]	CG10, CG11, U7, U8, U9, U10, U11/U12, U13, U14, U18, H12, H13, H16, H19, H20, H22, M7, M15, M16, M18, M31, M32, M33, W19, W20, Siliceous rock-crevice communities, Siliceous scree, Calcareous rock-crevice communities	H4010, H4030, H4060, H4080, H5130, H6150, H6210, H6230, H6430, H7130, H7220, H7240, H8110, H8210, H8220	15
2. Caenlochan	CG14, U7, U8, U11/U12, U13, U14, U15, U17, H19, M7, M8, M11, M12, M38, W20, OV40, Calaminarian grassland, Calcareous rock-crevice communities, Calcareous scree, Siliceous rock-crevice communities, Siliceous scree	H4030, H4060, H4080, H6130, H6150, H6230, H6430, H7130, H7230, H7240, H8110, H8120, H8210, H8220	14
3. Beinn a' Ghlo	CG10, CG11, CG14, U9, U10, U11/U12, M10, M11, H12, H13, H19, H22, OV40, Calcareous rock-crevice communities, Siliceous rock-crevice communities, Siliceous scree	H4030, H4060, H6150, H6210, H6230, H7130, H7220, H7230, H7240, H8110, H8210, H8220	12
4. Drumochter Hills	U7, U8, U10, U11/U12, H12, H13, H19, H20, CG11, M7, M15, M17, W20, Siliceous rock-crevice communities, Siliceous scree	H4010, H4030, H4060, H4080, H6150, H6230, H6430, H7130, H8110, H8220	10
5. Morrone Birkwood	H12, H13, H22, W19, M10, M11, CG10, CG11	H4060, H5130, H6210, H7220, H7230, H7240	6
6. Ballochbuie	H12, H16, H21, M16, M19, Calcareous rock-crevice communities, Siliceous rock-crevice communities,	H4010, H4030, H7130, H8210, H8220	5
7. Tulach Hill and Glen Fender Meadows	H12, M9, M10, M11, CG10, Limestone pavement	H4030, H6210, H7230, H8240	4
8. Ladder Hills	H12, H13, H22, M19	H4030, H4060, H7130	3
9. Green Hill of Strathdon	H12, W19, Calaminarian grassland	H4030, H5130, H6130	3
10. Glen Tanar	H12, H16	H4010, H4030, H7130	3
11. Monadhliath	CG11, U7, U10, U11/U12, U13, U15, H12, H19, H20, M7, M8, M19, W20, Calcareous rock-crevice communities	H7130	1
12. Morven and Mullachdubh	H12, H13, H16, H19, H22, M19, W19	H5130	1
13. Muir of Dinnet	H12, H16, M18	H4030	1
14. Coyles of Muick	H10 (species-rich), Calaminarian grassland	H6130	1
15. Creag nan Gamhainn	M37	H7220	1
16. The Maim	H16	H4030	1
17. Lochnagar[4]	H12, H13, H16, H19, H20, H22, M7, U10, U11/U12, U7, U8, Siliceous rock-crevice communities		
18. Glen Callater	U8, U17, H12, H13, H19, H20, M10, rock habitats		
19. Ben Vrackie	H12, H18, M8, M10, M32, OV40, Calcareous rock-crevice communities		
20. Craig Leek	H10 (species-rich), CG10, M10, M11, M37, Calcareous rock-crevice communities		
21. Creag Dhubh	H12, H21, M15, M10, M11		
22. Coire Bhachdaidh	CG11, H13		
23. Glas Tulaichean	H13, Calcareous rock-crevice communities		
24. Glen Ey Gorge	H12, U17		
25. Cairnwell	M8, CG14		

[1] NVC categories are listed in Annex 6.1.
[2] EC habitat codes and names are listed in Annex 6.2.
[3] Cairngorms SAC includes Cairngorms, Eastern Cairngorms, Inchrory, Northern Corries, North Rothiemurchus Pinewood, Glenmore Forest and Abernethy Forest SSSIs.
[4] Lochnagar is a Special Protection Area but not an SSSI.

and Cairngorm vegetation, nationally and internationally. Following on from this, a more comprehensive attempt to describe and classify upland plant communities was carried out by McVean and Ratcliffe (1962). Large numbers of relevés were collected from upland sites throughout the Highlands, including many from the Cairngorms, and analysed to give a phytosociological classification to which all upland vegetation could be related. This large body of data on the floristics of the vegetation of upland sites formed much of the basis for the descriptions and assessment of the conservation value of some of the most important upland sites, given in Ratcliffe (1977). Prior to this Ratcliffe (1974) gave a descriptive account of the vegetation of the Cairngorms. Huntley (1979) and Huntley and Birks (1979a,b) described the plant communities of Caenlochan and Morrone Birkwood, respectively.

More comprehensive plant community classifications have followed. These include Birse (1980, 1984) and Robertson (1984) for Scotland and *British Plant Communities* (Rodwell 1991a,b, 1992, 1994, 2000) for the whole of Britain. *British Plant Communities*, with its National Vegetation Classification (NVC), provides a basis for the description and evaluation of conservation value of plant communities in all upland areas. The NVC describes about 400 plant communities from Britain. About 80 of these are characteristic of the uplands in different parts of the UK, while about 60 occur in the Cairngorms. The latter include scrub, but not upland woodland communities, aquatic communities or swamps.

As part of more general work on altitudinal zonation, studies on relict woodland, scrub and the natural tree-line are important for forming a picture of what the vegetation may have been like prior to their widespread loss. Such studies are also important for assessing the conservation importance of relict types, their potential for restoration, and appropriate restoration targets. Studies of relict montane (or alpine) scrub above the potential tree-line are reviewed by Gilbert *et al.* (1997) and Gilbert (2002).

Vegetation surveys

Broad-scale vegetation mapping of the Cairngorms was carried out as part of the Land Cover of Scotland 1988 (LCS88) project (MLURI, 1993a,b) and the Countryside Survey 2000 (CS2000) (Haines-Young *et al.*, 2000) based on the interpretation of aerial photographs and satellite images, respectively (see Chapter 5). The LCS88 maps provide a broad picture of the main kinds of vegetation cover across the whole of the Cairngorms. Mapping categories especially relevant to the uplands are: Heather moorland, Peatland, Montane, Good rough grassland, Poor rough grassland and Bracken.

[1] See: http://www.gloria.ac.at/res/gloria_home/

More detailed vegetation maps are available for all of the larger upland SSSIs and many of the smaller ones. The Nature Conservancy Council carried out vegetation survey and mapping of many upland SSSIs in the 1980s (Nature Conservancy Council, 1982 to 1991). Stands of vegetation were classified and grouped into vegetation types, whose boundaries formed map polygons. An unpublished classification of upland vegetation types (Birks & Ratcliffe, 1980) was used prior to the first drafts of the National Vegetation Classification becoming available in 1986. Birks and Ratcliffe (1980) was based on the published upland vegetation classifications of McVean and Ratcliffe (1962) and Birks (1973), together with unpublished data gathered from southern Scotland, England and Wales.

Aerial photographs were used for navigation in the field and to assist in drawing the map polygons. From these, area measurements were produced for each plant community within SSSIs. These data form the basis for the evaluation of the plant communities on upland sites.

More recently, NVC surveys have been carried out to fill in unsurveyed areas or to add detail for SSSIs (Birse, 1986, 1987; McPhail, 1992; Loizou, 1996a,b,1999; McCrae *et al.*, 1996; Rae, 1996a). NVC survey of land outside of SSSIs has been undertaken for the Angus Glens (Holl, 1991) and for most of the Cairngorms Core Area (Rae, 1995, 1996b, 1997; Gill *et al.*, 1998).

Trends

The Allt a' Mharcaidh catchment, taking in almost 1,000 ha of submontane and montane habitat on the western flanks of the Cairngorms SAC, is an Environmental Change Network site. Monitoring of the vegetation and plant species occurs at intervals, with the aim of building up a long-term dataset (Bayfield *et al.*, 2003). These data have yet to be summarised. In general, no data on trends in the distributions of individual plant communities are available for the Cairngorms.

The Cairngorms is one of the target areas of the Global Observation Research Initiative in Alpine Environments (GLORIA). This is a Europe-wide long-term observation network to determine climate-induced threats on high mountain biodiversity. A report on GLORIA-Europe is available from the project's web site[1].

Hester *et al.* (1996) derived broad land cover change, from interpretation of aerial photographs taken in 1946 and 1988, for 1,000 km² of the core area of the Cairngorms (Chapter 5). The land cover categories used were those defined in the *Land cover of Scotland 1988* (MLURI, 1993a,b). The major changes detected were due to human impacts, with conifer plantation showing the greatest increase in net area. Successional changes in semi-natural vegetation did occur but none totalled more than 5 km² for any one category. Changes for four open-ground upland habitats (with net change in brackets) were as follows: *Agrostis-Festuca* grassland (+1.2 km²; +9%), Bracken *Pteridium aquilinum* (+1.4 km²; +467%), heather (-63.8 km²; -22%) and *Nardus-Molinia* grassland (+4.8 km²; +130%)[2]. The major net loss of heather was to conifer plantation (51.4 km²) with losses of between 0.4 and 2 km² of the two grassland and three semi-natural woodland types for each category. These trends differ from those described in Chapter 5, which were derived from a sample of NCMS squares drawn from throughout the National Park.

Conservation issues

Climate change. Under a scenario of rising temperatures montane or alpine communities could become more restricted in extent than they are at present (see Chapter 20). Many Arctic-alpine plant species are also under threat, because they are restricted to high altitudes in the UK. Some species may be able to migrate upslope if suitable ground is present, or into different plant communities from those they currently occupy. Plants likely to be favoured include Bracken, Gorse *Ulex europaeus* and Broom *Cytisus scoparius*, which are currently restricted by their susceptibility to frost. This suggests that the current species composition of upland communities could change, as some plants are able to adapt to changing conditions, while others are excluded.

Deer management and numbers. Long-term effects of grazing by deer and sheep in the uplands include the prevention of tree and scrub regeneration, and the restriction of grazing-sensitive species, including tall-herbs and many trees and shrubs, to localities inaccessible to grazing animals. Current effects of grazing include the suppression of growth and flowering, and the loss of plants such as heather and Blaeberry. Red Deer *Cervus elaphus* and sheep can also cause changes in plant composition of communities and damage to soils by trampling, dunging and urination (Chapter 21).

Culling, especially of hinds, has consistently lagged behind the recruitment rate, and hence has generally failed to prevent an increase in overall Red Deer numbers (Staines & Balharry, 2002). However, numbers have fallen in parts of the West Grampian area (Youngson & Stewart, 1997) and in the Northern Corries (Watson, 1997). Numbers of Red Deer did start to increase again in the late 1980s in the Northern Corries, but not before one of the most remarkable examples of tree and scrub regeneration occurred, demonstrating the dramatic regeneration that can occur when deer numbers are reduced to low levels. Scrubby trees and shrubs regenerated from the woodland edge at around 500 m, up to the potential tree-line and above, at around 850 m (Miller & Cummins 1982; Bayfield *et al.* 1998). French *et al.* (1997) believe that the population of young pines in the Northern Corries is likely to develop into a true subalpine scrub zone or tree-line, so long as colonisation continues, grazing pressure remains low and no catastrophic mortality occurs.

Sheep management and numbers. Sheep numbers are variable in the Cairngorms. In some areas numbers are low compared with many areas of upland Scotland. Large parts of the core granite area with poor acid soils have no sheep at all. The main concentrations of high densities of hill sheep in the Cairngorms are along the southern and south-western edges of the Cairngorms, especially in ground lying between the boundaries of the National Park and the Cairngorms area. The richer rocks of Clova, Glen Shee and Atholl support the largest numbers of sheep. The Angus Glens (especially Glen Clova), Tulach Hill, Beinn a' Ghlo, West Drumochter and Coire Bhachdaidh are examples of areas with high numbers of sheep. Changes to the vegetation due to high grazing pressure, including the replacement of heather moorland by grassland, can be identified in all of these areas.

Built development. This is mainly a landscape issue, since the area of upland habitat affected is small. There is a scattering of shepherds' huts, shooting huts, bothies, lodges and telecommunication masts across the uplands of the Cairngorms, and their associated access tracks. The main intrusions are caused by skiing developments at Cairngorm, Glen Shee and the Lecht. These developments are all located in areas with a range of plant communities similar to those developed on adjacent SSSIs and SACs. Indeed, the skiing area of the Lecht once forming part of the Ladder Hills SSSI, before erosion of peaty habitat led to management problems and caused it to be excised from the statutory site.

Wind farms are a potential threat to plant communities in the Cairngorms area outside of the National Park. Schemes have been proposed for areas of

---

[2] These figures assume that primary and secondary components of mosaics were 60% and 40% respectively.

low upland (on submontane ground around 300–500 m), where the main vegetation is blanket mire and dwarf-shrub heath, dominated by *Calluna*.

Downhill skiing. Skiing, ski-fencing and piste development results in localised damage to the vegetation cover and soil erosion (Watson, 1985, 1990; Bayfield, 1997) (see Chapter 22). The buildings, uplift facilities and service tracks result in local habitat loss. In the early years of development, bulldozing of pistes and insensitive use of snow-moving machines caused damage to soils and vegetation (Bayfield, 1980; Nethersole-Thompson & Watson, 1981; Bayfield, 1996).

Another cause of damage to plant communities is through increased footpath development, in response to an increasing number of walkers being attracted by the availability of car parks and uplift facilities (Lance *et al.*, 1989, 1991; Watson, 1984, 1991).

Ski-fencing is erected to encourage more snow to lie and can result in a loss of vegetation susceptible to prolonged snow cover, for example in the replacement of heather by the more snow-tolerant Blaeberry or Mat-grass *Nardus stricta*. Such effects may accentuate existing vegetation trends, but tend to favour a higher proportion of snow-tolerant vegetation. Changes like this have taken place at the Lecht, and to a lesser extent at Cairn Gorm and Glen Shee (Watson, 1990).

The loss of vegetation cover and soil erosion within the pistes is localised, with recovery taking place in many areas in recent years. Peaty soils at the Lecht and Glen Shee are the most susceptible to erosion. Sheep can congregate in the shelter of fences where they may change vegetation types by dunging and trampling (Welch *et al.*, 1995; van der Wal *et al.*, 2003).

Management agreements, Local Plans and Government guidance seek to minimise the ecological impacts of skiing developments.

Hunting and management. Throughout much of the Cairngorms the principal form of land-use, other than recreation, is hunting. Agricultural usage, chiefly sheep rearing, tends to occur alongside management for hunting, but is often subordinate to it. The main hunting interests are Red Grouse *Lagopus lagopus* shooting and Red Deer stalking. Large tracts of *Calluna*-dominated vegetation, prevalent throughout much of the Cairngorms, both on mineral and on peaty soils, favours Red Grouse. The Cairngorms massif is predominantly granite and, despite extensive *Calluna*-rich vegetation, tends to support low stocks of grouse, perhaps reflecting the nutrient-poor status of the rocks and the relatively high altitude.

Management for Red Grouse results in impacts on the vegetation, mostly through burning. Good burning practice following published guidelines (Scottish Executive, 2001a,b; Scotland's Moorland Forum, 2003) can help to maintain the species and structural diversity of heather moorland. Poor practices can result in a loss of quality and productivity because tall heather and unproductive old woody heather tends to predominate, providing few niches for other species.

Damage to plant communities can occur when burning guidelines are not followed, or when fires run out of control. One of the most common causes of damage is from fires running upslope from tall heather into montane prostrate heather on the windswept ridges and summits above. This can result in the loss of all vegetation cover and, in some cases, the thin organic soil layer may also be consumed. Recovery of heather cover is slow on this kind of exposed ground and characteristic lichens may take many decades to come back. Such bared areas are prone to soil erosion. Fire damage to prostrate heather of this kind has occurred in Glen Clunie, in the Eastern Cairngorms, on Drumochter and in Glen Shee.

Fires may also run up from gentle slopes on to steep, rocky slopes with thin, peaty soils. Heaths rich in bryophytes may occur in these localities, where recovery of the bryophyte species may be slow. Such steep slopes are also prone to soil erosion after fire, leading to scree development. Examples of burning on steep slopes can be seen in Glen Feshie and Glen Shee.

Burning of wetter areas of blanket bog, with bog-moss *Sphagnum* or pools, has also taken place in the past. Such burning can turn bog-moss *Sphagnum*-rich blanket bog into wet heath lacking the characteristic species of the blanket mire. Bare peat can also be exposed by fire, and may then be damaged further by Red Deer trampling. Examples of burning damage to blanket bog occur in upper Deeside, Glen Feshie and Glen Avon. There is evidence from Scotland and the Pennines that major peat erosion was initiated around 1500 AD to 1700 AD (Tallis, 1985, 1987; Stevenson *et al.*, 1990) corresponding to climate change associated with the Little Ice Age, or to an increase in the intensity of burning. The widespread peat erosion that occurs on high plateaux, such as on Drumochter and on Mòine Mhór, occurs above the altitudinal limit of *Calluna* growth. Burning is therefore unlikely to be a cause of the onset of erosion, suggesting past climate change as a more likely cause, though this needs investigation. Moor-gripping occurs widely in lower-altitude blanket bogs, where drainage channels cause a slight lowering of the water table and localised effects on the flora close to the drains. More severe effects can be caused by the drainage of fens, such as *Juncus-* and *Carex-Sphagnum* flushes, causing loss of characteristic wetland species.

Recreation. Walking for recreation in the hills has increased, at least in the last few decades (Chapter 22). The main effects on the plant communities are due to trampling, resulting in the development of paths and trample zones around paths. The damage in and along paths is usually small relative to the area of the habitat as a whole.

Short, montane vegetation is highly susceptible to damage from trampling. This includes lichen-rich dwarf-shrub heaths, Stiff-sedge-Woolly-fringe Moss *Racomitrium lanuginosum* heath and Three-leaved Rush *Juncus trifidus* heath with low growing mosses and hepatic and lichen crusts. The lichens and bryophytes are especially susceptible to damage and around clearly-defined paths zones of trampling damage due to loss of these may be perceptible.

Generally, ill-defined paths in the montane zone, such as on a broad ridge or plateau where people tend to spread out, pose some of the greatest risks to susceptible montane vegetation. Damage has been caused in this way to lichen-rich Three-leaved Rush *Juncus trifidus* heath and prostrate heather heaths on the Cairngorms SSSI and Drumochter SSSI. Sometimes, rare and highly valuable plant communities, such as late-lie mossy snow-beds, are crossed by footpaths. In the case of snow-beds, damage may by reduced by the presence of protective snow for much of the year. Blanket bog is also susceptible to trampling, and damage occurs locally on popular paths, as once occurred in the Northern Corries. There, ongoing footpath repair and restoration has considerably reduced damaging effects.

Legg (1998) reviews published work on human trampling impacts with special reference to the Cairngorms.

Bulldozed tracks. Most estates have built bulldozed tracks into upland areas, particularly since the 1960s. They are there to facilitate management and sport, notably the removal of Red Deer carcases, and to provide vehicular access to shooting butts. The area of upland habitat directly impacted by tracks is relatively small. The greatest impact of tracks is the loss of a perception of wilderness. Tracks which ascend up into the montane zone on high ridges or plateaux may impact on plant communities that are nationally scarce. The vegetation of one such track, cutting through *Juncus trifidus* rush-heath on Beinn a' Bhuird, has recently been restored, as have tracks in Abernethy. However, other damaging high-level tracks still occur in the Cairngorms. Tracks can disrupt the hydrology of upland fens and blanket bogs. Impacts can be minimised by the use of best practice in design and construction.

All Terrain Vehicles (ATVs). The use of ATVs in the uplands has become popular recently, and they have generally replaced ponies for extraction of Red Deer carcases. Peatland plant communities, especially those developed on deep peat, are highly susceptible to ATV use. ATVs do a great deal of damage, especially to wet peat plant communities at high altitude that recover only very slowly, if ever. All montane communities, especially those dominated by moss or with a high cover of lichens, are susceptible. Damage to Woolly-fringe Moss *Racomitrium lanuginosum* communities has been observed on the Drumochter Hills in the form of scuffing, cutting and detachment of the vegetation surface and breakage of lichens.

Many estates in the Cairngorms have bulldozed tracks up into the montane zone, on high ridges or plateaux, impacting both on the landscape and on nationally scarce plant communities.
Photo: *L. Gill*

Forestry. Commercial forestry of non-native conifer species occurs in the uplands of the Cairngorms, mainly along the southern and south-western edges outside of the National Park. Native trees, especially Scots Pine, are also used for forestry, especially on Speyside and Deeside.

Knowledge gaps. The more notable gaps in our knowledge of upland plant communities in the Cairngorms are as follows.

- Many upland areas outside of statutory sites lack floristic data.

- Impacts of grazing and trampling on vegetation have been poorly documented.

- Long-term data on trends for upland plant communities are lacking, especially on the extent and floristics of snow-beds in the montane zone.

- The dynamics of montane vegetation in response to grazing, nutrient inputs, atmospheric pollution and human trampling are poorly known.

- The ecology of montane scrub and tall-herb communities, and potential techniques for restoration require investigation.

- There is much uncertainty concerning the likely impacts of climate change on upland vegetation.

- The causes of erosion in high-altitude blanket bogs require further study.

References

Bayfield, N.G. (1980). Replacement of vegetation on disturbed ground near ski lifts in the Cairngorm mountains, Scotland. *Journal of Biogeography* 7: 249–260.

Bayfield, N.G. (1984). The dynamics of heather (*Calluna vulgaris*) stripes in the Cairngorm mountains. *Journal of Ecology* 72: 515–527.

Bayfield, N.G. (1996). Long-term changes in colonization of bulldozed ski pistes at Cairn Gorm, Scotland. *Journal of Applied Ecology* 33: 1359–1365.

Bayfield, N.G. (1997). *Recreation Impact Mapping of the Cairn Gorm-Ben Macdui Area: A Reconnaissance Study*. ITE Report to SNH, Hill of Brathens, Banchory.

Bayfield, N.G., Fraser, N.M. & Calle, Z. (1998). High altitude colonisation of the Northern Corries of Cairn Gorm by Scots pine (*Pinus sylvestris*). *Scottish Geographical Magazine* 114: 172–179.

Bayfield, N., Brooker, R. & Milne, L. (2003). Cairngorms ECN Site handbook. ECN Report.

Birks, H.J.B. & Ratcliffe, D.A. (1980). Classification of upland vegetation types in Britain. Unpublished report. Nature Conservancy Council: Peterborough.

Birks, H.J.B. (1973). *Past and Present Vegetation of the Isle of Skye A Palaeoecological Study*. Cambridge University Press: Cambridge.

Birse, E.L. (1980). *Plant Communities of Scotland. A Preliminary Phytocoenonia*. Macaulay Institute for Soil Research: Aberdeen.

Birse, E.L. (1984). *The Phytocoenonia of Scotland. Additions and Revisions*. Macaulay Institute for Soil Research: Aberdeen.

Birse, E.L. (1986). Vegetation monitoring Glenshee. Unpublished report to North East Scotland Region, Nature Conservancy Council.

Birse, E.L. (1987). Vegetation of Garbh Choire, Glen Shee. Unpublished report to North East Scotland Region, Nature Conservancy Council.

Burgess, A. (1951). The ecology of the Cairngorms III. The *Empetrum – Vaccinium* zone. *Journal of Ecology* 39: 271–284.

French, D.D., Miller, G.R. & Cummins, R.P. (1997). Recent development of high-altitude *Pinus sylvestris* scrub in the northern Cairngorm Mountains, Scotland. *Biological Conservation* 79: 133–144.

Gilbert, D. (ed.) (2002). *Montane Scrub: The Challenge above the Treeline*. Highland Birchwoods: Munlochy.

Gilbert, D., Horsfield, D. & Thompson, D.B.A. (eds.) (1997). *The ecology and restoration of montane and subalpine scrub habitats in Scotland*. SNH Review No. 83. SNH: Perth.

Gill, J.P., Sales, D. & Horsfield, D. (1998). *Cairngorms Montane and Moorland Habitat Survey and Impact Assessment* Unpublished ESS Report to SNH. SNH: Perth.

Haines-Young, R.H., Barr, C.J., Black, H.I.J., Briggs, D.J., Bunce, R.G.H., Clarke, R.T., Cooper, A., Dawson, F.H., Firbank, L.G., Fuller, R.M., Furse, M.T., Gillespie, M.K., Hill, R., Hornung, M., Howard, D.C., McCann, T., Morecroft, M.D., Petit, S., Sier, A.R.J., Smart, S.M., Smith, G.M., Stott, A.P., Stuart, R.C. & Watkins, J.W. (2000). *Accounting for Nature: Assessing Habitats in the UK Countryside*. Department of the Environment, Natural Environmental Research Council: Rotherham.

Hester, A.J., Miller, D.R. & Towers, W. (1996). Landscape-scale vegetation change in the Cairngorms, Scotland, 1946–1988: Implications for land management. *Biological Conservation* 77: 41–51.

Holl, K. (1991). *A botanical survey of the Angus uplands*. Unpublished report to the Nature Conservancy Council. SNH: Perth.

Huntley, B. (1979). The past and present vegetation of the Caenlochan National Nature Reserve, Scotland I. Present vegetation. *New Phytologist* 83: 215–283.

Huntley, B. & Birks, H.J.B. (1979a). The past and present vegetation of the Morrone Birkwoods National Nature Reserve, Scotland. I. A primary phytosociological survey. *Journal of Ecology* 67: 417–446.

Huntley, B. & Birks, H.J.B. (1979b). The past and present vegetation of the Morrone Birkwoods National Nature Reserve. II. Woodland vegetation and soils. *Journal of Ecology* 67: 447–467.

Ingram, M. (1958). The ecology of the Cairngorms. The *Juncus* zone: *Juncus trifidus* communities. *Journal of Ecology* 46: 707–737.

Lance, A.N., Baugh, I.D. & Love, J.A. (1989). Continued footpath widening in the Cairngorm mountains, Scotland. *Biological Conservation* 49: 201–214.

Lance, A.N., Thaxton, R. & Watson, A. (1991). Recent changes in footpath width in the Cairngorms. *Scottish Geographic Magazine* 107(2): 106–109.

Legg, C. (1998). *Review of published work in relation to trampling impacts and change in montane vegetation.* Unpublished report. SNH: Perth.

Loizou, T. (1996a). Report on the plant communities of Glen Feshie Special Area for Conservation. Unpublished report. SNH: Perth.

Loizou, T. (1996b). Report on the plant communities of Glen Lui Special Area for Conservation. Unpublished report. SNH: Perth.

Loizou, T. (1999). The habitats and plant communities of the corries and glens round Caenlochan SSSI. Unpublished report. SNH: Perth.

McCrae, G., Gray, D. & Graham, K. (1996). Vegetation survey of Beinn a' Ghlo pSAC. Unpublished report. SNH: Perth.

McPhail, P. (1992). Glen Fender Meadows. Unpublished vegetation map. SNH: Perth.

McVean, D.N. & Ratcliffe, D.A. (1962). *Plant Communities of the Scottish Highlands (Monographs of the Nature Conservancy No 1).* HMSO: London.

Metcalfe, G. (1950). The ecology of the Cairngorms, II. The mountain Callunetum. *Journal of Ecology* 38: 46–74.

Miller, G.R. & Cummins, R.P. (1982). Regeneration of Scots pine *Pinus sylvestris* at a natural tree-line in the Cairngorm mountains, Scotland. *Holarctic Ecology* 5: 27–34.

MLURI (1993a). *The Land Cover of Scotland 1988: Executive Summary.* Macaulay Land Use Research Institute: Aberdeen.

MLURI (1993b). *The Land Cover of Scotland 1988: Final Report.* Macaulay Land Use Research Institute: Aberdeen.

Nature Conservancy Council (1982). *Creag Dhubh. Upland Vegetation Survey, Vegetation Map File.* Unpublished report to the Nature Conservancy Council. SNH: Perth.

Nature Conservancy Council (1983a). *Coyles of Muick. Upland Vegetation Survey, Vegetation Map File.* Unpublished. SNH: Perth.

Nature Conservancy Council (1983b). *Monadhliath/Carn Coire na Creiche. Upland Vegetation Survey, Vegetation map file.* Unpublished. SNH: Perth.

Nature Conservancy Council (1984a). *Ben Vrackie. Upland Vegetation Survey, Vegetation Map File.* Unpublished. SNH: Perth.

Nature Conservancy Council (1984b). *Cairnwell. Upland Vegetation Survey, Vegetation Map File.* Unpublished. SNH: Perth.

Nature Conservancy Council (1984c). *Glen Callater. Upland Vegetation Survey, Vegetation map file.* Unpublished. SNH: Perth.

Nature Conservancy Council (1984d). *Green Hill of Strathdon. Upland Vegetation Survey, Vegetation Map File.* Unpublished. SNH: Perth.

Nature Conservancy Council (1984e). *Ladder Hills. Upland Vegetation Survey, Vegetation Map File.* Unpublished. SNH: Perth.

Nature Conservancy Council (1985a). *Coire Bhachdaidh. Upland Vegetation Survey, Vegetation Map File.* Unpublished. SNH: Perth.

Nature Conservancy Council (1985b). *Lochnagar. Upland Vegetation Survey, Vegetation Map File.* Unpublished. SNH: Perth.

Nature Conservancy Council (1986a). *Beinn a' Ghlo. Upland Vegetation Survey, Vegetation Map File.* Unpublished. SNH: Perth.

Nature Conservancy Council (1986b). *Caenlochan – Clova. Upland Vegetation Survey, Vegetation Map File.* Unpublished. SNH: Perth.

Nature Conservancy Council (1986c). *Eastern Cairngorms. Upland Vegetation Survey, Vegetation Map File.* Unpublished. SNH: Perth.

Nature Conservancy Council (1986d). *Morven and Peter's Hill. Upland Vegetation Survey, Vegetation Map File.* Unpublished. SNH: Perth.

Nature Conservancy Council (1986e). *Tulach Hill. Upland Vegetation Survey, Vegetation Map File.* Unpublished. SNH: Perth.

Nature Conservancy Council (1987a). *Cairngorms NNR Ben Macdui. Upland Vegetation Survey, Vegetation Map File.* Unpublished. SNH: Perth.

Nature Conservancy Council (1987b). *Inchrory. Upland Vegetation Survey, Vegetation Map File.* Unpublished. SNH: Perth.

Nature Conservancy Council (1987c). *Drumochter Hills. Upland Vegetation Survey, Vegetation Map File.* Unpublished. SNH: Perth.

Nature Conservancy Council (1987d). *Northern Corries. Upland Vegetation Survey, Vegetation Map File.* Unpublished. SNH: Perth.

Nature Conservancy Council (1988a). *Cairngorms NNR Braeriach. Upland Vegetation Survey, Vegetation Map File.* Unpublished. SNH: Perth.

Nature Conservancy Council (1988b). *Morrone Birkwood. Upland Vegetation Survey, Vegetation Map File.* Unpublished. SNH: Perth.

Nature Conservancy Council (1988c). *Muir of Dinnet. Upland Vegetation Survey, Vegetation Map File*. Unpublished. SNH: Perth.

Nature Conservancy Council (1991). *Craig Leek. Upland Vegetation Survey, Vegetation Map File*. Unpublished. SNH: Perth.

Nethersole-Thompson, D. & Watson, A. (1981). *The Cairngorms: Their Natural History and Scenery*. Melven Press: Perth.

Poore, M.E.D. & McVean, D.N. (1957). A new approach to Scottish mountain vegetation. *Journal of Ecology* 45: 401–439.

Rae, S. (1995). *Cairngorms Moorland and Montane Habitat Survey and Condition Assessment Carn Dearg, Geldie and Braemar Survey Areas*. Unpublished report. Contract RASD/063/96 CNG. SNH: Perth.

Rae, D. (1996a). *Drumochter Hills NVC survey and mapping of sub-arctic willow scrub*. Unpublished report. SNH: Perth.

Rae, S. (1996b). *Cairngorms Project: Continuation of Moorland and Montane Habitat Survey and Condition Assessment South Geldie Area*. Unpublished report. Contract RASD/091/97 CNG. SNH: Perth.

Rae, S. (1997). *Cairngorms Project: Montane and Moorland Habitat Survey and Condition Assessment Inchrory Area*. Unpublished report. Contract RASD HT/97/98/52. SNH: Perth.

Ratcliffe, D.A. (1974). The Vegetation. In: Nethersole-Thompson, D. & Watson, A. *The Cairngorms: Their Natural History and Scenery*. Collins: London.

Ratcliffe, D.A. (ed.) (1977). *A Nature Conservation Review. Vol. 1 and 2*. Cambridge University Press: Cambridge.

Robertson, J.S. (1984). *A Key to Common Plant Communities of Scotland*. Macaulay Institute for Soil Research: Aberdeen.

Rodwell, J. (1991a). *British Plant Communities. Vol. 1. Woodland and Scrub*. Cambridge University Press: Cambridge.

Rodwell, J. (1991b). *British Plant Communities. Vol. 2. Mires and Heaths*. Cambridge University Press: Cambridge.

Rodwell, J. (1992). *British Plant Communities. Vol. 3. Grasslands and Montane communities*. Cambridge University Press: Cambridge.

Rodwell, J. (1994). *British Plant Communities. Vol. 4. Aquatic communities, Swamps and Tall Herb Fens*. Cambridge University Press: Cambridge.

Rodwell, J. (2000). *British Plant Communities. Vol. 5. Maritime Communities and Vegetation of Open Habitats*. Cambridge University Press: Cambridge.

Scotland's Moorland Forum (2003). *Scotland's Moorland Forum: Principles of Moorland Management*. SNH: Perth.

Scottish Executive (2001a). *Prescribed Burning on Moorland. Supplement to the Muirburn Code: A Guide to Best Practice*. Scottish Executive: Edinburgh.

Scottish Executive (2001b). *The Muirburn Code*. Scottish Executive: Edinburgh.

Staines, B.W. & Balharry, R. (2002). Red Deer and Their Management in the Cairngorms. In: C.H. Gimingham (ed.), *The Ecology, Land Use and Conservation of the Cairngorms*. Packard Publishing Limited: Chichester.

Stevenson, A.C., Jones, V.J. & Battarbee, R.W. (1990). The cause of peat erosion: a palaeolimnological approach. *New Phytologist* 114: 727–735.

Tallis, J.H. (1985). Mass movement and erosion of a southern Pennine blanket peat. *Journal of Ecology* 73: 283–315.

Tallis, J.H. (1987). Fire and flood at Holme Moss: erosion processes in an upland blanket mire. *Journal of Ecology* 75: 1099–1129.

van der Wal, R., Pearce, I., Brooker, R., Scott, D., Welch, D. & Woodin, S. (2003). Interplay between nitrogen deposition and grazing causes habitat degradation. *Ecology Letters* 6: 141–146.

Watson, A. (1984). Paths and people in the Cairngorms. *Scottish Geographical Magazine* 100: 151–160.

Watson, A. (1985). Soil erosion and vegetation damage near ski lifts at Cairn Gorm, Scotland. *Biological Conservation* 33: 363–381.

Watson, A. (1991). Increase of people on Cairn Gorm plateau following easier access. *Scottish Geographical Magazine* 107: 99–105.

Watson, A. (1990). Human Impact on the Cairngorms Environment above Timber Line. In: Conroy, J.W.H., Watson, A. & Gunson, A.R. (eds.), *Caring for the High Mountains Proceedings of the conference on Conservation of the Cairngorms*. Centre for Scottish Studies: Aberdeen.

Watson, A. (1997). Human-induced changes in numbers of Red deer in the Cairn Gorm area. *Deer* 10: 278–281.

Watt, A.S. & Jones, E.W. (1948). The ecology of the Cairngorms, I. The environment and the altitudinal zonation of the vegetation. *Journal of Ecology* 36: 283–304.

Welch, D., Scott, D. & Watson, A. (1995). *Monitoring the effects of snow fencing on vegetation, herbivores and soils at Glas Maol in 1994*. SNH Research, Survey and Monitoring Report. No. 35. SNH: Perth.

Youngson, R.W. & Stewart, L.K. (1997). Trends in red deer populations within the Cairngorms core area. *Botanical Journal of Scotland* 48(1): 111–116.

Annex 6.1.

Upland National Vegetation Classification (NVC) types in the Cairngorms[1].

NVC code	NVC name	Common name
W19	*Juniperus communis-Oxalis acetosella* woodland	Juniper-Wood Sorrel woodland
W20	*Salix lapponum-Luzula sylvatica* scrub	Downy Willow-Great Wood-rush scrub
H10	*Calluna vulgaris-Erica cinerea* heath	Heather-Bell Heather heath
H12	*Calluna vulgaris-Vaccinium myrtillus* heath	Heather-Blaeberry heath
H13	*Calluna vulgaris-Cladonia arbuscula* heath	Prostrate Heather-Lichen heath
H16	*Calluna vulgaris-Arctostaphylos uva-ursi* heath	Heather-Bearberry heath
H18	*Vaccinium myrtillus-Deschampsia flexuosa* heath	Blaeberry-Wavy Hair-grass heath
H19	*Vaccinium myrtillus-Cladonia arbuscula* heath	Blaeberry-Lichen heath
H20	*Vaccinium myrtillus-Racomitrium lanuginosum* heath	Blaeberry-Woolly-fringe Moss heath
H21	*Calluna vulgaris-Vaccinium myrtillus-Sphagnum capillifolium* heath	Heather- Blaeberry-Bog Moss heath
H22	*Vaccinium myrtillus-Rubus chamaemorus* heath	Blaeberry-Cloudberry heath
U4	*Festuca ovina-Agrostis capillaris-Galium saxatile* grassland	Sheep's Fescue-Common Bent-Heath Bedstraw grassland
U5	*Nardus stricta-Galium saxatile* grassland	Matgrass-Heath Bedstraw grassland
U6	*Juncus squarrosus-Festuca ovina* grassland	Heath Rush-Sheep's Fescue grassland
U7	*Nardus stricta-Carex bigelowii* grass-heath	Matgrass-Stiff Sedge Grass-heath
U8	*Carex bigelowii-Polytrichum alpinum* grass-heath	Stiff Sedge-*Polytrichum* Grass-heath
U9	*Juncus trifidus-Racomitrium lanuginosum* rush-heath	Three-leaved Rush-Woolly-fringe Moss heath
U10	*Carex bigelowii-Racomitrium lanuginosum* moss-heath	Stiff Sedge-Woolly-fringe Moss-heath
U11	*Polytrichum norvegicum-Kiaeria starkei* snow-bed	Late-lie moss-dominated snow-beds
U12	*Salix herbacea-Racomitrium heterostichum* snow-bed	Late-lie moss-dominated snow-beds
U13	*Deschampsia cespitosa-Galium saxatile* grassland	Tufted Hair-grass-Heath Bedstraw grassland
U14	*Alchemilla alpina-Sibbaldia procumbens* dwarf-herb community	Alpine Lady's Mantle-*Sibbaldia* dwarf-herb community
U15	*Saxifraga aizoides-Alchemilla glabra* banks	Yellow Mountain Saxifrage banks
U16	*Luzula sylvatica-Vaccinium myrtillus* community	Great Wood Rush-Blaeberry community
U17	*Luzula sylvatica-Geum rivale* tall-herb community	Great Wood Rush-Water Avens tall-herb community
U18	*Cryptogramma crispa-Athyrium distentifolium* snow-bed	Parsley Fern-Alpine Lady-fern snow-bed community
U19	*Thelypteris limbosperma-Blechnum spicant* community	Mountain Fern-Hard Fern community
U20	*Pteridium aquilinum-Galium saxatile* community	Bracken-Heath Bedstraw community
M1	*Sphagnum auriculatum* bog-pool community	*Sphagnum auriculatum* bog-pool community
M2	*Sphagnum cuspidatum/recurvum* bog-pool community	*Sphagnum cuspidatum/recurvum* bog-pool community
M3	*Eriophorum angustifolium* bog-pool community	Common Cotton Grass bog-pool community
M4	*Carex rostrata-Sphagnum recurvum* mire	Bottle Sedge-*Sphagnum recurvum* mire

NVC code	NVC name	Common name
M6	*Carex echinata-Sphagnum recurvum/auriculatum* mire	Star Sedge-Bog Moss mire
M7	*Carex curta-Sphagnum russowii* mire	White Sedge-Bog Moss mire
M8	*Carex rostrata-Sphagnum warnstorfii* mire	Bottle Sedge-*Sphagnum warnstorfii* mire
M9	*Carex rostrata-Calliergon cuspidatum* mire	Bottle Sedge-*Calliergon* mire
M10	*Carex dioica-Pinguicula vulgaris* mire	Dioecious Sedge-Butterwort mire
M11	*Carex demissa-Saxifraga aizoides* mire	Yellow Sedge-Yellow Mountain Saxifrage mire
M12	*Carex saxatilis* mire	Russet Sedge mire
M15	*Scirpus cespitosus-Erica tetralix* wet heath	Deer Grass-Cross-leaved Heath wet heath
M16	*Erica tetralix-Sphagnum compactum* wet heath	Cross-leaved Heath-Bog Moss wet heath
M17	*Scirpus cespitosus-Eriophorum vaginatum* blanket mire	Deer Grass-Cotton Grass blanket mire
M18	*Erica tetralix-Sphagnum papillosum* raised and blanket mire	Cross-leaved Heath-Bog Moss blanket mire
M19	*Calluna vulgaris-Eriophorum vaginatum* blanket mire	Heather-Cotton Grass blanket mire
M23	*Juncus effusus/acutiflorus-Galium palustre* rush-pasture	Soft Rush/ Sharp-flowered Rush-Marsh-bedstraw rush-pasture
M25	*Molinia caerulea-Potentilla erecta* mire	Purple Moor-grass-Tormentil mire
M31	*Anthelia julacea-Sphagnum auriculatum* spring	White Sedge-Bog Moss flushes
M32	*Philonotis fontana-Saxifraga stellaris* spring	*Philonotis*-Starry Saxifrage spring
M33	*Pohlia wahlenbergii* var. *glacialis* spring	*Pohlia wahlenbergii* var. *glacialis* spring
M37	*Cratoneuron commutatum/filicinum-Festuca rubra* spring	*Cratoneuron*-Red Fescue spring
M38	*Cratoneuron commutatum-Carex nigra* spring	*Cratoneuron*-Common Sedge spring
OV40	*Asplenium viride-Cystopteris fragilis* community	Green Spleenwort-Brittle Bladder-fern community
CG10	*Festuca ovina-Agrostis capillaris-Thymus praecox* grassland	Sheep's Fescue-Common Bent-Thyme grassland
CG11	*Festuca ovina-Agrostis capillaris-Alchemilla alpina* grass-heath	Sheep's Fescue-Common Bent-Alpine Lady's Mantle grassland
CG12	*Festuca ovina-Alchemilla alpina-Silene acaulis* dwarf-herb community	Sheep's Fescue-Alpine Lady's Mantle-Moss Campion dwarf-herb community
CG14	*Dryas octopetala-Silene acaulis* ledge community	Mountain Avens-Moss Campion ledge community

[1] Including scrub but excluding woodland

Annex 6.2.

Habitats listed in Annex I of the EC Habitats Directive, and for which Special Areas of Conservation have been designated in the Cairngorms.

EC Code	EC Habitat Directive Annex I habitat name	Corresponding NVC types
H4010	Northern Atlantic wet heaths with *Erica tetralix*	M15, M16
H4030	European dry heaths	H10, H12, H16, H18
H4060	Alpine and Boreal heaths	H13, H19, H20, H22
H4080	Sub-Arctic *Salix* spp. scrub	W20
H5130	*Juniperus communis* formations on heaths or calcareous grasslands	W19
H6130	Calaminarian grasslands of the *Violetalia calaminariae*	
H6150	Siliceous alpine and boreal grasslands	U7, U8, U9, U10, U11, U12, U14
H6170	Alpine and subalpine calcareous grasslands	CG12, CG14
H6210	Semi-natural dry grasslands and scrubland facies: on calcareous substrates (*Festuco-Brometalia*)	CG10
H6230	*Species-rich *Nardus* grassland, on siliceous substrates in mountain areas (and submountain areas in continental Europe)	CG10, CG11
H6430	Hydrophilous tall herb fringe communities of plains and of the montane to alpine levels	U17
H7130	*Blanket bog	M17, M18, M19
H7220	*Petrifying springs with tufa formation (*Cratoneurion*)	M37, M38
H7230	Alkaline fens	M9, M10, M11
H7240	*Alpine pioneer formations of *Caricion bicoloris-atrofuscae*	M11, M12
H8110	Siliceous scree of the montane to snow levels (*Androsacetalia alpinae* and *Galeopsietalia ladani*)	U18
H8120	Calcareous and calcshist screes of the montane to alpine levels (*Thlaspietea rotundifolii*)	
H8210	Calcareous rocky slopes with chasmophytic vegetation	OV40
H8220	Siliceous rocky slopes with chasmophytic vegetation	
H8240	*Limestone pavements	

* Priority habitat; blanks denote no corresponding NVC type.

7. FORESTS AND WOODLANDS

Jeanette Hall

Introduction

The Cairngorms encompass the most extensive tracts of Caledonian pine forest in Britain, as well as the best examples in Scotland of bog woodland, montane willow scrub and Aspen *Populus tremula* woodland. Several woodland species, including Pict Moss *Pictus scoticus*, the Scented Knight Fungus *Tricholoma apium* and the hoverfly *Blera fallax*, have been recorded nowhere else in Britain.

Birch *Betula* spp., Juniper *Juniperus communis* and willow *Salix* spp. re-colonised the Cairngorms area after the last glaciation, some 9-10,000 years ago, and were later followed by Scots Pine *Pinus sylvestris*, which expanded into Strathspey and Deeside about 7,500 years ago. Woodland cover in Scotland peaked between 7,000 and 5,000 years ago, when it extended to about 790 m above sea level. During the pre-Roman period, a change to cooler, wetter conditions, together with the effects of woodland clearances for agriculture, timber and fuel, encouraged the formation of blanket peat in the Highlands. Smout (1997) suggests that considerably more than half of the original forest cover of Scotland may have vanished by the beginning of the first century AD. This decline continued throughout the middle ages, as more land was cleared for agriculture and browsed by domestic animals. By the mid-17th century, woodland covered only about 8% of the Highlands (Smout & Watson, 1997). Although much of Donside, lower Deeside and Strathspey were then virtually devoid of trees, pine and birch woods survived in the upper glens, where the stony, infertile soils were unsuitable for cultivation (Cairngorms Partnership, 1999).

Tree felling increased dramatically from the mid-18th century, and by the mid-19th century most of the useable timber had gone. Regeneration was often prolific, however, except where prevented by grazing and browsing animals. It was this, rather than continued felling, that limited the return of forest cover in the Highlands (Smout, 1997).

The Cairngorms area contains a large share of Scotland's semi-natural woodland, concentrated mainly in Strathspey and upper Deeside. In places, mature native pines dwarf neighbouring plantations, physically, aesthetically, and in their species diversity.

Photo: *L. Gill*

Recent trends

During the First and Second World Wars, renewed felling continued to reduce woodland cover, which reached its lowest level in 1946. An urgent reforestation programme was subsequently initiated, leading to dramatic increases in Scotland's woodland cover between 1950 and 1990. The Scottish Semi-Natural Woodland Inventory (SSNWI: Caledonian Partnership, 1999) estimated that, by 1988, woodland covered 109,672 ha of the Cairngorms area, accounting for 17% of the land (Table 7.1); a proportion similar to that occurring in the rest of Scotland. The proportion of *semi-natural* woodland in the Cairngorms was greater, however; while the Cairngorms area covers only 8% of Scotland's land area, it contained almost 12.5% of the country's semi-natural woodland and only 5.6% of its plantation. Most of the semi-natural woodland is concentrated in upper Strathspey and Deeside, with smaller areas along the Avon, and in the very south of the Cairngorms area (Figure 7.1). The natural altitudinal limit of tree growth is likely to be around 650 m, although this is expressed only at Creag Fhiaclach, above Glen Feshie, where the Highlands' only truly natural treeline occurs, at 600-640 m.

Woodland habitats

The Cairngorms contain some of the most important woodland areas in Britain. Under the EC Habitats Directive, 12 Special Areas of Conservation (SACs) have been designated for their woodland interest. The main types are pine and oak/birch woodland, but there are also important areas of bog woodland, Aspen, Juniper, montane scrub and wet Alder *Alnus glutinosa* woodland (Table 7.2).

Pine forest

In 1988, the Cairngorms area contained 19,341 ha of semi-natural woodland dominated by conifers, representing about half of Scotland's semi-natural

Hall, J. (2006). Forests and woodlands. In: Shaw, P. & Thompson, D.B.A. (eds.). *The Nature of the Cairngorms: Diversity in a changing environment.* The Stationery Office. pp. 91-107.

Table 7.1. The area of woodland within the Cairngorms in 1988 (from the Ancient Woodland Inventory, SNH; Scottish Semi-Natural Woodland Inventory (SSNWI), Caledonian Partnership, 1999)

Woodland type		Cairngorms area (ha)	Cairngorms National Park (ha)
Semi-natural woodland	Ancient	18,033	15,153
	Total	49,876	36,274
Mixed woodland	Ancient	2,417	2,019
	Total	5,827	4,651
Plantation	Ancient	20,309	14,454
	Total	53,902	34,219
All woodland	Ancient	40,763	31,629
	Total	109,672	75,202

pinewood. Most of this (13,258 ha) lies within Caledonian Pinewood Inventory (CPI) sites; considered to be remnants of the original Caledonian pine forest (Steven & Carlisle, 1959). While the remainder may be more recent in origin, it represents an important resource of semi-natural woodland. More than 80% of the semi-natural pine forest in the Cairngorms area lies within the National Park (Figure 7.2). The CPI contains a category of Planted Areas, where the planted pine was of local origin and comprises less than one-third of the pinewood. Regeneration Zones extend 100 m from pinewood fragments and, along with the fragments themselves, should be managed according to guidance given in the native pinewood *Forest Practice Guide* (Forestry Authority, 1994). Buffer zones extend a further 500 m, and in order to protect the pinewoods' genetic integrity, only native genotypes of Scots Pine should be planted in these areas.

Several restricted northern species occur in semi-natural pine forest, including Creeping Lady's-tresses *Goodyera repens*, Twinflower *Linnaea borealis* and Ostrich-plume Feather-moss *Ptilium crista-castrensis*. Some stands support important populations of notable bird species, such as the Capercaillie *Tetrao urogallus*, Parrot Crossbill *Loxia pytyopsittacus*, Scottish Crossbill *L. scotica* and Crested Tit *Parus cristatus* (Chapter 18).

Native pine woodlands are a priority habitat for the UK Biodiversity Action Plan, and are listed in the Habitats Directive as Caledonian Forest, which comprises relict, indigenous forests of Scots Pine and associated birch and

Juniper woodlands. Caledonian Forest occurs only in Scotland, and represents genetically distinct oceanic variants of the 'heathy pinewoods'[1] that extend across the Boreal region of northern Europe.

Native pine is a notified feature on 12 SSSIs in the Cairngorms, while Caledonian Forest is a qualifying feature on four SACs: Ballochbuie, Cairngorms, Glen Tanar and Kinveachy.

Oak/birch woodland

Oak/birch woodland is the dominant type of broadleaved woodland in the Cairngorms, as it is in upland Scotland generally. It has been estimated that the Cairngorms area encompassed about 17,110 ha of oak/birch woodland in 1998. Since none of the Scottish woodland inventories record woodland type, this estimate was derived from the Scottish Semi-Natural Woodland Inventory (Caledonian Partnership, 1999) in conjunction with the Native Woodland Model (NWM) (Towers *et al.*, 2004), which uses soil and land cover data to predict the woodland type likely to develop under current site conditions.

Upland oakwood *Quercus* spp. and upland birchwood are both priority habitat types in the UK Biodiversity Action Plan. In practice it is often difficult to delineate the two types, and it may be more appropriate to treat them as a single type, whose dominant canopy species vary in proportion. Birch is almost always present, and is generally the dominant, or only, broadleaved tree at high altitude in northern areas. As a pioneer species, it is also often the main canopy species in recent woodland. It is less palatable to grazing animals than oak, and so may increase in relative proportion in moderate- or heavily-grazed woodland.

The richest sites for upland oakwoods are in the west of Scotland. Although the more eastern examples tend to be smaller and less distinctive in their species composition, particularly in their bryophyte assemblages, they represent an important part of the habitat's range, with characteristic northern species such as Intermediate Wintergreen *Pyrola media* and Chickweed Wintergreen *Trientalis europaea*.

Upland birch is a notified feature on 10 SSSIs within the Cairngorms area, while upland oak is a notified feature on five SSSIs. Dinnet Oakwood has been designated as an SAC for western acidic oak woodland. Its fungal flora is of national importance (Chapter 11) and contains several rare species dependent on oak and charcoal.

---

[1] Pinewoods occuring on impoverished acid sands and drier peaty soils, with ground flora characterised by dwarf heathy shrubs, especially *Vaccinium* spp., *Calluna vulgaris* and *Erica* spp.

Figure 7.1. The distribution of woodlands in the Cairngorms in 1988 (SSNWI)

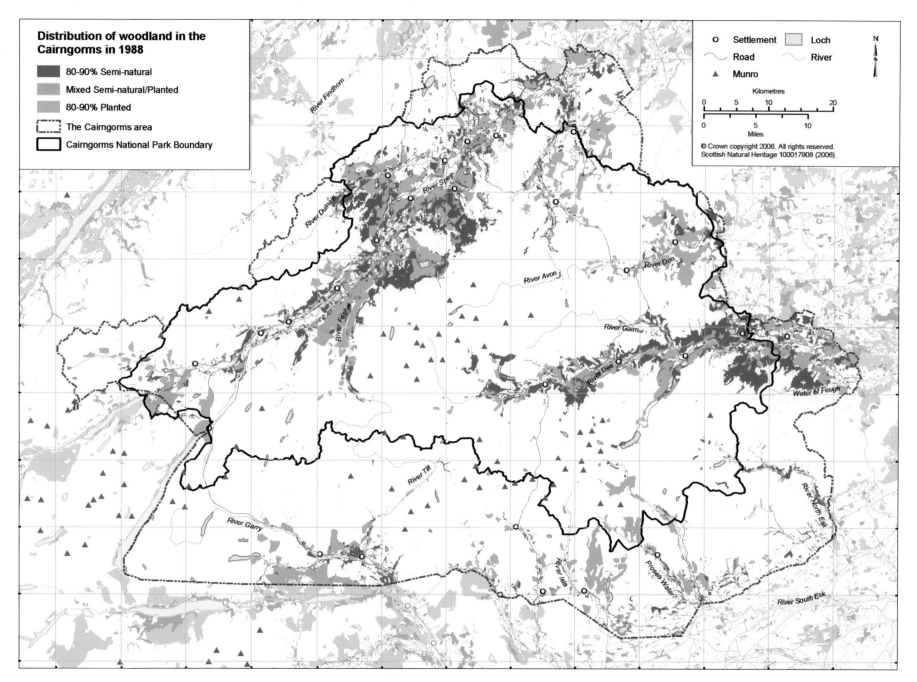

Distribution of woodland in the Cairngorms in 1988

- 80-90% Semi-natural
- Mixed Semi-natural/Planted
- 80-90% Planted
- The Cairngorms area
- Cairngorms National Park Boundary

Settlement Loch N
Road River
Munro

Kilometres
0   5   10   20
0   5   10
Miles

© Crown copyright 2006. All rights reserved.
Scottish Natural Heritage 100017908 (2006).

Table 7.2. The area of native woodland and forest habitats in 1988 (SSNWI: Caledonian Partnership, 1999).

BAP Priority:	Biodiversity Action Plan Priority habitat types.	
Habitats Directive:	Habitats listed in Annex I of the EC Habitats Directive.	
Percentage of UK range:	The percentage of the habitat's UK range (in 10-km squares) occurring within the Cairngorms area: *** 50-100%; ** 20-50%; * 10-20%.	

Type	BAP Priority	Habitats Directive	Cairngorms area (ha)	National Park (ha)	Percentage of UK range
Pine	Native pine woodlands	Caledonian forest	19,341	15,776	***
Oak/birch	Upland oakwood	Old sessile oak woods with Holly *Ilex* and hard fern *Blechnum* in the British Isles	17,110	10,279	*
Juniper	*Juniperus communis*	Juniper *Juniperus communis* formations on heaths or calcareous grasslands	888 [1]	888 [1]	***
Wet woods	Wet woodland	Alluvial forests with Alder *Alnus glutinosa* and Ash *Fraxinus excelsior* (*Alno-Padion, Alnion incanae, Salicion alvae*)			
		Bog woodland	438 [2]	>410 [2]	***
Aspen	-	-	123	?	***
Scrub	Woolly Willow *Salix lanata*	Sub-Arctic willow *Salix* spp. scrub	4.2 [3]	>1 [3]	**

[1] Area within Cairngorms SACs
[2] All but one of the bog woodland SACs in the Cairngorms area (in Kinveachy Forest) also lie within the National Park.
[3] The Cairngorms and Caenlochan montane scrub SACs lie wholly within the National Park, while that in Creag Meagaidh and Drumochter Hills SACs lie only partly within the National Park.

Aspen woodland

Aspen is found throughout Britain, but is most common in the Scottish Highlands, where it occurs at up to 550 m. Since it tolerates a wide range of soil types and climatic conditions, its current, sparse distribution is probably the result of deforestation and grazing pressure.

There are only about 21 remnant Aspen stands individually covering more than 1.5 ha in the Highlands. Together, they cover a total area of 159.5 ha (MacGowan, 1997). Fourteen stands are in Strathspey and Deeside, which together account for 77% of the total area of Aspen. The largest stands are in Strathspey, between Newtonmore and Grantown-on-Spey. Although Aspen is also quite common throughout upper Deeside the stands there are typically smaller, perhaps reflecting the topography of Deeside, where fertile ground suitable for Aspen is largely confined to a narrow area beside the river; in contrast to the wider Strathspey.

Aspen is a particularly important habitat for insects, including the BAP Priority hoverfly *Hammerschmidtia ferruginea* and the Dark Bordered Beauty Moth *Epione paralellaria* (Chapter 15). The saproxylic community associated with Aspen, characterised by 33 insect species, is especially rich. However, only 14 sites in the Scottish Highlands reach the minimum area (4.5 ha) considered necessary to maintain the full saproxylic community.

Aspen is listed as a feature (but not as a notified interest) on six SSSIs in the Cairngorms area, and is a component of upland birchwood on four of these. On one site it occurs within upland mixed Ash, and on another is a component of wet woodland. Aspen is not specifically covered by the UK Biodiversity Action Plan or the Habitats Directive, but is protected by the same mechanisms applicable to all semi-natural woodland in Britain[2]. The main concern is a lack of regeneration rather than the impact of direct destruction. Although Aspen suckers freely, it sets seed infrequently in Scotland. If protected from grazing it will, therefore, spread rapidly from existing stands of trees via its suckers, but cannot easily colonise new areas.

Bog woodland

Under certain circumstances scattered trees can occur in a relatively stable ecological relationship as open woodland on the surface of a bog, without the loss of bog species. This situation is much rarer than the progressive invasion of bogs by trees, through natural colonisation or afforestation, which is associated with changes in the drainage pattern, leading eventually to the loss of the bog community (Jackson & Macleod, 2002). Detailed definitions of bog woodland are given in Annex 7.1.

This habitat type is not well documented in the UK, and knowledge of its distribution and ecological characteristics is limited. Pine is the most frequent

[2] A licence is required to fell more than 5 m^3 of any woodland within a single year, and clearance of broadleaved woodland without restocking is not generally permitted. In addition, an Environmental Impact Assessment is required for certain forestry operations.

Figure 7.2. The distribution of semi-natural pine forest in Strathspey and Deeside in 1988.

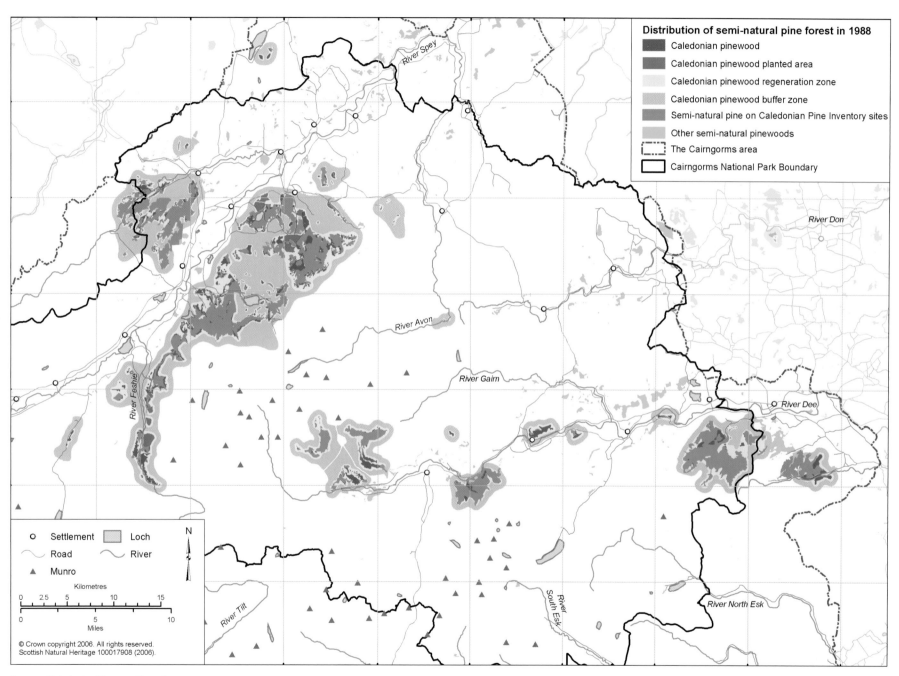

Source: Caledonian Pinewood Inventory

Birch re-colonised the Cairngorms area after the last glaciation, some 9–10,000 years ago, in advance of Scots Pine. Craigellachie birchwood, shown here, is one of the Cairngorms' most species-rich areas.
Photo: *L. Gill*

tree species in bog woodland, although birch or willow may also occur. In either case, the trees are generally slow-growing and widely-spaced, since much of the surface is too wet for them to become established. Although stunted in form, these trees may be of considerable age, with the oldest individuals in Scotland estimated at 350 years old. Despite their small size, the weight of the trees gradually depresses the peat locally, leading to progressive water-logging of the root system and eventual death. Dead trees may therefore be common in this woodland type (Jackson & Macleod, 2002).

Bog woodland is a priority habitat under the Habitats Directive. Although it is not specifically covered by the UK Biodiversity Action Plan, most examples are likely to fall within upland birchwood or native pine forest. Some examples may be considered as 'wet woodland'.

Knowledge of the distribution and extent of this habitat type is limited. Bog woodland is listed as an interest feature (but not a notified interest) on three SSSIs in the Cairngorms area, and on 10 Scottish SACs. Three of these (Ballochbuie, Cairngorms and Kinveachy Forest SACs) lie within the Cairngorms area. The Cairngorms SAC holds by far the largest extent of bog woodland in Scotland, habitat patches being interspersed with areas of Caledonian Forest, particularly at Inshriach and Abernethy Forest.

Juniper woodland

Juniper often occurs as low scrub on heathland or acidic grassland, but where it is long-established it forms a clear woodland canopy, often with Downy Birch *Betula pubescens* and Rowan *Sorbus aucuparia*. The understorey is often rich in acid-loving species and characteristic northern species occur locally, including Chickweed Wintergreen, Twinflower and Lesser Twayblade *Listera cordata*. On flushed lower slopes, and on more base-rich substrates, the flora contains species associated with an increased base-status, such as Common Dog-violet *Viola riviniana*, Dog's Mercury *Mercurialis perennis* and Northern Bedstraw *Galium boreale*. It can also occur as a much reduced version of Caledonian pinewood where the tree element has been removed or prevented from regenerating. This is the case in the lower parts of Kinveachy SAC, although a transition to a more natural Juniper canopy occurs with increasing altitude.

Juniper is a Biodiversity Action Plan priority species, and is also protected under the EC Habitats Directive, where it is defined as '*Juniperus communis* formations on heaths or calcareous grasslands'. This definition includes the southern English habitat type of Juniper on chalk, as well as upland Juniper formations occurring in more acidic conditions characteristic of the Cairngorms.

Juniper is a notified feature on five SSSIs in the Cairngorms area (Abernethy Forest, Crathie Wood, Kinveachy Forest, Morrone Birkwood, and Morven and Mullachdubh), and on four SACs (Cairngorms, Green Hill of Strathdon, Morrone Birkwood and Morven and Mullachdubh). Together these contain 888 ha of Juniper, representing almost 95% of Juniper contained within SACs in Scotland. and Morven and Mullachdubh SAC is particularly important, supporting the largest known area of Juniper scrub in the UK; about double the extent occurring at any other site.

Creag Fhiaclach has the most natural altitudinal tree-line in the UK. At around 640 m there is mixed tree-line woodland with stunted Scots Pine and Juniper, giving way at higher altitude to Juniper scrub. In these areas it often occurs in a stunted form, transitional between the nominate sub-species and the less common prostrate sub-species *J. communis nana*, which is largely restricted to north-west Scotland. Green Hill of Strathdon is also notable for its Juniper scrub, which has a species-rich flora associated with base-rich soil, influenced by the underlying serpentine rocks.

Montane scrub

The UK's highest-altitude shrubby vegetation, occurs on moist, relatively base-rich soils, on ungrazed ledges in the low montane zones. Grazing is believed to have reduced and restricted its occurrence, and at many sites its future is precarious, as it is confined to often unstable rock ledges. The largest continuous stand of this very local habitat type is about 0.5 ha in extent, but most stands are very much smaller. Their distribution is shown in Figure 7.3.

The most abundant willow species varies between sites, according to the base-richness of the underlying substrate, the altitude of the stands or, more locally, the effects of grazing. Downy Willow *Salix lapponum* is the most widespread species as it can grow on lime-poor schist, which is widely distributed in Scotland. Woolly Willow *S. lanata*, Dark-leaved Willow *S. myrsinifolia* and Net-leaved Willow *S. reticulata* are more lime-demanding and, consequently, rarer.

While montane scrub is not a priority habitat under the UK Biodiversity Action Plan, there is a Species Action Plan for Woolly Willow, the rarest of its

constituent willows, recorded from only 12 locations in Scotland. All but one of these populations are very small (less than 100 plants). Four 'populations' are of single individuals.

Montane scrub is protected under the Habitats Directive as Sub-Arctic *Salix* species scrub. It consists of a mixture of willows (including Mountain Willow *S. arbuscula*, Woolly Willow, Downy Willow, Dark-leaved Willow, Whortle-leaved Willow *S. myrsinites*, Tea-leaved Willow *S. phylicifolia* and Net-leaved Willow) growing amongst a rich mixture of dwarf shrubs, grasses, rushes and broad-leaved herbs. The habitat supports many rare plants and animals of northern latitudes and high mountains.

Within the Cairngorms area four sites (Caenlochan, Cairngorms, Creag Meagaidh and Drumochter Hills) have been designated as SACs for montane willow scrub, which is listed as an interest feature (although not as a notified interest) on three SSSIs. Together, these SACs contain 4.2 ha of willow scrub; about 20% of all SAC willow scrub in Scotland. A high proportion of the Scottish resource is contained within the SAC series.

Creag Fhiaclach, above Glen Feshie, has the most natural treeline in Britain, at 600–640 m. Here, stunted Scots Pine and Juniper woodland gives way to Juniper scrub.
Photo: *L. Gill*

The two largest patches of montane willow scrub remaining in the UK are both on SACs in the Cairngorms. The largest (*c.* 0.5 ha) is at Corrie Sharroch in Caenlochan National Nature Reserve, and the second largest is in the Drumochter Hills. Caenlochan is thought to hold the second largest population of Woolly Willow in the UK.

Plantations

In 1988, coniferous plantations covered 53,902 ha; 49% of all woodland in the Cairngorms area. Of this, 20,309 ha (38%) were classed as Plantations on Ancient Woodland Sites (Ancient Woodland Inventory (AWI); SSNWI). Plantations are more widely dispersed than semi-natural woodland, and are concentrated in the north-east of the Cairngorms area around the Don and Avon, and in the south of the area, between the South Esk and the River Garry.

Large-scale forestry was introduced by the 'Planting' Dukes of Atholl in the early 18th century, when large areas of Norway Spruce *Picea abies* and European Larch *Larix decidua* were established around Blair Atholl and Dunkeld (Atholl Estates, 2004). Although planting continued through the 19th and early 20th century, tree cover in the Cairngorms continued to decrease, notably during the First and Second World Wars. An urgent reforestation programme was initiated, leading to substantial increases in Scotland's woodland cover between 1950 and 1990. In the Cairngorms, Sitka Spruce *P. sitchensis*, larch *Larix* spp. and Douglas Fir *Pseudotsuga menziesii* were planted on the more fertile soils in the south of the area, whereas Scots Pine was more commonly planted on the poorer, drier soils of Deeside and Strathspey (Cairngorms Partnership, 1999).

Young commercial plantations tend to support little wildlife. The dense canopy prevents light from reaching the forest floor and inhibits the development of a ground layer. Many older plantations have developed a more interesting ground flora, however, particularly in glades and rides, and some support scarce or endangered bird species, such as Scottish Crossbill, Crested Tit and Capercaillie. Clear-felled and early growth stages can provide habitats for Hen

Grazing and browsing by Red Deer has prevented natural regeneration of native woodland throughout much of Strathspey and Deeside. Fortunately, where such pressures are reduced regeneration can be prolific, as here at Rothiemurchus.

Photo: *N. Mcintyre*

Figure 7.3.   The distribution of montane scrub species in 1995.

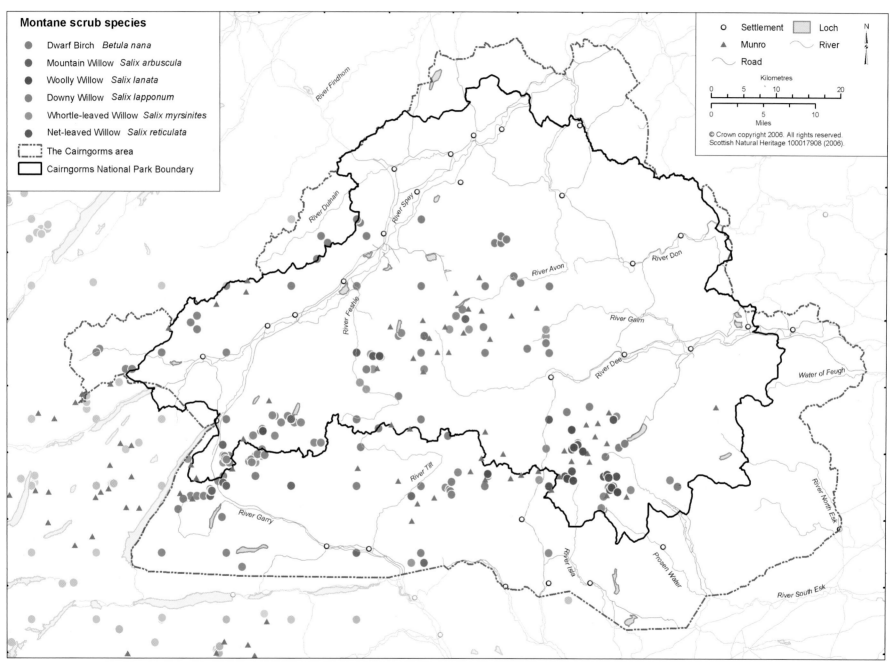

Source: Biological Records Centre

Table 7.3. Important catchments in the Cairngorms for woodland outside of designated sites (SSNWI; Caledonian Partnership, 1999)

Catchment	Area of semi-natural woodland (ha)
Strathspey (including River Dulnain)	8,700
Deeside (Including River Gairn)	5,400
River Avon	1,350
River Don	1,300

Harrier *Circus cyaneus* and Short-eared Owl *Asio flammeus*, although these species soon move out once the thicket growth stage is reached.

Callendar and MacKenzie (1991) found that Deeside's Scots Pine plantations are largely of local or north-east Scotland origin, and are mostly on former native pinewood sites. The combination of semi-natural and plantation woodlands in Deeside and Strathspey represents an unusually high degree of forest continuity, of exceptional value.

Important woodland areas

The Cairngorms area contains about one-eighth of Scotland's semi-natural woodland, concentrated mainly within the National Park, especially Strathspey and Deeside (Table 7.3). Much of this resource lies outside of the SSSI series, but is protected by the general regulations that apply to all forestry.

The high proportion of woodland cover, and its connectivity, is perhaps the most important aspect of woodland in the Cairngorms. Many woodland specialist species, including Capercaillie and Red Squirrel *Sciurus vulgaris*, require extensive forest networks, which may include plantations as well as semi-natural woodland. Woodland species often have a very limited ability to cross open ground, and so the fragmented resource of much of Scotland is unable to sustain viable populations.

Woodland is near-continuous along Deeside, from Banchory to Braemar. In Strathspey there are few major gaps between Kingussie and Spey Bay, although the semi-natural woodland is concentrated mainly within the National Park. This represents the most extensive area of boreal forest in Scotland.

Woodland is a notified feature on 30 SSSIs in the Cairngorms area, of which 20 lie at least partly within the National Park (Table 7.4). An additional six SACs have been designated for their woodland interest (including montane scrub).

Recent research and survey findings

In recent years, four major wooded peatland areas (Abernethy, Inshriach, North Rothiemurchus Pinewood SSSI and part of Mar Lodge Estate), all within the Cairngorms SAC, have been the subject of detailed survey and research. Parts of Inshriach and Abernethy Forest have also been the focus of restoration through the Wet Woods Restoration Life Project.

Abernethy. At least 20 discrete bogs, with varying densities of pine cover, lie in the north-western part of the RSPB's Abernethy Forest Reserve. Extensive fieldwork was undertaken on these areas in 2000, under the aegis of the EC Wet Woods Restoration Life Project in 2000. Drains were blocked over a total of 208 ha and trees removed from an area of 117 ha. McHaffie *et al.* (2000) mapped vegetation and tree densities, and analysed water quality and data from permanent quadrats, in order to monitor changes subsequent to 'restoration' works. It was concluded that bog woodland vegetation was more widespread than had previously been thought. As a result of this work, McHaffie *et al.* (2000) proposed the adoption of a tripartite classification of 'bog woodland' based on relative tree or seedling densities. This has yet to gain widespread acceptance.

Inshriach. This Wet Woods Restoration Project site lies between Loch an Eilein and Feshiebridge. The mosaic of pine and birch woodland, bog, fen and loch has been identified as an area of sufficient quality to merit its inclusion in an extended Cairngorms SSSI. The forest is owned by the Forestry Commission and largely comprises young Lodgepole Pine *Pinus contorta* and Scots Pine plantation, with significant remnants of bog woodland in varying condition.

Wells (2001) carried out detailed peat stratigraphical studies of five areas of mire in this area, to determine whether their characteristics conformed to the definition of 'bog woodland' consistent with *Natura 2000* guidelines. Two sites, and part of a further composite site, encompassed pine woodland developed on true ombrotrophic mires, while the others were developed over

Table 7.4. Statutory sites with significant areas of woodland in the Cairngorms. SSSIs designated at least partly for their woodland interest are shown in bold. On the remaining SSSIs woodland is not a designated interest, but is within a related SAC.

SSSI Name	Habitats present	Site area (ha)	Percentage of site within:		Other designations for woodland habitats
			Cairngorms area	National Park	
Abernethy Forest	Juniper woodland, Native pinewood	579	100	100	SAC
Alvie	Upland oak woodland	339	100	100	
Ballochbuie	Bog woodland, Native pinewood	1,882	100	100	SAC
Beinn a' Ghlo	Lowland mixed broadleaved woodland	8,085	100	0	
Bochel Wood	Upland birch woodland	198	100	100	
Caenlochan	Montane willow scrub	4,975	100	90	SAC
Cairngorms	Native pinewood, Montane willow scrub	29,028	100	100	SAC
Coire Bhachdaidh	Scrub	1,722	100	0	
Craig Leek	Native pinewood	185	100	100	
Craigellachie	Upland birch woodland	380	100	100	
Craigendarroch	Upland oak woodland	67	100	100	
Crathie Wood	Juniper woodland, Native pinewood, Upland birch woodland	193	100	100	
Creag Clunie and the Lion's Face	Native pinewood	252	100	100	SAC
Creag Dhubh	Upland birch woodland	1,052	100	100	
Creag Meagaidh	Montane willow scrub	7,033	25	7	SAC
Creag Nan Gamhainn	Upland birch woodland	16	100	100	
Crossbog Pinewood	Native pinewood	63	100	0	
Den of Ogil	Scrub	6	100	0	
Dinnet Oakwood	Upland oak woodland	20	100	100	SAC
Drumochter Hills	Montane willow scrub	9,688	100	36	SAC
Eastern Cairngorms	Native pinewood	16,503	100	100	SAC
Glen Tanar	Native pinewood	4,180	100	100	SAC
Glen Tilt Woods	Upland birch woodland	15	100	0	
Glenmore Forest	Native pinewood	1,440	100	100	SAC
Greenhill of Strathdon	Juniper woodland	641	100	100	SAC
Insh Marshes	Alder woodland on floodplains	1,159	100	100	SAC
Kinveachy Forest	Juniper woodland, Native pinewood	5,326	100	70	SAC
Lower Strathavon Woods	Upland birch woodland, Upland mixed ash woodland, Upland oak woodland, Wet woodland	293	100	0	
Morrone Birkwood	Juniper woodland, Upland birch woodland	328	100	100	SAC
Morven and Mullachdubh	Moorland juniper	2,508	100	94	SAC
North Rothiemurchus Pinewood	Native pinewood	1,510	100	100	SAC
Northern Corries, Cairngorms	Native pinewood	1,966	100	100	SAC

SSSI Name	Habitats present	Site area (ha)	Percentage of site within:		Other designations for woodland habitats
			Cairngorms area	National Park	
Pass of Killiecrankie	Upland oak woodland	62	72	0	
Quithel Wood	Upland mixed ash woodland, Wet woodland	13	100	0	
Shannel	Upland birch woodland	62	100	0	
Struan Wood	Upland birch woodland	83	100	0	

weakly minerotrophic poor-fen communities. The peat record indicated that all of the Inshriach sites had suffered major disturbance in the past (probably from peat cutting) and that none could be regarded as a 'relict' community. Instead, it seemed likely that the current bog woodland communities had developed in historically recent times, possibly aided by the development of commercial forestry. Nevertheless, all, or significant parts of the Inshriach sites could be said to fulfil the current statutory criteria encompassed by the term 'bog woodland'.

Other work, carried out under the EC 'Wet Woods' initiative during 2000-2001, included the removal of mixed conifers and non-native regeneration over an area of 40 ha, and the heavy thinning of planted Scots Pine, together with the blocking of key drains in this area. Conditions for the development of bog woodland were 'restored' over an area of 52 ha.

North Rothiemurchus Pinewood. North Rothiemurchus Pinewood SSSI contains a mosaic of habitats, including semi-natural woodland, mire, heathland and grassland. Substantial areas of lower-lying ground to the south of the Coylumbridge to Loch Morlich road are occupied by ombrotrophic mires, several of which are characterised as bog woodland. Taken together, these discrete wooded mires form an extensive area, estimated at around 170 ha, representing the largest example of bog woodland in Scotland.

Glimmerveen (1995) undertook systematic vegetation mapping of the estate, categorising plant communities using National Vegetation Classification (NVC) protocols. This work identified several areas of potential 'bog woodland' which Wells (2001) examined. Six areas where Scots Pine grow over Cross-leaved Heath-Bog Moss blanket mire (M18) communities were subjected to stratigraphic study. The peat stratigraphy indicated that morphologically, the peatlands occurring at Rothiemurchus were best described as conforming to the 'intermediate mire' type. Some of the sites produced evidence of prior pine growth at peat depths of 0.5 m or lower, indicating that 'bog woodland' habitats had a long history. The peat analyses also revealed that fires had been a notable feature during much of the history of most of the mires examined, while old peat cuttings had affected several areas, particularly in the northern sector of the estate, within easy access of the river. Although most sites could be said to conform to the broad definition of 'bog woodland', one mire could not, and another was found to be treeless. Nevertheless, it seemed likely that recent management changes enacted to reduce grazing pressure from deer (Ratcliffe, 1999), will promote the advance of low-density tree growth over most mire areas within the survey area. It was concluded that this may represent merely the latest event in a series of regeneration cycles, resulting from an extended sequence of intensive felling episodes affecting the Rothiemurchus woodland (Smout, 1999).

Mar Lodge. Pinewoods on the Mar Lodge Estate were surveyed in 1997 (Hepburn & Brooks, 1997) and a small area (*c.* 12 ha) of wooded peatland was considered to conform to 'bog woodland', based on superficial appearance. Wells (2001) established that peat occupied perhaps half of this area and appeared to have suffered a long history of burning, as well as damage from drainage and possibly peat cutting. It was difficult to characterise the current area of wooded peatland as any variant of true 'bog woodland', in view of the dry and partly eroded nature of the peatland, and the obviously vigorous growth of the pine, which showed no signs of stress, given the shallow depth (< 2 m) and dryness of the peat. The pines and ground flora were not appreciably different from adjacent stands occupying mineral ground, and it was concluded that the site was perhaps best regarded as an area of degraded mire that had been colonised by pine.

It was impossible to tell whether the site could have formerly carried a form of 'natural' pine-bog woodland, on a wet, actively growing mire, and it was considered that the current tree cover did not represent any form of relict system.

Trends

Woodland area. Between 1991 and 2003 new woodland was established over 2% of the Cairngorms area, comprising 6,174 ha of broadleaves and 7,975 ha of conifers. New woodland also accounts for 2% of the National Park, comprising 3,126 ha of broadleaves and 4,718 ha of conifers.

Condition. During 1999-2004, SNH assessed the condition of 28 notified woodland features on 24 SSSIs in the Cairngorms area. Fifteen features (on 12 sites) were judged to be in favourable condition, while 13 features (on 12 sites) were judged to be in unfavourable condition, in relation to the natural heritage objectives set. Twelve features (on nine sites) remained to be assessed. These include all of the sites notified for Juniper woodland.

Woodland types varied with regard to condition. While seven out of 10 pinewoods were judged to be in unfavourable condition, only two out of seven birchwoods and neither of the two ashwoods assessed were considered to be unfavourable. The reasons for woods being judged unfavourable also varied between types, and were related mainly to levels of grazing or browsing, regeneration and woodland structure. These categories have essentially a common cause – a long history of grazing preventing tree regeneration. Whilst periods of high grazing intensity are not necessarily damaging, the long absence of successful tree regeneration (for two centuries on some sites) has clearly damaged the woodland and caused a slow decline in its richness and robustness. Since widespread overgrazing continues on many sites, they will continue to decline for the foreseeable future.

Conservation issues

The Cairngorms woodland and forest framework (Cairngorms Partnership, 1999) discusses the major issues for woodland conservation and expansion. These are summarised below.

Grazing and browsing. In many areas, Red Deer *Cervus elaphus* have prevented natural regeneration of native woodland for at least 70 years. Since deer are wide-ranging, management policies are unlikely to succeed unless co-ordinated between neighbouring estates. Deer fencing is a major cause of death in woodland grouse (Chapter 18), has potentially damaging effects on landscape and access, and is costly to erect and maintain. It is recommended that fencing should only be used when alternative methods cannot be applied (see Chapter

21). In addition, employing stalkers to control deer may yield substantially more socio-economic benefits than using fences to control deer.

Other wild herbivores that can restrict regeneration include Mountain Hare *Lepus timidus*, Roe Deer *Capreolus capreolus*, Sika Deer *Cervus nippon*, feral goats *Capra hircus* and Rabbits *Oryctolagus cuniculus*. They are all less widely distributed in the Cairngorms than are Red Deer, but local damage to seedlings and saplings can be severe. In some upland areas sheep densities have been too high to allow woodland to regenerate, despite woodland being valued for shelter and an 'early bite'.

The conservation value of other habitats. Woodland expansion must proceed in a sensitive manner, pursuing an appropriate spatial balance between woodland and open habitats, to enhance the biodiversity and landscape value of the whole area.

Sporting value of open land. Deer stalking and grouse shooting are traditional

Bog woodland is an unusual habitat, in which trees - mainly pine - are thinly distributed across the bog surface, in a relatively stable ecological relationship. The Cairngorms area holds by far the largest extent of bog woodland in Scotland, habitat patches being interspersed with areas of Caledonian Forest, particularly at Inshriach and Abernethy.

Photo: *L. Gill*

Scottish field sports which attract many paying clients from elsewhere in Europe. There is some concern that woodland expansion close to open hill areas may encroach on 'deer forest' and heather moorland, leading to a loss of income on sporting estates.

Agriculture. 'Improved' land forms a small part of the total agricultural area (Chapter 8), and there is understandable resistance to the establishment of extensive tracts of woodland on such land. There are, however, opportunities for small-scale woodlands, which could provide shelter for stock, timber, sport, ecological and landscape benefits, and recreation. Issues affecting the ability of farmers to become more involved with woodland management and expansion include: constraints on tenant/landlord schemes under Agricultural Holdings legislation; complex and (at times) restrictive grant schemes operated by different agencies, and the need for training in aspects of woodland management.

Water and soil. Woodland expansion must be carried out in a way that protects water quality and quantity. Native woodlands can help to protect water quality, but some past forestry practices have been damaging to the aquatic environment. The greatest remaining concern is soil disturbance and movement, from new plantings and large-scale timber extraction. This is likely to become less of a problem in future, given the general trend towards diverse woodlands, smaller felling coupes and larger areas of open land.

Landscape. Some old plantations are poorly scaled and shaped, and inappropriately located in the landscape. Opportunities for re-stocking or restructuring of existing plantations, and careful consideration of landscape character when locating new woodlands, have led to significant improvements that look set to continue.

Cultural and built heritage. Forestry planting should avoid important sites. Where regeneration is planned it may be necessary to ensure that trees do not regenerate over archaeological sites. However, since the archaeological record is incomplete there is a danger that important sites will be lost, unless surveys are undertaken prior to regeneration and planting.

Sources

The *Ancient Woodland Inventory* was compiled by the Nature Conservancy Council and is maintained by SNH. It was derived from a desk-based exercise, which examined woodland cover shown on the Military Survey of Scotland maps (the 'Roy maps') from 1750, the OS First Edition from *c.* 1860, and the OS 1970 1:25,000 maps (Caledonian Partnership, 1999). It shows ancient woodland of semi-natural origin, which dates from either the 1750 or 1860 maps, and long-established woodland of plantation origin, again dating from either 1750 or 1860, but shown as plantation on these maps (Roberts *et al.* 1992; Kupiec, 1999).

The *Caledonian Pinewood Inventory* (CPI) was produced by the Forestry Commission, and shows pine woodland believed to be descended from the original Caledonian pine forest which spread across much of mainland Scotland after the last glaciation (Jones, 1999).

The *Native Woodland Model* (NWM; Towers *et al.*, 2004) was produced by the Macaulay Institute. It relates soil and land cover data to the requirements of different types of native woodland, to predict potential woodland types – the woodland NVC types which would be expected to develop under current soil and vegetation conditions, with no or minimal ground intervention, including fertilisation, ground preparation and drainage.

The *Scottish Semi-Natural Woodland Inventory* (SSNWI) was compiled by Highland Birchwoods on behalf of the Caledonian Partnership and the Millennium Forest for Scotland Trust (Caledonian Partnership, 1999). It was derived from the LCS88 aerial photography, at a capture scale of 1:25,000. Despite its name, SSNWI covers all woodland down to a minimum size of 0.1 ha.

Apart from the CPI, none of these inventories contains information on the woodland types (oak, ash etc). However, if semi-natural polygons are extracted from SSNWI and overlaid with NWM predictions, this provides what is thought to be a reasonable indication of the distribution of different woodland types.

Information on Habitats Directive Annex I habitats and on Scottish SACs was extracted from http://www.jncc.gov.uk/ProtectedSites/SACselection/SAC_habitats.asp.

Information on UKBAP priority habitats and species was extracted from http://www.ukbap.org.uk/.

References

Atholl Estates (2004). *Atholl Estates. A Famous Scottish Estate in the Heart of Highland Perthshire.* http://www.athollestates.co.uk/athollestates

Cairngorms Partnership (1999). *Cairngorms woodland and forest framework.* Cairngorms Partnership: Grantown-on-Spey.

Caledonian Partnership (1999) The Scottish Semi-natural Woodland Inventory. Unpublished, data held by Highland Birchwoods. Available from: www.scotlandswoods.org.uk

Callander R.F. & MacKenzie, N.A. (1991) The Native Pine woodlands of Highland Deeside. NCC report. Scottish Natural Heritage: Perth.

Forestry Authority (1994) *The management of semi-natural woodlands: Native pinewoods.* Forestry Authority: Edinburgh.

Glimmerveen, I. (1995). *Vegetation survey - North Rothiemurchus.* Internal Report for SNH. SNH: Perth.

Hepburn, L.V. & Brookes, B.S. (1997). *Mar Lodge Pinewoods National Vegetation Survey.* Internal Report for SNH. SNH: Perth.

Jackson, D.L. & McLeod, C.R. (2002). *Handbook on the UK status of EC Habitats Directive interest features: provisional data on the UK distribution and extent of Annex 1 Habitats and the UK distribution and population size of Annex II species: Version 2.* JNCC Report No 312. JNCC: Peterborough.

Jones, A.T. (1999). The Caledonian Pinewood Inventory of Scotland's Native Scots Pine Woodlands. *Scottish Forestry* 53(4): 237-242.

Kupiec, J. (1999). Further Development of the Inventory of Ancient and Long Established Woodland Sites and the Semi-natural Woodland Inventory. *SNH Information & Advisory Note 104.* SNH: Perth.

MacGowan I. (1997). *The Entomological value of Aspen in the Scottish Highlands. Malloch Society Research Report No 1.* The Malloch Society: Edinburgh. 23 pp. http://www.mallochsociety.org.uk/files_cms/10/1MALLOCH_REPORT_11.pdf

McHaffie, H., Legg, C. & Worrell, R. (2000). *Classification of bog woodland habitat and review and analysis of restoration management at the RSPB Abernethy Forest Reserve.* Report for EC Life Project Wet Woods Restoration.

Ratcliffe, P.R. (1999). Rothiemurchus: the Forest, its Ecology and Future management. In: Smout, T.C. & Lambert, R.A. (eds), *Rothiemurchus, Nature and people on a Highland Estate 1500-2000.* Scottish Cultural Press: Dalkeith. pp. 79-208.

Roberts A.J., Russell, C., Walker G.J. & Kirby, K.J. (1992). Regional Variation in the Origin, Extent and Composition of Scottish Woodland. *Botanical Journal of Scotland,* 46(2): 167-189.

Smout, T.C. (1997). Highland land-use before 1800. In: Smout, T.C. (ed.). *Scottish woodland history.* Scottish Cultural Press: Edinburgh.

Smout, T.C. (1999). The History of the Rothiemurchus Woodlands. In: Smout, T.C. & Lambert, R.A. (eds), *Rothiemurchus, Nature and people on a Highland Estate 1500-2000.* Scottish Cultural Press: Dalkeith. pp. 60-78.

Smout, T.C. & Watson, F. (1997) Exploiting semi-natural woods 1600 – 1800. In: Smout, T.C. (ed.) *Scottish woodland history.* Scottish Cultural Press: Edinburgh.

Steven, H.M. & Carlisle, A. (1959). *The Native Pinewoods of Scotland.* Hartnolls Ltd.: Cornwall.

Towers, W., Hall, J., Hester, A., Malcolm, A., & Stone, D. (2004). *The potential for native woodland in Scotland: the native woodland model.* SNH: Battleby.

Wells, C.E. (2001). *A survey of the peat stratigraphy of seven 'bog woodland' sites in Scotland.* Report for SNH.

Annex 7.1.

Definitions of Bog Woodland

EC 'Life' Wet Woods Restoration Project

'Bog woodland' is generally defined as areas of coniferous or broadleaved trees growing on peatlands where the high level of the water table and the natural low fertility restrict tree growth. It has the appearance of open woodland with scattered trees occurring across the surface of a bog in a relatively stable ecological relationship, without the loss of bog species. This true bog woodland habitat is distinct from the progressive invasion of bog by trees, either by natural colonisation or afforestation, following changes in the drainage pattern.'
Source: www.wetwoods.org

The EC Habitats Directive

'Coniferous and broad-leaved forests on a humid to wet peaty substrate, with the water level permanently high and even higher than the surrounding water table. The water is always very poor in nutrients (raised bogs and acid fens). These communities are generally dominated by *Betula pubescens, Frangula alnus, Pinus sylvestris, Pinus rotundata* and *Picea abies*, with species specific to bog or, more generally, to oligotrophic environments, such as *Vaccinium* spp., *Sphagnum* spp., *Carex* spp. *Vaccinio-Piceetea*: *Piceo-Vaccinienion uliginosi* (*Betulion pubescentis, Ledo-Pinion*).'
Source: http://eunis.eea.eu.int

UK SAC Selection Criteria

'Under certain combinations of physical circumstances in the UK, scattered trees can occur across the surface of a bog in a relatively stable ecological relationship as open woodland, without the loss of bog species. This true Bog woodland is a much rarer condition than the progressive invasion of bogs by trees, through natural colonisation or afforestation following changes in the drainage pattern which leads eventually to the loss of the bog community. The habitat type has not previously been well described in the UK, and consequently knowledge of its ecological characteristics is limited.'
Source: www.jncc.gov.uk/ProtectedSites/SACselection/SAC_habitat.asp

8. FARMLAND

Claudia Rowse

Introduction

Agriculture has been practised for thousands of years in the Cairngorms. With over 70% of the area in agricultural use (Cosgrove, 2002), changes in farming practice and management have had profound effects on natural habitats and landscapes. The main form of agriculture in the Cairngorms is livestock farming, with extensive sheep farming on the hills, and beef production or mixed sheep and beef units lower down. Rough grazing is the most widespread habitat, with arable land and agriculturally 'improved' grassland occurring mainly in the straths.

Agricultural practices in the Cairngorms have created habitats important for a range of species of conservation concern, including the Pink Waxcap *Hygrocybe calyptriformis*, Olive Earthtongue fungus *Microglossum olivaceum*, Pearl-bordered Fritillary *Boloria euphrosyne*, the mason bee *Osmia inermis*, its parasite, the Ruby-tailed Wasp *Chrysura hisuta*, and Black Grouse *Tetrao tetrix*. All are Biodiversity Action Plan priority species with populations in the Cairngorms (Cosgrove, 2002). Lowland grassland in the straths also supports some of the densest populations of breeding waders in mainland Britain. In recent years, management of these habitats has been strongly influenced by the provision of farming subsidies, and will continue to be so in the foreseeable future. This chapter describes trends in farming practices in the Cairngorms, and the incentive schemes that underpin them.

Land use

There are approximately 570 farm holdings in the Cairngorms area, with an average area of 847 ha, 90% of which is classified as rough grazing. Their large average size is due to the existence of extensive areas of upland grazing, which tend to be much larger than enclosed land holdings lower down. In the north and west of the area, between Grantown-on-Spey and Laggan, crofting is a significant land use, with over 100 registered crofts and seven Common Grazings. The June Census (Scottish Executive, 2003a) shows that Cairngorms National Park supported 27,770 beef cattle and 189,390 sheep, with small numbers of pigs, poultry and dairy cattle. Over half of the 210 farm businesses in the National Park were classified as sheep or cattle holdings (SEERAD, pers. comm.). Principal forms of land use in the Cairngorms Partnership Board Area (which encompasses 21 agricultural parishes, either wholly or partially) are shown in Table 8.1.

Agriculture in the Cairngorms is constrained by a range of factors, principally climate, topography, soil type and distance from markets. Macaulay Land Capability Maps classify most of the Cairngorms as Class 7, i.e. land of very limited agricultural value (Bibby *et al.*, 1982). The other predominant land use is rough grazing (Class 6) with some limited potential for improved grassland (Class 5). On lower-lying land, with more favourable climate and soils, some limited arable cropping is possible (Class 3). More extensive agriculture is based primarily on grassland production (Class 4).

On account of the disadvantages facing agriculture, the whole of the Cairngorms area is classified by the European Union (EU) as Severely Disadvantaged within Less Favoured Areas (LFA). Despite the natural constraints it faces, agriculture plays a significant role in the economy and environment of the area. In 1991, 6.9% of the workforce in the Cairngorms was employed in agriculture, compared with 8.2% in 1981. Comparable figures for Scotland were 2.2% and 2.6% respectively. By 2002, agriculture employed only about 5% of the workforce in the Cairngorms (CNPA, pers. comm.), illustrating the continued decline in agricultural employment within the area.

Arable fields and improved grassland near Blair Atholl. Much of the Cairngorms area can support rough grazing, with limited potential for improved grassland and, in the more favourable areas, some arable cropping.

Photo: *L. Gill*

Rowse, C. (2006). Farmland. In: Shaw, P. & Thompson, D.B.A. (eds.). *The Nature of the Cairngorms: Diversity in a changing environment.* The Stationery Office. pp. 109-117.

Table 8.1. Land use in the Cairngorms Partnership Board Area[1], based on census data from June 1990 (from Bayfield & Conroy, 1996)

Land type	Area (ha)	Percentage of total
Rough grazing	429,818	67%
Permanent improved grassland	15,720	2%
Temporary improved grassland	13,302	2%
Farm woodland	8,058	1%
Annual crops	6,233	1%
Other land	5,150	1%
Land not included in census[2]	164,485	26%
Total area:	642,766	

[1] This does not coincide with the Cairngorms Partnership Area.
[2] Includes a large area of land not in agricultural use.

Old semi-improved grasslands are important for species such as the Pink Waxcap Hygrocybe calyptriformis; *a Biodiversity Action Plan species, and one of 30 grassland fungi of conservation concern in the Cairngorms.*

Photo: *L. Gill*

One of the main factors influencing agriculture and land use in the Cairngorms is national government and EU policy, most importantly the Common Agricultural Policy (CAP). A number of agricultural schemes supported through the CAP have had a significant influence on the type of agriculture practised. They include the Sheep Annual Premium, Beef Special Premium, Extensification Payments, Suckler Cow Premium Scheme, Less Favoured Areas Support Scheme and the Arable Area Payments Scheme. It is likely that agri-environment schemes will become more important to the area's economy in the future.

The economics of agriculture in the Cairngorms

Farms in the Cairngorms typically generate low incomes and are highly dependent on subsidy (Table 8.2) (Bayfield & Conroy, 1996). By 2002–03, farmers' incomes had largely recovered from a severe drop experienced during the late 1990s, although those for LFA specialist sheep farmers remained unsustainably low. Based on Census data for June 2002, subsidy figures for the National Park were estimated at £5 million, with a gross margin estimated at £8.5 million. Income from agri-environment schemes was estimated at £0.75 million, accounting for 15% of the total subsidy figure; proportionately much higher than in the UK as a whole, where agri-environmental subsidies account for 4–5% of income. To put this in context, income from agriculture was very much lower than tourism revenue, which, in Badenoch and Strathspey, was valued at £82 million in 2001 (SEERAD, pers. comm.). The implications of CAP reforms for farmers' incomes, and the consequences for farmed habitats and species in the Cairngorms, are discussed below.

Agri-environment Schemes
In the 1980s, as part of the reform of the CAP, the EU required all Member States to implement a programme of agri-environment schemes, which led to the establishment of the Environmentally Sensitive Area (ESA) Scheme in 1986. Breadalbane was designated as an ESA in 1987, followed by the Cairngorms Straths in 1994 (Figure 8.1). The purpose of ESAs was to encourage measures that enhance the environment and support the continuation of farming practices that have helped to create distinctive landscapes and to maintain wildlife habitats and historic features. Under the ESA Scheme, farmers entered into voluntary agreements with the Scottish Executive and received payments for carrying out environmentally-friendly farming practices. Agreements lasted for 10 years, with a five-year opt-out clause. General environmental objectives were formulated for each ESA. Those identified for Breadalbane and the Cairngorms

Straths ESAs were aimed at protecting and enhancing woodland, wetland and herb-rich unimproved grassland. A detailed list of the objectives for both the Breadalbane and Cairngorms Straths ESA Schemes was provided by Scottish Office Agriculture, Environment and Fisheries Department (1997).

Cairngorms Straths ESA covers approximately 2,361 km² and includes Strathspey, Strath Avon, Glenlivet, Strathdon and upper Deeside, as well as the southern fringe of the Monadhliath mountains, the foothills of Cairn Gorm and the montane summits of Glas Maol and Lochnagar. The area thus varies considerably in climate, geology, soils, vegetation and agriculture. Four distinctive features of land cover have been identified in the Cairngorms ESA (Bell *et al.*, 2000):

- a diverse and intricate association of agricultural and semi-natural habitats;
- important areas of enclosed grasslands, supporting a diversity of species;
- a predominance of dry moorland vegetation, often forming a mosaic with grassland; and
- many areas of broadleaved and semi-natural coniferous woodland.

Uptake of ESA scheme agreements was initially slow in the Cairngorms, but reached 90% by the time the Scheme closed. A similarly high level of uptake (86%) occurred in the Breadalbane ESA. Uptake appears to be related partly to the size of the land holding, being high among relatively small farms and lower in the more upland areas, which are dominated by large estates (Nolan *et al.*, 2000).

Breadalbane ESA overlaps with the southern boundary of the Cairngorms area, most of its 140,000 ha falling outside of the Cairngorms, in highland Perthshire.

Table 8.2. Net farm income in Scotland, in relation to type (from Bayfield & Conroy, 1996; Scottish Executive, 2003b)

Farm Type	Net farm income[1]		
	1993–94	2000–01	2002–03
LFA sheep farm	£11,100	£100	£8,600
LFA mixed cattle & sheep farm	£15,300	£11,900	£17,000

[1] For a definition of Net Farm Income, see Annex 2, Economic Report on Scottish Agriculture (Scottish Executive, 2003b).

The ESA Scheme was closed to new entrants in December 2000 and has now been replaced by the Rural Stewardship Scheme (RSS). By 2003, there were 43 RSS agreements within the Cairngorms, covering 63,000 ha (SEERAD, pers. comm.).

There has been an increasing interest in organic farming in the Cairngorms, supported by attractive payments through the Organic Aid Scheme (OAS). By 2003 there were 21 farm agreements for OAS, covering 47,100 ha in nine Cairngorms parishes: Abernethy, Birse, Blair Atholl, Crathie and Braemar, Cromdale, Glenisla, Inveravon, Kingussie and Kirkmichael (SEERAD, pers. comm.).

Farmland habitats

Many UK and Local Biodiversity Action Plan priority habitats and species are associated with farming and crofting in the Cairngorms, which has generally been less intensive than in other parts of the UK. Some of the more important farmland habitats for biodiversity are described below.

Figure 8.1. Environmentally Sensitive Areas in the Cairngorms.

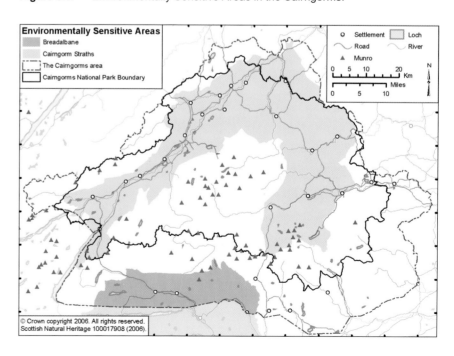

Arable land

Arable land covers less than 2% of the Cairngorms National Park (Cosgrove, 2002), and is restricted to Strathspey, Strath Avon, Donside and Deeside. Spring barley is the main cereal crop, with smaller areas of oats and winter barley. Fodder crops such as turnips, swedes, rape, kale and cabbage are also grown for feeding stock. Several BAP priority species, including Black Grouse, Linnet *Carduelis cannabina* and Brown Hare *Lepus europaeus*, are at least partly associated with this habitat, and the continuation of traditional arable production has an important role to play in sustaining biodiversity. Other notable species associated with arable land in the Cairngorms include Twite *C. flavirostris* and Snow Bunting *Plectrophenax nivalis*, which depend partly on the weeds, spilt grain and cover provided by arable stubbles and fodder crops during the winter.

Key issues relating to arable production are the reduction in fodder kale, turnips and their associated weeds and, to a lesser extent, the change from spring sowing to autumn sowing. The recent reduction in the overall area of cropping in the Cairngorms is probably the most significant issue affecting species that rely on arable land for a significant part of their winter diet.

Improved grassland

There are approximately 30,000 ha of improved grassland within the National Park. Improved grassland can be an important habitat for ground-nesting birds such as Lapwing *Vanellus vanellus*, Redshank *Tringa totanus* and Skylark *Alauda arvensis*, but tends to be very poor for vascular plants, fungi and invertebrates.

Unimproved grassland

Unimproved species-rich grasslands are those that have been managed traditionally, without agricultural 'improvements', such as re-seeding, or the application of artificial fertilisers. Of these, Lowland and Upland Hay Meadows are priority habitats in the UK BAP, and are represented in the Cairngorms by a number of small, fragmented sites. Their small size means that most Cairngorms hay meadows are unlikely to be of national significance, but are locally important for biodiversity. Grazed, rough, unimproved grasslands are also important for breeding species such as Lapwing, Redshank and Skylark, and, when associated with rushy pastures, can hold Snipe *Gallinago gallinago* and Curlew *Numenius arquata*.

Both over- and under-grazing have an adverse effect on the condition of unimproved grasslands. The change from hay to silage and the increased use of artificial fertilisers have been major causes of the decline in species-rich grasslands, as silage fields are less floristically diverse than hay. UK priority species associated with unimproved grassland, and which have significant UK populations in the Cairngorms, include Black Grouse, Pearl-bordered Fritillary and Northern Brown Argus *Aricia artaxerxes*.

Boundary features

After fences, drystane dykes are the most common boundary feature in the Cairngorms area, totalling some 30,000 km, much of it in Deeside. Although many of the dykes are in a poor state of repair, their value remains significant, providing a habitat for flowering plants, ferns, mosses and lichens, as well as providing a wildlife corridor, shelter, feeding and breeding sites for a range of invertebrates, reptiles, birds and mammals (Cosgrove, 2002). They are also important cultural and historical features. However, they require substantial resources to maintain and, given the continuing downturn in agricultural employment and structural change in the rural economy, are likely to continue to suffer from neglect.

Drystane dykes provide a habitat for flowering plants, ferns, mosses and lichens, and a wildlife corridor for invertebrates, reptiles, birds and mammals. Their value was recognised under the Environmentally Sensitive Areas Scheme, which helped subsidise the repair and maintenance of dykes in the Cairngorms.

Photo: *H. MacKay / SNH*

Recent research and survey findings

Monitoring the Cairngorms Straths ESA

In 1994, a comprehensive 10-year monitoring programme was commissioned by the Scottish Office Agriculture and Fisheries Department (SOAFD) to monitor the performance of ESAs in Scotland. This was designed to assess the effectiveness of the ESA Scheme, with monitoring resources apportioned between three elements: landscape and vegetation (75%); archaeology (20%); and farmland wading birds (5%). After five years of monitoring the Cairngorms Straths ESA, Bell *et al.* (2000) reported the following results for farms within the Scheme.

- Few statistically significant botanical changes were detected.

- There was little conclusive evidence of a change in wetlands (with respect to wetness, acidity, calcareousness, grazing tolerance or nutrients), although there had been a reduction in grazing pressure.

- There were no significant differences in the number of species or the degree of cover of the most dominant species in species-rich grassland, within and outwith the scheme.

- There was a slight increase in heather height on moorland entered into positive management.

- Water margins showed an increase in tree and rush cover, and a decrease in poaching (i.e. trampling).

- The four wader species surveyed (Lapwing, Oystercatcher *Haematopus ostralegus*, Redshank and Curlew) reached their highest densities on reverted, improved (rushy) pastures.

- Oystercatcher, Lapwing and Redshank numbers remained stable, in contrast to national declines recorded for these species by the BTO Breeding Bird Survey.

These results were subject to the following constraints.

- The initial monitoring round covered only two or three years; a relatively short timescale in ecological terms.

- The methodology and sampling effort applied were unlikely to reveal fine-scale changes.

- Sample sizes were small.

- Bird surveys were restricted to four species of farmland waders; passerines and moorland birds were excluded.

The lack of statistically significant results does not imply that the ESA scheme failed to deliver environmental benefits. Perhaps its greatest achievement was its support for farming systems that helped maintain existing environmental interests, as opposed to conversion to more intensive farming systems that could have reduced the environmental value. Within the short timescale, it would have been surprising if some of the indicators had demonstrated an improvement in environmental interests, and it is likely that the moorland management measure will have reduced overgrazing of heather and resulted in an improvement in heather condition.

Structural change in agriculture: implications for the Cairngorms

There has been accelerating change in the agricultural sector recently, which is likely to lead to significant restructuring. This will affect land use and management, which will in turn affect rural economies, landscapes and the environment across Britain. In order to determine what changes are taking place, research was commissioned by SNH and conducted by FPDSavills (2001), with the aim of: considering what changes had occurred, and were likely to occur in the next 5–10 years; identifying drivers of change; and determining the consequences of these changes for the countryside, particularly with regard to the natural heritage.

The work was initiated in February 2001, before the outbreak of Foot and Mouth Disease (FMD), and reported on in December 2001. The research spanned mainland Britain, covering 650 farms, including 85 farms within Badenoch and Strathspey. The main findings for Badenoch and Strathspey were that there had been a withdrawal from farming (due to land sales), a switch to part-time farming, and more off-farm employment or diversification into other businesses. Farm size had grown, with greater specialisation, while the number of mixed farms had fallen. The report concluded that the main driver of these changes was a decline in agricultural profitability. Other drivers included new technology, changing agricultural policies and differing management performance amongst individual farmers.

There is a relatively high proportion of tenanted land in Badenoch and Strathspey, carrying extra land costs which owner/occupiers do not bear. This makes future change highly likely, as gross margins become increasingly important.

Strathspey Breeding Farmland Wader Survey

The aim of the Strathspey Breeding Farmland Wader Survey 2000 was to estimate population densities of nesting waders in Strathspey, and to compare these with wader density estimates from similar surveys elsewhere in Britain and Ireland (RSPB, 2000). This would enable Strathspey wader populations to be viewed in a national context. The survey was co-ordinated by the RSPB and involved input from farmers, landowners and local volunteers. None of the 50 sites surveyed (9,000 ha in total) lay within SSSIs. The survey suggests that Strathspey is the most important mainland breeding site in Britain and Ireland for Lapwing, Redshank, Curlew and Snipe.

Partnership for Breeding Wading Birds

The Partnership for Breeding Wading Birds is a collaborative project involving SNH, RSPB, FWAG and the Cairngorms Biodiversity Action Group. It was established in December 2002 and is due to report in May 2006. Its objectives are: to improve our knowledge of breeding wader numbers on farmland in Tomintoul and Glenlivet; to promote awareness of the importance of the Cairngorms Straths for breeding waders; and to extend suitable habitat and management practices.

The project proposes to achieve this by surveying the area for wading birds, and by drawing up wader plans for farms that contain key breeding sites requiring management, and whose owners are keen to participate.

The upland grain project

In 2000–04, the Cairngorms Local Biodiversity Action Plan (LBAP) and the Farming and Wildlife Advisory Group (FWAG) ran a joint project, aimed at conserving several declining bird species in the Cairngorms. Its objectives were: to encourage grain production at higher altitudes; to demonstrate the value of relatively small areas of grain for biodiversity on crofts and farms in the uplands; and to encourage farmers and crofters to grow oats. Stooks were then built along field margins next to woodlands, providing food and shelter for Capercaillie *Tetrao urogallus* and Black Grouse during the winter.

The project identified 12 suitable sites for growing oats, stooking oats or leaving crops unharvested, spanning a total of about 12 ha. These sites were monitored

weekly for birds during October–January each year. Seven UK BAP priority species were recorded on the sites: Capercaillie, Black Grouse, Grey Partridge, Linnet, Skylark, Song Thrush *Turdus philomelos* and Reed Bunting *Emberiza schoeniclus*. A further 27 species of conservation concern, plus concentrations of finches and buntings, were recorded. The project demonstrated that small-scale initiatives can be very successful in addressing specific issues relating to declining farmland biodiversity on upland sites.

BioScene: Scenarios for reconciling the conservation of biodiversity with declining agricultural use in the mountains of Europe

This three-year project started in December 2002 with the aim of investigating the implications of agricultural restructuring and decline for biodiversity conservation in Europe's mountain areas. The project examined the relationship between biodiversity and farming in six study areas across Europe, including the Cairngorms. Project outputs will describe the opportunities and threats arising from further agricultural contraction, and will evaluate the ecological, economic and political sustainability of different regional management scenarios (or 'BioScenes'[1]).

Rural Stewardship Scheme Monitoring

In 2004, SEERAD awarded a five year contract to Scott Wilson and Associates to monitor and evaluate the environmental impacts of the Rural Stewardship Scheme (RSS), Organic Aid Scheme (OAS) and Countryside Premium Scheme (CPS). One of its objectives is to assess the contribution of agri-environment schemes to the delivery of UK Biodiversity Action Plans.

Cairngorms National Park Authority Projects

In addition, the CNPA have managed the following agricultural projects.

Project	Aim	End date
Direct marketing research and workshop	To develop direct marketing of agricultural goods.	September 2003
Crofting baseline survey	To collect baseline information on crofting in Badenoch & Strathspey.	October 2003
Agriculture waste scheme	To assist farmers in disposing of sheep dip and black plastic.	April 2004
Moorland project	To demonstrate good moorland management.	December 2005

[1] See www.bioscene.co.uk for details

Trends

The adoption of Common Agricultural Policy proposals, in combination with technical developments and economic pressures, has led to a rapid, widespread transformation of European agriculture characterised by intensification, concentration and specialisation of production. This trend has been mirrored in the Cairngorms area and has taken the form of an increase in the number of hill sheep, increased use of silage, a reduction in mixed farming, a decline in cultivated and cropped land, an increase in permanent grassland and a switch to forestry.

The reduction in arable cropping is likely to be the most significant of these changes for wildlife dependent on farmland in the Cairngorms, and was probably the main cause of the loss of three farmland breeding bird species from the Cairngorms (Corncrake *Crex crex*, Tree Sparrow *Passer montanus* and Corn Bunting *Miliaria calandra*), and for a significant decline in breeding Yellowhammer *Emberiza citrinella* (Dennis, 1995). In addition, the change from spring to autumn sowing has had an adverse effect on many farmland birds, by reducing the availability of winter stubble – important as a feeding habitat.

In line with national trends, the number of farm businesses is decreasing, while their average size has increased. The number of small upland farms, in particular, has declined markedly. The impacts of such changes may have been partly mitigated by agri-environment schemes which, as noted above, have a higher than average uptake in the Cairngorms.

Other trends in the Cairngorms area include a rise in sheep numbers during 1980–90, driven largely by Sheep Annual Premium and Hill Livestock Compensatory Allowances (HLCA). In 2001, as part of the Agenda 2000 reforms of the CAP, the HLCA scheme was replaced by the Less Favoured Area Support Scheme (LFASS), under which support is provided on an area basis rather than on a headage basis. This has largely reduced the incentive to maintain artificially high sheep stocking levels, and is likely to have contributed towards a 15% decline in sheep numbers between 1990 and 2003 (Figure 8.2). It is likely that sheep numbers will continue to decline as financial support is decoupled from production (Cook, 2003), as part of the Mid-term Review of the Common Agricultural Policy (see below). With the decline in sheep numbers, over-grazing by sheep is no longer likely to be as significant a problem. The downturn in the profitability of sheep farming has led many estates to focus on the management of the uplands for grouse rather than for continued sheep production.

Farm diversification

The continued decline in farm incomes over many years has led farmers in Scotland to diversify into activities other than farming, providing an additional source of income. Whilst no figures exist in relation to the Cairngorms area specifically, data on diversification within Less Favoured Areas suggest that the trend has also occurred there. The most common form of diversification is to seek off-farm employment, yielding additional income from investments, retainers and state benefits (such as pensions). In contrast, few farmers secure any substantial income from on-farm diversification (such as bed and breakfast or farm shops). Compared to farming, non-farming activities can provide a stable source of income. Figures relating to the whole of the Less Favoured Areas for 2002–03 show that farmers with cattle and sheep earned an average of around £6,000 from activities other than farming, while sheep farmers, whose income from farming was lower (Table 8.2), earned an average of around £11,600 outside of farming (including earnings by farmers' spouses; SEERAD, 2004).

Applications to Moray, Badenoch and Strathspey Enterprise for non-agricultural diversification projects, funded through the Agricultural Business Development Scheme (ABDS), give an indication of the type of diversification projects taking place in this area. During 2001–2004, projects funded through ABDS included seven applications for tourist accommodation and 18 for rural services (e.g. contractors, kennels and cattery, clay pigeon shooting, horse breeding) (SEERAD, pers. comm.).

Conservation issues

The Cairngorms Local Biodiversity Action Plan identifies six main farmland and grassland biodiversity issues: habitat loss and fragmentation; lack of data; awareness-raising; access to appropriate funds; pollution and climate change; and the introduction of alien species (Cosgrove, 2002).

Conservation issues relating to farmland are as follows.

Land-use change. Changes in land use are likely to occur as a result of the Mid-term Review (MTR) of the Common Agricultural Policy. This is likely to be the single-most important policy change in agriculture since

Figure 8.2. Trends in the number of cattle, sheep and lambs recorded within Cairngorms National Park during 1985-2003.

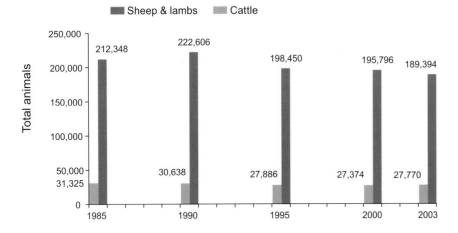

Source: SEERAD

the UK joined the CAP in the early 1970s. The MTR proposals were implemented in January 2005. Projected impacts are: a likely 20% drop in total agricultural output across different sectors in the Highlands and Islands Enterprise area (Cook, 2003); an intensification of existing trends, with an increase in specialisation and farm size; and a further decline in beef cattle numbers within the National Park, which dropped by 9% during 1990–2003 (Figure 8.2). It is hard to predict environmental impacts until farmers' reactions to the MTR proposals have been assessed. A reduction in over-grazing may bring some environmental benefits, however there is concern that some features that depend on grazing or cropping may be left unmanaged. Conversely, the decoupling of subsidies from production may provide farmers with greater opportunities to join incentive schemes for positive land management.

Agri-environment schemes. The first ESA scheme agreements expired in 2004. Those involved were given the option of automatic entry into the Rural Stewardship Scheme. This will be critical in safeguarding natural heritage interests previously protected through ESA agreements.

Land Management Contracts (LMCs). These have been piloted on 25 Scottish farms and crofts, one of which lies within the Cairngorms. It is likely that LMCs will be implemented in 2005–06 and will continue to be developed from 2007 onwards.

Habitat loss and fragmentation. Some grassland habitats in the Cairngorms are found only in small, isolated sites. Habitat fragmentation may pose significant problems for natural ecological processes and species dispersal, leaving specialist species particularly vulnerable to change (Cosgrove, 2002). The loss of grassland habitats – such as traditionally managed hayfields – has a direct effect on biodiversity, as a number of species depend on these floristically diverse grassland habitats.

The Cairngorms National Park Authority (CNPA) will play an important role in supporting and developing agricultural schemes in the area. The Scottish Executive (2001) states that "projects will be developed in the … National Park … to find new approaches to land management which are tailored to the ends of land managers, the environment and the wider rural economy".

Abandonment and under-utilisation. Abandonment or under-utilisation of agricultural land is likely to be occurring already in the Cairngorms, with both gains and losses for biodiversity. The extent to which this continues will depend largely on how the CAP Mid-term Review is implemented and, in particular, on how successful Cross Compliance and Good Agricultural and Environmental Condition are in preventing abandonment.

References

Bayfield, N.G. & Conroy, J.W.H. (eds.) (1996). *The Cairngorms Assets.* The Cairngorms Partnership: Grantown-on-Spey.

Bell, J.S., Hewison, R.L., Cummins, R.P., Martin, I.S., French, D.D., Picozzi, N., Catt, D.C., Rees, T. & Mills, C. (2000). *Monitoring Environmentally Sensitive Areas in Scotland, Vol 4: The Cairngorms Straths ESA Monitoring Report 1994–1999.* Report to the Scottish Executive, Rural Affairs Department.

Bibby, J.S., Douglas, H.A., Thomasson, A.J. & Robertson, J.S. (1982). *Land Capability for Agriculture. Soil Survey of Scotland Monograph.* The Macaulay Institute for Soil Research: Aberdeen.

Cook, P. (2003). *Update of Agricultural Forecasts for the HIE Area, the impact of the July 2003 MTR Agreement.* Scottish Agricultural College, Rural Business Unit.

Cosgrove, P. (ed.) (2002). *The Cairngorms Local Biodiversity Action Plan.* The Cairngorms Partnership: Grantown-on-Spey.

Dennis, R. (1995). *The Birds of Badenoch and Strathspey.* Colin Baxter Photography: Lanark.

FPDSavills (2001). *Structural Change in Agriculture and the Implications for the Countryside.* Scottish Natural Heritage Commissioned Report F00AA105A. SNH: Perth.

Nolan, A.J., Hewison, R.L., Rees, T., Mills, C. & Murray, T. (2000). *Monitoring Environmentally Sensitive Areas in Scotland, Vol 3: The Breadalbane ESA Monitoring Report 1994–1999.* Report to the Scottish Executive Rural Affairs Department.

RSPB (2000). *Strathspey Breeding Farmland Wader Survey 2000.* RSPB: Edinburgh.

Scottish Executive (2001). *A Forward Strategy for Scottish Agriculture.* The Stationery Office: Edinburgh.

Scottish Executive (2003a). *Agriculture Census.* The Stationery Office: Edinburgh.

Scottish Executive (2003b). *Economic Report on Scottish Agriculture.* The Stationery Office: Edinburgh.

Scottish Office, Agriculture, Environment and Fisheries Department (1997). *Environmentally Sensitive Areas: explanatory leaflet for farmers, crofters and common grazings committees.* The Stationery Office: Edinburgh.

SEERAD (2004). *Farm Incomes in Scotland 2002/03.* Scottish Executive: Edinburgh.

Additional reading
Leaper, G. (1999). *Biodiversity of the Cairngorms.* The Cairngorms Partnership: Grantown-on-Spey.

O'Brien, M.G. (1995). *Survey of breeding waders on Scottish lowlands.* Interim unpublished report to RSPB. RSPB: Edinburgh.

RSPB (2003). *The Future of ESAs in Scotland.* RSPB: Edinburgh.

Scottish Executive (2003). *Key Scottish Environment Statistics.* The Stationery Office: Edinburgh.

Scottish Executive (2003). *New Directions for Land Management in Scotland's National Parks.* The Stationery Office: Edinburgh.

9. FRESHWATERS

Colin Bean

Introduction

The distribution of freshwater habitats in the UK is determined mainly by climate and geology. Scotland has a temperate maritime climate, characterised by relatively mild temperatures and high precipitation, much of which falls on the hills. As a result, Scottish freshwaters account for 90% of the volume and 70% of the total surface area of freshwater in the UK, and include some 950 river systems that drain directly into the sea. Standing waters, ranging from small pools to deep, expansive lochs, account for 2% of Scotland's surface area.

The alignment of Scottish rivers north of the Highland Boundary Fault is strongly influenced by the Caledonian orogeny, which has produced a south-west to north-east geological graining (SEPA, 1996). Rivers and streams are a common feature throughout Scotland, particularly in the West and north-east Highlands, which host the largest number of river systems. These tend to be relatively small and steep in comparison with the larger catchments typical of the east coast. As a result of their small size and the underlying geology and land-use characteristics of their catchments, these rivers tend to be relatively unproductive (oligotrophic) systems.

The alignment of rivers draining to the east of the country is strongly influenced by the montane character and geology of high altitude areas such as the Cairngorms. Generally, those rivers that drain towards the east originate in a number of base-poor upland sub-catchments, and the main stems become progressively larger and more biologically diverse and productive as they flow through lowland areas.

The vast majority of standing water bodies in Scotland are small pools and lochans, associated with upland and peatland areas in the north and west. Standing waters account for approximately 50% (by surface area) of the Scottish total (Lyle & Smith, 1994). The distribution and chemistry of standing waters in Scotland has been strongly influenced by their glacial history, geology, climate and catchment land use. The location and geology of underlying bedrock has a profound effect on the size and shape of the loch system, as well as its water chemistry and overall productivity. Most Scottish lochs are of glacial origin, and the majority are considered to be nutrient-poor.

The rivers and lochs of the Cairngorms are important not only in a regional or national context, but are considered to be a global asset (Davidson *et al.,* 2002). The Cairngorms are the premier mountain range in the UK, and their scale, altitude and value as a wilderness offer unique opportunities for scientific study, nature conservation and recreation. Water has, in a number of ways, contributed to the unique landscape of the Cairngorms. Over the last four glacial cycles, glaciers enveloped the entire area, resulting in the formation of a wide variety of characteristic glacial and peri-glacial landforms. These, in turn, have strongly influenced the distribution, character and chemistry of the Cairngorms' rivers and lochs, and hence their biodiversity, much of which is more typical of alpine environments.

Freshwater habitats

Rivers
Rivers draining the Cairngorms area are among the largest in Scotland. In terms of mean flow level (measured in cumecs: cubic metres per second), the Tay and the Spey, for example, are larger than the Clyde (49 cumecs) and Forth (47 cumecs) (Table 9.1).

Bean, C. (2006). Freshwaters. In: Shaw, P. & Thompson, D.B.A. (eds.). *The Nature of the Cairngorms: Diversity in a changing environment.* The Stationery Office. pp. 119-131.

The rivers and lochs of the Cairngorms are considered to be a global as well as a national asset. Rivers like the Feshie offer unique opportunities for scientific study, nature conservation and recreation, and contribute to the area's exceptional landscape.

Photo: *P. Cairns*

Table 9.1. The lengths and flow levels of rivers draining the Cairngorms area, in descending order of mean flow level.

River	Total length (km)	Mean flow levels (cumecs[1])
Tay	193	168
Spey	160	64
Dee	154	46
South Esk	79	19
Don	132	14
North Esk	47	12

[1] Cubic metres per second.

The Cairngorms area encompasses 5,677 km of river habitat, of which 2,315 km lie outside of the National Park; along the River Tay, the North Esk, South Esk, and along small sections of the Deveron and Findhorn.

Lochs

The Cairngorms area includes 37 lochs, 14 of which lie outside of the National Park. These figures do not include smaller water bodies, such as small lochans and peat pools, which provide important habitats for a wide variety of specialised aquatic flora and fauna. Only one loch – Loch Muick – is ranked among the largest 50 lochs in Scotland (Murray & Pullar, 1910). However it is not the size or volume of lochs in the Cairngorms that give these habitats their particular natural heritage value. The morphological characteristics of standing waters in the Cairngorms area vary remarkably in terms of basin shape (e.g. scoured depressions, kettleholes, high corrie lochans), chemistry, nutrient status (e.g. oligotrophic, eutrophic, dystrophic) and thermal regime which, in some cases, is influenced by semi-permanent ice cover. In total, standing waters account for only about 34 km^2 and 20 km^2 (0.01%) of the Cairngorms area and the National Park, respectively, but contribute disproportionately to the Cairngorms' biodiversity.

Important areas

Rivers

In common with other river systems, the physical and chemical characteristics of Cairngorms river systems are reflected in the range and variety of their aquatic and riparian biological communities.

The River Spey catchment dominates Cairngorms National Park in terms of scale, covering 54% of the Park area. The Spey is considered to be nationally important for nature conservation on account of its water quality, rich plant and invertebrate communities (Chapter 15), bird communities (Chapter 18) and the diversity of its fluvial geomorphological features (Chapter 2). The latter include the forested alluvial fan and active braided channels at its confluence with the River Feshie. Much of the river is also considered to be of European importance, having been identified under the EC Habitats Directive as a Special Area of Conservation (SAC) for its Atlantic Salmon *Salmo salar*, Sea Lamprey *Petromyzon marinus*, Otter *Lutra lutra* and Freshwater Pearl Mussel *Margaritifera margaritifera* populations. Loch Insh, an expansion of the River Spey, has also been identified as an SAC, as well as a Ramsar site, a Special Protection Area (SPA) and an SSSI.

The catchments of the rivers Dee, Don, North Esk and South Esk, and a small sub-catchment of the Tay, also lie within the National Park. The rivers Dee, South Esk and Tay host particularly important Atlantic Salmon populations and have been accorded SAC status for that species (Chapter 16). The River Tay SAC extends only as far north as the Allt a Ghlinne Bhig, however, and therefore lies outwith the National Park. Other qualifying interests for these SAC rivers include the Brook Lamprey *Lampetra planeri* (Tay), River Lamprey *Lampetra fluviatilis* (Tay), Sea Lamprey (Tay and Spey), Freshwater Pearl Mussel (Dee, Spey and South Esk) and the Otter (Dee, Spey and Tay). The River Tay SAC also contains the Habitats Directive Annex I habitat 'Oligotrophic to mesotrophic standing waters with vegetation of the *Littorelletea uniflorae* and/or of the *Isoëto-Nanojuncetea*'.

The headwaters of the River Dee, which drain the southern Cairngorm and north Grampian mountains, are particularly important for their larger, early running Atlantic Salmon. The River South Esk drains a moderate-sized catchment, and has a strong nutrient gradient along its length, rising in the nutrient-poor Grampians and flowing through the fertile lower catchment area of Strathmore, before entering the sea. This enables it to support a full range of Atlantic Salmon life-history types and an internationally important Freshwater Pearl Mussel population (Chapter 15). All of the catchments arising in the Cairngorms area support nationally important Atlantic Salmon fisheries (Chapter 16).

Lochs

Standing waters throughout the UK are usually classified according to their nutrient status, although other classification methods can be used. Most are assigned to one of three classes: oligotrophic (nutrient-poor), mesotrophic (intermediate nutrient levels) and eutrophic (nutrient-rich). 'Dystrophic' lochs also occur in the Cairngorms, and are slightly different from the other nutrient categories, being distinguished by their smaller size, higher colouration, acidity, and association with peatland areas. Whilst most lochs in the Cairngorms area are oligotrophic, reflecting the base-poor geology on which they and their feeder streams are located, a small number of mesotrophic, eutrophic and dystrophic lochs occur.

Oligotrophic water bodies in the Cairngorms include some of the highest standing waters in the UK. High corrie lochs, such as those near the summits of Lochnagar, Ben Macdui (e.g. An Lochan Uaine) and Braeriach (e.g. Loch Coire an Lochan), are particularly unproductive, and a combination of coarse substrates, high-energy wave action, low temperatures and frequent ice cover allow only a few macrophytes to survive. Davidson *et al.* (2002) consider that the real value of high altitude lochs lies in their unique algal flora. Loch Etchachan is the highest of the corrie lochs and, although lacking in fish, hosts a number of macroinvertebrate species characteristic of high altitude habitats. These include the mayfly *Ameletus inopinatus*, the net-spinning caddis *Plectrocnemia conspersa* and the stonefly *Capnia atra*.

An Lochan Uaine, Loch Coire an Lochan and Loch Etchachan are listed in the Nature Conservation Review (NCR) (Ratcliffe, 1977), reflecting their Arctic-alpine character, unique in Great Britain. All are included in the Cairngorms SAC. At lower altitudes, lochs Einich and Avon are good examples of large oligotrophic glacial water bodies. Despite being relatively unproductive, they host a more diverse range of flora and fauna than higher altitude systems. As a function of their bathymetry and their more sheltered shoreline habitats, these lochs host a variety of macrophyte, invertebrate and fish species, characteristic of nutrient-poor systems. Lochs Einich and Avon are also listed in the NCR for their high altitude glacial trough characteristics (Ratcliffe, 1977), and are SAC qualifying features on account of their nutrient status and unique macrophyte flora.

Lochs in the straths enjoy more sheltered conditions and have finer sediments, allowing higher plants to become established. Although most are oligotrophic, some, such as lochs Vrotachan, Davan and Kinord, are now classified as Type 5A (mesotrophic) (Ratcliffe, 1977; Bailey-Watts *et al.*, 1992; Palmer *et al.*, 1992; Bennion *et al.*, 2001). Key species for these high altitude oligotrophic lochs include Quillwort *Isoetes lacustris*, Shoreweed *Littorella uniflora* and the

rare Six-stamened Waterwort *Elatine hexandra*, which is present in Loch Einich (altitude 500 m). The lochs in this area are generally classified as Type 3 (Oligotrophic/base poor with *Myriophyllum alterniflorum*, *Isoetes lacustris* and *Fontinalis antipyretica*). They include lochs Muick, Callater, Bhrodainn, Morlich, an Eilein, Alvie, Insh, Garten, Lochindorb and Loch an Duin. A few, such as Loch Avon, are classified as Type 2 (Oligotrophic/base poor with *Juncus bulbosus*, *Potamogeton polygonifolius*, *Littorella uniflora*, *Lobelia dortmanna* and *Potamogeton natans*).

Compared with the number and distribution of oligotrophic water bodies, mesotrophic lochs are relatively scarce in the Cairngorms area, since they are not associated with montane areas and are more commonly located in areas underlain with less resistant bedrocks, thicker overlying deposits and with catchment soils supporting greater plant productivity and agricultural activities. Lochs Davan and Kinord are the largest of four mesotrophic loch systems in the National Park. These lochs are fine examples of 'kettlehole lakes', and pollen preserved in the sediments of Loch Kinord record an almost complete sequence of Devensian late-glacial and Flandrian vegetation

Low temperatures, frequent ice cover and high wave action make high corrie lochs like Lochan Uaine on Angel's Peak biologically unproductive. Nonetheless, such lochs are considered important for their unique algal flora.

Photo: *P. & A. MacDonald*

history. Both lochs are important reference sites for reconstructing changing environmental conditions in north-east Scotland since the last glacial period, and are important refuges for passage and wintering wildfowl (Chapter 18). Loch Kinord possesses a particularly rich aquatic flora, as yet undamaged by eutrophication, and a full range of hydroseral plant communities, ranging from emergent fens dominated by Bottle Sedge *Carex rostrata* and Slender Sedge *Carex lasiocarpa* to Bog Myrtle *Myrica gale* scrub, fen carr and birch woodland (Chapter 10). Loch Davan is particularly noteworthy for its extensive areas of Common Reed *Phragmites australis*. As well as being designated as SAC, SPA and Ramsar sites, both are NCR sites, included in the Muir of Dinnet SSSI.

Loch Insh is unique in the Cairngorms area in that it lies in the extensive morainic deposits of Strathspey and forms an expansion of the River Spey. It has a relatively low average gradient (*c.* 2.6 m km^{-1}) over a 40 km stretch upstream of Grantown-on-Spey (Davidson *et al.*, 2002). In conjunction with other fluvial processes, this has led to lateral flooding, the creation of Loch Insh, and an extensive flood plain: the Insh Marshes. The loch receives water from the upper portion of the Spey catchment, which has a shallow gradient. As a result, the loch basin acts as a major deposition area for silt, resulting in a build-up of nutrients, and hence the loch's mesotrophic status.

Together, Loch Insh and Insh Marshes constitute a major wetland site of international importance (see Chapter 10). Loch Insh is an NCR site and is part of the River Spey and Insh Marshes SSSI, the Insh Marshes SAC, and is designated under the Ramsar Convention as a wetland site of international importance. The site supports one of the few populations of Arctic Charr *Salvelinus alpinus* in Scotland known to spawn in running waters (Chapter 16).

Lochs Con, Mor and Loch of Lintrathen are also classed as mesotrophic. Mesotrophic lochs are priority habitats and subject to Habitat Action Plans (HAPs) under the UK's Biodiversity Action Plan, led by SEPA. While lochs Davan, Kinord and Vrotachan are all designated as naturally mesotrophic lochs in favourable status, Loch of Lintrathen is the subject of an Environmental Improvement Plan by SEPA. Under this plan, SEPA will undertake chemical and botanical surveys of the loch, and assess the sources of phosphorus, the main enriching pollutant, within the loch's catchment. The long-term aim of this project is to identify and implement measures required to reduce the inputs of phosphorus to the loch to a level consistent with an unimpacted mesotrophic standing water.

Eutrophic water bodies are not uncommon in lowland areas throughout the UK, particularly where intensive agriculture is the dominant form of land use. These lochs are characterised by high levels of primary production (by algae and macrophytes) and of secondary production (by zooplankton and macroinvertebrates). A change in dominance from salmonid fish species to cyprinids (e.g. Roach *Rutilus rutilus*, Bream *Abramis brama*) and percids (e.g. Perch *Perca fluviatilis*) also occurs. Eutrophic water bodies offer enhanced feeding opportunities and habitat diversity for a variety of bird species, particularly waterfowl.

Despite the abundance of eutrophic water bodies throughout lowland Britain, *naturally* eutrophic water bodies are relatively rare. None exists in Cairngorms National Park, and there is only one – Loch of Kinnordy – in the wider Cairngorms area. Loch of Kinnordy is a naturally eutrophic system located in the south-east of the Cairngorms area. As well as being an NCR site and an SSSI, it is an SPA on account of its wintering goose populations (Chapter 18). Associated with the open water are extensive and relatively undisturbed rich fen and carr plant communities which are becoming increasingly rare nationally. The site also hosts several rare plants, such as Cowbane *Cicuta virosa*, Greater Spearwort *Ranunculus lingua*, Nodding Bur-marigold *Bidens cernua*, Greater Tussock Sedge *Carex paniculata*, Lesser Tussock Sedge *Carex diandra* and Water Sedge *Carex aquatilis*.

Recent research and survey findings

Medium to long-term freshwater research and monitoring programmes in the Cairngorms have tended to focus on relatively few subject areas, such as the monitoring of water quality, invertebrate or fish populations. However, a considerable number of short-term (1-3 year) or one-off or programmes have been implemented.

Water quality monitoring
Water quality has been monitored at several locations in the Cairngorms for many decades. Prior to the formation of SEPA in 1996, routine water quality monitoring in this area was undertaken by the North East River Purification Board. Scottish Water also monitors the quality of raw water sources in the Cairngorms area. These data are available in a variety of forms, dating from the 1970s. They include rivers (e.g. the Spey, Dee and Tay) as well as standing waters (e.g. Loch Lee). SEPA has reported good progress towards meeting its targets for water quality in the Cairngorms and in Scotland as a whole

(SEPA 1996, 1999, 2001 *et seq.*). This has been achieved, in part, through the development of more effective pollution control legislation, including the Pollution Prevention and Control (Scotland) Regulations 2000 and the EC Nitrates Directive. Further improvements may result once the Water Framework Directive comes into force.

Nutrient enrichment in standing waters can be regarded as a natural process, but can be accelerated by a number of factors, such as agricultural run-off. Water quality studies (Bailey-Watts *et al.*, 1992) and palaeolimnological studies (Bennion *et al.*, 2001) have shown that Loch Davan is now more enriched than in the past, and that Loch Kinord should be classed as mesotrophic. Studies of diatom communities in sediment cores (Bennion *et al.*, op. cit.) also suggest that lochs Einich and Muick are oligotrophic systems showing some evidence of past acidification. Water chemistry is routinely monitored by SEPA in lochs Morlich, Davan, Kinord, Insh, Muick, Alvie and an t-Seilich, and above Spey Dam, either monthly or bi-monthly throughout the year. Invertebrates are sampled less frequently.

Acidification and climate change

Other long-term water quality datasets available for freshwaters in the Cairngorms area generally relate to the monitoring of acidification and climate change, and to detailed hydrological and hydrochemical studies. Bodies such as SEPA, the Environmental Change Research Centre, the SEERAD Fisheries Research Laboratory, Aberdeen University, CEH and MLURI, hold chemical, invertebrate or fish data sets for freshwaters in the Cairngorms. Much of these data relate to Allt a'Mharcaidh and Lochnagar, which are part of the UK Acid Waters Monitoring Network (UKAWMN). Data have been collected from these sites since 1988 and form part of the UK's contribution to the UNECE International Cooperative Programmes (ICPs) on *Integrated Monitoring* (Allt a'Mharcaidh) and *Assessment and Monitoring of Acidification of Rivers and Lakes* (Lochnagar). They also contribute to a requirement, under the Second Sulphur Protocol, to monitor the extent and impact of acid deposition in Europe.

Lochnagar has also been selected as a representative site within the Environmental Change Network (ECN) and has been included in two large-scale EU-funded projects: Mountain Lakes Research and Monitoring (MOLAR) and its successor, the European Mountain Lake Ecosystems: Regionalisation, Diagnostic and Socio-Economic Evaluation (EMERGE). Acidification records for Allt a'Mharcaidh and Lochnagar from the period 1988–2003 are available in Shilland *et al.* (2003).

Both Allt a'Mharcaidh and Lochnagar have been studied as part of the Surface Waters Acidification Project. This was a collaborative research programme established by the UK, Norway and Sweden to evaluate the factors responsible for fish population declines in acidified streams and lochs (see Patrick *et al.*, 1996).

Studies of trace metal distribution in sediment cores from Lochnagar have shown increased levels of mercury, lead, copper and zinc since the 1860s (Yang *et al.*, 2002a). The flux of mercury and lead concentrations in core samples was greatest between 1880 and 1970, since when levels have stablised (Yang *et al.*, 2002b).

Invertebrate and water chemistry data have been collected from up to 17 streams in the Cairngorms area since 1984 (Soulsby *et al.*, 1997). These provide invaluable insights into the seasonality of water quality trends and biological responses to acidification, showing that subtle differences in macroinvertebrate community structure exist between and within catchments, and from year to year (Gibbins *et al.*, 2001; Soulsby *et al.*, 2002). Soulsby *et al.* (op. cit.) also provide evidence that a reduction in sulphate concentrations in stream water is occurring at a rate consistent with declining levels of atmospheric deposition.

Vives *et al.* (2004) examined organochlorine compounds found in the muscle and liver tissue of Brown Trout *Salmo trutta* from high altitude lakes in 11 European countries, plus Greenland. They showed that fish from Lochnagar contained higher levels of the flame retardant Polybromodiphenyl Ether (PBDE) than any of the other fish sampled. An observed link between organochlorine concentration and ambient temperature suggests that a remobilisation of organochlorines accumulated in the sediments of Lochnagar may occur as a consequence of climate change.

Catchment management

In addition to long-term water quality and macroinvertebrate studies, rivers and streams in the Cairngorms have been used to test and develop a variety of approaches to managing both water resources and water quality at different spatial scales. Wade *et al.* (2001), for example, used a model of Integrated Nitrogen in Catchments as a tool for catchment management in the River Dee. Smart *et al.* (2001) extended this work, using GIS modelling to examine water chemistry at a number of sites in the Dee catchment. This, together with earlier studies (e.g. Smart *et al.*, 1998), showed that the Dee basin could be neatly separated into upland and lowland regions in terms of land use, reflecting clear differences in the water chemistry of each region. This work also demonstrated that sub-catchments of the River Dee could be grouped in terms of temporal variation in stream water chemistry. It is likely that similar patterns can be found in the catchments of the Spey, Don, North Esk, South Esk and Tay.

In addition to studies at the catchment level, work has taken place in discreet sub-catchments to elucidate run-off processes and flow paths in the Feshie, Feugh and Allt a'Mharcaidh systems, using a variety of approaches, including the measurement of geochemical tracers and oxygen (O_2^{18}) isotopes (e.g. Soulsby *et al.*, 2000, 2003, 2004).

Groundwater

While most of the research on river and stream systems in the Cairngorms area has focussed on surface waters, the hydrodynamics of groundwater sources has also been examined. Interactions between groundwater and surface water in rivers such as those of the Cairngorms are not yet well understood, and it is acknowledged that these zones of interaction play an important role as potential buffer zones in relation to water quality impacts (Walker, 2000). They can also have implications for water supply, flood management and river engineering works. It is essential that interactions between groundwater and surface water

An examination of the water chemistry at a number of sites in the Dee catchment has shown that clear differences in water chemistry reflect patterns of land use in different parts of the Dee basin.

Photo: *L. Gill*

---

[1] The saturated zone under a river or stream.
[2] Whether oligotrophic, mesotrophic, eutrophic or dystrophic.

are better understood if appropriate water level management plans in wetland environments are to be developed.

Early work by Soulsby *et al.* (1998a,b) considered the influence of groundwater on the quality and quantity of streamflow and its relationship with potable supplies in rural areas. Later research focussed on spatial and temporal variability in interactions between groundwater and surface water in the hyporheic zone[1] of salmonid spawning streams (e.g. Moir *et al.*, 1998; Malcolm *et al.*, 2002, 2003a,b). These studies suggest that watershed management strategies and river restoration schemes focussing solely on surface water characteristics risk overlooking sub-surface processes that may be critical to the survival of fish and other stream fauna.

Monitoring natural heritage features

A considerable number of surveys of freshwater habitats have been carried out in the Cairngorms area. These range from extensive programmes, such as the SNH-funded Loch Survey in 1997, to small, one-off projects, such as the 1985 survey of lochs in Strathspey (Charter, 1988).

Macrophyte data were obtained from a number of standing waters in the Cairngorms area, as part of the 1997 Lochs Survey. Data from Scottish lochs, which included lochs Etchachan, Vrotachan, Davan and Kinord, were integrated into a larger dataset, derived from 1,100 lakes around Britain. This was used by Palmer *et al.* (1992) to develop a classification system for lake types. A new classification system is currently being developed, using data from more than 3,000 standing waters, including those situated in the Cairngorms area.

The classification system developed by Palmer *et al.* (op. cit.) is currently being used to assess the condition of lochs designated as SSSIs or SACs for their macrophyte interests or lake typology[2]. Condition is assessed by comparing the results with targets set for each loch's macrophyte community composition and structure, extent, hydrology, substrate, sediment load and local distinctiveness (i.e. the presence of rare plants). A number of standing waters in the Cairngorms area have been assessed, including lochs Kinord, Davan, Buildg, Callater, Insh, Einich, and two un-named lochans adjacent to lochs Buildg and Insh.

Site Condition Monitoring is also carried out on fish and Freshwater Pearl Mussel populations on designated sites in the Cairngorms area. Fluvial-geomorphological research in the Cairngorms, including works carried out on the River Feshie, is reviewed in Chapter 2.

Trends

Water quality

Water quality measurements are the most reliable way of assessing the potential for change in aquatic habitats. The classification scheme currently used by SEPA divides each river network into stretches. Each stretch is assigned a monitoring point, where chemical and/or ecological samples are taken and aesthetic appearance is recorded. During 2004, 1,425 km (88.8%) of the *c.* 1,605 km of river and stream habitat within the National Park was classified as being either 'excellent' (Class A1) or 'good' (Class A2) (SEPA, pers. comm.). A further 3.7 km (0.2%) was considered to be 'fair' (Class B). Only 2.8 km (0.2%) of monitored watercourses were considered to be of 'poor' quality (Class C), and no waters were considered to be 'seriously polluted' (Class D). Not all watercourses are monitored however, and 173.6 km (10.8%) was unclassified. Most of the unclassified watercourses are located in rural upland catchments. SEPA aims to progressively reduce the extent of unclassified rivers prior to full implementation of the EC Water Framework Directive. This is evidenced by a 50% reduction in the total length of unclassified reaches within the National Park during 2003–04.

The first national survey of water quality in standing waters within Scotland took place during 1995. This was largely restricted to the 150 lochs in Scotland that have a surface area greater than 1 km², although a limited number of smaller lochs of particular local interest were also included. Of the 10 lochs within the Cairngorms area that are monitored by SEPA as part of their Standing Waters Classification Scheme, seven (lochs Alvie, An t-Seilich, Davan, Einich, Kinord, Muick and Spey Dam) were considered to be of WQ Class 1 (excellent). The remaining three lochs (Insh, Lintrathen and Morlich) were downgraded to WQ Class 2 (fair) because they display evidence of past or ongoing nutrient enrichment. Between 1995 and 2000 there was no change in any of these classifications. SEPA report on the condition of these standing waters on a quinquennial basis.

The EC Water Framework Directive came into force in December 2000, with the primary aim of protecting and restoring freshwater, marine and wetland biodiversity. The Directive introduced a new approach to European water management and led to the development of new statutory measures to set and achieve 'ecological status' targets for the water environment. Those activities affecting the water environment will be addressed through the preparation of River Basin Management Plans and sub-Basin Management Plans. Each contains a 'programme of measures' to prevent deterioration and

to achieve 'good status' for all recognised water bodies by 2015. It is unclear how existing Catchment Management Plans, such as those for the Spey and Dee catchments, will be incorporated into the sub-Basin Management Plans. The Directive requires that activities which could affect the ecological status of aquatic and wetland habitats be considered, regardless of whether the activity takes place on water or on the surrounding land.

The Directive has been transposed into Scottish law by primary legislation, as the Water Environment & Water Services (Scotland) Act 2003 (WEWS). Secondary legislation, such as the Water Environment (Controlled Activities) (Scotland) Regulations 2004, is already under development and this will enable the environmental objectives associated with water abstraction, river engineering and diffuse pollution to be achieved.

Good water quality in rivers and lochs in the Cairngorms is a reflection of the relatively low number of industrial effluent discharges in the area. Industrial effluent discharges in the National Park consist of a small number of fish farms or hatcheries and whisky distilleries. Thermal discharges from distilleries are also a form of pollution, whose seasonal and long-term impacts on aquatic flora and fauna are currently unknown. Water bodies in the National Park also receive treated sewage effluent from a number of small- to medium-sized settlements, which are thought to have a relatively minor impact on water quality (Davidson *et al.*, 2002).

Eutrophication

Although water quality in the National Park is generally classified as being 'excellent' or 'good', some nutrient enrichment may occur. This may be part of a natural process, or accelerated through the input of nutrients from elsewhere. Algal blooms, a feature more commonly associated with eutrophic water bodies, occur in Cairngorms lochs that have no obvious external nutrient source (Davidson *et al.*, 2002). Nutrient enrichment is generally associated with sewage effluent from settlements. Loch Insh, for example, receives sewage effluent from Kingussie, Newtonmore, Lynchat, Insh and a number of smaller developments, and it is clear that a large part of the nutrient budget of this system originates from these sources. In the case of Loch Insh, the impact of nutrient enrichment is ameliorated by the short time taken for complete water exchange (flushing) to take place within the loch (Bailey-Watts *et al.*, 1993). Other waters, such as Loch Morlich, receive nutrient inputs from mountain streams polluted by visitor facilities located on Cairn Gorm itself. Additional nutrient inputs, both direct and diffuse, may originate from forestry and farming activities. Adherence to the new *Forests and Water Guidelines* (Forestry Commission, 2003) should reduce the potential for negative impacts. The EC Water Framework Directive, through the WEWS Act and the Water Environment (Controlled Activities) (Scotland) Regulations 1994, will introduce new controls over point- and diffuse pollution sources.

Extensive areas to the north-east and south-east of the Cairngorms area have been designated as Nitrate Vulnerable Zones (NVZs). These zones, designated in accordance with the requirements of the EC Nitrates Directive, aim to reduce water pollution caused by nitrates from agricultural sources. Surface water, originating from the Cairngorms, drains into the Moray, Aberdeenshire, Banff & Buchan NVZ to the north-east, and into the Strathmore & Fife NVZ to the south-east.

Acidification

Acid conditions are not uncommon in running and standing waters in the Cairngorms area. Some of this can be attributed to the surrounding geology and soil composition. It is clear, however, that acidification, caused primarily by the atmospheric deposition of pollutants originating from distant sources,

has occurred in the Cairngorms area over much of the last century (Patrick *et al.*, 1989; Jones *et al.*, 1993) and that critical loads have been exceeded regularly during this period. In the Cairngorms, four standing water sites that have shown clear evidence of acidification are Lochnagar, An Lochan Uaine, Loch nan Eun and Dubh Loch (Jones *et al.*, op. cit.). Fluctuations in pH levels can have an impact on the ecology of standing waters on a number of levels, by, for example, reducing algal biomass, species composition and invertebrate diversity, and increasing the mortality rates of resident Brown Trout.

Acidification is not restricted to standing waters. Morrison and Harriman (1992) and Harriman *et al.* (1992) described the impact of acidification and short-term, low pH episodes on the fauna of streams in the Cairngorms area. Both studies noted a reduction in invertebrate and salmonid production. Soulsby *et al.* (1997) provides a review of acidified streams in the Cairngorms area.

As noted above, two sites in the Cairngorms – Allt a'Mharcaidh and Lochnagar – are part of the UK Acid Waters Monitoring Network and the UNECE Integrated Monitoring Programme. Together with lochs Davan and Kinord,

In a survey of water quality in 1995, Loch Morlich was one of three lochs in the Cairngorms downgraded from 'excellent' to 'fair' as a result of nutrient enrichment. The loch receives nutrient inputs from mountain streams polluted by visitor facilities on Cairn Gorm.

Photo: *P. Cairns*

and the River Spey at Fochabers, they also form part of the UK Environmental Change Network.

Water quantity

Many lowland wetlands have been drained and converted to agricultural use in the past, although the extent of this loss has not been quantified (Leaper, 1999). Some small open water habitats may also have been lost, but data to support this view are lacking. While it is possible that small areas of the littoral zones of lochs may have been lost, due to large scale drainage, there is no evidence for this. Temporary losses of water may occur in modified water bodies used as reservoirs or impoundments for hydropower generation. For example, the British Alcan Hydro-power Scheme diverts water from the upper reaches of the River Spey at Spey Dam and the River Mashie, to serve the Pattack-Laggan system. Scottish and Southern Energy transfer water from the rivers Tromie and Truim, as well as a number of smaller sources (e.g. Loch Cuaich and Allt Bhran), to support production in the Ericht-Tummel system. This represents a net loss of water from the Cairngorms area. The EC Water Framework Directive, through the WEWS Act and the Water Environment (Controlled Activities) (Scotland) Regulations 1994, will initiate new controls over water impoundment and abstraction in future years.

Climate change may also play an increasing role in changing the pattern and volume of rainfall and of snow deposition, and the timing of snow-melt in the Cairngorms area (Chapter 20). This is likely to have profound effects on the rate at which water flows through and out of the Cairngorms area, and on the biota that depend on it.

Conservation issues

Pressures on the freshwater resources of the Cairngorms area are varied. Walker (2000) and Davidson et al. (2002) give an overview of those issues particularly relevant to aquatic habitats and freshwater resources in the wider Cairngorms. Leaper (1999), in a detailed assessment of biodiversity in the Cairngorms, describes priority aquatic habitats and species, and highlights areas of concern, some of which are described below.

Industrial or domestic pollution.
Nutrient enrichment can occur by natural means, but it is clear that anthropogenic sources of nutrients have resulted in enrichment in some localities. To comply with the EC Water Framework

Directive, areas where water quality is a continuing issue will be identified, environmental objectives set, and a programme of measures undertaken to achieve these objectives by 2015.

Land use.
Erosion is an important issue in areas where thinly vegetated, shallow soils are damaged by deer or sheep grazing. Anthropogenic damage also occurs as a result of hill walking, skiing and poorly controlled muirburn. Ballentyne (1991) suggests that accelerated erosion may be a consequence of climate change as well as of poor land management. The transport of coarse and fine sediment can lead to the loss of stream habitats for invertebrates and fish. It may also lead to the silting up, shallowing or loss of standing water habitats, and may negatively impact on their associated flora and fauna.

Erosion and siltation can be a feature in streams or rivers that receive run-off from forestry plantations or agricultural land. The Cairngorms Forestry Framework and the new Forest and Water Guidelines (Forestry Commission, 2003) reduce the potential for future forestry operations to damage freshwater habitats.

The Environmentally Sensitive Area scheme and its successor, the Rural Stewardship Scheme (Chapter 8), provide landowners with incentives to manage wetlands, water margins and flood plains as wildlife habitats. Improved riparian management may help to reduce the potential for erosion in future years.

Forestry and farming issues are perhaps most effectively dealt with at the catchment level. The Cairngorms Rivers Project was established by the Cairngorms Partnership to help develop an integrated and sustainable management strategy, which balanced economic, social and environmental pressures on rivers in the Partnership area (Walker, 2000). A number of issues identified in its 'Phase I' report were incorporated into the River Spey Catchment Management Plan, launched in 2003. Although a catchment management plan is also under development for the River Dee, no plans have been developed for other rivers originating in the Cairngorms area. Plans for the Spey and Dee catchments may, in any case, be superseded by the development of sub-Basin Management Plans, developed by SEPA through the Water Framework Directive.

Acid deposition.
Surface water acidification has occurred in the Cairngorms area over much of the last century. Since the waters of the Cairngorms are

generally poorly buffered and naturally acidic, they require little additional acid input to cause them to exceed their critical loads. Long-term monitoring at Allt a'Mharcaidh and Lochnagar has revealed differing trends in acid levels at these sites. Regular monitoring by Aberdeen University and others, at Allt a'Mharcaidh and at a number of other sites in the Cairngorms, suggests that sulphate concentrations in stream water is occurring at a rate consistent with declining levels of atmospheric deposition, but that biological recovery is occurring at a slower rate. Similar studies of acidified standing waters, such as Lochnagar, reveal that whilst these habitats are no longer undergoing acidification, recovery is not yet apparent.

Abstraction and flood alleviation. The abstraction of water for hydro-electricity production by British Alcan and Scottish and Southern Energy is the biggest example of abstraction and cross-catchment water transfer in the Cairngorms area. These activities will now be subject to licence controls, as part of the requirement of the Water Environment (Controlled Activities) (Scotland) Regulations 1994. Abstraction for potable water supplies also occurs in several of the catchments originating in the Cairngorms, most notably the River Dee.

Deforestation and land drainage have, over time, increased the risk of flooding in the Cairngorms area and several major floods have occurred in the Spey, Dee and Tay in recent decades. Flood alleviation is a major issue for those individuals or communities affected. Some conflict has arisen between the need to protect sites of nature conservation interest and to alleviate the risk of flood damage, most notably on the River Spey at Insh Marshes and at the Spey-Feshie confluence.

Climate change. The impacts of climate change on aquatic habitats are difficult to predict. As noted above, changes in the distribution and quantity of rain and snow deposition in the Cairngorms may result in temperature increases in some low altitude standing waters, leading to changes in their flora and fauna. Post-glacial relict species and habitats are likely to be lost, and it is possible that ombrotrophic systems, such as blanket bog, will also be lost or damaged.

References

Bailey-Watts, A.E., May, L., Kirika, A. & Lyle, A.A. (1992). *Eutrophication Case Studies: Phase II An Assessment Based on Desk Analysis of Catchments and Summer Limnological Reconnaissances. Volume II Limnological Profiles of the Sites With Special Reference to Eutrophication and Phosphorus.* Report to NCC by the Institute of Terrestrial Ecology: Edinburgh.

Bailey-Watts, A.E., Lyle, A.A., Kirika, A. & Gunn, I.D.M. (1993). *Sensitivity of Lentic Waters.* Report to SOED by the Institute of Terrestrial Ecology: Edinburgh.

Ballentyne, C.K. (1991). Holocene geomorphic activity in the Scottish Highlands. *Scottish Geographical Magazine* 107: 84–98.

Bennion, H., Fluin, J., Appleby, P. & Ferrier, R. (2001). Paleolimnological Investigations of Scottish Freshwater Lochs. Report to the Scottish and Northern Irish Forum for Environmental Research (SNIFFER).

Charter, E. (1988). *Survey of the Spey Valley Lochs, 1985.* Nature Conservancy Council Survey Report No. 16. NCC: Peterborough. 79pp.

Davidson, M.B., Owen, R.P. & MacKay, D.W. (2002). Ecology of Aquatic and Sub-aquatic Habitats. In: Gimingham, C. (ed.), *The Ecology, Land Use and Conservation of the Cairngorms.* Pachard Publishing Ltd.: Chichester. pp. 67–84.

Forestry Commission (2003). *Forests and Water Guidelines.* 4th Edition. Forestry Commission: Edinburgh.

Gibbins, C., Dilks, C., Malcolm, R., Soulsby, C. & Juggins, S. (2001). Invertebrate communities and hydrological variation in Cairngorm mountain streams. *Hydrobiologia* 462: 205–219.

Harriman, R., Gillespie, E. & Morrison, B.R.S. (1992). Factors affecting fish survival in Scottish catchments. In: Mason, B.J. (ed.), *The Surface Waters Acidification Programme.* Cambridge University Press. pp. 343–355.

Jones, V.J., Flower, R.J., Appleby, P.G., Natkanski, J., Richardson, N., Rippey, B., Stevenson, A.C. & Battarbee, R.W. (1993). Paleolimnological evidence for the acidification and atmospheric contamination of lochs in the Cairngorm and Lochnagar areas of Scotland. *Journal of Ecology* 81: 3–24.

Leaper, G. (1999). Biodiversity in the Cairngorms: an assessment of priority habitats and species. Report to the Cairngorms Partnership. 224 pp.

Lyle, A.A. & Smith, I.R. (1994). Standing Waters In: Maitland, P.S., Boon, P.J. & McLusky, D.S. (eds.), *The Fresh Waters of Scotland: A National Resource of International Significance.* Wiley & Sons: Chichester. pp. 35–50.

Malcolm, I.A., Soulsby, C. & Youngson, A.F. (2002). Thermal regime in the hyporheic zone of two contrasting salmonid spawning streams: Ecological and hydrological implications. *Fisheries Management and Ecology* 9: 1–10.

Malcolm, I.A., Soulsby, C., Youngson, A.F. & Petry, J. (2003a). Heterogeneity in ground water-surface water interactions in the hyporheic zone of a salmonid spawning stream. *Hydrological Processes* 17: 601–617.

Malcolm, I.A., Youngson, A.F. & Soulsby, C. (2003b). Survival of salmonid eggs in a degraded gravel-bed stream: effects of groundwater-surface water interactions. *River Research and Applications* 19: 303–316.

Moir, H.J., Soulsby, C. & Youngson, A. (1998). Hydraulic and sedimentary characteristics of habitat utilized by Atlantic salmon for spawning in the Girnock Burn, Scotland. *Fisheries Management and Ecology* 5: 241–254.

Morrison, B.R.S. & Harriman, R. (1992). Fish populations and invertebrates in some headwaters of the Rivers Dee and Spey. *Scottish Fisheries Research Report* No. 53.

Murray, J. & Pullar, L. (eds.) (1910). *Bathymetrical Survey of the Scottish Fresh-Water Lochs.* Vols. 1–6. Challenger Office: Edinburgh.

Palmer, M.A., Bell, S.L. & Butterfield, I. (1992). A botanical classification of standing waters in Great Britain: applications for conservation and monitoring. *Aquatic Conservation: Marine and Freshwater Ecosystems* 2: 125–143.

Patrick, S., Battarbee, R.W., & Jenkins, A. (1996). Monitoring acid waters in the U.K.: An overview of the U.K. acid waters monitoring network and summary of the first interpretative exercise. *Freshwater Biology* 36: 131–150.

Patrick, S.T, Flower, R.J., Appleby, P.G., Oldfield, F., Rippey, B., Stevenson, A.C., Darley, J. & Battarbee, R.W. (1989). *Palaeoecological evaluation of the recent acidification of Lochnagar, Scotland.* Palaeoecology Research Unit, University College London. Research Paper No. 34.

Ratcliffe, D. (1977). *A Nature Conservation Review: the selection of biological sites of national importance to nature conservation in Britain.* 2 Volumes. Cambridge University Press: London.

SEPA (1996). *State of the Environment Report.* SEPA: Stirling.

SEPA (1999). *Improving Scotland's Water.* SEPA: Stirling.

SEPA (2001 *et seq.*). Water Quality Classification. (website: www.sepa.org.uk/data/classification/index.htm).

Shilland, E.M., Monteith, D.T., Smith, J. & Beaumont W.R.C. (2003). UKAWMN Summary of Data for Year 15 (2002–2003). Report to Defra (Contract EPG 1/3/160) and DENI (Contract CON 4/4 (38)).

Smart, R.P., Soulsby, C., Neal, C., Wade, A., Cresser, M.S., Billett, M.F. Langan, S.J., Edwards, A.C., Jarvie, H.P. & Owen, R. (1998). Factors regulating the spatial and temporal distribution of solute concentrations in a major river system in NE Scotland. *Science of the Total Environment* 221: 93–110.

Smart, R.P., Soulsby, C., Cresser, M.S., Wade, A.J., Townend, J., Billett, M.F. & Langan, S. (2001). Riparian zone influence on stream water chemistry at different spatial scales: A GIS-based modelling approach, an example for the Dee, NE Scotland. *Science of the Total Environment* 280: 173–193.

Soulsby, C., Chen, M., Ferrier, R.C., Helliwell, R.C., Jenkins, A. & Harriman, R. (1998a). Hydrogeochemistry of shallow groundwater in an upland Scottish catchment. *Hydrological Processes* 12: 1111–1127.

Soulsby, C., Malcolm, R., Helliwell, R., Ferrier, R.C. & Jenkins, A. (2000). Isotope hydrology of the Allt a'Mharcaidh catchment, Cairngorms, Scotland: Implications for hydrological pathways and residence times. *Hydrological Processes* 14: 747–762.

Soulsby, C., Moir, H., Chen, M. & Gibbins, C. (1998b). Impact of groundwater development on Atlantic salmon spawning habitat in a Scottish river. In: Wheater, H. & Kirby, C. (eds.), *Hydrology in a Changing Environment: Hydrological and Ecological Interactions.* J. Wiley & Sons Ltd.: Chichester. pp. 3–16.

Soulsby, C., Rodgers, P., Smart, R., Dawson, J. & Dunn, S. (2003). A tracer-based assessment of hydrological pathways at different spatial scales in a mesoscale Scottish catchment. *Hydrological Processes* 17: 759–777.

Soulsby, C., Rodgers, P.J., Petry, J., Hannah, D.M., Malcolm, I.A. & Dunn, S.M. (2004). Using tracers to upscale flow path understanding in mesoscale mountainous catchments: Two examples from Scotland. *Journal of Hydrology* 291: 174–196.

Soulsby, C., Turnbull, D., Langan, S.J. & Owen, R. (1997). Reversibility of stream acidification in the Cairngorm region of Scotland. *Journal of Hydrology* 195: 291–311.

Soulsby, C., Malcolm, R., Gibbins, C. & Dilks, C. (2002). Seasonality, water quality trends and biological responses in four streams in the Cairngorm mountains, Scotland. *Hydrology and Earth System Sciences* 5: 433–450.

Vives, I., Grimalt, J.O., Catalan, J., Rosseland, B.O. & Battarbee, R.W. (2004). Influence of altitude and age in the accumulation of organochlorine; compounds in fish from high mountain lakes. *Environmental Science & Technology* 38: 690–698.

Wade, A.J., Neal, C., Soulsby, C., Langan, S.J. & Smart, R.P. (2001). On modelling the effects of afforestation on acidification in heterogeneous catchments at different spatial and temporal scales. *Journal of Hydrology* 250: 149–169.

Walker, S. (2000). Cairngorms Rivers Project: Phase I Report. Report to the Cairngorms Rivers Task Force and Cairngorms Partnership. 69 pp.

Yang, H., Rose, N.L., Battarbee, R.W. & Monteith, D. (2002a). Trace metal distribution in the sediments of the whole lake basin for Lochnagar, Scotland: A palaeolimnological assessment. *Hydrobiologia* 479: 51–61.

Yang, H., Rose, N.L., Battarbee, R.W. & Boyle, J.F. (2002b). Mercury and lead budgets for Lochnagar, a Scottish mountain lake and its catchment. *Environmental Science & Technology* 36: 1383–1388.

Additional reading

Brown, I.M. & Clapperton, C.M. (2002). The Physical Geography. In: Gimingham, C. (ed.), *The Ecology, Land Use and Conservation of the Cairngorms*. Packard Publishing Ltd.: Chichester. pp. 8–22.

Gardiner, R. & Mackay, D.W. (2002). Fish Populations. In: Gimingham, C. (ed.), *The Ecology, Land Use and Conservation of the Cairngorms*. Packard Publishing Ltd.: Chichester. pp. 148–159.

Gimingham, C. (2002). *The Ecology, Land Use and Conservation of the Cairngorms*. Packard Publishing Ltd.: Chichester.

Juggins, S., Flower, R.J. & Battarbee, R.W. (1996). Palaeolimnological evidence for recent chemical and biological changes in U.K. acid waters monitoring network sites. *Freshwater Biology* 36: 203–219.

Smith, I.R. & Lyle, A.A. (1979). *Distribution of Freshwaters in Great Britain*. Institute of Terrestrial Ecology, Cambridge.

Smith, I.R. & Lyle, A.A. (1994). Running Waters In: Maitland, P.S., Boon P.J. & McLusky D.S. (eds.), *The Fresh Waters of Scotland: A National resource of International Significance*. J. Wiley & Sons Ltd.: Chichester. pp. 19–34.

Soulsby, C. & Dunn, S.M. (2003) Towards integrating tracer studies in conceptual rainfall-runoff models: recent insights from a sub-arctic catchment in the Cairngorm mountains, Scotland. *Hydrological Processes* 17: 403–416.

Soulsby, C., Turnbull, D., Langan, S.J., Owen, R. & Hirst, D. (1995). Long-term trends in stream chemistry and biology in northeast Scotland: Evidence for recovery. *Water, Air, & Soil Pollution* 85: 689–694.

10. FENS AND LOWLAND RAISED BOGS

Colin Wells

Introduction

Fens and Bogs are both types of *mire*, that is to say, peat-forming ecosystems. They are distributed widely across the wetter parts of the United Kingdom, in both uplands and lowlands. This chapter deals with those types occurring predominantly at low altitudes (floodplain fens, basin fens and raised bogs). Their higher altitude counterparts (soligenous flushes and blanket bogs) are described in Chapter 6.

Britain's cool temperate maritime climate and consequent high average rainfall help ensure that precipitation exceeds evaporation for most of the year in the north and west, encouraging peat formation in areas of impeded drainage. Many mires began to form in wet, low-lying depressions around 4–8,000 years ago, although some small basin mires contain organic deposits dating back to the end of late Devensian glacial period, around 12–13,000 years ago.

Before the era of intensive agricultural reclamation, beginning in the late 18th century, large areas of the lowlands in north-west Britain were occupied by raised bogs, while areas of impeded drainage associated with rivers and streams supported fens. Subsequent human activity has vastly reduced the extent of bog and fen vegetation. An indication of the scale of the habitat decline is provided by Lindsay & Immirzi (1996), who suggest that the area of undisturbed lowland raised bog might have diminished by around 90% (from about 95,000 ha to perhaps 6,000 ha at the present time). The precision of these figures must be treated with some caution as they are based on potentially unreliable proxy indicators, including geological and soil survey maps of peat soils, rather than extensive field survey.

Historically, most of this decline is attributable to agricultural intensification, followed by afforestation and commercial peat extraction. Future losses are most likely to be the result of the gradual desiccation of bogs damaged by a range of drainage activities and/or a general lowering of groundwater tables.

Within the Cairngorms area, lowland raised bogs, by definition, are always likely to have been uncommon, thanks to the area's predominantly upland topography. Instead, most acid, ombrotrophic mires that occur are of the blanket bog type. Fen communities have always been significant components of the landscape, however, due to the major river systems of the Spey and Dee. The habitat has shown dynamic changes in extent over time, both positive and negative, due to periods of attempted reclamation followed by the abandonment of drainage. Currently, fens in the Cairngorms represent 10–25% of the UK resource (Table 10.1). The Insh Marshes, especially, are nationally significant. They currently represent the largest contiguous area of floodplain 'poor-fens'[1] in the UK and are notable for supporting large populations of important wildfowl, insects, plants and mammals, such as Otter *Lutra lutra*.

Habitat definitions

Fens and Raised Bogs are the two major divisions of peat-forming systems normally to be found occupying almost permanently saturated lowland terrestrial wetlands. The difference between them lies in their predominant mode of irrigation. Whereas the vegetation of raised bogs depends almost entirely on atmospheric precipitation for nutrients (an ombrotrophic mire) and their peats tend to be predominantly acidic, fen vegetation is supplied by relatively nutrient-rich groundwater (a minerotrophic mire) and grows in

---

Wells, C. (2006). Fens and lowland raised bogs. In: Shaw, P. & Thompson, D.B.A. (eds.). *The Nature of the Cairngorms: Diversity in a changing environment*. The Stationery Office. pp. 133-143.

---

[1] 'Poor-fens' occur where the water source is derived from base-poor rocks such as granites. They are characterised by short vegetation with a high proportion of *Sphagnum* bog mosses and acid water (pH 5 or lower). They are differentiated from 'Rich-fens', which are fed by mineral-enriched calcareous waters (pH 5 or more) and a vegetation normally characterised by tall sedges, grasses and hypnoid mosses.

A mosaic of wetland plant communities stretching along the floodplain of the Spey, Insh Marshes are, for the most part, not a 'marsh' but a complex of fens; the largest contiguous area of flood-plain 'poor-fens' in the UK.

Photo: *L. Campbell*

Table 10.1. The estimated area of fen and lowland raised bog in the Cairngorms.

Habitat	Estimated area in the Cairngorms area (ha)	Estimated area in Cairngorms National Park (ha)	Percentage of UK resource
Fen	500-1000	500-1000	10-25%
Raised bog	16	-	<5%

a less acidic or calcareous peat substrate. This results in two distinct types of vegetation. Fens are generally characterised by sedges, hypnoid mosses and tall herbs and grasses, while raised bogs are dominated by *Sphagnum* bog-mosses, cotton-grasses and dwarf shrubs such as heathers.

In strict floristic terms, fen vegetation also generically encompasses *Reedbeds* and *Swamp*, which are differentiated into separate habitat categories under the JNCC's 'key habitats' classification. For the purposes of clarity, these two habitats are encompassed within the broad umbrella term 'Fen' in this report. The term 'Marsh' is often also included in broad wetland habitat reporting categories used by agencies such as SNH (e.g. 'Fen, marsh and swamp.'). In ecological terms, a 'Marsh' refers to vegetation on periodically saturated ground, which remains rooted in mineral soil, i.e. it is not a peat-forming system, or mire, like fens and bogs. The situation is further complicated by the use of the term 'Grazing Marsh' by the Biodiversity Steering Group, a definition based on NVC communities found in England and which refers to periodically inundated pasture or meadow with species-rich ditches maintaining water levels. Although there are considerable areas of marshy grassland in the floodplains of the Spey and the Dee, it seems that there may not be any habitat in the Cairngorms area that exactly fits this definition. Because of this ambiguity, 'Marshes' are excluded from this report, although it is probable that variants of 'marsh vegetation', important especially for wading birds and wildfowl, form a minor part of some of the fen locations discussed here.

Developmentally, fens and bogs are closely related; most raised bogs have developed over fen systems, the surface vegetation changing to bog communities once the level of peat accumulation had raised it above the influence of ground water. Thus, given enough time (in the order of perhaps 1,000 years), it is likely that many present-day fen systems might eventually evolve into bogs if left undisturbed. Conversely, some present-day fens are derived from old peat cuttings in bogs, which have lowered the peat surface back to a level where it is once more subject to groundwater influence.

Major fen complexes are further distinguished according to their hydromorphological characteristics. *Floodplain mires* occupy permanently saturated floodplains, while *basin mires* are found in waterlogged basins with slow water flows. Fens are also subdivided according to the degree to which their water tends towards alkalinity or acidity. The less base-rich systems ('poor-fens') are generally less species-rich than their more calcareous cousins ('rich-fens'). Most types present within the Cairngorms area can be classified as 'poor-fens.'

The principal definitions of bog and fen habitat under different statutory frameworks are given in Annex 10.1.

Important areas

Fens
1. Insh Marshes. Although traditionally and colloquially known as the Insh Marshes, the mosaic of wetland plant communities stretching for 5 km along the floodplain of the Spey between Kingussie and Kincraig (Figure 10.1) is, for the most part, not a 'marsh' in the technical ecological sense of the word[2] but a complex of fens. As such, the site comprises the most significant area of fen habitat within the Cairngorms, both in terms of size and national importance (Table 10.2).

Despite a long history of drainage initiatives and the construction of a railway line across part of the site, the wetland has recovered well and represents an unusually large area of semi-natural habitats, considered to be 'the most important tract of flood-plain mire in northern Britain' (Ratcliffe, 1977).

Covering a total area of about 900 ha, the complex supports the most expansive contiguous area of 'Transition Mire' (*sensu* JNCC) vegetation communities in the UK (Fojt, 1988). The site has considerable habitat diversity, with a variety of other fen, swamp and wet wood communities occurring. Part of the Marshes also forms a home for the String Sedge *Carex chordorrhiza*, (found at only one other site in Scotland; Chapter 14), as well as other rare species such as Cowbane *Cicuta virosa*, Narrow Small-reed *Calamagrostis stricta*, Least Water-lily *Nuphar pumila*, Awlwort *Subalaria aquatica* and Shady Horsetail *Equisetum pratense*. Also present in abundance is Water Sedge *Carex aquatilis*; a very local northern species.

As a consequence, Insh Marshes is designated as an SSSI, as well as a National Nature Reserve. It has also been selected as an SAC, on the grounds of its 'Transition Mire' communities. In addition, Insh Marshes forms a Ramsar site and a Special Protection Area. Around half of the wetland is owned and managed by the RSPB for its bird interest and for the conservation of fen vegetation.

2. Alvie. The other significant area of fen associated with the Spey catchment within the Cairngorms occurs at Alvie. This SSSI encompasses a mosaic of habitats, including wet woodland and three freshwater lochs (lochs Alvie, Beag and the Bogach), notable for their mycological, entomological and ornithological value. In contrast to Insh (where all the communities can be characterised as occupying 'floodplain mire'), the Alvie fen vegetation occupies a series of basin mires. As yet, no systematic survey work relating to the fen communities has been undertaken at this site, and so current estimates of both community composition and their area remain approximate, having been derived from aerial photographs and qualitative ground observations. Thus, although the total area of the SSSI is 343 ha, the exact area occupied by fen remains undetermined. However, up to 20 ha of Transition Mire occurs in association with the open water bodies.

The Dee flood plain and Quoich wetlands once comprised a complex of wetland habitats. Attempts are underway to recreate some of the former fen interest by ditch blocking. If successful, this will add considerably to the area of poor-fen present in the Cairngorms area.
Photo: *L. Gill*

[2] True 'marshes' comprise periodically inundated ground in which the vegetation is rooted in mineral soil, rather than in peat.

Figure 10.1.   Important fen and lowland raised bog sites.

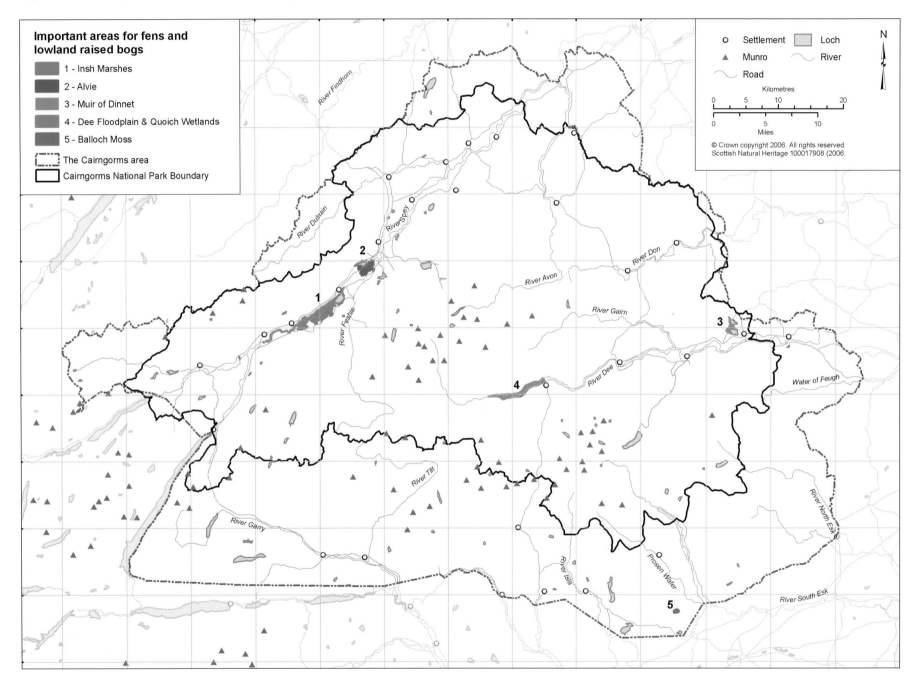

Important areas for fens and lowland raised bogs
1 - Insh Marshes
2 - Alvie
3 - Muir of Dinnet
4 - Dee Floodplain & Quoich Wetlands
5 - Balloch Moss
The Cairngorms area
Cairngorms National Park Boundary

Table 10.2. Important fen and lowland raised bog sites in the Cairngorms area.

Area name	Habitats	Area	Percentage within National Park	Partly/wholly within:		
				SSSI	NNR	SAC
1. Insh Marshes	Fen, swamp	c. 900 ha	100%	wholly	wholly	wholly
2. Alvie	Fen, swamp	c. 20 ha	100%	wholly	-	-
3. Muir of Dinnet	Fen, swamp	c. 50 ha	100%	partly	partly	-
4. Dee Floodplain & Quoich Wetlands	Wet grassland, fen	c. 200 ha	100%	-	-	-
5. Balloch Moss	Raised bog	c. 16 ha	0%	wholly	-	-

3. Muir of Dinnet. The Muir of Dinnet forms a diverse range of habitats in which fens blend with freshwater lochs, heathland and pine and birch woodland in a moraine-strewn topography partly enclosed by low granite hills. The fen communities occupy basin and valley mires surrounding the lochs, and comprise a mosaic of reedbeds, transition mire and carr woodland. Reedbeds alone are estimated to cover approximately 19 ha of the Dinnet site, although precise figures for the extent of all fen communities are currently unavailable. Much of the wetland area is designated as both SSSI and NNR, although there are also some unmanaged fens which fall outside the statutorily protected zone, which are especially valuable for their ornithological interest (Francis, 1999) (Chapter 18). Muir of Dinnet is also an SAC, on which transition mire and raised bogs are qualifying features.

4. Dee Floodplain and Quoich Wetlands currently comprise 205 ha of predominantly rank wet *Molinia* grassland stretching from Mar Lodge to Invercauld near Braemar. Formerly a complex of wetland habitats, including bog and fen, a history of partial drainage and use for rough grazing has degraded the site, reducing much of its conservation interest. The RSPB, in association with SNH and the estates, however, is currently undertaking a long-term initiative to attempt to recreate some of the former fen interest by ditch blocking. This is designed to encourage the re-wetting of much of the area and, if successful, will add considerably to the total area of poor-fen present in the Cairngorms area.

Other fen sites
Loch of Kinnordy and Loch an Leathain contain areas of reedbed and fen of importance to wildfowl. Other poorly-defined areas of wetland vegetation occur adjacent to Loch Vaa, Loch Morlich, Loch an Eilein, Loch Pityoulish, Loch Muick, Loch Callater and Loch Garry. Detailed surveys are required before the exact nature of possible fen or bog components of these sites can be determined.

Raised Bogs

5. Balloch Moss. Raised bogs are largely absent from the Cairngorms, with most ombrotrophic peats being represented by blanket mires (see Chapter 6). An exception occurs at Balloch, Angus, where a small (16 ha) mire exists. Although the central section of this site appears to retain untruncated peat stratigraphy, the peripheral areas have been cut for peat, which has allowed the peat surface to become desiccated, resulting in the modification of characteristic raised bog communities. Nevertheless, relict bog vegetation remains around wetter hollows in the central part of the site and remediation measures are being attempted in the form of ditch blocking. The site is designated as an SSSI.

Recent research and survey findings

Most of the recent research relating to lowland wetlands in the Cairngorms has taken place at Insh Marshes. The last decade has seen a considerable expansion of interest in the fen complex, mainly concerned with gaining a sound descriptive vegetative baseline and obtaining information relevant to bird conservation. Other biological groups have not been neglected however, and baseline surveys of insects and fish have all been carried out in recent years. The major pieces of research are summarised below.

Vegetation studies
National Vegetation Classification mapping. Building on original surveys by Fojt (1988), Wood (1989) and Rieley and Page (1991), Loizou (1997) undertook a detailed, systematic survey of the vegetation of most of the Insh Marshes, using the National Vegetation Classification (NVC) scheme. This established a baseline on which future monitoring and management initiatives could be based.

Willow scrub encroachment. Hodge (1993) investigated concerns that willow scrub encroachment might have been causing deterioration of the conservation value of parts of the Insh Marshes. The study compared evidence from a time-series of aerial photographs dating from 1946 and concluded that significant scrub encroachment had occurred after 1964. The report recommended scrub control measures, which were subsequently implemented (commencing in 1995).

String Sedge. Cowie and Sydes (1995) focused on the status, distribution, ecology and management of Insh Marshes' best-known rarity, the String Sedge *Carex chordorrhiza* (see Chapter 14).

Long-term monitoring. Maier (in prep.) has initiated long-term monitoring of vegetation and species for the RSPB, designed to chart the effects of management and hydroseral succession on habitat quality in the Insh Marshes, using a 5–10 year sampling interval. Adopting a pragmatic approach, Maier modified NVC communities to produce 24 simplified habitat types, whose distribution was mapped across the site. Thirty-four permanent transects were implemented, along with 41 randomly chosen habitat polygons. Fixed-point photography locations have also been selected.

Initial results of the early monitoring work, based on partial comparison with earlier data, suggest that scrub clearance in the Insh Marshes has promoted the area of open fen, while areas of scarce *Carex lasiocarpa*-dominated communities have increased at the expense of *Phalaris arundinacea* communities.

Other studies

The last decade has seen numerous studies related to the bird interest of Insh Marshes, together with surveys of dragonflies, beetles, butterflies and moths, spiders, aquatic invertebrates and fish. Their findings have been published in Maitland (1991), Baines (1992), Bhatia (1992), Breslin (1993), Prescott (1993), Tunmore (1993), Smith and Smith (1994), Bridge (1996), Langridge (1996) and French (1997).

Recreation impact and flood defence studies

Hill *et al.* (1987) have studied the effects of water-based recreation on waterfowl on Loch Insh. Recent studies relevant to the role of the Insh Marshes as downstream flood protection for Speyside include those of Gilvear (1994), Johnson *et al.* (1991) and Stubbs (1991).

Trends

Historically, fens and bogs have suffered nationally and locally from drainage intended to improve grazing for livestock, to help convert peatland into agricultural use, or to aid peat cutting. Because of its reliance on groundwater, fen vegetation is also particularly sensitive to changes in run-off from agricultural land, both in terms of volume and chemistry. Problems may be caused by the eutrophication of water sources, which can prompt undesirable changes in the composition of the plant communities. Another widespread challenge to fen conservation has been presented by changes to their traditional land management. The reduction of summer grazing regimes, for example, has led to the advance of scrub woodland across many sites, shading out light-dependent species, and thereby reducing biodiversity.

The Cairngorms' most significant site, Insh Marshes, is managed in ways sympathetic to its conservation interests, thanks to its part ownership by the RSPB and management as an SPA, SSSI and NNR. Current monitoring initiatives, together with experimentation on management techniques, mean that the conservation effort at this site is considerably advanced compared to that on many fen sites in the UK. Examples of ongoing 'experiments' with management include scrub removal, grazing controls and 'topping' (the physical removal of rank vegetation in order to promote plant species diversity).

The fens at Alvie and Dinnet have not enjoyed the same degree of management attention, although both are now subject to SNH's Site Condition Monitoring programme, designed to identify the state of the ecological health of habitats within SSSIs. However, an initiative to try to reverse the trend towards eutrophication at Loch Davan, which supports much fen vegetation, has been undertaken. Some concern has been expressed over potential eutrophication effects at Alvie, thanks to its vulnerable position surrounded by farmland (Bayfield & Conroy, 1996; Leaper, 1997), although evidence remains largely observational or anecdotal at present, and any effects remain to be quantified.

Potentially one of the most important initiatives relating to the future of Cairngorms wetlands is that being undertaken by the RSPB at Quoich Wetlands, Dee Floodplain near Braemar, described above. Acting in collaboration with the National Trust for Scotland, Invercauld Estate and SNH, the RSPB are attempting wetland recreation on the Dee Floodplain by blocking drainage dikes and raising the general water level in an area that was formerly fen (Francis & Urquhart, 1996). If successful, this could provide a model for similar initiatives elsewhere. As well as helping to re-create fen communities, this initiative may also provide improved nesting habitat for wading birds.

The RSPB has undertaken scrub removal to restore fen communities at Loch of Kinnordy, an operation which also includes the removal of incipient marginal fen from the loch itself, to prevent infilling of open water. The overall objective of this work is to achieve a balance for breeding and wintering birds.

The number of lowland raised bogs within the Cairngorms is unlikely ever to have been large, due to the topographical characteristics of the region. Nevertheless, the most significant site remaining, Balloch Moss, has suffered from much the same damage as most UK lowland bogs; namely partial drainage and peat cutting around its periphery. This has resulted in surface desiccation and a concomitant loss or reduction in its characteristic flora, fauna and structure. As in all bog SSSIs however, Balloch is now subject to Site Condition Monitoring in order to assess the conservation quality of the site. Attempts are being made to improve this by raising the water table by means of ditch blocking.

Further positive trends for the habitats include the fact that 'Active raised bogs' and several types of fen are priority habitats under the EC Habitats Directive. Bogs and fens are also capable of benefiting from carefully targeted and designed agri-environment incentives. Whole-catchment planning for water resources and agriculture are especially important for bogs and fens and, in their catchment and shoreline management plans, SEPA has been encouraged to incorporate fen and bog protection, management or creation. In the near future it seems likely that the forthcoming EC Water Framework Directive will require a common approach to protecting surface- and groundwater across Europe. This might provide an opportunity to place integrated catchment management in a statutory framework, which will require a multi-sectoral, integrated approach to managing water quality, quantity and physical habitat in the Cairngorms. A catchment management plan has been developed for the Spey (SEPA, 2003), and is under development for the Dee.

Conservation issues

Fens
The relatively small total area of the habitat means that there may be critically small population sizes of several key species dependent on it. Due to their nature as dynamic semi-natural systems, fens often require active management in order to maintain the open plant communities prized for their high biodiversity. Without such intervention (e.g. mowing, grazing, burning, peat cutting, scrub clearance), natural succession may lead to fen carr woodland occupying sites, and shading out light-demanding species. In addition to such actions, other factors that can affect this habitat type include the following.

- Loss of area by drainage and conversion to intensive agriculture.

- Water abstraction from aquifers drying or reducing spring line flows and generally lowering water tables.

- A vulnerability to nutritional enrichment from agricultural or industrial pollution. (The catchment of Loch Insh, for example, receives treated sewage effluent from Newtonmore, Kingussie, Lynchat and Insh).

Another key issue is the lack of a comprehensive inventory of fens in the Cairngorms; a characteristic shared with the rest of Scotland.

Bogs
In the past, agricultural drainage, afforestation and peat extraction have been the major threats to lowland raised bog systems which, in some areas, have also been targeted as priority sites for landfill developments. Great strides have been made in combating these threats in the past decade, but the legacy of this history continues to damage many sites. The indirect effects of drainage around their perimeter, for example, may limit the 'rewetting' potential of many sites. The direct effects of existing forestry plantations on deep peat also have a continuing impact on adjacent peatland, as successive rotations dry out these neighbouring areas and act as an invasive seed source. Other key concerns include the following.

- *Dereliction*. Bogs drained either directly or indirectly can degenerate without active intervention. The conservation potential of such areas is frequently constrained by complex tenure and a lack of management resources.

- *Livestock and game management* (such as Pheasant rearing and rough grazing). This is frequently accompanied by drainage, trampling, burning and surface contamination with feed and droppings.

Sources

Consultation and discussions with Ian Francis and Carl Mitchell (RSPB) were extremely valuable in locating a number of important unpublished pieces of research, and for general discussion of the status and distribution of the habitats in the Cairngorms area. This review was, nevertheless, constrained by the lack of a detailed systematic inventory of fen habitats for the Cairngorms. Estimates of area and descriptions of the type and condition of fen vegetation expressed here therefore necessarily remain approximate in most areas outside of the Insh Marshes complex. To a lesser degree, the same caveat applies to data for raised bogs, as the information relating to lowland peatland contained in Lindsay & Immirzi (1996) has been found to be unreliable in many parts of Scotland.

Habitat Action Plans were consulted for *Coastal and Floodplain Grazing Marsh* (http://www.ukbap.org.uk/UKPlans.aspx?ID=9), *Lowland Wetland, Lowland raised bog, Fens* and *Reedbeds* (www.jncc.gov.uk/habitats/agency/low_wet.htm).

References

Baines, M. (1992). *A beetle survey of the Insh Marshes RSPB Reserve*. Report for RSPB Scotland. RSPB: Edinburgh.

Bayfield, N.G. & Conroy, J.W.H. (eds.) (1996). *The Cairngorm Assets*. The Cairngorms Partnership: Grantown-on-Spey.

Bhatia, Z. (1992). *Breeding Waterfowl Survey, River Spey/Insh Marshes SSSI 1992*. Unpublished report. RSPB: Edinburgh.

Breslin, J.J. (1993). *Survey of the Aquatic Invertebrates and Fish Communities in the Insh Marshes Lochans*. Report for SNH by Department of Zoology, University of Aberdeen: Aberdeen.

Bridge, D. (1996). *Insh Marshes Whooper Swan Survey – Winter 1995/96*. Unpublished report. RSPB: Edinburgh.

Commission of the European Communities, Directorate-General for Environment, Nuclear Safety and Civil Protection (1991). *The Corine Biotypes Manual*. Office for Official Publications of the European Communities: Luxembourg.

Cowie, N.R. & Sydes, C. (1995). *Status, distribution, ecology and management of string sedge Carex chordorrhiza*. Unpublished report. SNH: Perth.

Fojt, W. (1988). *A vegetation survey of the Insh Marshes SSSI*. Unpublished Report. NCC: Peterborough.

Francis, I. (1999). *Confidential report to RSPB*. RSPB: Aberdeen.

Francis, I. & Urquhart, U. (1996). *The Dee Floodplain and Quoich Wetland, Braemar*. RSPB: Aberdeen.

French, P. (1997). *Breeding Success of Lapwing* Vanellus vanellus *in part of Strathspey*. SOC Project Report. SOC: Edinburgh.

Gilvear, D.J. (1994). *Hydrological Survey of the Insh Marshes*. Department of Environmental Science, University of Stirling.

Hill, D., Bloor, P. & Lambton, S. (1987). *The Effects of Water-based Recreation on Waterfowl on Loch Insh, Speyside*. RSPB Reserves Ecology, Scotland. RSPB: Edinburgh.

Hodge, J.G.W. (1993). *Scrub encroachment at Insh Marshes Nature Reserve*. RSPB Reserves Ecology, Scotland. RSPB: Edinburgh.

Johnson, R.C., Piper, B.S., Acreman, M.C. & Gilman, K. (1991). *Flood Alleviation in Upper Strathspey – Modelling and Environment Study, Vol. I*. Report prepared for the Nature Conservancy Council for Scotland by the Institute of Hydrology. NCCS: Edinburgh.

Langridge, A. (1996). *The Status of the Breeding Population of Goldeneye* Bucephala clangula *in Scotland from 1974–1995*. RSPB: Edinburgh.

Leaper, G. (1997). *Biodiversity of the Cairngorms Partnership Area*. Commissioned Report for the Cairngorms Partnership. Cairngorms Partnership: Grantown.

Lindsay, R. & Immirzi, P. (1996). *An inventory of lowland raised bogs in Great Britain*. SNH Research, Survey and Monitoring Report, 78. SNH: Perth.

Loizou, T. (1997). *Report on the Plant Communities of part of the Insh Marshes SSSI for Scottish Natural Heritage*. Commissioned report for SNH. SNH: Perth.

Maier, R. (in prep.). *Long-term vegetation monitoring of the Insh Marshes RSPB Reserve*. Commissioned report for RSPB. RSPB: Edinburgh.

Maitland, P.S. (1991). *Assessment of Impact on Aquatic fauna – Supporting Report SR2, Flood Alleviation in Upper Strathspey – Modelling and Environmental Study Vol II*. Report prepared for the Nature Conservancy Council for Scotland by the Institute of Hydrology. NCCS: Edinburgh.

Nature Conservancy Council (1989). *Guidelines for the Selection of Biological SSSIs*. NCC: Peterborough.

Prescott, T. (1993). *Macrolepidoptera of Insh Marshes Nature Reserve – 1991*. RSPB: Sandy, Bedfordshire.

Ratcliffe, D. (1977). *A Nature Conservation Review*. Nature Conservancy Council: Peterborough.

Rieley, J. & Page, S. (1991). Terrestrial Plant Communities: A Botanical Description and Evaluation. In: Johnson, R.C., Piper, B.S., Acreman, M.C. & Gilman, K. (eds.), *Flood alleviation in Upper Strathspey – modelling and environmental study*. Vol. II Supporting Reports. Report for NCC Scotland by the Institute of Hydrology. NCCS: Edinburgh.

SEPA (2003). *River Spey: Towards a Catchment Management Plan.* http://www.sepa.org.uk/pdf/publications/technical/spey/speyreport.pdf.

Smith, E.M. & Smith, R.W.J. (1994). *Odonata at Insh Marshes.* RSPB: Edinburgh.

Stubbs, A. (1991). *Terrestrial Entomology – Supporting report SR4, Flood Alleviation in Upper Strathspey – Modelling and Environment Study, Vol. II.* Report prepared for the Nature Conservancy Council for Scotland by the Institute of Hydrology. NCCS: Edinburgh.

Tunmore, N. (1993). *Moth trapping at Insh Marshes Nature Reserve.* RSPB: Edinburgh.

Wood, D. (1989). *A Vegetation survey of Insh Marshes RSPB Reserve, 1988–1989.* Reserves Ecology Department, Reserves Division. RSPB: Sandy.

Additional reading

Alexander, G., Leaper, G., Francis, I. & Tulloch, M. (1998). *Biodiversity in North-East Scotland.* NE Scotland Local Biodiversity Action Plan Committee: Aberdeen.

Cosgrove, P. (2002). *The Cairngorms Local Biodiversity Action Plan.* Cairngorms Partnership: Grantown-on-Spey.

Fojt, W., Kirby, K., McLean, I., Palmer, M. & Pienkowski, M. (1987). *The national importance of the Insh Marshes, Scotland.* Chief Scientist's Directorate, unpublished report. NCC: Peterborough.

Gimingham, C.H. (ed.) (2002). *The Ecology, Land Use and Conservation of the Cairngorms.* Packard Publishing: Chichester.

Grampian Regional Council (1987). *A Natural Habitat Survey of Grampian.* Grampian Regional Council: Aberdeen.

Hepburn, L.V. & Brookes, B.S. (1997). *Mar Lodge Pinewoods National Vegetation Survey.* Unpublished report. SNH: Perth.

JNCC (2002). *Habitat Action Plan: Coastal and Floodplain Grazing Marsh, Lowland Wetland, Lowland raised bog, Fens, Reedbeds.* http://www.ukbap.org.uk/GenPageText.aspx?id=95].

SNH (2002). *Lowland Raised Bog Inventory.* www.snh.org.uk/Peatlands/wc-lrbi.htm .

Annex 10.1.

Statutory definitions of fens and raised bogs

SSSI Guidelines

Fens (also termed 'minerotrophic' mires) occur in waterlogged situations such as basins, valleys and flood plains where they receive nutrients from the surrounding catchment, as well as from rainfall.

Bogs ('ombrotrophic' mires) occur in areas where water inputs (almost exclusively from precipitation) have a low nutrient content and the local climate is generally cool and damp, or where the rainfall is sufficient to maintain the ground surface in a waterlogged condition. These can form above fen peats. Bog vegetation is characterised by acid tolerant plant communities in which the genus *Sphagnum* usually is, or has been, a significant component.

Source: NCC (1989)

The EC Habitats Directive (*Natura 2000*)

Fens. The EC Habitats Directive uses several definitions for fen types, encompassing variation in broad habitat type across Europe. The most relevant to the Cairngorms is as follows.

Transition Mire and Quaking Bog. 'Peat-forming communities developed at the oligotrophic to mesotrophic water surfaces, with characteristics intermediate between soligenous and ombrogenous types. They present a large and diverse range of plant communities. In large peaty systems, the most prominent communities are swaying swards, floating carpets or quaking mires formed by medium-sized or small sedges, associated with *Sphagnum* or brown mosses. They are generally accompanied by aquatic and amphibious communities.'

Raised bogs. 'Active Raised Bogs: Acid bogs, ombrotrophic, poor in mineral nutrients, sustained mainly by rainwater, with a water level generally higher than the surrounding water table, with perennial vegetation dominated by colourful Sphagna hummocks allowing for the growth of the bog. Typically, pools may be present in western UK, Ireland, Finland and Sweden. The term 'active' must be taken to mean still supporting a significant area of vegetation that is normally peat forming, but bogs where active peat formation is temporarily at a standstill, such as after a fire or during a natural climatic cycle e.g. a period of drought, are also included.'

Source: Commission of the European Communities, Directorate-General for Environment, Nuclear Safety and Civil Protection (1991).

JNCC: Habitat Action Plan

Fens. 'Fens are peatlands which receive water and nutrients from the soil, rock and ground water as well as from rainfall: they are minerotrophic. Two types of fen can broadly be distinguished: topogenous and soligenous. Topogenous fens are those where water movements in the peat or soil are generally vertical. They include basin fens and floodplain fen. Soligenous fens, where water movements are predominantly lateral, include mires associated with springs, rills and flushes in the uplands, valley mires, springs and flushes in the lowlands, trackways and ladder fens in blanket bogs and laggs of raised bogs.

Fens can also be described as 'poor-fens' or 'rich-fens'. Poor-fens, where the water is derived from base-poor rock such as sandstones and granites occur mainly in the uplands, or are associated with lowland heaths. They are characterised by short vegetation with a high proportion of bog mosses *Sphagnum* spp. and acid water (pH of 5 or less). Rich-fens, are fed by mineral-enriched calcareous waters (pH 5 or more) and are mainly confined to the lowlands and where there are localised occurrences of base-rich rocks such as limestone in the uplands. Fen habitats support a diversity of plant and animal communities. Some can contain up to 550 species of higher plants, a third of our native plant species; up to and occasionally more than half the UK's species of dragonflies, several thousand other insect species, as well as being an important habitat for a range of aquatic beetles.'

Bogs. 'Lowland raised bogs are peatland ecosystems which develop primarily, but not exclusively, in lowland areas such as the head of estuaries, along river flood-plains and in topographic depressions. In such locations drainage may be impeded by a high groundwater table, or by low permeability substrata such as estuarine, glacial or lacustrine clays. The resultant waterlogging provides anaerobic conditions which slow down the decomposition of plant material which in turn leads to an accumulation of peat. Continued accrual of peat elevates the bog surface above regional groundwater levels to form a gently curving dome from which the term 'raised' bog is derived. The thickness of the peat mantle varies considerably but can exceed 12 m. In the UK lowland raised bogs are a particular feature of cool, rather humid regions such as the north-west lowlands of England, the central and north-east lowlands of Scotland, Wales and Northern Ireland, but remnants also occur in some southern and eastern localities, for example Somerset, South Yorkshire and Fenland.'

Source: www.jncc.gov.uk/habitats/agency/low_wet.htm

11. FUNGI

Elizabeth M. Holden

Introduction

Fungi are a highly diverse group, with around 2,500 species of macrofungi already recorded in Britain and Ireland, and many more microfungi known to be present (Watling & Ward, 2003). For the most part microfungi have not been included in this review, although some reference has been made to the montane Slime Moulds (Myxomycetes) since they have been relatively well-studied and, being intimately linked to the duration of snow-lie in the higher corries, would be particularly vulnerable to climate change. Many fungi grow in association with a host plant or tree and are thus bound to particular habitats. The management of these habitats can influence the fungal diversity therein, but further research is needed to fully understand the dynamics and implications of fungal ecology.

Important species and habitats

Reference to the British Mycological Society (BMS) managed fungal records database (BMSFRD) and other sources, as outlined below, suggests that areas of semi-natural pine forest within the Cairngorms support the largest numbers of interesting or important fungal species. These include 75 species listed in the Provisional British Red Data List (PBRL)[1] (Ing, 1992) and a further 25 species either rarely recorded in Scotland or recorded recently for the first time. It should be noted, however, that compared with similar areas elsewhere in Europe, wood-decomposing fungi are under-represented in Scottish pine forests; a direct reflection of the lack of dead timber available for colonisation. Scottish pine forests have been managed for many years for their timber, not only through the felling of good quality standing timber, but also through the removal of dead standing and fallen timber. On Mar Lodge Estate for example, Urquhart et al. (2001) quote an auction of timber in 1786 which included 'the decayed trees in the Black Park'. Recent changes in management activities, which take account of conservation objectives, should see a gradual increase in the amount of available dead wood. This will be of great benefit to the diversity of fungi and invertebrates.

The Scottish pine forest has been described as boreal by Worrell (1996), with affinities to the same habitat in Eurasia. Worrell notes however, that the climate in Scotland is more oceanic than in other regions where boreal forest occurs, and that there has been a high degree of disruption to the migration of tree species, caused by glaciation and the isolation of Britain from Western Europe, post-glaciation. There has been very little serious fungal survey work undertaken in Scotland, and only limited comment can be made on the effects of such variables in relation to the importance of the Cairngorms mycota in a national or international context. Some species within the Cairngorms are thought to be of global significance. For instance, a review by Coppins et al. (2003) of the status of Black Falsebolete Boletopsis leucomelaena[2], whose only two British sites both lie within the Cairngorms, quotes Ryvarden & Gilbertson (1993) in saying that it is 'circumboreal in the conifer zone but everywhere rare'.

The Cairngorms contain other important habitats for fungi. The high mountain plateaux, large areas of which are still under-recorded for fungi, contain populations of Arctic-alpine species, including 38 species of conservation concern. The relative lack of this habitat in Britain means that the Cairngorms are of outstanding importance for these species in a British context, and the majority of British records are from here. In comparison with other parts of Europe, where this habitat is more extensive, the British montane mycota would appear to be impoverished, with only one macrofungus of European concern being recorded from the Cairngorms. As Ing (2003) points out however, with regard to Slime Moulds (Myxomycetes), the low

---

The spectacular Fibrous Waxcap Hygrocybe intermedia *has been recorded from several sites in the Cairngorms, including Rothiemurchus, Abernethy Forest and Dunachton.*

Photo: *L. Gill*

Holden, E.M. (2006). Fungi. In: Shaw, P. & Thompson, D.B.A. (eds.). *The Nature of the Cairngorms: Diversity in a changing environment.* The Stationery Office. pp. 145-175.

---

[1] The BMS is currently developing a revised Red List of British fungi, which will supersede the PBRL

[2] The Scottish collections referred to in this text as *Boletopsis leucomelaena* do not agree with *B. grisea* found with pine in Continental Europe nor with *B. leucomelaena* growing with spruce in Europe. The Scottish collections would appear to be a separate species, presently being formally described (R.Watling pers. comm.).

number of snow-line species recorded in Scotland (21 compared with 60 species known from the Alps) may also be associated with the removal of high-level montane forest and scrub in Scotland – a very productive habitat in the Alps. Two globally rare montane micro-species do occur in the Cairngorms; Bearberry Redleaf *Exobasidium sydowianum* and the slime mould *Physarum albescens* (Ing, pers. comm.). Watling (1988) presents an overview of montane fungi in Scotland and also notes the reduction of high-level shrubs such as Net-leaved Willow *Salix reticulata* as a result of human activity. Such shrubs in Scandinavia and the Alps are rich hosts for ectomycorrhizal fungi, and their return to the montane scrub zone of Scottish mountains would undoubtedly benefit fungal biodiversity here.

Old semi-improved grasslands are another important habitat in Scotland as a whole, and the Cairngorms contain examples that are provisionally considered to be of national or European conservation importance, based on an initial analysis of the data collected by Newton *et al.* (2003a)[3] (S. Ward, pers. comm.). A reflection of the concern surrounding this habitat in Europe is that the Provisional European Red Data list (PERL) (Ing, 1993) includes 16 species of waxcap, while PBRL only includes two. Some sites, which might not be considered of outstanding importance in Scotland, are thus significant in a European context. There are 30 grassland species of conservation concern[4] in the Cairngorms (Table 11.1), two of which, Pink Waxcap *Hygrocybe calyptriformis* and Olive Earthtongue *Microglossum olivaceum*, are grassland Biodiversity Action Plan (BAP) species, described by Newton *et al.* (2000) and Silverside (2000) as being globally widespread, but nowhere common and often very rare.

Birch-dominated woodland within the Cairngorms contains 38 species of conservation concern. Most of these have been recorded either from the woodlands of Strathspey or from Morrone on upper Deeside. Birch woodland in Scotland has a number of distinctive fungi in the genera *Cortinarius* (Webcaps), *Lactarius* (Milkcaps), *Leccinum* (Boletes) and *Russula* (Brittlegills) (Watling, 1984a; Orton, 1986). *Cortinarius* is particularly well-represented among the species of conservation concern listed in Table 11.1.

Oak woodland is relatively restricted in the Cairngorms, however sites such as Dinnet, Glen Tanar and Killiecrankie support rare oakwood species thought to be at the northern limits of their distribution, particularly in the case of Dinnet. They include Gilded Bolete *Aureoboletus gentilis*, Oak Bolete *Boletus appendiculatus* and *B. aereus*. These oak woodlands are thus of considerable importance, and provide an interesting baseline for comparison with the unique Scottish Atlantic oakwoods.

Important areas

Important areas for fungi in the Cairngorms are presented in Table 11.2 and Figure 11.1, and are described below in descending order of international importance, in terms of the number of PERL species present. Since fungi distribution data are much less complete than that for many other species groups, this list should be viewed as provisional, pending more extensive, systematic survey coverage.

1. Rothiemurchus (including Glenmore and Loch an Eilein). Some of the older records for this area give an indication of the length of time for which it has been a focus of interest amongst mycologists. As is the case at Abernethy Forest (below), the large number of interesting species present is partly a reflection of this attention. The species listed reflect the presence of extensive Caledonian pinewood as well as birch forest, with smaller areas of Aspen *Populus tremula*, riverine woodland and semi-improved grassland being a part of the habitat mosaic.

Loch an Eilein is worthy of particular mention as it supports a rich pinewood mycota. Of special interest is Black Falsebolete *Boletopsis leucomelaena*[5], recorded here in 1938 and 1963; the first of two known sites in Britain (see Mar Lodge: Inverey Wood below). Giant Knight *Tricholoma colossus* has also been recorded.

The northern shores of Loch Morlich and the lower stretch of the Lairig Ghru path near Coylumbridge are also worthy of particular mention. The latter site includes a relatively short stretch of young pine trees that have naturally regenerated on an old pinewood site supporting eight BAP fungi; Drab Tooth *Bankera fuligineoalba*, Blue Tooth *Hydnellum caeruleum*, Mealy Tooth *H. ferrugineum*, Devil's Tooth *H. peckii*, Grey Tooth *Phellodon melaleucus*, Woolly Tooth *P. tomentosus*, Greenfoot Tooth *Sarcodon glaucopus* and Pine Tooth *S. squamosus*[6]. Giant Knight *Tricholoma colossus* is also recorded here.

---

[3] Data collected during this survey are being used to develop thresholds and criteria for recognising sites of national and European conservation importance, based on the number of species (e.g. of waxcaps *Hygrocybe*) recorded during a single visit (S. Ward, pers. comm.).

[4] Species that are listed in the PERL or PBRL, or else are BAP Priority or Nationally Rare.

[5] Since many common names for fungi have only recently been proposed, common and scientific names are both given throughout this chapter.

[6] Previously recorded as *S. imbricatus*, this fungus is now known to be *S. squamosus* (Watling & Milne, 2005).

2. Abernethy Forest (including Loch Garten, Boat of Garten, Dell Wood, Forest Lodge and Rynettin areas). This important area has been surveyed almost annually since 1968 by some of Britain's leading field mycologists (Orton *et al.*, 1968–2003), raising the number of rare and interesting species recorded. Allison (2001) lists 33 European and 49 British provisional Red Data List species. These totals have increased to 44 and 72 respectively, (Table 11.2), illustrating how our understanding of the distribution and occurrence of species has improved, as more focused work is undertaken and old records gradually incorporated into the national database.

Abernethy Forest is the largest Caledonian pine forest remaining, and contains many of the fungi associated with this habitat. Thirteen species of stipitate hydnoid tooth fungi are listed for the area, 11 of which have a Species Action Plan. The tooth fungi present include all of the species considered by Newton *et al.* (2002a,b) to be 'endangered' (having fewer than five localities; *Hydnellum aurantiacum*, *H. concrescens*, *Phellodon confluens* and *Sarcodon scabrosum*) or 'vulnerable' (fewer than ten localities; *H. caeruleum*, *H. scrobiculatum*, *Phellodon melaleucus*, *P. niger* and *Sarcodon glaucopus*). *H. auratile* is no longer considered British (Dickson & Emmett, 2004).

Other particularly interesting species from the pine forest at Abernethy include *Phellodon atratus*, Lilac Domecap *Calocybe onychina*, Woolly Rosette *Cotylidia pannosa*, Roothole Rosette *Stereopsis vitellina* and Conifer Roundhead *Stropharia hornemanii*.

Abernethy Forest also encompasses a mosaic of other habitats. These include: birchwoods, containing Violet Webcap *Cortinarius violaceus* and a number of other rarely recorded mycorrhizal species; mire containing *Ombrophila violacea* and *Sarcoleotia turficola*; and areas of old, semi-improved grassland with an impressive suite of grassland fungi. The latter include 29 *Hygrocybe* species, collected over a period of 16 years, one of which is the BAP species Pink Waxcap *Hygrocybe calyptriformis*. It is not clear whether the grassland sites are still extant or whether the reduction in grazing has made them unsuitable for fungal fruiting. Two other species occurring in particular microhabitats are worthy of mention. One is *Rickenella pseudogrisella*, located in 2003 growing with the liverwort *Blasia pusilla* on streamside gravels. This is an Arctic-alpine fungus with one other collection known from the Beinn a' Ghlo area (R. Watling, pers. comm.). The other is Aspen Tongue *Taphrina johansonii*; a parasitic fungus that causes the enlargement of the carpels of Aspen catkins. Abernethy is one of two known Scottish sites for the latter fungus, for which a further three sites are known in England.

Eight BAP fungi have been recorded from the Lairig Ghru path near Coylumbridge, including the Blue Tooth Hydnellum caeruleum.
Photo: L. Gill

The Pine Tooth Sarcodon squamosus *occurs at Rothiemurchus and Mar Lodge Estate, and is one of three BAP fungi recorded from Glen Tanar.*
Photo: L. Gill

3. Mar Lodge: Inverey Wood. This is a relatively small (approx 10 ha) area of woodland on the south side of the River Dee near Braemar. It is an extraordinarily rich area for pine-associated fungi on the PBRL, with 32 recorded so far, 12 of which are BAP species. One of the latter, Black Falsebolete *Boletopsis leucomelaena* is known from only one other site in Britain (Loch an Eilein, Rothiemurchus) and is of the highest level of concern according to the PERL. There is also an area of acid, semi-improved grassland immediately to the west, containing a further four interesting species: Violet Coral *Clavaria zollingeri*, Olive Earthtongue *Microglossum olivaceum*, Mealy Meadowcap *Porpoloma metapodium* and Dark Purple Earthtongue *Thuemenidium atropurpureum*.

The history of the area is unknown, but the present stand of mature pine is thought to have been planted. This is a somewhat unusual habitat, in that the substrate is of flat river gravels. The soils are therefore poor, but well-drained, with linear undulations throughout the wood dipping close to the water table and thus helping to maintain humidity. Being accessible, the area lends itself well to research and education, and has been forayed

The Gypsy fungus Rozites caperatus. *A pine forest species, this fungus is locally abundant in the Cairngorms but rarely recorded elsewhere.*

Photo: *L. Gill*

regularly since 1964. An interesting management dilemma exists as to whether to allow the wood to regenerate, expand or fall down. There is anecdotal evidence to suggest that a reduction in grazing levels, allowing natural regeneration within the wood, is likely to suppress the fruiting of mycorrhizal fungi (Orton, 1986).

Recent survey and foraying in the wood has located three species new to Britain: *Mycena viridimarginata*, *Russula vinosobrunnea* and *Tubulicrinis propinquus*. There are undoubtedly more interesting species awaiting discovery in this area.

4. Glen Tanar. The extensive semi-natural pine woodland and semi-improved grassland in Glen Tanar both contain interesting and important fungi. There is some dead wood beginning to accumulate under the pinewood canopy and this should be encouraged. The important pinewood species include three BAP species: Mealy Tooth *Hydnellum ferrugineum*, Woolly Tooth *Phellodon tomentosus* and Pine Tooth *Sarcodon squamosus*, as well as PBRL species Giant Knight *Tricholoma colossus*.

Glen Tanar and Dinnet (see below) are the only known Scottish localities of Gilded Bolete *Aureoboletus gentilis*. Glen Tanar has a number of other species that would appear to fruit more regularly in the south of England, including *Boletus aereus*, *B. pseudosulphureus*, *B. reticulatus*, Upright Coral *Ramaria stricta* and Bearded Seamine *Ripartites tricholoma*.

5. Morrone. Essentially ancient birch woodland, this area, near Braemar, contains exposures of Dalradian limestone and a mosaic of habitats of mycological interest. Bare soil amongst the limestone outcrops supports *Geopora arenosa s.s.*, known from similar microhabitats at three other Scottish sites (see Craig Leek below). An area of both mature and regenerating Aspen is present, and supports Aspen Bracket *Phellinus tremulae* and *Leccinum aurantiacum*. Areas of deer-grazed, semi-improved grassland support 52 grassland species, including Big Blue Pinkgill *Entoloma bloxamii*, a species that seems to favour base-rich sites. The first Scottish record of *Peziza granulosa* was from this location in a base-rich flush, and *Perrotia flammea* also occurs here. Dennis (1986) notes that the latter species used to be common in the Central Highlands in the 19th century but that it is now rarely recorded. Rooting Poisonpie *Hebeloma radicosum* is an interesting fungus that is thought to be associated with mole runs, and has been recorded at Morrone - one of 12 known sites in Scotland. Lurid Bolete *Boletus luridus* is mainly a southern species,

Table 11.1. Important fungal species known to fruit within the Cairngorms area. A provisional assessment of the national importance of these species is given. Species for which the UK has an international responsibility are highlighted in bold. Notable areas outside of the National Park, but within the wider Cairngorms area, are identified.

Nationally rare:	Recorded from 1-15 10-km squares in the UK
PERL:	Species on the Provisional European Red Data List (Ing, 1993)
PBRL:	Species on the Provisional British Red Data List (Ing, 1992)
BAP:	Biodiversity Action Plan. P = Species Action Plan prepared; S = Species Statement
Percentage of UK range:	The percentage of the species' UK range (in 10-km squares) occurring with the Cairngorms area or in the National Park *** >75%; ** 25-75%; * 10-24%; '-' <10%

Habitat	Species	Recommended English Name	Status				Percentage of UK range in:		Notable areas outside of the National Park	Comments
			Nationally rare	PERL	PBRL	BAP	Cairngorms area	National Park		
Broadleaved woodland, particularly birch	*Amanita flavescens*		Y				***	***		Morrone is the only confirmed British site.
	Boletus pseudosulphureus		Y	Y	Y		-	-		Likely to be removed from revised British red list; data deficient.
	Boletus queletii	Deceiving Bolete	Y				-	-		A southern species that rarely fruits in Scotland.
	Cheimonophyllum candidissimum		Y				*	-	Struan Wood	Widespread, but rarely recorded.
	Clavariadelphus pistillaris	Giant Club					-	-	Killiecrankie	Widespread, but rarely recorded in Scotland.
	Collybia aquosa						*	-	Killiecrankie	Widespread, but rarely recorded in Scotland.
	Coltricia montagnei		Y				**	**		Old record from 1912. Rarely recorded.
	Coprinus lilatinctus		Y				**	**		Three British sites known.
	Cortinarius caerulescens	Mealy Bigfoot Webcap			Y		*	*	Atholl & Glen Tilt	Likely to be removed from revised British red list; data deficient.
	Cortinarius crassus		Y		Y		**	**		Likely to be removed from revised British red list; data deficient.
	Cortinarius cyanites		Y	Y	Y		**	**	Killiecrankie	
	Cortinarius infractus				Y		*	-	Struan Wood	Likely to be removed from revised British red list; least concern.
	Cortinarius olidus		Y		Y		*	*		Likely to be removed from revised British red list; data deficient.
	Cortinarius orellanus	Fool's Webcap	Y	Y			*	*		Old records from 1890, 1900.
	Cortinarius porphyropus		Y		Y		**	**	Struan Wood	Old record from 1927.
	Cortinarius rubicundulus		Y				*	*		Widespread, but rarely recorded.
	Cortinarius saporatus		Y		Y		*	*		Likely to be removed from revised British red list; data deficient
	Cortinarius talus	Honey Webcap			Y		**	*	Struan Wood	Likely to be removed from revised British red list; least concern
	Cortinarius violaceus	Violet Webcap		Y	Y		*	*	Struan Wood	
	Cortinarius xanthocephalus		Y		Y		*	-	Struan Wood	Likely to be removed from revised British red list; data deficient.
	Cotylidia pannosa	Woolly Rosette	Y	Y	Y		**	**		Old record from 1900.
	Entoloma tjallingiorum		Y				*	*	Quithel Wood	Widespread, but rarely recorded. Likely to be included in revised British red list.
	Gloeoporus dichrous		Y	Y			**	**		Likely to be included in revised British red list.

Habitat	Species	Recommended English Name	Status				Percentage of UK range in:		Notable areas outside of the National Park	Comments
			Nationally rare	PERL	PBRL	BAP	Cairngorms area	National Park		
Broadleaved woodland, particularly birch	Gyromitra infula	Pouched False Morel	Y		Y		**	**	Quithel Wood	Likely to be removed from revised British red list; least concern.
	Gyroporus cyanescens						-	-		Widespread, but rarely recorded.
	Hebeloma radicosum	Rooting Poisonpie					-	-		Widespread, but rarely recorded in Scotland.
	Helvella cupuliformis		Y				*	-	Atholl & Glen Tilt	Widespread, but rarely recorded.
	Hyalopsora aspidiotus	Oak Fern Rust	Y		Y		**	**		Likely to be listed as extinct on the revised British red list.
	Hygrophorus hedreychii		Y		Y		**	**		Likely to be removed from revised British red list; data deficient.
	Hypholoma epixanthum						-	-	Atholl & Glen Tilt	Widespread, but rarely recorded.
	Inocybe calospora				Y		-	-		Likely to be removed from revised British red list; data deficient.
	Inocybe leptophylla		Y				*	*		Widespread, but rarely recorded.
	Lactarius flavidus		Y				-	-	Struan Wood	Widespread, but rarely recorded.
	Ochropsora ariae				Y		**	*	Quithel Wood, Killiecrankie	Living on *Anemone nemorosa* leaves. Likely to be removed from revised British red list; least concern.
	Perrotia flammea		Y				***	***	Struan Wood	Rarely recorded Scottish species often associated with dead attached willow branches.
	Phellinus laevigatus		Y				*	*	Struan Wood	Widespread, but rarely recorded.
	Phellinus pomaceus	Cushion Bracket					-	-		Rarely recorded in Scotland. Often associated with *Prunus* spp.
	Phellodon confluens	Fused Tooth		Y	Y	P	*	*		
	Rhodocybe hirneola		Y				**	*	Struan Wood	Widespread, but rarely recorded.
	Russula font-queri		Y				**	**		
	Russula intermedia		Y		Y		**	**	Quithel Wood, Killiecrankie	
	Russula scotica		Y				*	*	Ben Vrackie	Type specimen from Craigellachie. Rarely recorded in Scotland.
	Russula violaceoides		Y		Y		**	**		Type specimen from Rothiemurchus. Dubious species likely to be removed from revised British red list.
	Scutellinia decipiens		Y				**	-	Struan Wood	Two Scottish records only. Associated with wet peat rather than birch.
Aspen woodland	Phellinus tremulae	Aspen Bracket		Y			**	**		New to Britain in 2000.
	Taphrina johansonii	Aspen Tongue	Y				**	**		Rarely recorded. Abernethy and Braemar are the only Scottish sites.
Riparian woodland	Cortinarius alnetorum						*	-	Quithel Wood	Rarely recorded, but probably overlooked.
	Cytidia salicina	Scarlet Splash	Y				**	**		Relocated at Kinrara after 100 years. Other recent records from Insh, Rannoch and Keilder only.

Habitat	Species	Recommended English Name	Status				Percentage of UK range in:		Notable areas outside of the National Park	Comments
			Nationally rare	PERL	PBRL	BAP	Cairngorms area	National Park		
Riparian woodland	Entoloma dysthales		Y				-	-	Quithel Wood	Widespread but rarely recorded.
	Entoloma euchroum			Y			-	-		Old record from 1927; habitat not recorded.
	Lactarius aspideus			Y			*	*		Widespread, but rarely recorded.
	Lycoperdon echinatum	Spiny Puffball					-	-	Quithel Wood, Killiecrankie	Occurring at its most northerly confirmed site.
	Mycena alexandrii		Y				***	***	Quithel Wood	New to Britain if confirmed. Located in river debris.
	Naucoria striatula (incl. N. scolecina)	Striate Aldercap			Y		-	-		Likely to be removed from revised British red list; least concern.
	Phellinus punctatus		Y				-	-		Widespread, but rarely recorded in Scotland.
	Pholiota heteroclita		Y				*	-	Killiecrankie	Widespread but rarely recorded in Scotland.
	Plicatura crispa						*	*	Quithel wood	Recently removed from PBRL.
	Scytinostroma portentosum	Mothball Crust	Y	Y	Y		*	*	Quithel Wood	Likely to be removed from revised British red list; least concern.
	Vibrissea truncorum			Y			*	*		
Broadleaved woodland, particularly oak	Amanita pachyvolvata		Y				**	-	Atholl & Glen Tilt	Widespread but rarely recorded in Scotland. Grows with *Fagus* as well.
	Amanita phalloides	Deathcap					-	-	Atholl & Glen Tilt, Killiecrankie	Rarely recorded in Scotland.
	Aureoboletus gentilis	Gilded Bolete		Y			-	-		
	Boletus aereus						-	-		Widespread but rarely recorded in Scotland.
	Boletus appendiculatus	Oak Bolete		Y			-	-		
	Boletus radicans	Rooting Bolete		Y			-	-		Old record from 1900, habitat unclear.
	Calocybe constricta						-	-	Killiecrankie	Widespread but rarely recorded in Scotland.
	Cystolepiota seminuda						-	-	Killiecrankie	Widespread but rarely recorded in Scotland.
	Euepixylon udum (=Hypoxylon udum)						-	-		Widespread, but rarely recorded.
	Grifola frondosa	Hen of the Woods		Y			-	-		
	Hygrophorus nemoreus	Oak Woodwax	Y	Y	Y		*	-	Killiecrankie	
	Leccinum atrostipitatum		Y				**	*		Widespread but rarely recorded in Scotland.
	Microglossum viride			Y					Atholl & Glen Tilt	
	Otidia phlebophora		Y		Y		*	-	Killiecrankie	
	Phylloporus pelletieri	**Golden Gilled Bolete**		Y			-	-		Likely to be added to revised British red list.
	Porphyrellus porphyrosporus	Dusky Bolete		Y			-	-	Killiecrankie	
	Pseudocraterellus undulatus	Sinuous Chanterelle			Y		-	-	Atholl & Glen Tilt	Likely to be removed from revised British red list; least concern.

Habitat	Species	Recommended English Name	Status				Percentage of UK range in:		Notable areas outside of the National Park	Comments
			Nationally rare	PERL	PBRL	BAP	Cairngorms area	National Park		
Broadleaved woodland, particularly oak	*Ramaria botrytis*	Rosso Coral		Y			-	-	Killiecrankie	Only known Scottish site. Recorded with *Quercus* and *Fagus*.
	Russula solaris				Y		-	-	Killiecrankie	Probably with *Fagus*. Likely to be removed from revised British red list; least concern.
	Strobilomyces strobilaceus	Old Man of the Woods		Y	Y		-	-	Atholl & Glen Tilt, Killiecrankie	Likely to be removed from revised British red list; least concern.
	Tricholoma acerbum						-	-		Southern distribution. Rarely recorded in Scotland.
Conifer plantations	*Bankera violascens*	Spruce Tooth	Y				***	***		Only 2 British locations: Glenmore (extinct?) and Inver (extant), associating with spruce.
	Gomphidius maculatus			Y			*	*	Killiecrankie	
	Psathyrella caput-medusae	Medusa Brittlestem	Y	Y	Y		**	**		
	Pseudoplectania nigrella	Ebony Cup	Y		Y		**	**		Two records from Braemar area.
	Suillus bresadolae var. *flavogriseus*	Bearded Bolete	Y		Y		*	*		One of the 3 known Scottish sites is Linn of Dee. Likely to be removed from revised British red list – alien.
Semi-natural pine woodland	*Antrodia ramentacea*		Y				**	**		Widespread, but rarely recorded.
	Boletopsis leucomelaena	**Black Falsebolete**	Y	Y	Y	S	***	***		Only 2 locations in Britain, both in Cairngorms: Inverey & Loch an Eilein.
	Bankera fuligineoalba	**Drab Tooth**		Y	Y	P	**	**		
	Buchwaldoboletus lignicola				Y		-	-		Likely to be removed from revised British red list; least concern.
	Calocybe onychina	Lilac Domecap	Y		Y		***	***		
	Cantharellus aurora	Golden Chanterelle			Y		*	*		Likely to be removed from revised British red list; least concern.
	Cantharellus ferruginascens				Y		**	*		
	Chrysomphalina chrysophylla	Golden Navel	Y		Y		**	**		
	Collybia acervata				Y		*	*	Struan Wood	Likely to be removed from revised British red list; least concern.
	Collybia alpina		Y				**	**		8 records, all in Scotland.
	Collybia prolixa		Y		Y		**	**		Likely to be removed from revised British red list; data deficient.
	Collybia putilla		Y		Y		**	**		
	Collybia racemosa	Branched Shanklet	Y		Y		*	*		Widespread but rarely recorded in Scotland.
	Collybia tergina		Y				**	**		Widespread, but rarely recorded.
	Conocybe pinetorum		Y				**	**		Recorded twice from Abernethy.
	Cortinarius balteatocumatilis		Y		Y		*	*		Likely to be removed from British red list; data deficient.
	Cortinarius caledoniensis		Y		Y		**	**		Likely to be removed from revised British red list; data deficient.
	Cortinarius camphoratus	Goatcheese Webcap	Y		Y		**	**		
	Cortinarius durus		Y		Y		**	**		Likely to be removed from revised British red list; data deficient.

Habitat	Species	Recommended English Name	Status				Percentage of UK range in:		Notable areas outside of the National Park	Comments
			Nationally rare	PERL	PBRL	BAP	Cairngorms area	National Park		
Semi-natural pine woodland	*Cortinarius fervidus*	Dyer's Webcap	Y		Y		***	***		Likely to be removed from revised British red list; data deficient.
	Cortinarius glaucopus		Y		Y		**	*	Atholl & Glen Tilt	Likely to be removed from revised British red list; data deficient.
	Cortinarius laniger		Y		Y		**	**		
	Cortinarius limonius	Sunset Webcap			Y		**	**		
	Cortinarius scaurus	Green Webcap	Y	Y	Y		**	**		Likely to be removed from revised British red list; least concern.
	Cortinarius spilomeus	Freckled Webcap	Y				**	**	Struan Wood	Rarely recorded, mostly in Scotland.
	Cortinarius subtortus		Y		Y		**	**		Likely to be removed from revised British red list; data deficient.
	Cortinarius variicolor		Y		Y		*	*		Likely to be removed from revised British red list; data deficient.
	Cudonia circinans	Redleg Jellybaby	Y	Y	Y		**	**		
	Cudonia confusa	Cinnamon Jellybaby	Y		Y		**	**		
	Cystoderma cinnabarinum		Y		Y		**	**		
	Dacrymyces confluens		Y				***	**		Only known British record at Curr – no voucher
	Dacrymyces estonicus		Y				**	**		Widespread, but rarely recorded.
	Entoloma nitidum				Y		-	-		Likely to be removed from revised British red list; least concern.
	Fayodia bisphaerigera				Y		*	*		
	Flammulaster limulatus		Y		Y		**	*	Atholl & Glen Tilt	
	Gloeophyllum odoratum	Anise Mazegill	Y		Y		**	**		Mar Lodge is one of two Scottish records.
	Gymnosporangium clavariiforme						*	*		A rust fungus, uncommon in Scotland.
	Gymnosporangium cornutum						**	*		A rust fungus, uncommon in England.
	Gyromitra ambigua		Y				***	***		Old record (1907); rarely recorded. Likely to be listed as extinct on revised British red list.
	Gyromitra infula	Pouched False Morel	Y		Y		**	**	Quithel Wood	Likely to be removed from revised British red list.
	Hapalopilus salmonicolor	Salmon Bracket	Y		Y		**	**		
	Hebeloma birrus						-	-		Widespread but rarely recorded in Scotland.
	Hebeloma pallidoluctuosum						-	-		Widespread but rarely recorded in Scotland.
	Hebeloma sordescens		Y				**	**		2 Scottish records, both in the Cairngorms, of 4 records in total.
	Hydnellum aurantiacum	Orange Tooth	Y	Y	Y	P	***	***		
	Hydnellum caeruleum	Blue Tooth	Y	Y	Y	P	**	**		
	Hydnellum concrescens	**Zoned Tooth**		Y	Y	P	*	*	Killiecrankie	
	Hydnellum ferrugineum	Mealy Tooth	Y	Y	Y	P	**	**	Bruar	
	Hydnellum peckii	**Devil's Tooth**		Y	Y	P	**	**		

Habitat	Species	Recommended English Name	Status				Percentage of UK range in:		Notable areas outside of the National Park	Comments
			Nationally rare	PERL	PBRL	BAP	Cairngorms area	National Park		
Semi-natural pine woodland	*Hydnellum scrobiculatum*	**Ridged Tooth**		Y	Y	P	*	*		
	Hygrophorus camarophyllus	Arched Woodwax	Y	Y	Y		**	**		Growing with Bearberry at 700 m near Cairn Gorm, 2005.
	Hypomyces viridis		Y				**	**		Widespread, but rarely recorded.
	Inocybe jacobi		Y		Y		**	**		Likely to be removed from revised British red list; data deficient.
	Lactarius badiosanguineus		Y				***	***		Known in Britain only from Abernethy & Rothiemurchus.
	Lactarius hysginus				Y		*	*	Atholl & Glen Tilt, Struan Wood, Bruar	
	Lactarius mammosus						*	*	Straun	Widespread, but rarely recorded.
	Lactarius musteus	Pine Milkcap	Y	Y	Y		**	**		
	Leccinum vulpinum	Foxy Bolete	Y		Y		**	**		
	Leucocortinarius bulbiger	White Webcap	Y	Y	Y		**	**		
	Metacoleroa dickiei		Y				***	***		Rarely recorded microfungus, limited by host (Twinflower) distribution.
	Mucronella calva						-	-		Widespread, but rarely recorded in Scotland.
	Mycena purpureofusca				Y		**	**		Likely to be removed from revised British red list; least concern.
	Mycena rosella	Pink Bonnet			Y		**	**		Likely to be removed from revised British red list; least concern.
	Mycena rubromarginata	Red Edge Bonnet			Y		*	*		Likely to be removed from revised British red list; least concern.
	Mycena septentrionalis		Y				**	**		Rarely recorded. Occurs in Scottish pinewoods.
	Mycena urania	Violet Bonnet	Y		Y		**	**		
	Mycena viridmarginata		Y				***	***		New to Britain in 2001, at Inverey.
	Peniphora pini		Y				*	*		Widespread, but rarely recorded.
	Phellodon atratus		Y				***	***		Recorded from Abernethy and Glenmore only. Taxonomically uncertain
	Phellodon melaleucus	**Grey Tooth**		Y	Y	P	**	**		International responsibility.
	Phellodon niger	**Black Tooth**		Y	Y		**	**	Struan Wood	International responsibility.
	Phellodon tomentosus	**Woolly Tooth**		Y	Y	P	**	**		International responsibility.
	Pholiota astragalina		Y		Y		**	**		Likely to be removed from revised British red list; data deficient.
	Pleurocybella porrigens	Angels Wings	Y				*	*		Not uncommon in Scotland.
	Psathyrella solitaria (= P. rannochii)		Y		Y		**	**		Likely to be removed from revised British red list; data deficient.
	Ramaria stricta	Upright Coral					-	-		Widespread but rarely recorded in Scotland.
	Ramaria suecica		Y		Y		***	***		Likely to be removed from revised British red list; data deficient.
	Ripartites tricholoma						-	-		Widespread but rarely recorded in Scotland.
	Rozites caperatus	The Gypsy			Y		**	**	Killiecrankie	Likely to be removed from revised British red list; least concern.
	Russula amythestina		Y		Y		**	**		Likely to be removed from revised British red list; data deficient.

Habitat	Species	Recommended English Name	Nationally rare	PERL	PBRL	BAP	Cairngorms area	National Park	Notable areas outside of the National Park	Comments
			Status				Percentage of UK range in:			
Semi-natural pine woodland	*Russula aquosa*			Y	Y		*	*	Atholl & Glen Tilt	Likely to be removed from revised British red list; least concern.
	Russula badia	Burning Brittlegill	Y		Y		**	**		
	Russula cessans				Y		*	*		Likely to be removed from revised British red list; least concern.
	Russula decolorans	Copper Brittlegill			Y		**	**		Likely to be removed from revised British red list; least concern.
	Russula fusconigra		Y				***	***		New to Britain in 2001, at Curr.
	Russula integra				Y		*	*	Atholl & Glen Tilt	Likely to be removed from revised British red list; data deficient.
	Russula vinosa	Darkening Brittlegill			Y		**	**		
	Russula vinosobrunnea		Y				**	**		One Scottish record - from Inverey.
	Russula xenochlora		Y				***	***		In Britain known only from Curr Wood & Abernethy.
	Sarcodon glaucopus	Greenfoot Tooth	Y	Y	Y	P	***	***		
	Sarcodon scabrosus	Bitter Tooth	Y	Y	Y	P	**	**		Scottish records may refer to *S. glaucopus*.
	Sarcodon squamosus	**Pine Tooth**		Y	Y	P	**	**		
	Sistotrema muscicola		Y				*	*		One Scottish record, from Lui Bridge.
	Spathularia flavida	Yellow Fan	Y	Y			**	**	Struan Wood	
	Stagnicola perplexa		Y		Y		***	***		
	Stereopsis vitellina	Roothole Rosette	Y	Y	Y		***	***		
	Stropharia hornemannii	Conifer Roundhead	Y		Y		***	***		
	Suillus flavidus			Y	Y		**	**		Likely to be removed from revised British red list; least concern.
	Tricholoma apium	Scented Knight	Y	Y	Y		***	***		
	Tricholoma colossus	Giant Knight	Y	Y	Y		***	***		
	Tricholoma focale	Booted Knight		Y	Y		**	**		
	Tricholoma nauseosum		Y							Last vouchered collection in 1927 at Abernethy & Rothiemurchus, as *T. caligatum*.
	Tricholoma pessundatum				Y		**	**		
	Tricholoma sejunctum	Deceiving Knight		Y	Y		-	-	Atholl & Glen Tilt; Killiecrankie	Likely to be removed from revised British red list; least concern
	Tricholoma stans	Upright Knight	Y		Y		***	***		
	Tubulicrinis propinquus		Y				***	***		New to Brtain in 2003, at Inverey Wood.
	Xeromphalina campanella		Y		Y		**	**		Likely to be removed from revised British red list; least concern.
	Xeromphalina cauticinalis		Y		Y		***	***		Likely to be removed from revised British red list; least concern.
Bog	*Armillaria ectypa*		Y	Y	Y	Y	**	**		First Scottish record from Insh Marshes, 2005.
	Ombrophila violacea				Y		-	-		Likely to be removed from revised British red list; least concern.
	Omphalina mutila		Y				**	**		Widespread, but rarely recorded.

Habitat	Species	Recommended English Name	Status				Percentage of UK range in:		Notable areas outside of the National Park	Comments
			Nationally rare	PERL	PBRL	BAP	Cairngorms area	National Park		
Bog	*Phaeogalera stagnina* (incl. *P. zetlandica*)			Y			**	**		Widespread, but rarely recorded.
	Sarcoleotia turficola		Y				*	*		Widespread, but rarely recorded.
Moss cushions on limestone boulders	***Tulostoma niveum***	**White Stalkball**	Y	Y	Y	P	**	**		Second site in Britain (Craig Leek) located in 1998; the other is at Inchnadamph.
Upland Heath	***Discina leucoxantha***		Y				**	**		One vouchered collection from Perth, 1924. Species refound in 2004, near Crathie.
	Exobasidium expansum	Northern Bilberry Redleaf	Y				***	***		Recorded on Cairngorm in 1994; the only known British site.
	Exobasidium sydowianum	**Bearberry Redleaf**	Y		Y		**	**		A globally rare species with 3 British sites: in W. Ross and Cairngorms.
Montane	*Amanita nivalis*	Mountain Grisette	Y		Y		**	*v		
	Boletus luridus	Lurid Bolete					-	-	Atholl & Glen Tilt, Glen Shee, Killiecrankie	Notably growing with Rock Rose in base-rich situations.
	Cortinarius favrei		Y				**	**		Rarely recorded; occurs in Scottish mountains.
	Cortinarius gausapatus		Y				***	***		New to Britain in 1984.
	Cortinarius helvelloides f. Favre		Y				***	***		Rarely recorded; occurs in Scottish mountains. This taxonomic interpretation not dealt with by Checklist.
	Cortinarius phaeopygmaeus		Y				***	***		New to Britain in 2002
	Cortinarius rufostriatus		Y				***	***		New to Britain in 1984.
	Cortinarius scotoides		Y				***	***		New to Britain in 1984.
	Galerina harrisonii		Y				**	**		Rarely recorded; occurs in Scottish mountains.
	Geopora arenosa s.s.		Y				***	**	Beinn a' Ghlo	Rarely recorded, in bare, base rich soil on Scottish mountains.
	Hygrocybe citrinopallida		Y				*	*		One Scottish record from Beinn a' Bhuird.
	Hygrocybe lilacina		Y				**	**		Rarely recorded; occurs in Scottish mountains.
	Hygrocybe salicis-herbaceae	Mountain Waxcap	Y				***	***		New to Britain in 1997, from Glas Maol.
	Inocybe dulcamara f. squamosoannulata Favre		Y				***	***		New to Britain in 1984. Included in Checklist under *I. dulcamara*
	Inocybe scabella var. fulvella s. Heim		Y				***	***		Possibly new to Britain in 1984. Included in Checklist under *I. fulvella*.
	Laccaria proximella		Y				**	**		New to Britain in 1984, but taxonomically uncertain. Included in Checklist under *L. proxima*.
	Lichenomphalia alpina						*	*	Ben Vrackie	Widespread but uncommon; in Scottish mountains only.
	Nyssopsora echinata		Y		Y		**	**	Glen Shee	
	Omphaliaster asterosporus						*	*		Rarely recorded; occurs in Scottish mountains.
	Omphaliaster borealis		Y				**	**		Widespread, but rarely recorded.
	Psathyrella nolitangere		Y				-	-		Widespread, but rarely recorded.

Habitat	Species	Recommended English Name	Status				Percentage of UK range in:		Notable areas outside of the National Park	Comments
			Nationally rare	PERL	PBRL	BAP	Cairngorms area	National Park		
Montane	*Rickenella pseudogrisella*		Y				***	**	Beinn a' Ghlo	Second British record, Abernethy, 2003.
	Russula nana	Alpine Brittlegill	Y		Y		**	**	Struan Wood, Ben Vrackie	
	Russula norvegica		Y		Y		**	**		Included in Checklist under *R. laccata*.
	Russula pascua		Y				***	**	Ben Vrackie	Four Scottish sites, plus one in N. Ireland.
	Russula persicina		Y		Y		**	*	Struan Wood	Likely to be removed from revised British red list; data deficient.
	Scutellinia patagonica		Y				**	**		Widespread, but rarely recorded.
Montane Myxomycetes (Slime Moulds)	*Dianema nivale*		Y		Y		**	**		
	Diderma lyallii (=*D. fallax*)		Y				**	**		Recorded from 3 Scottish sites, including Cairngorms.
	Diderma microcarpum		Y				***	***		Only 2 known British sites, both in Cairngorms.
	Diderma niveum s.s.		Y				***	***		Only 2 known British sites, both in Cairngorms.
	Didymium nivivola		Y				*	*		Only 7 British sites, all Scottish, including Cairngorms.
	Lamproderma atrosporum		Y		Y		**	**		Only 2 known British sites, including Cairngorms.
	Lamproderma carestiae		Y				**	**		Only 4 British sites, all Scottish, including Cairngorms.
	Lamproderma cribrarioides		Y				***	***		Only 2 British sites, both in Cairngorms.
	Lamproderma ovoideum		Y				***	***		The only British record is in Cairngorms.
	Lamproderma sauteri		Y		Y		***	***		Only 4 known British records; 3 in Cairngorms.
	Lepidoderma aggregatum		Y				***	***		Only 5 known British records; 4 in Cairngorms
	Lepidoderma carestianum				Y		**	**	Ben Vrackie	Ten British records (all Scottish); 5 in Cairngorms.
	Physarum albescens		Y				***	***		The only British record is from Glas Maol.
	Physarum alpestre		Y				***	***		The only British record is from the Cairngorms.
Calcareous grassland	*Camarophyllopsis micacea*		Y		Y		**	**		Not restricted to grassland; also occurs with shrubs.
	Entoloma bloxamii	**Big Blue Pinkgill**		Y	Y		-	-		
Acid/neutral grassland	*Clavaria rosea*	Rose Spindles					-	-	Glen Shee	Widespread, but not common.
	Clavaria straminea	Straw Club			Y		-	-		
	Clavaria zollingeri	Violet Coral		Y	Y		-	-	Atholl & Glen Tilt	Likely to be removed from revised British red list; least concern.
	Clavulinopsis umbrinella				Y		-	-	Corrie Fee	Likely to be removed from revised British red list; least concern.
	Entoloma griseocyaneum	Felted Pinkgill		Y			*	*	Ben Vrackie, Quithel Wood, Struan Wood	
	Entoloma prunuloides	Mealy Pinkgill		Y			-	-	Struan Wood	
	Gamundia striatula						**	*	Struan Wood	Widespread, but rarely recorded.
	Geoglossum atropurpureum	**Dark Purple Earthtongue**		Y	Y		**	*	Atholl & Glen Tilt	
	Geoglossum fallax				Y		-	-		Common in Scotland.

Habitat	Species	Recommended English Name	Status				Percentage of UK range in:		Notable areas outside of the National Park	Comments
			Nationally rare	PERL	PBRL	BAP	Cairngorms area	National Park		
Acid/neutral grassland	Geoglossum glutinosum			Y			-	-		Common in Scotland.
	Geoglossum starbaeckii		Y		Y		*	*		
	Geoglossum umbratile	Plain Earthtongue		Y			-	-		Common in Scotland.
	Hygrocybe aurantiosplendens	Orange Waxcap		Y			-	-		
	Hygrocybe cantharellus	Goblet Waxcap		Y			-	-	Struan Wood	Common in Scotland.
	Hygrocybe calyptriformis	**Pink Waxcap**			Y	P	-	-		
	Hygrocybe fornicata	Earthy Waxcap		Y			*	*		
	Hygrocybe ingrata			Y			-	-		
	Hygrocybe insipida	Spangle Waxcap		Y			-	-		Common in Scotland
	Hygrocybe irrigata	Slimy Waxcap		Y			-	-		Common in Scotland
	Hygrocybe lacmus	Grey Waxcap		Y			-	-		
	Hygrocybe nitrata	Nitrous Waxcap		Y			-	-	Atholl & Glen Tilt	
	Hygrocybe ovina	Blushing Waxcap		Y			-	-	Atholl & Glen Tilt, Struan Wood	
	Hygrocybe punicea	Crimson Waxcap		Y			*	-	Aboyne Playing Fields, Atholl & Glen Tilt, Corrie Fee, Struan Wood	
	Hygrocybe quieta	Oily Waxcap		Y			-	-	Atholl & Glen Tilt	Common in Scotland
	Lepista panaeola						-	-		Widespread, but rarely recorded in Scotland.
	Microglossum olivaceum	**Olive Earthtongue**		Y	Y	P	-	-		
	Mycena latifolia		Y				**	**		Widespread, but rarely recorded.
	Porpoloma metapodium	Mealy Meadowcap		Y	Y		*	*		Likely to be removed from revised British red list; least concern.
	Squamanita contortipes	Contorted Strangler	Y		Y		***	***		One record only from Britain, in grassland in old pine forest. Likely to be listed as extinct on revised British red list.
	Squamanita paradoxa	Powdercap Strangler	Y		Y		*	*		
	Squamanita pearsonii	Strathy Strangler	Y		Y		**	**		Two British records both in Scotland.
On horn	Onygena equina	Horn Stalkball		Y			*	-	Struan Wood	Not uncommon in Scotland.
On soil	Peziza granulosa		Y				*	*		Morrone is the only known Scottish location. Rarely recorded in the rest of Britain.

where it is associated predominantly with broadleaved woodland. Many of the 24 Scottish records in this dataset, including the Morrone record, occur in a base-rich habitat in which it associates with Rock Rose *Helianthimum nummularium*. Morrone is also the only confirmed site in Britain for *Amanita flavescens*.

6. Mar Lodge: Lui Flats. This area is outstanding for its semi-improved grassland. It has been used as winter/spring grazing for Red Deer *Cervus elaphus* and has been limed in the past. The National Trust for Scotland has managed the area since 1995, with conservation as a priority. There is some naturally occurring base-rich influence and the areas least affected by any agricultural improvement, for instance around the ruined settlements, are particularly rich in grassland fungi. The area has been surveyed over a six-year period, yielding 58 grassland fungi, and is provisionally classified as being of European importance. It supports one grassland BAP species – Olive Earthtongue *Microglossum olivaceum* – and a number of other interesting species, including Powdercap Strangler *Squamanita paradoxa*, *Lepista panaeola*, *Gammundia striatula* and Rose Spindles *Clavaria rosea*. The presence of scheduled ancient monuments means that woodland within the immediate vicinity of these ruins will not be encouraged. It is therefore likely that grazing will continue on Lui Flats, despite an overall estate management intervention to reduce the grazing and encourage natural regeneration of the nearby pine woodland.

7. Inverey Flats (Golf Course). This area was part of the Mar Lodge golf course until the Second World War. Since then it has been used as winter/spring grazing for Red Deer and is occasionally limed and topped. There is some base-rich influence, and the periphery of the area is particularly rich in herbs and fungi. The area has been surveyed over a six-year period and 60 grassland fungi have been recorded. There are two grassland BAP species – Pink Waxcap *Hygrocybe calyptriformis* and Olive Earthtongue *Microglossum olivaceum* – the latter present in both the green form and the brown variety, *fuscorubens*. Alpine Brittlegill *Russula nana*, usually thought of as a montane species, is also present, probably growing with Viviparous Bistort *Polygonum viviparum* and Rock Rose. A strip of Aspen growing beside the river supports *Phellinus tremulae* and *Leccinum aurantiacum*.

8. Dunachton, near Insh Marshes, contains an area of semi-improved grassland and areas of oak and birch on well-drained, poor, moraine soils. *Gyroporus cyaneus* occurs, and this is also one of three British sites for *Russula font-queri* (see Insh Marshes below). The grassland contains two of the five species that

Newton *et al.* (2003a) suggest are associated with particularly diverse sites; Blushing Waxcap *Hygrocybe ovina* and *H. ingrata*.

9. Dinnet. This area includes Muir of Dinnet and Dinnet Oakwood. Oak, pine and Aspen woodland in the area all contain interesting fungal associates. The oakwood, south of the Dee, is an unusual Scottish oakwood with many charcteristic oak fungi at their northern limit, including *Boletus aereus* and Oak Bolete *B. appendiculatus* (see Glen Tanar). A further range of interesting mycorrhizal species occur, including *Cortinarius crassus*, Honey Webcap *C. talus*, Oak Woodwax *Hygrophorus nemoreus* and *Russula aquosa*. The Wood Anemone *Anemone nemorosa* growing beneath the canopy supports a rarely recorded rust, *Ochropsora ariae*, and the area of Aspen north of Loch Kinord contains Aspen specialists such as *Leccinum aurantiacum*, *Phellinus tremulae* (first recorded in Britain in 2000) and the encrusting *Peniophora polygonia*. A strip of pine along the A97 supports BAP species Devil's Tooth *Hydnellum peckii* and BPRL Booted Knight *Tricholoma focale*. The BAP grassland species Pink Waxcap *Hygrocybe calyptriformis* occurs near to New Kinord House (M. Faulkner, pers. comm.).

10. Atholl and Glen Tilt. This is a large area of diverse habitat, encompassing the policies of Blair Castle, the base-rich unimproved pasture in Glen Tilt and areas of woodland around Kincraigie. Exact locations are difficult to determine from the records and further research would be needed to locate the most interesting areas. *Amanita pachyvolvata* is the only Scottish record out of three British records, and *Helvella cupuliformis* is one of only two records, both from Scotland.

11. Mar Lodge: Quoich Bridge. The area around the Quoich Water, just before it joins the Dee, contains semi-improved grassland and semi-natural pine woodland, both of which support a range of interesting fungi. The area of grassland is provisionally classified as being of national importance. The pine woodland contains a range of important pine associates, including BAP species Devil's Tooth *Hydnellum peckii*, Woolly Tooth *Phellodon tomentosus* and Pine Tooth *Sarcodon squamosus*. Areas of semi-natural pine woodland further up the glen (including the Dubh Ghleann and Beachan Wood) also contain significant populations of PBRL species.

12. Killiecrankie. It should be noted that part of this site lies outside of the Cairngorms area. The site itself contains an interesting mix of oak, ash and Hazel *Corylus avellana* and several rare fungal species more normally of a southern distribution.

13. Struan Wood. Predominantly an important area of old birchwood, this area (on Atholl Estate) also contains interesting unimproved pasture, and a conifer plantation at which PBRL species Black Tooth *Phellodon niger* has been recorded.

14. Craig Leek. This area, near Braemar, contains a large exposure of Dalradian limestone. Scree of large limestone boulders beneath the south-east facing cliffs provides the moss cushion habitat required by the BAP species White Stalkball *Tulostoma niveum*, considered to be globally threatened (Palmer, 1994). Worldwide it is known from only 23 localities; 20 in Sweden, one in Finland (Kers, 1978) and two in Scotland.

Another interesting species from this area is *Geopora arenosa* (*sensu strictu*) (Yao & Spooner, 2003), recorded from bare, base-rich soils, and on three other Scottish montane sites (see Morrone above).

Craig Leek contains a mosaic of mycologically interesting habitats, with pinewood species such as Sunset Webcap *Cortinarius limonius*, *Mycena purpureofusca* and Copper Brittlegill *Russula decolorans*, and a range of grassland fungi, including

Blushing Waxcap *Hygrocybe ovina*; one of five species linked to sites of national importance for their grassland mycota (Newton *et al.*, 2003a). There are also areas of semi-natural birchwood.

15. Glen Clunie. An area of riverside grassland was located in Glen Clunie during the survey of Scottish waxcap grasslands (Newton *et al.*, 2003a) and provisionally classified as being of national importance. Glen Clunie contains other similar areas of grassland that have yet to be surveyed and grades into montane habitats on the Cairnwell and other mountains. On the southern side of the watershed, the A93 runs through Gleann Beag. This area is known to contain Rose Spindles *Clavaria rosea* and also Spignel Rust *Nyssopsora echinata*; a rare rust of the montane grassland plant Spignel *Meum athamanticum*. The semi-improved grasslands of the glen would undoubtedly benefit from further survey. Lurid Bolete *Boletus luridus* is recorded from Gleann Beag, growing in base-rich grassland with Rock Rose.

16. Mar Lodge: Lui Bridge. This area is part of the extensive semi-natural pinewoods of upper Deeside, which include Glen Derry and Glen Luibeg.

The BAP Priority Devil's Tooth Hydnellum peckii *is named after the red droplets that form on young fruit bodies. A pinewood specialist, it has been recorded from six of the Cairngorms' important areas for fungi.*
Photo: *L. Gill*

Tooth fungi are often found fruiting in mineral soil beside paths or rivers. The Black Tooth Phellodon niger, *shown here, has been recorded from fewer than ten British localities.*
Photo: *L. Gill*

Known to contain significant populations of PBRL species, Lui Bridge includes an area of mixed pine and birch, raising the fungal diversity of the area. Of particular interest is Giant Knight *Tricholoma colossus*, the two BAP species Drab Tooth *Bankera fuligineoalba* and Pine Tooth *Sarcodon squamosus*, and *Sistotrema muscicola*. Lui Bridge is the only known Scottish site for the latter, with only four other locations known in England.

17. Curr Wood is an area of mature pine plantation with some larch, near to Dulnain Bridge. The presence of extensive areas of Twinflower *Linnaea borealis* and the range of interesting pine-associating fungi found in this area suggest that there may be a link with Caledonian pine forest. They include Golden Navel *Chrysomphalina chrysophylla*, Sunset Webcap *Cortinarius limonius*, Pine Milkcap *Lactarius musteus*, *Mycena purpureofusca*, Copper Brittlegill *Russula decolorans* and *Tricholoma pessundatum*. *Russula fusconigra* is a new British record and *Metacoleroa dickiei* is a microfungus that associates with Twinflower. The rare occurrence of this microfungus is linked to the limited occurrence of the plant. The site is now being managed as a model pine plantation and for conservation purposes.

18. Cairngorms and Cairnwell/ Glas Maol. This extensive area (Figure 11.1: 18a) encompasses parts of the Cairngorms SSSI and NNR, Caenlochan and Eastern Cairngorms SSSIs, and includes several localities known to be of particular fungal interest (18b). The high tops include large areas of montane habitat, with pockets of Dwarf Birch *Betula nana* and Dwarf Willow *Salix herbacea* (Figure 7.3). Whilst unlikely to support the diversity of fungi associated with lowland woods, these pockets contain relict populations of associated fungi. Mycorrhizal fungi are an important component of such habitats and must play an important role in nitrogen transfer and the release of phosphate (Watling, 1988). Since areas around Cairngorm itself and Cairnwell/Glas Maol are relatively accessible, many of the records come from these areas. Other areas are relatively inaccessible and consequently under-recorded. There is one British record of Northern Bilberry Redleaf *Exobasidium expansum* from this area, and also one of only four British records of the globally rare Bearberry Redleaf *E. sydowianum*. Bearberry *Arctostaphylos uva-ursi* has also been found to support mycorrhizal fungi more normally associated with pine. Species such as Foxy Bolete *Leccinum vulpinum* and Arched Woodwax *Hygrophorus camarophyllus* have been recorded at 700 m in the vicinity of Cairn Gorm (R. Watling pers. comm.; E. Holden in prog.).

Although not strictly fungi, the Slime Moulds (Myxomycetes) have traditionally been studied by mycologists and, since they include a particularly important group of snow-line specialists recorded from the Cairngorms, it would seem appropriate

Moss growing on limestone boulders provides suitable habitat for the BAP Priority species White Stalkball Tulostoma niveum.
Photo: *L. Gill*

White Stalkball is considered to be globally threatened, and is known from only 23 localities worldwide.
Photo: *L. Gill*

to include them in this chapter. The lowest altitude that these Myxomycetes have been found in Scotland is 500 m (Ing, 2003) and they require at least three months of continuous snow cover to become established. Cairngorms NNR includes the best sites for these organisms in Britain, with 16 species recorded, out of a total of 21 known in Britain. Glas Maol is also an excellent site, containing two species not yet found on Cairn Gorm; *Lepidioderma chailletti* and *Physarum albescens* (Ing, 2002 and pers. comm.). Many of the species found within the Cairngorms are widespread in montane areas of Europe, the Americas, Australasia, Japan and the Himalayas, but *Physarum albescens* is scattered and uncommon in other countries also. Within Britain, the species listed in Table 11.2 are rarely recorded outside of Scotland and the Cairngorms hold a considerable proportion of the known British populations.

19. Craigellachie. Comprising ancient, predominantly birch woodland, this is one of several discrete areas on Strathspey that contain a range of rare and interesting species. The type collection for *Russula scotica* is from here, but further collections are required to confirm the validity of the taxon, since the type has been lost.

In Britain, the pinewood specialist Scented Knight Tricholoma apium *has been recorded from only four locations – all within the Cairngorms.*

Photo: *L. Holden*

20. Kinrara, near Alvie, contains a mosaic of interesting habitats for fungi, including semi-natural pine woodland, as illustrated by the presence of the two BAP species Devil's Tooth *Hydnellum peckii* and Woolly Tooth *Phellodon tomentosus*. An area of fen has so far proved to be the most interesting mycologically, however. This includes dead wood on old willows in a humid habitat, and supports several colonies of Scarlet Splash *Cytidia salicina* and *Phellinus punctatus* (see Insh Marshes below). The discovery of *C. salicina* here in 2002 was particularly interesting as it is very possibly the same location as that from which the species was recorded in 1879 and 1900, i.e. 'Lynwilg'. It would seem quite likely that the fungus has been fruiting here, unrecorded, for over 100 years.

21. Corriemulzie (North and South). These two adjacent areas of semi-improved grassland in upper Deeside were located during the survey of Scottish waxcap grasslands (Newton *et al.*, 2003a) and provisionally classified as being of national importance. Upper Deeside contains several areas of semi-improved grassland that are of mycological interest. They are often acidic grasslands with some base-rich influence, and usually grazed by sheep, deer, rabbits or hare. They have been managed by grazing only, and a minimum of agricultural improvement has been undertaken.

22. Balneden is a small area of semi-improved grassland at the southern end of Strath Avon. It was located during a survey of Scottish waxcap grasslands (Newton *et al.*, 2003a) and is provisionally classified as being of European importance. The area of interest is on a steep hillside, surrounded on one side by conifer plantation and above, and to the other side, by flatter, improved grassland of no mycological interest. The site thus illustrates many of the threats to this kind of habitat, but is unlikely to be the only site of interest in the area.

23. Inver. This is an area of conifer plantation, including both Scots Pine *Pinus sylvestris* and Sitka Spruce *Picea sitchensis*, with small areas of intact old birch woodland. It is currently being managed to reduce the number of exotic species and to create a more natural vegetation structure. The presence of both pine and birch PBRL species in the area would certainly support this aim. Spruce Tooth *Bankera violascens*, a mycorrhizal associate of spruce, also occurs, this being only its second known British location. (The first, now clear-felled of spruce, is also in the Cairngorms, at Glenmore). Its discovery has led to some modification of the original management plan, so that some areas of spruce will be retained. The fungus is thought to be widespread but uncommon in Europe, and although it may have been introduced into Britain with its host, it is also

Figure 11.1. Important areas for fungi. See text for details and Table 11.2 for species lists.

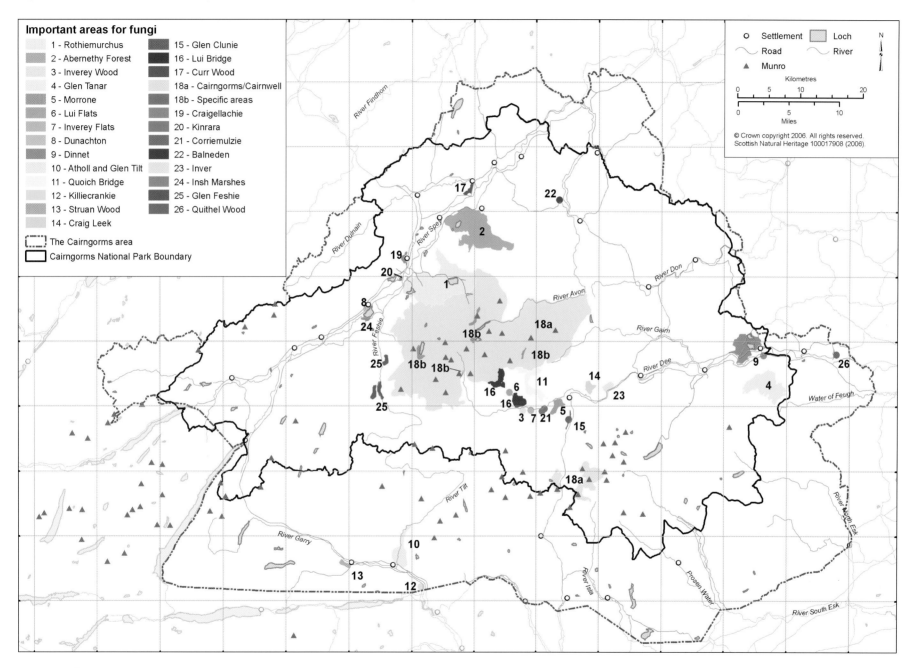

Important areas for fungi

1 - Rothiemurchus
2 - Abernethy Forest
3 - Inverey Wood
4 - Glen Tanar
5 - Morrone
6 - Lui Flats
7 - Inverey Flats
8 - Dunachton
9 - Dinnet
10 - Atholl and Glen Tilt
11 - Quoich Bridge
12 - Killiecrankie
13 - Struan Wood
14 - Craig Leek

15 - Glen Clunie
16 - Lui Bridge
17 - Curr Wood
18a - Cairngorms/Cairnwell
18b - Specific areas
19 - Craigellachie
20 - Kinrara
21 - Corriemulzie
22 - Balneden
23 - Inver
24 - Insh Marshes
25 - Glen Feshie
26 - Quithel Wood

The Cairngorms area
Cairngorms National Park Boundary

Settlement Loch
Road   River
Munro

N

Kilometres
0   5   10   20

0   5   10
Miles

Aspen Tongue Taphrina johansonii *is a parasitic fungus which causes enlargement of the carpels of Aspen catkins. Its five known British sites include Abernethy and Braemar.*

Photo: *E. Emmet*

In 2002 the Scarlet Splash Cytidia salicina *was rediscovered at Kinrara; possibly the same location at which it had been found in 1900. The species has been recorded from just four British sites, which include Insh Marshes.*

Photo: *L. Holden*

possible that it developed from independent spore sources. Further discussion of the importance of exotic tree and shrub species and their associated fungi in Scotland is given in Watling (1997).

24. Insh Marshes*.* Peripheral to the open water are wet areas containing old willows. There are extensive stands of Aspen, with both habitats including some dead wood. This is reflected in the presence of three interesting dead wood species: *Ceriporiopsis aneirina* growing on dead Aspen; Scarlet Splash *Cytidia salicina* growing on the underside of dead willow branches in humid conditions; and *Phellinus punctatus*, also on willow. Insh is one of four British sites for Scarlet Splash *Cytida salicina*, one of two Scottish sites for *Phellinus punctatus* (see Kinrara) and for *Russula font-queri* (see Dunachton). The first Scottish record of BAP species Marsh Honey Fungus *Armillaria ectypa* was found during a visit to the site by the BMS in August, 2005.

25. Glen Feshie (including Badan Mosach). Mycologists have neglected this area, which consequently has relatively few records. There are large areas of semi-natural pine woodland, and the presence of five PBRL species associated with pinewoods, including two BAP species (Devil's Tooth *Hydnellum peckii* and Woolly Tooth *Phellodon tomentosus*), suggests that the area warrants further survey.

26. Quithel Wood*.* This base-rich, mixed broadleaf, riverine woodland, which includes old coppiced Hazel and a relatively large area of Alder carr, is an interesting site in the eastern Cairngorms. A collection of the litter-decomposing *Mycena alexandrii* (still to be finally confirmed) would be new to Britain, while a record of *Scytinostroma portentosum* is the first for Scotland of this nationally rare fungus. A wood-decomposing fungus, it is possible that the sheltered, humid nature of a site, with a relatively high accumulation of dead wood, has encouraged its growth.

There are, in addition, outstanding sites for fungi around Kindrogan Field Studies Centre, which lie on the boundary of the Cairngorms area and have not been included in this review.

Recent research and survey findings

The BAP programme has stimulated a considerable amount of research and survey work on fungi (Fleming, 2001), which has included sites within the Cairngorms. In response to this and to the increasing need for land managers to know how their management interventions will affect fungal communities, field mycologists have had to look again for methodologies which overcome the well-documented difficulties of surveying fungi (Watling, 1990; Cannon, 1997; Feest, 2000). Much of the work outlined below has focussed on gathering baseline data on the distribution of species of interest and further studies are anticipated to better inform the relevant Species Action Plans (SAPs). The initial results of these surveys indicate that the Cairngorms area is of great mycological importance, particularly for its pinewood, montane and unimproved grassland species.

One of the important results of the increased interest in fungal survey work has been the location of several new or important species within the Cairngorms. These include: *Cortinarius phaeopygmaeus,* found on the Cairngorm plateau; *Mycena viridimarginata, Tubulicrinis propinquus* and *Russula vinosobrunnea,* recorded on Mar Lodge Estate; and Aspen Bracket *Phellinus tremulae, Russula font-queri* and *R. fusconigra* from Strathspey. All are new to Britain and recorded since 1999. White Stalkball *Tulostoma niveum* and Black Falsebolete *Boletopsis leucomelaena,* both BAP species, were each known from only one location, until surveys in 1998 and 2001 uncovered sites at Craig Leek and Mar Lodge (Holden, 1999, 2002a). The recording efforts of interested individuals, local recording groups[7] and the BMS have also made a significant contribution to recording new species and enhancing our knowledge of the distribution of fungi.

Desk Studies. Considerable effort has been invested in entering existing records onto a database system (e.g. Watling *et al.,* 1995; Davy, 2003). However, there is still a large number of collections of great significance at the RBGE which require incorporation (R. Watling, pers. comm.). Some have already been analysed (Watling, unpublished data).

The publication of lists of Scottish Priority Fungi and Species of Conservation Concern (Ward, 1999) and, more recently, of the Cairngorms LBAP (Cosgrove, 2002), has highlighted the mycological importance of the Cairngorms. In Ward (1999) 22 Priority Fungi are listed and defined as being globally threatened or declining, and in need of species action plans. One of these, a single collection of *Sarcodon versipellis,* is now accepted as being a misidentification. Of the remaining 21, 19 have been recorded in the Cairngorms, the exceptions being Hazel Gloves *Hypocreopsis rhododendri* and Date Waxcap *Hygrocybe spadicea.*

Fungi are listed as a notified feature on only four SSSIs in the Cairngorms area. *Important Fungus Areas* (Evans *et al.,* 2001) lists 16 areas in the Cairngorms that are considered to be of national importance, and 43 such areas in Scotland as a whole. A further 24 areas were considered likely to be of national importance but were data deficient. In an attempt to highlight these areas and to provide the next step towards further action by the statutory conservation agencies, SNH commissioned the compilation of a dossier of 107 such areas in Scotland (Holden, 2003a), including 18 areas within the Cairngorms.

Fungal diversity in Scottish conifer plantations (1995-1999). This survey was commissioned by the Forestry Commission as a part of a larger study of the biodiversity associated with plantations. Permanent sample plots were established in eight woodland sites, including Queen's Forest, Glenmore. Detailed analysis of the data is presented in Humphrey *et al.* (2000) while Newton *et al.* (2003b) present a useful summary of the main findings relevant to fungal conservation. The finding that many fungal species, including threatened taxa, are able to colonise plantation forests, particularly those closest to areas of semi-natural pinewood, will help to inform the management of plantation woodlands of the Cairngorms.

Another key result of this survey was the high degree of variation recorded between sites, with respect to the composition of fungal communities (Newton

Quithel Wood is the only known Scottish site for the nationally rare Mothball Crust Scytinostroma portentosum.
Photo: *L. Holden*

Table 11.2. Important areas for fungi in the Cairngorms, listed in descending order of the number of species on the Provisional European Red List. Species for which there is a UK Species Action Plan are indicated in bold.

Note that species may occur both in column 2 (PERL) and in column 3 (BAP/PBRL). Column 4 lists species that do not appear on published lists of conservation concern but are nevertheless of interest (see Table 11.1). Note also that the more extensive areas (e.g., Rothiemurchus, Abernethy, Cairngorms) are not strictly comparable with smaller, more discrete areas.

Percentage of area occurring within the National Park: *** >75%; ** 25-75%; * 10-24%; '-' <10%

Area	Species on the Provisional European Red List	BAP and/or Provisional British Red List species	Other species of interest	% of area within NP
1. Rothiemurchus	*Bankera fuligineoalba*, **Boletopsis leucomelaena**, *Boletus appendiculatus, B. radicans, Clavaria zollingeri, Cortinarius cyanites, C. orellanus, C. scaurus, Cudonia circinans, Entoloma bloxamii, E. euchroum, E. prunuloides, Gloeporus dichrous, Gomphidius maculatus,* **Hydnellum aurantiacum, H. caeruleum, H. concrescens, H. ferrugineum, H. peckii, H. scrobiculatum,** *Hygrocybe cantharellus, H.fornicata, H. intermedia, H. irrigata, H. nitrata, H. ovina, H. punicea, H. quieta, Lactarius aspideus, L. hysginus, L. musteus, Leucocortinarius bulbiger, Phellinus tremulae,* **Phellodon confluens, P. melaleucus,** *P. niger,* **P. tomentosus,** *Pleurocybella porrigens, Porpoloma metapodium, Psathyrella caput-medusae, Russula aquosa,* **Sarcodon glaucopus, S. squamosus, S. scabrosus,** *Stereopsis vitellina, Suillus flavidus, Tricholoma apium, T. colossus, T. focale, T. sejunctum, Vibrissea truncorum* **(51 species)**	*Bankera fuligineoalba*, **Boletopsis leucomelaena,** *Camarophyllopsis micacea, Cantharellus aurora, Clavaria zollingeri, Collybia acervata, C. prolixa, C. putilla, Cortinarius balteatocumatilis, C. caerulescens, C. caledoniensis, C. camphoratus, C. cyanites, C. durus, C. fervidus, C. glaucopus, C. laniger, C. limonius, C. porphyropus, C. scaurus, C. subtortus, C. talus, C. saporatus C. variicolor, C. violaceus, Cudonia circinans, C. confusa, Cystoderma cinnabarinum, Entoloma bloxamii, Fayodia bisphaerigera, Flammulaster limulatus, Hapalopilus salmonicolor,* **Hydnellum aurantiacum, H. caeruleum, H. concrescens, H. ferrugineum, H. peckii, H. scrobiculatum,** *Hygrophorus hedrychii, Hypholoma epixanthum, Inocybe calospora, Lactarius musteus, Leccinum vulpinum, Leucocortinarius bulbiger, Mycena purpureofusca, M. rosella, M. rubromarginata, M. urania, Naucoria scolecina, Stagnicola perplexa,* **Phellodon confluens, P. melaleucus,** *P. niger,* **P. tomentosus,** *Pholiota astragalina, Porpoloma metapodium, Psathyrella caput-medusae, P. solitaria, Pseudocraterellus undulatus, Ramaria stricta, R. suecica, Rozites caperatus, Russula aquosa, R. badia, R. decolorans, R. mustelina, R. integra, R. vinosa, R. violaceoides,* **Sarcodon glaucopus, S. squamosus, S. scabrosus,** *Squamanita contortipes, S. pearsonii, Stereopsis vitellina, Suillus flavidus, Tricholoma acerbum, T. apium, T. nauseosum, T. colossus, T. focale, T. pessundatum, T. sejunctum, Vibrissae truncorum, Xeromphalina campanella, X. cauticinalis* **(86 species)**	*Antrodia ramentacea, Bankera violascens, Boletus luridus, Collybia aquosa, C. hariolorum, C. tergina, Coltricia montagnei, Cortinarius rubicundulus, C. spilomeus, Gamundia striatula, Gymnosporangium cornutum, G. clavariiforme, Gyromitra ambigua, G. infula, Hebeloma radicosum, Hydnum mucidum, Lactarius badiosanguineus, L. mammosus, Lichenomphalia alpina, Mucronella calva, Omphalina mutila, Peniophora pini, Perrotia flammea, Phellinus pomaceus, Phellodon atratus, Ramaria stricta, Rhodocybe hirneola, Ripartites tricholoma* **(28 species)**	***
2. Abernethy Forest	*Bankera fuligineoalba, Clavaria zollingeri, C. scaurus, Cortinarius violaceus, Cotylidia pannosa, Cudonia circinans, Entoloma griseocyaneum, Gomphidius maculatus,* **Hydnellum aurantiacum, H. caeruleum, H. concrescens, H. ferrugineum, H. peckii, H. scrobiculatum,** *Hygrocybe aurantiosplendens, H. cantharellus, H. fornicata, H. insipida, H. intermedia, H. irrigata, H. lacmus, H. nitrata, H. punicea, H. quieta, Lactarius musteus, Microglossum viride, Phaeogalera stagnina, Phellinus tremulae,* **Phellodon confluens, P. melaleucus,** *P. niger,* **P. tomentosus,** *Pleurocybella porrigens, Psathyrella caput-medusae, Russula aquosa,* **Sarcodon glaucopus, S. squamosus, S. scabrosus,** *Spathularia flavida, Stereopsis vitellina, Suillus flavidus, Tricholoma apium, T. focale, T. sejunctum* **(44 species)**	*Bankera fuligineoalba, Calocybe onychina, Cantharellus lutescens, Chrysomphalina chrysophylla, Clavaria straminea, C. zollingeri, Collybia acervata, C. prolixa, Cortinarius caerulescens, C. caledoniensis, C. camphoratus, C. durus, C. fervidus, C. glaucopus, C. laniger, C. limonius, C. talus, C. scaurus, C. subtortus, C. porphyropus, C. purpurascens, C. violaceus, Cotylidia pannosa, Cudonia circinans, C. confusa, Cystoderma cinnabarinum, Entoloma nitidum, Flammulaster limulatus,* **Hydnellum aurantiacum, H. caeruleum, H. concrescens, H. ferrugineum, H. peckii, H. scrobiculatum, Hygrocybe calyptriformis,** *Inocybe jacobi, Lactarius musteus, Leccinum vulpinum, Mycena purpureofusca, M. rosella, M. rubromarginata, M. urania, Naucoria striatula, Ombrophila violacea,* **Phellodon confluens, P. melaleucus,** *P. niger,* **P. tomentosus,** *Psathyrella caput-medusae, Psathyrella solitaria, Rozites caperatus, Russula badia, R. aquosa, R. cessans, R. decolorans, R. vinosa, R. integra, R. violaceoides,* **Sarcodon glaucopus, S. squamosus, S. scabrosus,** *Stereopsis vitellina, Stropharia hornemannii, Suillus flavidus, Tricholoma apium, T. nauseosum, T. focale, T. pessundatum, T. sejunctum, T. stans, Xeromphalina campanella, X. cauticinalis* **(72 species)**	*Antrodia ramentacea, Collybia alpina, C. tergina, Conocybe pinetorum, Cortinarius rubicundulus, C. spilomeus, Gymnosporangium cornutum, G. clavariiforme,* **Hebeloma sordescens,** *Hypomyces viridis, Lactarius badiosanguineus, Leccinum atrostipatum, Lepista panaeola, Phellodon atratus,* **Rhodocybe hirneola,** *Rickenella pseudogrisella, Russula scotica, R. xenochlora, Sarcoleotia turficola, Taphrina johansonii* **(20 species)**	***

Area	Species on the Provisional European Red List	BAP and/or Provisional British Red List species	Other species of interest	% of area within NP
3. Mar Lodge: Inverey Wood	*Bankera fuligineoalba*, *Boletopsis leucomelaena*, *Buchwaldoboletus lignicola*, *Clavaria zollingeri*, *Cortinarius scaurus*, *Geoglossum atropurpureum*, *Gomphidius maculatus*, **Hydnellum aurantiacum, H. caeruleum, H. ferrugineum, H. peckii, H. scrobiculatum**, *Hygrocybe punicea*, *Lactarius musteus*, **Microglossum olivaceum**, *Onygena equina*, **Phellodon melaleucus**, *P. niger*, **P. tomentosus**, *Pleurocybella porrigens*, *Porpoloma metapodium*, **Sarcodon squamosus, S. scabrosus**, *Suillus flavidus*, *Tricholoma apium*, *T. focale*, *T. pessundatum*, *Xerophalina campanella* **(28 species)**	*Bankera fuligineoalba*, *Boletopsis leucomelaena*, *Buchwaldoboletus lignicola*, *Cantharellus aurora*, *Clavaria zollingeri*, *Collybia acervata*, *Cortinarius limonius*, *C. scaurus*, *Geoglossum atropurpureum*, **Hydnellum aurantiacum, H. caeruleum, H. ferrugineum, H. peckii, H. scrobiculatum**, *Lactarius musteus*, *Leccinum vulpinum*, **Microglossum olivaceum**, *Mycena purpureofusca*, *M. rubromarginata*, **Phellodon melaleucus**, *P. niger*, **P. tomentosus**, *Porpoloma metapodium*, *Rozites caperatus*, *Russula badia*, *R. decolorans*, *R. mustelina*, *R vinosa*, *R. integra*, **Sarcodon squamosus, S. scabrosus**, *Suillus flavidus*, *Tricholoma apium*, *T. focale*, *T. pessundatum*, *Xerophalina campanella* **(36 species)**	*Clavaria rosea*, *Collybia alpina*, *Hypomyces viridis*, *Lactarius mammosus*, *Mycena septentrionalis*, *M. viridimarginata*, *Russula vinosobrunnea*, *Tubulicrinis propinquus* **(8 species)**	***
4. Glen Tanar	*Aureoboletus gentilis*, *Boletus pseudosulphureus*, *Entoloma griseocyaneum*, *E. prunuloides*, **Hydnellum ferrugineum**, *Hygrocybe cantharellus*, *H. lacmus*, *H. fornicata*, *Phaeogalera stagnina*, **Phellodon tomentosus**, *Pleurocybella porrigens*, **Sarcodon squamosus** *Spathularia flavida*, *Suillus flavidus*, *Tricholoma colossus*, *T. focale*, *T. sejunctum* **(17 species)**	*Boletus pseudosulphureus*, *Collybia acervata*, *Cortinarius caledoniensis*, *C. limonius*, **Hydnellum ferrugineum**, *Mycena purpureofusca*, **Phellodon tomentosus**, *Pholiota spumosa*, *Rozites caperatus*, *Russula decolorans*, *R. vinosa*, *R. integra*, **Sarcodon squamosus**, *Suillus flavidus*, *Tricholoma colossus*, *T. focale*, *T. pessundatum*, *T. sejunctum*, *Xeromphalina campanella* **(19 species)**	*Boletus aereus*, *B. luridus*, *Ramaria stricta*, *Ripartites tricholoma* **(4 species)**	***
5. Morrone	*Boletus queletii*, *Cortinarius cyanites*, *Entoloma bloxamii*, *E. prunuloides*, *Geoglossum atropurpureum*, *G. fallax*, *G. glutinosum*, *Gloeoporus dichrous*, *Hygrocybe cantharellus*, *H. insipida*, *H. irrigata*, *H. nitrata*, *H. punicea*, *H. quieta*, *Onygena equina*, *Phellinus tremulae*, *Russula aquosa* **(17 species)**	*Cortinarius cyanites*, *C. talus*, *C. olidus*, *C. porphyropus*, *Entoloma bloxamii*, *Geoglossum atropurpureum*, *Hyalopsora aspidiotus*, *Hygrophorus hedreychii*, *Leccinum vulpinum*, *Mycena rubromarginata*, *Rozites caperatus*, *Russula aquosa*, *R. decolorans*, *R. intermedia*, *R. persicina*, *R. nana*, *R. vinosa*, *R. integra* **(18 species)**	*Amanita flavescens*, *Boletus luridus*, *Clavariadelphus pistillaris*, *Coprinus lilatinctus*, *Cortinarius rubicundulus*, *C. spilomeus*, *Geopora arenosa s.s.*, *Gymnosporangium cornutum*, *G. clavariiforme Hebeloma radicosum*, *Inocybe leptophylla*, *Mycena latifolia*, *Omphalina mutila*, *Perrotia flammea*, *Peziza granulosa* **(15 species)**	***
6. Mar Lodge: Lui Flats	*Entoloma griseocyaneum*, *E. prunuloides*, *Geoglossum atropurpureum*, *G. fallax*, *G. glutinosum*, *G. umbratile*, *Hygrocybe cantharellus*, *H. fornicata*, *H. insipida*, *H. nitrata*, *H. punicea*, *H. quieta*, **Microglossum olivaceum**, *Porpoloma metapodium* **(14 species)**	*Geoglossum atropurpureum*, *G. starbaeckii*, **Microglossum olivaceum**, *Porpoloma metapodium*, *Squamanita paradoxa*, *Xeromphalina campanella* **(6 species)**	*Clavaria rosea*, *Gamundia striatula*, *Lepista panaeola* **(3 species)**	***
7. Inverey Flats	*Entoloma griseocyaneum*, *E. prunuloides*, *Geoglossum umbratile*, *Hygrocybe cantharellus*, *H. fornicata*, *H. irrigata*, *H. nitrata*, *H. punicea*, *H. quieta*, *H radiata*, **Microglossum olivaceum**, *Phellinus tremulae* **(12 species)**	*Clavulinopsis umbrinella*, **Hygrocybe calyptriformis, Microglossum olivaceum**, *Russula nana* **(4 species)**		***
8. Dunachton	*Entoloma griseocyaneum*, *Geoglossum glutinosum*, *G. umbratile*, *Hygrocybe cantharellus*, *H. ingrata*, *H. intermedia*, *H. irrigata*, *H. ovina*, *H. punicea*, *H. quieta*, *Phellinus tremulae*, *Porpoloma metapodium* **(12 species)**	*Cantharellus ferruginascens*, *Porpoloma metapodium* **(2 species)**	*Gyroporus cyanescens*, *Russula fontqueri* **(2 species)**	***

Area	Species on the Provisional European Red List	BAP and/or Provisional British Red List species	Other species of interest	% of area within NP
9. Dinnet	*Aureoboletus gentilis, Boletus appendiculatus, Grifola frondosa, Hydnellum scrobiculatum, Hygrocybe cantharellus, Hygrophorus nemoreus, Leucocortinarius bulbiger, Phellinus tremulae, Porphyrellus porphyrosporus, Russula aquosa, Tricholoma focale* (11 species)	*Cortinarius crassus, C. caledoniensis, C. limonius, C. melliolens, C. porphyropus,* **Hydnellum scrobiculatum, Hygrocybe calyptriformis,** *Hygrophorus nemoreus, Leccinum vulpinum, Leucocortinarius bulbiger, Ochropsora ariae, Pseudocraterellus undulatus, Russula aquosa, R. vinosa, Tricholoma focale, T. pessundatum* (16 species)	*Boletus aereus, Euepixylon udum, Hebeloma radicosum, Hemimycena cephalotricha* (unconfirmed record, 2003) (4 species)	***
10. Atholl and Glen Tilt	*Clavaria zollingeri, Geoglossum atropurpureum, Hygrocybe nitrata, H. ovina, H. punicea, H. quieta, Lactarius hysginus, Microglossum viride, Russula aquosa, Stobilomyces strobilaceus, Tricholoma sejunctum* (11 species)	*Clavaria zollingeri, Cortinarius caerulescens, C. glaucopus, C. variicolor, Flammulaster limulatus, Geoglossum atropurpureum, Pseudocraterellus undulatus, Russula aquosa, R. integra, Strobilomyces strobilaceus, Tricholoma sejunctum* (11 species)	*Amanita pachyvolvata, Amanita phalloides, Boletus luridus, Helvella cupuliformis, Hypholoma epixanthum* (5 species)	-
11. Mar Lodge: Quoich Bridge	*Geoglossum atropurpureum, G. fallax, G. glutinosum, G. umbratile,* **Hydnellum peckii,** *Hygrocybe cantharellus, H. punicea, H. quieta,* **Phellodon tomentosus, Sarcodon squamosus** (10 species)	*Cortinarius limonius, Collybia acervata, Geoglossum atropurpureum,* **Hydnellum peckii,** *Mycena rubromarginata,* **Phellodon tomentosus,** *Rozites caperatus, Russula decolorans, R. integra, R. vinosa,* **Sarcodon squamosus** (11 species)		***
12. Killiecrankie	*Cortinarius cyanites, Gomphidius maculatus,* **Hydnellum concrescens,** *Hygrocybe punicea, Hygrophorus nemoreus, Phylloporus pelletieri, Porphyrellus porphyrosporus,* **Ramaria botrytis,** *Strobilomyces strobilaceus, Tricholoma sejunctum* (10 species)	*Cortinarius cyanites, Flavoscypha phlebophora,* **Hydnellum concrescens,** *Hygrophorus nemoreus, Ochropsora ariae, Rozites caperatus, Russula lundellii, R. solaris, Strobilomyces strobilaceus, Tricholoma sejunctum* (10 species)	*Amanita phalloides,* **Boletus luridus,** *Calocybe constricta, Collybia aquosa, Clavariadelphus pistillaris, Cystolepiota seminuda, Leccinum atrostipitatum, Lycoperdon echinatum* (8 species)	-
13. Struan Wood	*Cortinarius violaceus, Entoloma griseocyanea, E. prunuloides, Hygrocybe cantharellus, H. ovina, H. punicea, Lactarius hysginus, Onygena equina, Phellodon niger, Spathularia flavida* (10 species)	*Collybia acervata, Cortinarius infractus, C. porphyropus, C. talus, C. variicolor, C. violaceus, C. xanthocephalus, Phellodon niger, Russula nana, R. persicina* (10 species)	*Cheimonophyllum candidissimum, Cortinarius spilomeus, Gamundia striatula, Lactarius flavidus, Perrotia flammea, Phellinus laevigatus, Rhodocybe hirneola, Scutellinia decipiens* (8 species)	-
14. Craig Leek	*Entoloma prunuloides, Gomphidius maculatus, Hygrocybe lacmus, H. nitrata, H. ovina, H. punicea, H. quieta,* **Tulostoma niveum** (8 species)	*Cortinarius camphoratus, C. limonius, Fayodia bisphaerigera, Mycena purpureofusca, Russula decolorans, R. nana, R. vinosa,* **Tulostoma niveum** (8 species)	*Geopora arenosa s.s., Mycena septentrionalis* (2 species)	***
15. Glen Clunie	*Entoloma prunuloides, Geoglossum atropurpureum, G. glutinosum, G. umbratile, Hygrocybe lacmus, H. nitrata, H. punicea, H. quieta* (8 species)	*Geoglossum atropurpureum, Nyssopsora echinata* (2 species)	*Boletus luridus, Clavaria rosea* (2 species)	**
16. Mar Lodge: Lui Bridge	**Bankera fuligineoalba,** *Cortinarius scaurus, Lactarius musteus, Russula aquosa,* **Sarcodon squamosus,** *Tricholoma apium, T. colossus* (7 species)	**Bankera fuligineoalba,** *Cantharellus aurora, Collybia acervata, Cortinarius camphoratus, C. limonius, C. scaurus, C variicolor, Cystoderma cinnabarinum, Lactarius musteus, Leccinum vulpinum, Mycena rubromarginata, Russula aquosa, R. decolorans, R. vinosa, R. integra,* **Sarcodon squamosus,** *Suillus flavidus, Tricholoma apium, T. colossus, T. pessundatum* (20 species)	*Sistotrema muscicola* (1 species)	***
17. Curr Wood	*Geoglossum fallax, Gomphidius maculatus, Hygrocybe cantharellus, H. insipida, Lactarius musteus, Pleurocybella porrigens, Russula aquosa* (7 species)	*Chrysomphalina chrysophylla, Collybia acervata, Cortinarius limonius, C. variicolor, Lactarius musteus, Mycena purpureofusca, Rozites caperatus, Russula amethystina, R. aquosa, R. badia, R. decolorans, R. vinosa, Tricholoma pessundatum, Xeromphalina cauticinalis* (14 species)	*Cortinarius rubicundulus, Dacrymyces confluens, Gymnosporangium cornutum, G. clavariiforme, Hebeloma birrum, Hebeloma pallidoluctuosum, H. sordescens, Hypomyces viridis, Lactarius mammosus, Metacoleroa dickiei, Russula fusconigra, R. xenochlora* (12 species)	***

Area	Species on the Provisional European Red List	BAP and/or Provisional British Red List species	Other species of interest	% of area within NP
18. Cairngorms and Cairnwell/ Glas Maol	*Geoglossum fallax, G. umbratile, Hygrocybe cantharellus, H. insipida, H. nitrata, H quieta, Hygrophorus camarophyllus* **(7 species)**	*Amanita nivalis, Exobasidium sydowianum, Hygrophorus camarophyllus, Russula nana, Russula norvegica (= montane variety of R. laccata?), R. persicina* Myxomycetes (Slime Moulds): *Dianema nivale, Lamproderma atrosporum, Lamproderma sauteri, Lepidoderma carestianum* **(10 species)**	*Collybia alpina, Cortinarius favrei, C. gausapatus, C. helvelloides f.* Favre, *C. phaeopygmaeus, C. rufostriatus, C. scotoides, Exobadium expansum, Galerina harrisonii, Hygrocybe citrinopallida, H. lilacina, Hygrocybe salicis-herbaceae, Inocybe dulcamara f. squamosoannualata, I.scabella var. fulvella, Laccaria proximella, Lichenomphalia alpina, Mycena latifolia, Omphaliaster asterosporus, O. borealis, Phaeogalera stagnina, Psathyrella nolitangere, Russula pascua, Scutellinia patagonica,* Myxomycetes (Slime Moulds) *Diderma lyallii, Lamproderma carestiae, Lamproderma cribrarioides, Physarum albescens* **(27 species)**	*** **
19. Craigellachie	*Hygrocybe cantharellus, H. punicea, Lactarius aspideus, L. hysginus, Leucocortinarius bulbiger, Russula aquosa, Tricholoma sejunctum* **(7 species)**	*Cortinarius talus, Leucocortinarius bulbiger, Russula aquosa, Tricholoma sejunctum* **(4 species)**	*Collybia aquosa, Dacrymyces estonicus, Russula scotica* **(3 species)**	***
20. Kinrara	***Hydnellum peckii**, Hygrocybe cantharellus, H. punicea, Phellinus tremulae, **Phellodon tomentosus**, Porphyrellus porphyrosporus* **(6 species)**	***Hydnellum peckii, Phellodon tomentosus**, Rozites caperatus, Suillus flavidus* **(4 species)**	*Cytidia salicina, Phellinus punctatus* **(2 species)**	***
21. Corriemulzie	*Entoloma prunuloides, Geoglossum fallax, G. glutinosum, G. umbratile, Hygrocybe punicea, H. quieta* **(6 species)**	***Hygrocybe calyptriformis** **(1 species)***		***
22. Balneden	*Entoloma prunuloides, Hygrocybe irrigata, H. nitrata, H. punicea, H. quieta* **(5 species)**			***
23. Inver	*Cortinarius violaceus, Hydnellum concrescens, **Phellodon melaleucus**, Pleurocybella porrigens* **(4 species)**	*Collybia acervata, Cortinarius camphoratus, C. violaceus, Mycena purpureofusca, **Phellodon melaleucus**, Tricholoma pessundatum* **(6 species)**	*Bankera violascens, Collybia alpina* **(2 species)**	***
24. Insh Marshes	*Armillaria ectypa, Hygrocybe cantharellus, H. punicea, Phellinus tremulae* **(4 species)**	*Armillaria ectypa* **(1 species)**	*Cytidia salicina, Lactarius mammosus, Mycena latifolia, Phellinus punctatus, Russula font-queri* **(5 species)**	***
25. Glen Feshie	***Hydnellum peckii, Phellodon tomentosus**, Pleurocybella porrigens* **(3 species)**	*Collybia acervata, **Hydnellum peckii, Phellodon tomentosus**, Russula decolorans, Xeromphalina campanella* **(5 species)**		***
26. Quithel Wood	*Entoloma griseocyaneum, Scytinostroma portentosum* **(2 species)**	*Gyromitra infula, Ochropsora ariae, Russula lundellii, Scytinostroma portentosum* **(4 species)**	*Cortinarius alnetorum, Entoloma dysthales, E. tjallingiorum, Lycoperdon echinatum, Mycena alexandrii, Plicatura crispa* **(6 species)**	-

et al., 2003b). Patterns of fungal diversity and community composition remained largely unexplained by the variables measured. For example, stand stage, crop type and climate zone had no significant effect on fungal species richness. Such results highlight the general lack of understanding of the processes influencing fungal diversity (Bruns, 1995). It should be noted, however, that there was a positive correlation between deadwood volume and wood saprotroph species richness.

Status and distribution of hydnoid tooth fungi in Scottish conifer forests (1998–2000).

Reports from northern and central Europe regarding the decline of *Bankera*, *Hydnellum*, *Phellodon* and *Sarcodon* species raised conservation concern for these species in Britain. A joint Species Action Plan has been prepared for 14 species in these genera, prompting SNH to commission a three-year field survey of Scottish pinewoods, including those at Abernethy, Craig Leek, Dinnet, Glen Feshie, Glen Tanar, Mar Lodge and Rothiemurchus. Details are given in Newton *et al.* (2002a,b) and summarised in Newton *et al.* (2003b). Interesting findings include: the location of 13 species of tooth fungi in plantation woods; the restriction of tooth fungi to particular microsites associated with exposed mineral soil; the positive correlation between forest area and the number of species recorded; and the outstanding importance of forests on Strathspey and Deeside for these fungi in Scotland.

Survey of grassland fungi in Scotland (1999 – 2001).

A suite of fungi associated with old, unimproved grasslands has also been the subject of conservation concern, as their decline has been recorded in northern Europe. They include the genera *Hygrocybe* (Waxcaps), *Entoloma* (Pinkgills), *Dermoloma* and the families Clavariaceae (Fairy Clubs) and Geoglossaceae (Earthtongues). Species Action Plans have been developed for three grassland species in Britain. As a contribution towards the implementation of these SAPs, SNH commissioned a three-year survey of Scottish grasslands (Newton *et al.*, 2003a), the results of which indicate that, whilst there is some evidence of habitat loss, Scotland is of exceptional importance for grassland fungi when compared with other countries in northern Europe. The survey also highlighted difficulties in characterising the fungal composition of individual sites. Species accumulation curves indicated that more than 16 visits might be required to fully characterise the fungal diversity of a given site, and to accurately define its conservation value.

The following grassland sites in the Cairngorms area are described above as provisionally being of European or national interest: Balneden, Corriemulzie (north and south), Glen Clunie, Inverey Flats, Mar Lodge: Lui Flats, Mar Lodge: Quoich Bridge and Morrone. Other areas within the Cairngorms known to include grassland assemblages are at Abernethy, Craig Leek, Glen Tanar, Dinnet, Muir Cottage Field (Mar Lodge) and Dunachton. It is likely that further sites await discovery.

Survey of the fungi of Mar Lodge Estate (1999-2001).

This survey was commissioned by the National Trust for Scotland to assess the fungal populations within the Mar Lodge Estate and to enable the impact of management interventions on the fungi to be monitored. Species collected during the fieldwork were added to those collated from a desk study, yielding a total of 734 species on the site. Of particular interest was the investigation into the plot size necessary to sample the fungal diversity within a particular pine woodland area (Holden *et al.*, 2000).

Scottish Forestry Alliance.

Areas of Abernethy and Glenmore are part of a woodland regeneration scheme funded by the Scottish Forestry Alliance. Work towards monitoring the long-term effects of woodland regeneration on the site's biodiversity began in 2003 (Holden & Stamm, 2003). A fungal monitoring methodology is under development.

Listed on the Provisional European Red List, Black Falsebolete Boletopsis leucomelaena *is known from only two British sites: at Loch an Eilein and Inverey Wood.*

Photo: *L. Gill*

Site Condition Monitoring of SSSIs. As noted above, fungi are notified interests on four SSSIs in the Cairngorms: Abernethy, Cairngorms, Glen Tanar and Rothiemurchus. Site dossiers are being prepared for each of these (Holden, 2002c,d; Holden, 2004a,b) and a monitoring methodology is under development (Holden, 2003c).

Fungi below ground. A team from Aberdeen University and the Macaulay Institute is using DNA fingerprinting to investigate the ecology of ectomycorrhizal fungi (I. Alexander, pers. comm.). They are particularly interested in the relationship between the fruiting of mycorrhizal fungi and the mycorrhizal connections with roots. Some of this work is based in a chronosequence of native Scots Pine stands in Glen Tanar. This fascinating area of research will be an important step in furthering the understanding of fungal ecology and its relationship with woodlands.

Biodiversity: Taxonomy, Genetics and Ecology of Sub-Arctic Willow Scrub. This project was funded by SEERAD and co-ordinated jointly by the Royal Botanic Garden Edinburgh and the Macaulay Institute, Aberdeen. The main conclusions from the mycological perspective are: that Dwarf Willow *Salix herbacea* supports a high diversity of mycorrhizal fungi; that the below-ground mycorrhizal community is dominated by species that either do not produce fruiting structures above-ground or else produce fruiting forms that are cryptic; that there is some evidence to support the principle of maintaining genetic diversity in willow populations in order to maintain the diversity of associated organisms, including fungi, and also to minimise the chances of catastrophic pathogen epidemics. It is recommended that trials are carried out to assess the benefits of mycorrhizal inoculum enhancement for willow establishment (Scottish Montane Willow Research Group, 2005). The study sites were mostly outwith the Cairngorms area, but collections of fruit bodies were made from *S. herbacea* sites around Scotland, including the Cairngorms. This will provide a reference database of identified fungal DNA, against which to compare the DNA extracted from root tips (J. Milne, pers. comm.).

Trends

Baseline data, necessary for illustrating trends in population or range size, are not yet available for fungi.

The waxcap and tooth fungi surveys (Newton *et al.*, 2002b, 2003a) found evidence that some species have persisted in certain pinewood and unimproved grassland sites for decades or even centuries. However, as Newton *et al.* (2003a) point out, there is insufficient evidence to conclude that there have been no declines in Scotland.

Changes in land management are also important to consider. Whilst there is evidence that suitable habitat for the species associated with coniferous woodland is increasing, and that plantation woodland can in the right circumstances provide suitable habitat for these fungi, there has been a significant decline in the area of rough grassland in Scotland between the 1940s and the 1980s (Mackey *et al.*, 1998).

As suggested for bryophytes (Chapter 13), it is very likely that the trend of discovering new species and new sites for rare species will continue, as focused fungal survey work gradually expands our knowledge to reflect true distribution patterns, rather than just those places that mycologists have visited.

Conservation issues

Pollution. Watling & Ward (2003) suggest that pollution, including air and water-borne exhaust gases and leachates, as well as the increased use of fertilisers, are a major threat to fungi. He notes that 'these adverse impacts can replace a high density of diverse fungi in the soil or on the roots of vascular plants with just two or three common, widespread and hence successful 'weedy' species'. Arnolds (1989b) suggests that tooth fungi are particularly intolerant of high nitrogen levels and thus any future increases in airborne pollution could have a significant effect on the communities of tooth fungi in the Cairngorms. The adverse effects of artificial fertilisers are well documented in relation to the fungi of old pastures (Arnolds, 1989a).

Climate Change. Arctic-alpine species are likely to be the most directly affected by climate change, assuming that winters become milder (Chapter 20). Competition from fungi associated with plants that are not specifically adapted for the present harsh environment would certainly impact on the montane fungi. The snow-line Myxomycetes would be particularly vulnerable, as they require a minimum of three months of snow-lie to become established (Ing, 2003).

Woodland management. Increasing the area of woodland, as is planned for example at Glenmore, Abernethy and Mar Lodge, is entirely in accordance with the evidence that the larger the area of forest, the greater the diversity of species such as tooth fungi. The creation of a more diverse woodland structure, in terms of species composition and age profile, and an increase in the amount of dead timber (Humphrey *et al.*, 2000) would also be welcome from a fungal perspective. Although some fungi are particularly adapted to burnt areas, the practice of burning dead wood should be discouraged, as this effectively shortens the woodland nutrient cycle (Hodgetts, 1996). The effect of controlled burning of woodland ground flora on fungal fruiting forms part of a current project at Abernethy Forest (A. Amphlett, pers. comm.). It should be noted that where woodland is planted or regenerated on ground that has not previously been wooded, or not wooded for some considerable time, the fungal community will take longer to develop fully. This is thought to be because many mycorrhizal fungi develop better from root stock inoculation than from airborne spore sources. Retaining some mature trees in any felling operations is thus recommended.

Niemälä *et al.* (2002) have described the specialised niche for fungi provided by ancient, decorticated pines on dry hillsides exposed to direct sunlight. It is not yet known whether any members of this fungal community exist in Scotland, although there is certainly potential, and the provision of this habitat should be taken into account when considering woodland management.

One area of concern is that a reduction in grazing pressure within woodlands, and the consequent development of a more luxuriant ground flora, may suppress the fruiting of mycorrhizal species (Orton, 1986). At present, it is not known whether the fungi affected would continue to thrive in a vegetative state. Such changes could impact upon the important populations of tooth fungi within the Cairngorms, as they distinctly prefer areas of bare mineral soil in which to fruit. In the long-term, the survival of woodland through regeneration is obviously essential to the fungi. It is also possible that the humidity created by the increased ground flora may promote the development of wood decomposing fungi. As Watling (2003) suggests, managing woodland habitats to create a mosaic of vegetational types may be the best option for fungal biodiversity.

Habitat fragmentation and loss. The loss of ancient woodland or unimproved pasture will inevitably have a negative effect on fungal populations. Current initiatives to expand native woodland in the Cairngorms are therefore a positive development although care should be taken to ensure that the expansion of the one important habitat is not at the expense of another. It is quite possible that grassland sites supporting important populations of fungi are still being lost, often through a lack of awareness of their value. The importance of the Scottish grassland communities in a European context should not be underestimated.

Awareness and education. Much work still has to be done to raise the profile of fungi with land managers and the statutory agencies. Initiatives such as the 'BAP Fungi, Tooth Fungi and Waxcaps Training Course', organised for conservation and forestry practitioners by SNH in 2003, are welcome events but require continued input to maintain interest. Public forays and educational packages designed for schools can be used to inform both visitors and the local community about the importance of fungi in the Cairngorms. The recording work of local fungus groups and centres such as North East of Scotland Biological Records Centre (NESBReC) also makes a valuable contribution in this respect.

Training and expertise. One of the major impediments to fungal surveys is a lack of expertise, both to undertake the fieldwork itself and to identify critical species. The Royal Botanic Garden Edinburgh (RBGE), for example, has experienced difficulties in filling the post of senior mycologist. This situation needs to be addressed so that future priorities for action can be realised.

Knowledge gaps. Newton *et al.* (2003a) present a comprehensive list of priorities for action, which has been used as a basis for the suggestions below.

*   *Surveys of threatened species.* Most species, including microfungi, are under-recorded in the Cairngorms, making it difficult to provide accurate information about their distribution or to inform management decisions. Although the tooth fungi of pine woodland have been surveyed recently, those species of tooth fungi associated with broadleaved woodland require investigation. Research into the relationship between what is fruiting above ground and the vegetative system below ground would also inform this process.

*   *Surveys of specific habitats.* Most habitats in the Cairngorms have not been rigorously surveyed for fungi. Habitats such as montane heath, semi-improved grassland and riverine woodland are either lacking in records or have large gaps in the areas surveyed. Survey of dead wood in all woodland habitats, by a specialist, would provide useful baseline data, given the likely future increase in this substrate as a result of changing management priorities.

*   *Development of monitoring approaches.* In order to provide useful baseline information, consistent, practical monitoring methods are required. Deciding on the best size of sample plot to use in each habitat might be a first step.

- *Management interventions.* Research into the impacts of management on fungal populations is required. For example, the effect, above and below ground, of changes in grazing in woodland habitats is particularly relevant, given recent management interventions to reduce grazing levels.

- *International comparisons.* Comparison of the lists of threatened species in Scandinavia and other comparable countries might help provide a more international perspective on the Cairngorms mycota. Discussion with mycologists in these countries might inform our conservation concerns.

These priorities should build upon recent, systematic surveys, so that fungi may be fully incorporated into conservation planning and management in the future.

Sources

The data presented in this chapter were derived primarily from the British Mycological Society (BMS) managed fungus record database (BMSFRD) and a database of Scottish records (Davy, 2003), which includes data from an earlier inventory developed for the Cairngorm Project (Watling *et al.*, 1995). There are, however, still many records in the RBGE, which have not been entered onto either database, and which were not consulted for this study (R. Watling, pers. comm.). Additional records from unpublished reports (Orton, 1968-2001; Watling, 1984a; Emmett & Emmett, 2002a,b,c; Holden, 2002b; Beker, pers. comm.; Milne, pers. comm.) and published literature (Ing, 1998a,b) have also been consulted.

Considerable effort has gone into the quality control of data in Tables 11.1 and 11.2, but no research has been undertaken to check the accuracy of the records they present. In some cases the recorder has remained anonymous and many of the records are not supported by dried specimens, retained for confirmation purposes. Common names follow those set out in Holden (2003b). The basidiomycete nomenclature follows the recommendations of the new Checklist (Legon & Henrici, 2005). It should be noted that both the European and British Provisional Red Data Lists, which have been used as the basis for demonstrating the conservation interest of species in the tables above, are currently being reviewed. Our understanding of the taxonomy, distribution and ecological needs of fungi is slowly improving, and the information given above should be updated in the light of these and other future developments.

References

Allison, M. (2001). The conservation of fungi on reserves managed by the Royal Society for the Protection of Birds (RSPB). In: Moore, D., Nauta, M.M., Evans, S.E. & Rotheroe, M. (eds.) *Fungal Conservation: Issues and Solutions.* Cambridge University Press: Cambridge.

Arnolds, E. (1989a). The influence of increased fertilisation on the macrofungi of a sheep meadow in Drenthe, the Netherlands. *Opera Botanica* 100: 7-21.

Arnolds, E. (1989b). Former and present distribution of stiptate hydnaceous fungi (Basidiomycetes) in the Netherlands. *Nova Hedwigia* 48: 107-142.

Bruns, T.D. (1995). Thoughts on the processes that maintain local species diversity of ectomycorrhizal fungi. *Plant and Soil* 170: 63-73.

Cannon, P.F. (1997). Strategies for rapid assessment of fungal diversity. *Biodiversity and Conservation* 6: 669 – 680.

Coppins, B.J., Watling, R. & Holden, E.M. (2003). *Species Dossier: Boletopsis leucomelaena.* Unpublished report. SNH: Edinburgh.

Cosgrove, P. (ed.) (2002). *The Cairngorms Local Biodiversity Action Plan.* Cairngorms Partnership: Findhorn.

Davy, L.M. (2003). *Database of Scottish Records of Non-lichenized fungi.* Unpublished report. SNH: Edinburgh.

Dennis, R.W.G. (1986). *Fungi of the Hebrides.* Royal Botanic Garden, Kew: London.

Dickson, G. & Emmett, E. (2004). *Hydnellum auratile* at last. *Field Mycology* 5(2).

Emmett, E.E. & Emmett, V.E. (2002a). *Survey of the fungi on Dunachton Estate.* Unpublished report. Dunachton Estate: Kingussie.

Emmett, E.E. & Emmett, V.E. (2002b). *Survey of the fungi on Insh Marshes RSPB Reserve* Unpublished report. RSPB: Edinburgh.

Emmett, E.E. & Emmett, V.E. (2002c). *Survey of the fungi on the Kinrara Estate.* Unpublished report. Kinrara Estate: Aviemore.

Evans, S., Marren, P. & Harper, M. (2001). *Important Fungus Areas (2001).* Report to Fungus Conservation Forum: Plantlife, Salisbury.

Feest, A. (2000). The assessment of the fungal value of sites for conservation. *Mycologist* 14(1): 14-15.

Fleming, L.V. (2001). Fungi and the UK Biodiversity Action Plan: the process explained. In: Moore, D., Nauta, M.M., Evans, S.E. & Rotheroe, M. (eds.) *Fungal Conservation: Issues and Solutions.* Cambridge University Press: Cambridge.

Hodgetts, N.G., (1996) *The Conservation of Lower Plants in Woodland.* JNCC, Peterborough.

Holden, E. (1999). *Craig Leek SSSI Fungus Survey.* Unpublished report. SNH: Aberdeen.

Holden, L. (2002a). *Boletopsis leucomelaena* rediscovered after 38 years. *Field Mycology* 3(2).

Holden, L. (2002b). *Fungus Survey of Quithel Wood SSSI*. Unpublished report. SNH: Aberdeen.

Holden, E.M. (2002c). *Site Condition Monitoring for fungi: Site Dossier North Rothiemurchus SSSI*. Unpublished report. SNH: Edinburgh.

Holden, E.M. (2002d). *Site Condition Monitoring for fungi: Site Dossier Abernethy SSSI*. Unpublished report. SNH: Edinburgh.

Holden, E. (2003a). *Compilation of a working database to safeguard fungal sites of national and European interest in Scotland*. Unpublished report. SNH: Edinburgh.

Holden, E.M. (2003b). *Recommended English Names for Fungi*. Plantlife International: Salisbury.

Holden, E. M. (2003c). *Site Condition Monitoring of SSSIs for Fungi: Methodology*. Unpublished second interim report. SNH: Edinburgh.

Holden, E.M. (2004a). *Site Condition Monitoring for fungi: Site Dossier Glen Tanar SSSI*. Unpublished report. SNH: Edinburgh.

Holden, E.M. (2004b). *Site Condition Monitoring for fungi: Site Dossier Culbin Sands, Forest and Findhorn Bay SSSI*. Unpublished report. SNH: Edinburgh.

Holden, L. & Stamm, M. (2003). *Scottish Forestry Alliance (SFA): baseline monitoring of biodiversity in native woodland / forest on SFA sites in Scotland*. Unpublished report. RSBP: Edinburgh.

Holden, L., Newton, A., Davy, L. & Watling, R. (2000). *Survey of woodland fungi, Mar Lodge Estate*. Unpublished first annual report. National Trust for Scotland: Edinburgh.

Humphrey, J., Newton, A.C., Peace, A. & Holden, E. (2000). The importance of conifer plantations in northern Britain as a habitat for native fungi. *Biological Conservation* 96: 241-252.

Ing, B. (1992). A provisional red data list of British fungi. *Mycologist* 6: 124-128.

Ing, B. (1993). Towards a red list of endangered European macrofungi. In: Pegler, D.N., Boddy, L., Ing, B. & Kirk, P.H. (eds.) *Fungi of Europe: Investigation, Recording and Conservation*. Royal Botanic Gardens, Kew: London.

Ing, B. (1998a). Exobasidium in the British Isles. *Mycologist* 12(2): 80-82.

Ing, B. (1998b). Exobasidium in Scotland. *Botanical Journal of Scotland* 51: 221-225.

Ing, B. (2002). The endangered myxomycetes of the British Isles. *English Nature Research Report No 466*. English Nature: Peterborough.

Ing, B. (2003). Snow-line Myxomycetes in Britain. *Field Mycology* 4(1): 7–13.

Kers, L.E. (1978). *Tulostoma niveum sp. nov. (Gasteromycetes)*, described from Sweden. *Bot. Notiser* 131.

Legon, N.W. & Henrici, A. (2005). *Checklist of the British and Irish Basidiomycota*. Royal Botanic Gardens: Kew.

Mackey, E.C., Shewry, M.C. & Tudor, G.J. (1998). *Land Cover Change: Scotland from the 1940s to the 1980s*. The Stationary Office: Edinburgh.

Newton, A., Davy, L., Silverside, A., Holden, L., Watling, R. & Ward, S. (2000). *Species Dossier: Pink meadow cap Hygrocybe calyptriformis* Unpublished report. SNH: Edinburgh.

Newton, A.C., Holden, E., Davy, L.M., Ward, S.D., Fleming, L.V. & Watling, R. (2002a). Status and distribution of stipitate hydnoid fungi in Scottish coniferous forests. *Biological Conservation* 107: 181–192.

Newton, A.C., Watling, R., Davy, L.M., Holden, E. & Ward, S. (2002b). Progress towards implementing the biodiversity action plan for stipitate hydnoid fungi in Scotland. *Botanical Journal of Scotland* 54(1): 89-110.

Newton, A.C., Davy, L.M., Holden, E., Silverside, A., Watling, R. & Ward, S.D. (2003a). Status, distribution and definition of mycologically important grasslands in Scotland. *Biological Conservation* 111: 11-23.

Newton, A.C., Holden, E., Watling, R. & Davy, L.M. (2003b). Fungal conservation in Scotland: recent progress and future priorities. *Botanical Journal of Scotland* 55(1): 39-53.

Niemelä,T., Wallenius, T. & Kotiranta, H. (2002). The Kelo Tree, a vanishing substrate of specified wood-inhabiting fungi. *Polish Botanical Journal* 47(2): 91-101.

Orton, P.D. (1986). Fungi of Northern Pine and Birch Woods. *Bulletin of the BMS* 20: 130 –145.

Orton, P.D., Dickson, G.C. & Leonard, A. (1968-2003). *Fungus List – Abernethy Forest Reserve*. Unpublished report. RSPB: Abernethy.

Palmer, M. (1994). *A UK Plant Conservation Strategy*. JNCC: Peterborough.

Ryvarden, L. & Gilbertson, R.L. (1993). *European Polypores: Part 1*. Fungiflora: Oslo.

Scottish Montane Willow Research Group (2005). *Biodiversity: taxonomy, genetics and ecology of sub-arctic willow scrub*. Royal Botanic Garden Edinburgh: Edinburgh.

Silverside, A. (2000). *Species Dossier: An Earthtongue* Microglossum olivaceum Unpublished report. SNH: Edinburgh.

Urquhart, U., Martin, E. & Ewen, G. (2001). *Mar Lodge Estate Woodland History Project 2001*. Unpublished report. National Trust for Scotland: Edinburgh.

Ward, S. (ed). (1999). *Local Biodiversity Action Plans – Technical information of species: 1. Cryptogamic Plants and Fungi*. Scottish Natural Heritage Review No. 70. SNH: Edinburgh.

Watling, R. (1984a). *Annotated list of montane fungi*. Unpublished report. NCC: Aviemore.

Watling, R. (1988). Presidential Address: A mycological kaleidoscope. *Transactions of the British Mycological Society* 90(1): 1–28.

Watling, R. (1990). On the way towards a Red Data Book on British fungi. *Transactions of the Botanical Society of Edinburgh.* 45: 463 – 471.

Watling. R. (1997). Biodiversity of lichenised and non-lichenised fungi in Scotland. In: *Biodiversity in Scotland: Trends and Initiatives.* Eds: Fleming, L.V., Newton, A.C., Vickery, J.A. & Usher, M.B. The Stationery Office: Edinburgh and SNH: Edinburgh.

Watling, R. (2003). Fungi. *Life Series.* The Natural History Museum: London.

Watling, R. & Ward, S.D. (2003). *Fungi: Naturally Scottish.* SNH: Battleby.

Watling, R. & Milne, J. (2005). Scottish *Sarcodon imbricatus* Under Scrutiny. *Botanical Journal of Scotland* 56(2): 175-181.

Watling, R., Coppins, B.J., Fleming, L.V. & Davy, L.M. (1995). *Cairngorm Project: inventory of restricted lower plants (larger fungi and lichenized fungi).* Unpublished report. SNH: Edinburgh.

Worrell, R. (1996). *The Boreal Forests of Scotland.* Forestry Commision Technical Paper 14. Forestry Commission: Edinburgh.

Yao, Y.-J. & Spooner, B.M. (2003). *The occurrence of* Geopora arenosa *in the British Isles.* Kew Bulletin 58:247-252.

Additional reading

Anon. (1999). *UK Biodiversity Group. Tranche 2 Action Plans. Vol III – Plants and Fungi.* English Nature: Peterborough, UK.

Boertmann, D. (1995). *The genus Hygrocybe. Fungi of Northern Europe, Vol 1.* Danish Mycological Society: Greve, Denmark.

Watling, R. (1984b). Macrofungi of Birchwoods. *Proceedings of the Royal Society of Edinburgh.* 85B: 129-140.

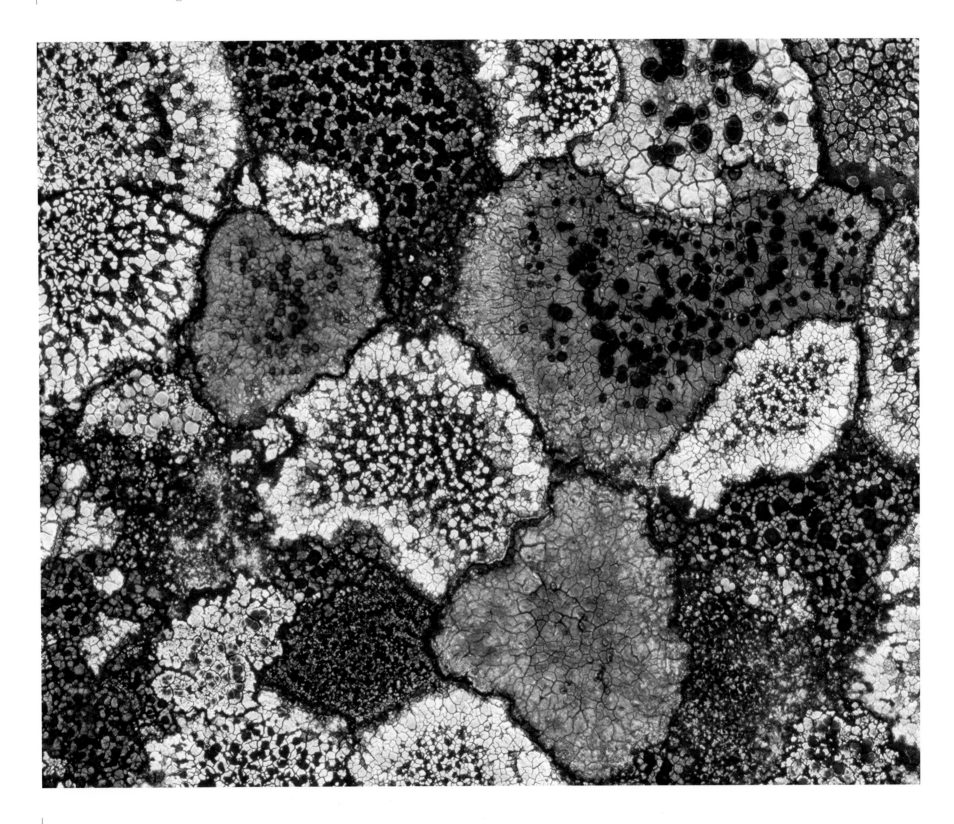

12. LICHENS

Alan Fryday

Introduction

The vast area of the Cairngorms encompasses a wide range of habitats: from the alpine heaths, late snow areas and damp corries of the high mountains, to the native pine and deciduous woodlands, and the relatively unpolluted rivers of the lowlands. These diverse habitats support correspondingly rich and diverse lichen vegetation that is of great national importance. From an international perspective, however, it is the western side of Britain and Ireland, with its uniquely oceanic climate, characterized by high precipitation and low seasonal temperature variation, that supports the most distinctive and important lichen vegetation, in both woodland and mountain habitats. As the Cairngorms are located in the most 'continental' part of Scotland, the 'oceanic' element of the flora is much reduced and largely confined to north- and east-facing corries. Most of the rare species and notable communities in the Cairngorms are composed of Arctic-alpine or boreal-montane taxa, which, although of very limited occurrence in the UK, are often widespread and abundant in the mountains and forests of mainland Europe, especially Scandinavia (Fryday, 2002).

Important species and habitats

The total number of lichen taxa recorded from Britain and Ireland is around 1,750 (Coppins, 2002), of which about 85 have over 50% of their British range within the Cairngorms area and 35 are known in Britain only from the Cairngorms. Of 400 taxa with at least 10% of their UK range in the area, over 180 are nationally rare and over 350 are nationally scarce species[1] (Table 12.1; Annex 12.1). Unfortunately, information on the lichen vegetation of the Cairngorms area is scarce and exists mostly in unpublished reports. The only recent published work is that of Gilbert & Fox (1985), Gilbert & Coppins (1992), Purvis *et al.* (1994) and Fryday (2001a,b, 2002).

Lichens form an important component of many ecosystems in the Cairngorms area, which supports lichen assemblages of considerable national importance. Chief among these are the epiphytic communities of native pine and deciduous woodlands in Strathspey and Deeside, and epilithic and epigaeic communities of the base-rich, mica-schist areas of the Angus Hills. Also of significant national interest are the lichen-rich epigaeic communities of the sub- to low alpine heaths, and areas of late snow-lie in the Cairngorm Mountains.

Native Pinewoods. There are two important areas of native Caledonian pinewoods in the Cairngorms, centred on Strathspey and Deeside. Of these, the lichen vegetation of Strathspey has been more thoroughly investigated, with Abernethy Forest, in particular, being the subject of a more detailed survey (Street & Street, 2000b) than those of, for example, Mar Lodge Estate near Braemar (Street & Street, 2000a).

Deciduous Woods. These are also centred on Strathspey and Deeside, but with some important areas on the southern edge of the Angus Hills (e.g. Munro, 2000). Although Deeside has not been surveyed, some of Strathspey's birch *Betula* and Aspen *Populus tremula* woods have been surveyed recently (Fryday, 1990; Coppins *et al.*, 2001, 2002).

Alpine Heaths. There are two nationally important areas of alpine heath for lichens in the Cairngorms area: the northern edge of the Cairngorms and the mid-alpine heaths of the eastern Cairngorms (Beinn a' Bhuird and Ben Avon). Elsewhere, the lichen vegetation of alpine heaths is largely unremarkable, consisting mostly of widespread species.

Late snow-lie. This habitat is rich in uncommon lichen species. However, most of the crustose, epigaeic species and those occurring on small stones and pebbles are primarily species of damp habitats, and are usually more widespread further west

Mosaics of crustose lichens on siliceous rock surfaces are a conspicuous feature of many of the Cairngorms' habitats.

Photo: *N. Benvie*

Fryday, A. (2006). Lichens. In: Shaw, P. & Thompson, D.B.A. (eds.). *The Nature of the Cairngorms: Diversity in a changing environment.* The Stationery Office. pp. 177-193.

[1] Nationally rare species are those recorded from 15 or fewer 10-km squares, while nationally scarce species are those recorded from 16-100 10-km squares in the UK. Note, however, that these categories are of limited value when applied to lichens. Because of the lack of systematic recording, for example, nearly two-thirds of all British lichen taxa fall into these categories.

(Fryday, 2001a, 2002). Only those species occurring on the tops of boulders in areas of late snow-lie can be considered true snow-bed specialists. These species have the centre of their distribution in Britain and Ireland in the Cairngorms, although they also occur in this habitat throughout the Scottish Highlands.

Base-rich substrata. As with most groups of plants, this habitat supports some of the rarest species in Britain and Ireland, for the obvious reason that the habitat is rare, especially at higher altitudes. The majority of the rare species of this habitat also occur – in greater abundance – in the Breadalbane Hills of Perthshire. The Cairngorms themselves are composed mostly of granite, and it is only at the periphery of the area that base-rich substrata occur in any appreciable amount. Important examples are the mica-schist of Caenlochan and the Angus Hills, and the metamorphosed limestone of the Blair Atholl area. Elsewhere, there are isolated areas of base-rich rock, but the only ones that have been surveyed for their lichen vegetation are three relatively low-altitude sites near Braemar: Lion's Face, Creag Clunie (Coppins & Coppins, 1999) and Craig Leek.

Important areas

Very few areas in the Cairngorms have had their lichen flora thoroughly investigated. The following descriptions deal only with areas for which there is sufficient information available to enable their importance to be assessed (Table 12.2, Figure 12.1).

1. Caenlochan Glen. The lichen vegetation of Caenlochan Glen was surveyed by Gilbert and Coppins (1992). They describe a vegetation rich in calcicole species, but which was scattered across many different micro-habitats in the glen. Although no single location was outstanding, together they comprise the third most important area in Britain and Ireland for alpine calcicole lichens (after Ben Lawers and Coire Cheap in the Ben Alder range). Subsequent fieldwork has emphasised the importance of other areas; notably in the Breadalbane Hills (e.g. Beinn Heasgarnich, Meall na Samhna), Glen Coe, Inchnadamph and Beinn Eighe. Nonetheless, Caenlochan remains one of Britain's most important areas for alpine calcicole lichens. It is of particular importance in being the only location in Britain and Ireland for *Rinodina parasitica*, *Rhizocarpon caeruleoalbum* and *R. chioneum*, and the only such location outside of the Ben Lawers range for *Acarospora badiofusca* and the British endemic *Halecania rhypodiza*. The importance of this

area is limited by two factors, however: its relatively low altitude, which favours the growth of vascular plants over cryptogams; and its location on the eastern side of Britain. This means that it is generally drier than the other important areas, and less rich in species favoured by a high-moisture regime.

2. The Main Cairngorms. The main area of the Cairngorm Mountains is composed of granite and is of limited interest lichenologically. However, two habitats are of special interest: areas of late snow-lie and low-alpine *Calluna* heath.

Areas of late snow-lie (Ciste Mhearad, Coire Domhain, Feith Buidhe and Garbh Uisge Mor). In Britain and Ireland, late snow-lie is most extensive in the Cairngorm mountains, and the numerous rare species that are restricted to this habitat are similarly most frequent here (e.g. *Ameliella andreaeicola* in ed., *Lecanora formosa* (*Lecidella bullata* auct.), *L. leptacina*, *Miriquidica griseoatra* and '*Toninia*' *squalescens*,). The above species occur on the tops of boulders protruding from the snow-bed, but two epigaeic macrolichens – *Cladonia maxima* and *C. trassii* (*C. stricta* auct Brit.) – also have their distribution in Britain and Ireland centred on the Cairngorms snowbeds. Indeed, the latter is known only from the Cairngorms. Most of the crustose epigaeic species (e.g. *Ameliella grisea* in ed.) and species that occur on small stones and pebbles (*Sterocaulon plicatile*, *S. tornense*) are associated primarily with damp habitats, and are generally more widespread further west (Fryday, 2001a, 2002).

Low-alpine Calluna *heath*. The prostrate *Calluna* heath of the northern slopes of the Cairngorms is the only British locality for *Alectoria ochroleuca*, a common circumpolar species abundant on the heaths of Scandinavia. This locality is also the only British location for the saxicolous species *Lecidea promiscua* and *Pseudephebe minuscula*, although the former has probably been overlooked elsewhere.

3. Creag Clunie, Lion's Face and Craig Leek. Creag Clunie and Lion's Face SSSI, near Braemar, was surveyed for SNH by Coppins & Coppins (1999) and found to be of national importance for its saxicolous lichen flora both on base-rich and siliceous rocks. This included the internationally important species *Gyalecta ulmi*, and three other Red Data Book species: *Chaenotheca gracilenta*, *Leptogium saturninum* and *Opegrapha paraxanthodes*. In addition, numerous other rare species were recorded from rocks, including the new species *Rimularia globulosa* and the first British record of *Ionaspis obtecta* (*Hymenelia obtecta*). Other rare species on rocks included *Acarospora macrospora*, *Caloplaca approximata*, *Chrysothrix chlorina*,

Lecanora atrosulphurea, Lecidea syncarpa, Miriquidica atrofulva, Polysporina cyclocarpa, Protoparmelia nephaea, Pyrrhospora rubiginans, Rinodina interpolata, Umbilicaria hirsuta, and *Umbilicaria nylanderiana.* The corticolous lichen flora was also found to be of significant interest, with *Chaenothecopsis vainioana, Pycnora sorophora, Sclerophora peronella* and *Xerotrema megalospora* being recorded, along with several Revised Index of Ecological Continuity (RIEC) species (Rose, 1976), which are rare in north-east Scotland. *Pleopsidium chlorophana* (second British record) and *Rhizocarpon ridescens* (first British record) were recently reported from nearby Creag Choinnich.

Craig Leek, on the north side of the Dee, has never been fully surveyed for lichens, but is known to support many important species, including *Acarospora macrospora, Adelolecia pilati, Aspicilia contorta* var. *hoffmanniana, Buellia uberior, Fuscidea austera, Gyalecta ulmi, Lecidella wulfenii, Miriquidica atrofulva, Parotoparmelia atriseda, P. nephaea, Rinodina interpolata, Sagiolechia protuberans, Strigula muscicola* (the only British locality) and *Umbilicaria hirsuta.* Many of these records are from siliceous rocks and walls below the limestone crags.

4. Abernethy Forest. Abernethy Forest RSPB Reserve was the subject of a report by Street & Street (2000b). The lichen flora of the whole reserve, which extends to the summit of Ben Macdui and includes several important late snow-lie areas, includes three species listed under Schedule 8 of the Wildlife & Countryside Act, four BAP species, 14 Red Data Book species, 35 nationally rare and 60 nationally scarce species. The native pine forest is the richest of any eastern forest in terms of native pinewood indicator species, and the third richest of any area in the UK. Among the important species recorded from trees and stumps were *Bacidia vermifera, Bryoria furcellata, Caloplaca flavorubescens, Catinaria neuschildii, Chaenotheca xyloxena, Cladonia botrytes, Lecidea leprarioides, Pycnora xanthococca, Rinodina laevigata, Schismatomma graphidioides* and *Xerotrema megalospora. Peltigera malacea* and *Stereocaulon glareosum* were recorded from soil.

5. Beinn a' Ghlo & Tulach Hill. The limestone outcrops in this area were surveyed by Purvis *et al.* (1994). Although they discovered several interesting montane calcicole species (e.g. *Brigantiaea fuscolutea, Caloplaca approximata, Collema parvum, Halecania alpivaga, Lecanora epibryon, Polysporina cyclocarpa, Sagiolechia protuberans* and *Toninia diffracta*) and an outlying population of *Flavocetraria nivalis,* they concluded that the outcrops were too small and at too low an altitude to support an extensive montane calcicole flora, and were of regional interest only.

6. Eastern Cairngorms (Beinn a' Bhuird – Ben Avon). This is one of two nationally important areas of alpine heath within the Cairngorms area. Mid-alpine heath on the summit of Beinn a' Bhuird supports *Ameliella grisea* in ed., *Catolechia wahlenbergii, Cladonia maxima, Cetrariella delisei, Micarea inquinans* and *Sterocaulon spathuliferum,* while its eastern corries support a substantial population of *Brodoa intestiniformis (Hypogymnia intestiniformis),* discovered there in 2005. Rocks near the summit of Ben Avon are the only other known location in Britain for *B. intestiniformis,* which was recorded there once in the 1960s, but not since, despite recent surveys. Also discovered in the eastern corries of Beinn a' Bhuird in 2005 were *Thelocarpon strasseri, Toninia squalescens* and several specimens of what appear to be *Arctoparmelia centrifuga;* a species not previously recorded correctly from Britain or Ireland. These records await confirmation.

The extensive limestone outcrops at Inchrory and the calcareous rocks on Creag an Dail Bheag appear not to have been visited recently by lichenologists.

The northern slopes of the Cairngorm mountains are the only British locality for the BAP Priority lichen Alectoria ochroleuca.

Photo: *A. Fryday*

Table 12.1. Lichen taxa whose populations in the Cairngorms area are of at least national importance. Those with an internationally important population on at least one site are shown in bold. Notable areas outside of the National Park, but within the Cairngorms area, are identified.

Nationally Rare:	Recorded from 1-15 10-km squares in the UK.
RDB:	National Red Data Book status. CR = Critical; EN = Endangered; VU = Vulnerable; DD = Data Deficient; NT = Near-threatened; LC = Least Concern. Sub-categories for CR, EN, and VU (e.g. 'CR A') refer to the justification for including the species in this threat category, given by IUCN (2001) and reproduced in Woods & Coppins (2003).
BAP:	Biodiversity Action Plan: P = Species Action Plan; S = Species statement.
WCA:	Protected under Schedule 8 of the 1981 Wildlife & Countryside Act
E/IR:	Endemic/International Responsibility for Conservation. E = Endemic to Britain. IR = Species whose British population probably accounts for more than 10% of the European and/or world population, based on a preliminary assessment of current knowledge (Woods & Coppins, 2003).
Percentage of UK range:	The percentage of the species' UK range (in 10-km squares) occurring within the Cairngorms area or in the National Park: *** >75%; ** 25-75%; * 10-24%; '-' <10%

Habitat General	Specific	Taxon	Status Nationally Rare	RDB	BAP	WCA	E/IR	Percentage of UK range in: Cairngorms area	National Park	Notable areas outside of the National Park
Coniferous trees	Rotting coniferous stumps	*Absconditella annexa*	Y	LC				***	-	Glenogil
	Conifer stumps and lignum	*Absconditella pauxilla*	Y	LC				***	***	
	Coniferous trees	*Alectoria sarmentosa* ssp. *sarmentosa*		NT				*	*	
	Coniferous trees	*Bryoria furcellata*	Y	VU D1				**	**	
	Coniferous trees and wood	*Calicium parvum*	Y	NT				**	**	
	Pinus and *Ilex*	*Chaenothecopsis vainioana*	Y	NT				***	***	
	Coniferous trees	**Chrysothrix chrysophthalma**	Y	NT			IR	*	*	
	Conifer stumps	*Cladonia botrytes*	Y	CR A	P			***	**	
	Rotting coniferous stumps	*Cladonia cenotea*	Y	NT				***	***	
	Conifer wood and posts	*Cyphelium tigillare*	Y	NT				**	**	
	Fence post	*Cyphelium trachylioides*	Y	CR D				***	-	Glen Prosen
	Coniferous stumps	*Hertelidea bortyosa*	Y	NT				**	**	
	Decorticate trunks	*Hypocenomyce anthrocophila*	Y	EN D				***	***	
	Coniferous trees	*Hypogymnia farinacea*	Y	NT				**	**	
	Coniferous trees	*Lecanora mughicola*	Y	NT				*	*	
	Conifer cones, bark and palings	*Lecidea antiloga*	Y	VU D2				**	**	
	Pinus	*Lecidea leprarioides*	Y	NT				***	***	
	Fallen and rotten *Pinus*	*Micarea contexta*	Y	LC				**	**	
	Fallen branches	*Micarea exima*	Y	DD				***	***	
	Hard lignum	*Pycnora sorophora*	Y	LC				**	**	
	Hard lignum	*Pycnora xanthococca*	Y	VU D2				***	***	
	Coniferous trees	*Vulpicida pinastri*	Y	NT				**	**	
	Coniferous trees	**Xerotrema megalospora**	Y	NT				**	**	
Deciduous trees	*Populus*	*Arthonia patellulata*	Y	DD				***	***	
	Deciduous trees	*Arthopyrenia atractospora*	Y	NT				**	**	
	Populus	*Bacidia igniarii*	Y	VU D2				***	**	
	Deciduous trees	*Bacidia subincompta*		VU C, D1				**	*	
	Juniperus and *Populus*	*Bacidia vermifera*	Y	EN D				***	***	

| Habitat | | | Status | | | | | Percentage of UK range in: | | |
General	Specific	Taxon	Nationally Rare	RDB	BAP	WCA	E/IR	Cairngorms area	National Park	Notable areas outside of the National Park
Deciduous trees	Deciduous trees	*Biatora efflorescens*	Y	NT				**	**	
	Deciduous trees	*Biatoridium delitescens*	Y	VU D1				**	**	
	Populus	*Caloplaca ahtii*	Y	DD				***	***	
	Deciduous trees	*Caloplaca cerinelloides*[1]	Y	LC				***	***	
	Deciduous trees	*Caloplaca flavorubescens*		EN A				**	**	
	Deciduous trees	*Catillaria globulosa*		NT				**	**	
	Juniperus and old *Salix* bark	*Catinaria neuschildii*	Y	VU D2				**	**	
	Deciduous trees	*Cliostomum flavidulum*	Y	DD				***	***	
	Deciduous trees	*Chaenotheca gracilenta*	Y	EN D				**	**	
	Deciduous and coniferous wood	*Chaenotheca xyloxena*	Y	VU D2				**	**	
	Deciduous trees	*Collema nigrescens*		NT				*	*	
	Deciduous trees	*Collema occultatum*		NT				**	-	Kindrogan
	Populus tremula	*Diplotomma pharcidum*	Y	DD				**	**	
	Deciduous trees	*Elixia flexella*	Y	NT				*	*	
	Populus	*Lecania dubitans*	Y	NE				***	***	
	Deciduous trees	*Lecanora conizaeoides* f. *variola*	Y	NE				**	**	
	Deciduous trees	*Lecanora horiza*	Y	NT				***	**	(8 km E of Kirriemuir, outside of Cairngorms area)
	Deciduous trees	*Lecanora populicola*	Y	NT				***	***	
	Populus and *Salix*	*Lecidella flavosorediata*	Y	NE				***	***	
	Deciduous trees	*Leptogium saturninum*		VU C2				*	*	
	Deciduous trees	*Melanelixia subargentifera* (=*Melanelia subargentifera*)	Y	CR D				-	-	The Burn[2] (River N. Esk)
	Betula	*Melanohalea septentrionalis* (=*Melanelia septentrionalis*)		LC				***	***	
	Deciduous trees	*Pachyphiale fagicola*	Y	NT				**	*	Glen Tilt
	Deciduous trees	*Rinodina degeliana*	Y	VU D				***	***	
	Populus	*Rinodina laevigata*	Y	DD				***	***	
	Deciduous trees	*Schismatomma graphidioides*		VU B, D1				*	*	
	Deciduous trees	*Sclerophora pallida*		VU C2, D1				*	*	Glen Tilt
	Deciduous trees	*Sclerophora peronella*		NT				*	*	
	Deciduous trees	*Strangospora deplanata*	Y	DD				***	-	Blair Atholl
	Betula and *Larix* trees	*Usnea chaetophora*	Y	DD				**	**	
Alpine heath	Low-alpine heath	*Alectoria ochroleuca*	Y	VU B	P	Y		***	***	
	Mid-alpine heath	**Ameliella grisea** in ed. (=*Amelia grisea* ad int.)	Y	NE			IR	**	**	
	Alpine heaths and mossy rocks	*Catolechia wahlenbergii*	Y	VU D1	P	Y		*	*	
	Mid-alpine heath	*Cetrariella delisei*	Y	NT				***	***	
	Acid soils and mossy scree	*Cladonia macrophylla*		LC				**	**	
	Mid-alpine heath	*Flavocetraria nivalis*		NT				***	**	Beinn a' Ghlo & Tulach Hill
	Over bryophytes	*Pertusaria geminipara*	Y	NT				**	**	

Habitat			Status					Percentage of UK range in:		
General	Specific	Taxon	Nationally Rare	RDB	BAP	WCA	E/IR	Cairngorms area	National Park	Notable areas outside of the National Park
Alpine heath	Alpine heaths	*Stereocaulon spathuliferum*	Y	NT				*	*	
Late snow-lie	Over bryophytes on siliceous boulders	***Ameliella andraeicola*** in ed. (=*Amelia andreaeicola* ad. int.)	Y	NE			IR	**	**	
	Siliceous pebble	*Bellemerea alpina*	Y	CR B	S			***	***	
	Nardus heath	*Cladonia maxima*	Y	VU D2				**	**	
	Terricolous	*Cladonia phyllophora*	Y	NT				**	**	
	Terricolous	*Cladonia trassii* (=*Cladonia stricta* auct. Brit.)	Y	VU D2		Y		***	***	
	Siliceous boulders	*Lecanora formosa* (=*Lecidella bullata* auct Brit.)	Y	NT				**	**	
	Over bryophytes on siliceous boulders	*Lecanora leptacina*	Y	LC				**	**	
Siliceous rocks	Mid-alpine siliceous boulders	*Arctoparmelia ?centrifuga*	Y	NE				***	***	
	Mid-alpine siliceous boulders	*Brodoa intestiniformis* (=*Hypogymium intestiniformis*)	Y	CR B,D	S			***	***	
	Siliceous rocks	*Buellia uberior*	Y	DD				*	*	
	Mid-alpine siliceous boulders	*Calvitimela armeniaca*	Y	LC				***	**	
	Siliceous rocks	*Chrysothrix chlorina*	Y	LC				**	**	
	Mossy siliceous boulders	*Cladonia metacorallifera*	Y	DD				**	**	
	Siliceous boulders	*Fuscidea austera*	Y	NT				**	**	
	Siliceous rocks	*Ionaspis obtecta* (=*Hymenelia obtecta*)	Y	NT				***	***	
	Siliceous rocks	*Lecanora atrosulphurea*	Y	NT				**	**	
	Siliceous rocks	*Lecanora swartzii*	1	LC				*	*	
	Siliceous boulders	*Lecidea luteoatra*	Y	LC				**	**	
	Siliceous boulders	*Lecidea promiscens*	Y`	DD				**	**	
	Siliceous boulders	*Lecidea promiscua*	Y	DD				***	***	
	Siliceous boulders	*Lecidea sarcogynoides*	Y	VU D2				**	**	
	Siliceous boulders (iron-rich)	*Lecidea silacea*		LC				**	**	
	Siliceous boulders	*Lecidea syncarpa*	Y	DD				**	**	
	Mossy siliceous rocks	*Lepraria cacuminum*	Y	LC				**	**	Beinn a' Ghlo & Tulach Hill
	Siliceous boulders	*Melanelia stygia*		NT				**	**	
	Siliceous boulders (iron-rich)	*Miriquidica atrofulva*	Y	LC				**	**	
	Siliceous boulders	*Miriquidica nigroleprosa* var. *liljenströemii* (=*Miriquidica liljenströemii*)	Y	DD				**	**	
	Semi-inundated siliceous rocks	*Phaeophyscia endococcina*	Y	VU D2				**	**	
	Retaining wall	*Pleopsidium chlorophana*	Y	DD				**	**	
	Semi-inundated siliceous rocks	*Polyblastia quartzina*	Y	DD				**	**	
	Siliceous boulders	*Protoparmelia memnonia*	Y	NT				**	**	
	Siliceous boulders (iron-rich)	*Protoparmelia nephaea*	Y	NT				**	**	
	Siliceous boulders	*Pseudophebe minuscula*	Y	NE				***	***	
	Siliceous rocks	*Pyrrhospora rubiginans*	Y	LC				***	**	

| Habitat | | Taxon | Status | | | | | Percentage of UK range in: | | Notable areas outside of the National Park |
General	Specific		Nationally Rare	RDB	BAP	WCA	E/IR	Cairngorms area	National Park	
Siliceous rocks	Siliceous boulders in streams	*Rhizocarpon amphibium*	Y	DD				**	**	
	Siliceous rock	*Rhizocarpon anaperum*	Y	LC				*	*	
	Iron-rich rocks	*Rhizocarpon ridescens*	Y	NE				***	***	
	Siliceous boulders	*Rhizocarpon submodestum*	Y	DD				**	**	
	Siliceous boulders	*Rhizocarpon subpostumum*	Y	DD				***	***	
	Siliceous boulders	*Rimularia globulosa*	Y	NE				***	**	
	Siliceous rock	*Rinodina interpolata*	Y	NT				*	*	
	Siliceous boulders	*Sporastatia polyspora*	Y	NT				**	**	
	Siliceous boulders	*Sporastatia testudinea*	Y	NT				***	***	
	Semi-inundated siliceous rocks	*Staurothele areolata*	Y	VU D2				**	**	
	Siliceous rock	*Stereocaulon plicatile*	Y	NT				*	*	
	Damp siliceous rock	*Umbilicaria hirsuta*	Y	NT				**	**	
	Siliceous boulders	*Umbilicaria hyperborea*		LC				**	**	
	Siliceous rock face	*Umbilicaria nylanderiana*	Y	DD				**	**	
Base-rich rocks	Base-rich rocks	*Acarospora badiofusca*	Y	NT				**	**	
	Base-rich rocks	*Acarospora macrospora*	Y	NT				**	-	Beinn a' Ghlo limestone
	Base-rich rocks	*Acrocordia subglobosa*	Y	NE				***	***	
	Over bryophytes	*Arctomia delicatula*	Y	NT				*	*	
	Over bryophytes	*Bryonora curvescens*	Y	VU D2				**	**	
	Base-rich rocks	*Caloplaca approximata*	Y	NT				**	**	Beinn a' Ghlo & Tulach Hill
	Base-rich rocks	**Catillaria gilbertii**	Y	NT			E/IR	**	**	
	Base-rich rocks	*Collema parvum*	Y	VU D				**	*	Beinn a' Ghlo & Tulach Hill
	Base-rich rocks and *Ulmus*	**Gyalecta ulmi**	Y	EN C2	P	Y	IR	**	-	Beinn a' Ghlo & Tulach Hill
	Base-rich rocks	*Gyalidea fritzei*	Y	NT				*	*	
	Base-rich rocks	*Halecania alpivaga*	Y	VU D2				**	-	Beinn a' Ghlo & Tulach Hill
	Base-rich rocks	**Halecania rhypodiza**	Y	VU D2	P		E/IR	**	**	
	Bryophytes on base-rich soil	**Jamesiella scotica** (=*Gyalideopsis scotica*)	Y	NT	P		E/IR	*	*	
	Base-rich rocks	*Lecanora atromarginata*	Y	VU D2				**	**	
	Over bryophytes	*Lecanora epibryon*	Y	VU D2				**	-	Beinn a' Ghlo & Tulach Hill
	Limestone	*Lecanora xanthostoma*	Y	LC				*	*	
	Mossy base-rich rocks	*Lecidella wulfenii*	Y	VU D2				**	**	
	Base-rich rocks	*Lempholemma cladodes*	Y	NT				*	*	Beinn a' Ghlo & Tulach Hill
	Base-rich rocks	*Lempholemma radiatum*	Y	NT				*	*	
	Base-rich soils	*Leptogium byssinum*	Y	LC				**	**	
	Over bryophytes	*Lopadium coralloideum*	Y	VU D2				**	**	
	Base-rich rocks	*Opegrapha paraxanthodes*	Y	NT				**	*	
	Base-rich rocks	**Pertusaria flavocorallina**	Y	DD			IR	**	**	
	Base-rich rocks	*Placynthium pannariellum*		NT				*	*	
	Base-rich rocks	*Polyblastia efflorescens*	Y	NT				**	*	

Habitat			Status					Percentage of UK range in:		
General	Specific	Taxon	Nationally Rare	RDB	BAP	WCA	E/IR	Cairngorms area	National Park	Notable areas outside of the National Park
Base-rich rocks	Bryophytes over base-rich rocks	*Polyblastia gothica*	Y	DD				***	***	
	Base-rich rocks	*Polyblastia inumbrata*		NT				*	-	
	Bryophytes and base-rich rocks	*Polyblastia terrestris*	Y	NT				*	*	
	Base-rich rocks	*Polysporina cyclocarpa*	Y	NT				***	**	Beinn a' Ghlo & Tulach Hill
	Base-rich rocks	*Protoblastenia cyclospora*	Y	DD				*	*	
	Base-rich rocks	*Rhizocarpon caeruleoalbum*	Y	DD				***	***	
	Base-rich rocks	*Rhizocarpon chioneum*	Y	DD				***	***	
	Base-rich rocks	*Sagiolechia protuberans*	Y	NT				**	**	Beinn a' Ghlo & Tulach Hill
	Base-rich rocks	*Staurothele bacilligera*	Y	NT				**	*	Beinn a' Ghlo & Tulach Hill
	On bryophytes	*Strigula muscicola*	Y	NE				***	***	
	Damp base-rich rocks	*Thelidium fumidum*	Y	NT				*	*	
	Base-rich rocks	*Thelocarpon sphaerosporum*	Y	LC				***	***	
	Over bryophytes	*Thelopsis melathelia*	Y	NT				**	**	
	Damp base-rich rocks	*Thermutis velutina*	Y	NT				*	-	
	Base-rich rocks	*Toninia coelestina*	Y	VU D1, D2				**	**	
	Base-rich rocks	*Toninia diffracta*	Y	DD				***	-	Beinn a' Ghlo & Tulach Hill
	Among bryophytes	*Toninia squalida*	Y	NT				**	**	
Base-rich soil	Bryophytes over calcareous soil	*Brigantiaea fuscolutaea*	Y	NT				*	-	Beinn a' Ghlo & Tulach Hill
	Base-rich soil	*Catapyrenium daedaleum*	Y	VU D1				*	*	
	Bryophytes on base-rich soil	*Fuscopannaria praetermissa* (= *Pannaria praetermissa*)	Y	NT				**	**	
	Bryophytes on base-rich soil	*Gyalecta foveolaris*	Y	NT				**	-	Beinn a' Ghlo & Tulach Hill
	Base-rich soil	*Megaspora verrucosa*		NT				**	-	Beinn a' Ghlo & Tulach Hill
	Base-rich soil	*Peltigera elisabethae*	Y	NT				*	*	
	Base-rich soil	*Peltigera malacea*	Y	EN B				*	*	
	Base-rich soil (among bryophytes)	*Peltigera venosa*		VU C1				**	*	Glen Shee (old record), Killiecrankie
	Bryophytes on base-rich soil	*Polyblastia wheldonii*		NT				*	*	Beinn a' Ghlo & Tulach Hill
	Base-rich soil	*Porina mammillosa*	Y	NT				**	**	
	Bryophytes on base-rich soil	*Rhexophiale rhexoblephara*	Y	NT				*	*	
Lichenicolous	*Stereocaulon evolutum*	*Arthonia stereocaulina*	Y	NE				***	***	
	Lecanora carpinea	*Arthonia subfuscicola*	Y	NE				***	***	
	Lecanora populicola	*Candelariella superdistans*	Y	DD				***	***	
	Amygdelaria spp.	*Dactylospora amygdalariae*	Y	NE				**	**	
	Dibaeis baeomyces	*Micarea inquinans*	Y	LC				**	**	
	Rhizocarpon geographicum	*Protoparmelia atriseda*	Y	VU D2				**	**	Old Struan
	Aspicilia caesiocinerea	*Rinodina parasitica*	Y	DD				***	***	
Acidic soil	River shingle	*Stereocaulon glareosum*	Y	NT				*	*	
	Over bryophytes	*Rinodina mniaracea* var. *mniaraeiza*	Y	DD				***	***	
Bryicolous	*Sphagnum* spp.	*Absconditella sphagnorum*	Y	NT				**	**	

[1] *Caloplaca cerinelloides*: dubious records, probably not of this species.
[2] Note that 'The Burn', River N. Esk, the site for *Melanelixia subargentifera* (=*Melanelia subargentifera*) lies on the boundary of the Cairngorms area.

7. Mar Lodge Estate Pinewoods and Crags. The Mar Lodge Estate Pinewoods are one of the largest areas of native pinewoods in Britain and Ireland. They were surveyed, in the winter, by Street & Street (2000a) and, although only a preliminary survey, they ranked the woods as the sixth most important in the UK for their lichen flora. Among the important species they recorded were *Absconditella pauxilla, Alectoria sarmentosa* ssp. *sarmentosa, Chrysothrix chrysopthalma, Cladonia botrytes, C. cenotea, C. macrophylla, C. phyllophora, Elixia flexella, Hertelidia botryosa* (*Lecidea botryosa*), *Pycnora sorophora* and *Sclerophora peronella. Lecidea silacea* and *Miriquidica atrofulva* also occurred, on iron-rich silicious rocks. Since then, several important additional species have been reported. They include *Hypocenomyce anthrocophila* (third British record), *Chaenotheciopsis vainioana* and *Cyphelium tigillare* from the pinewoods; *Acrocordia subglobosa* (first British record), *Arctomia delicatula, Lopadium coralloideum* and *Polysporina cyclocarpa* from the crags of Creag an Diuchd in Glen Lui; and *Pyrrhospora rubiginans* and the first British report of *Rhizocarpon amphibium*, from the Linn of Quoich.

8. Strathspey. Much of the work in this area has been incidental; records accruing during visits made for other purposes. A recent survey of the Aspen woods of Strathspey, however, revealed four species new to Britain and Ireland:

Arthonia patellulata, Caloplaca ahtii, Candelariella superdistans and *Rinodina laevigata.* There were also two extremely rare Red Data Book species: *Caloplaca flavorubescens* and *Schismatomma graphidioides* (Coppins *et al.*, 2001, 2002). The area would obviously benefit from a more thorough survey.

9. The Angus Hills. This area was the focus of collecting by the late R. Munro for many years. Unfortunately, only some of his material has been retained, of which the most important is in the herbarium of the RBGE, or in private herbaria (especially that of C.J.B. Hitch). Ecological and other notes are extremely brief. Some of his more important discoveries in the Angus Hills were of *Absconditella annexa, A. sphagnorum, Catapyrenium daedaleum, Cyphelium trachylioides, Dermatocarpon leptophyllodes, Gyalidea rivulosa, Porina mammillosa, Protoparmelia nephaea, Pyrrhospora rubiginans, Rhizocarpon subpostumum* and *Rinodina mniaracea* var. *mniaraeiza.* The lichen flora of this area has yet to be surveyed professionally.

10. Dinnet Oakwood. Surveyed by Coppins & Coppins (1994), this area was found to support several rare and threatened species, including *Bacidia igniarii, Catillaria globulosa, Catinaria neuschildii, Cliostomum flavidulum* and *Melanohalea septentrionalis* (*Melanelia septentrionalis*).

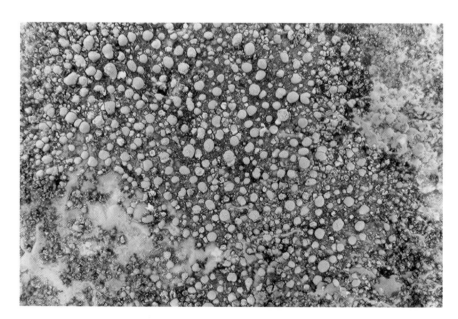

Rhizocarpon ridescens *is known in Britain only from Creag Choinnich, near Braemar*
Photo: *B. Coppins*

Flavocetraria nivalis *is found in alpine heath in the central and eastern Cairngorms, with an outlying population at Beinn a' Ghlo & Tulach Hill.*
Photo: *B. Coppins*

Figure 12.1. Important areas for lichens. See text for details and Table 12.2 for species lists.

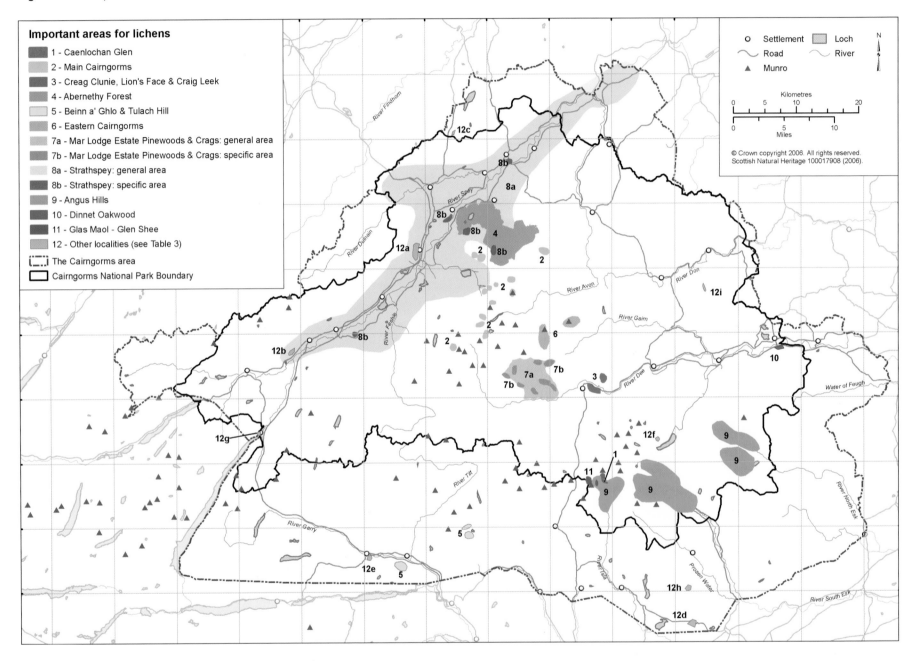

Important areas for lichens

1 - Caenlochan Glen
2 - Main Cairngorms
3 - Creag Clunie, Lion's Face & Craig Leek
4 - Abernethy Forest
5 - Beinn a' Ghlo & Tulach Hill
6 - Eastern Cairngorms
7a - Mar Lodge Estate Pinewoods & Crags: general area
7b - Mar Lodge Estate Pinewoods & Crags: specific area
8a - Strathspey: general area
8b - Strathspey: specific area
9 - Angus Hills
10 - Dinnet Oakwood
11 - Glas Maol - Glen Shee
12 - Other localities (see Table 3)
- - - The Cairngorms area
—— Cairngorms National Park Boundary

Settlement   Loch
Road   River
Munro

Kilometres
0   5   10   20

0   5   10
Miles

© Crown copyright 2006. All rights reserved.
Scottish Natural Heritage 100017908 (2006).

Table 12.2.   Important areas for lichens in the Cairngorms, listed in descending order of the number of internationally and nationally important species in each area.

Percentage of area occurring within the National Park: *** >75%; ** 25-75%; * 10-24%; '-' <10%

Area	Species of international importance	National importance	% of area within NP
1. Caenlochan Glen	*Catillaria gilbertii, Jamesiella scotica (Gyalideopsis scotica), Halecania rhypodiza, Pertusaria flavocorallina*	*Acarospora badiofusca, Brigantiaea fuscolutea, Bryonora curvescens, Caloplaca approximata, Collema parvum, Dactylospora amygdalariae, Fuscidea austera, Fuscopannaria praetermissa, Gyalidea fritzei, Lecidea silacea, Lecidella wulfenii, Lempholemma cladodes, L. radiatum, Lepraria cacuminum, Megaspora verrucosa, Miriquidica atrofulva, Peltigera elisabethae, P. venosa, Phaeophyscia endococcina, Polyblastia efflorescens, P. terrestris, P. wheldonii, Porina mammillosa, Rhizocarpon caeruleoalbum, Rhizocarpon chioneum, Rinodina parasitica, Sagiolechia protuberans, Sporastatia polyspora, S. testudinea, Staurothele bacilligera, Thelidium fumidum, Thelopsis melathelia* **(32 species)**	***
2. Main Cairngorms	*Ameliella grisea* in ed., *Ameliella andeaeicola* in ed.	*Alectoria ochroleuca, Bellemerea alpina, Calvitimela armeniaca, Cercidospora decolorella, Cladonia maxima, C. phyllophora, C. trassii, Flavocetraria nivalis, Lecanora formosa, L. leptacina, Lecidea luteoatra, L. promiscens, L. promiscua, L. syncarpa, Melanelia stygia, Miriquidica nigroleprosa var. liljenströemii, Pertusaria geminipara, Polyblastia gothica, Pseudephebe minuscula, Sporastatia polyspora, Staurothele areolata, Umbilicaria hyperborea* **(22 species)**	***
3. Creag Clunie, Lion's Face & Craig Leek	*Gyalecta ulmi*	*Acarospora macrospora, Adelolecia pilati, Aspicilia contorta ssp. hoffmanniana, Buellia uberior, Caloplaca approximata, Chaenotheca gracilenta, Chaenothecopsis vainioana, Chrysothrix chlorina, Cladonia cenotea, Cladonia metacorallifera, Dactylospora amygdalariae, Fuscidea austera, Ionaspis obtecta (Hymenelia obtecta), Lecanora atrosulphurea, L. swartzii, L. xanthostoma, Lecidea syncarpa, Lecidella wulfenii, Lepraria cacuminum, Leptogium saturninum, Miriquidica atrofulva, Melanelia stygia, Opegrapha paraxanthodes, Polysporina cyclocarpa, Protoparmelia atriseda, P. nephaea, Pycnora sorophora, Pyrrhospora rubiginans, Rimularia globulosa, Rinodina interpolata, Sagiolechia protuberans, Sclerophora peronella, Strigula muscicola, Thelocarpon sphaerosporum, Umbilicaria hirsuta, U. nylanderiana, Xerotrema megalospora* **(37 species)**	***
4. Abernethy Forest	*Chrysothrix chrysophthalma*	*Bacidia vermifera, Biatora efflorescens, Bryoria furcellata, Caloplaca flavorubescens, Catinaria neuschildii, Chaenotheca xyloxena, Chaenothecopsis vainioana, Cladonia botrytes, C. cenotea, Cyphelium tigillare, Elixia flexella, Hertelidea botryosa (Lecidea botryosa), Lecanora mughicola, Lecidea leprarioides, Micarea contexta, Melanohalea septentrionalis (Melanelia septentrionalis), Peltigera malacea, Pycnora xanthococca, Rinodina laevigata, Schismatomma graphidioides, Sclerophora pallida, S. peronella, Stereocaulon glareosum, Xerotrema megalospora* **(24 species)**	***
5. Beinn a' Ghlo & Tulach Hill	*Gyalecta ulmi*	*Acarospora macrospora, Brigantiaea fuscolutea, Caloplaca approximata, Flavocetraria nivalis, Collema parvum, Gyalecta foveolaris, Halecania alpivaga, Lecanora epibryon, Lempholemma cladodes, Lepraria cacuminum, Megaspora verrucosa, Pachyphiale fagicola, Polyblastia inumbrata, P. wheldonii, Polysporina cyclocarpa, Sagiolechia protuberans, Staurothele bacilligera, Strangospora deplanata, Toninia diffracta* **(19 species)**	-
6. Eastern Cairngorms	*Ameliella grisea* in ed.	*Arctoparmelia ?centrifuga, Brodoa intestiniformis, Calvitimela armeniaca, Catolechia wahlenbergii, Cetrariella delisei, Cladonia maxima, C. phyllophora, C. trassii, Flavocetraria nivalis, Lecanora formosa, L. leptacina, Lecidea luteoatra, Melanelia stygia, Micarea inquinans, Stereocaulon spathuliferum, Thelocarpon strasseri, Toninia squalescens* **(17 species)**	***
7. Mar Lodge Estate Pinewoods & Crags	*Chrysothrix chrysopthalma*	*Absconditella pauxilla, Acrocordia subglobosa, Alectoria sarmentosa ssp. sarmentosa, Arctomia delicatula, Cladonia botrytes, C. cenotea, C. macrophylla, C. phyllophora, Elixia flexella, Hertelidea botryosa (Lecidea botryosa), Lecidea silacea, Lopadium coralloideum, Miriquidica atrofulva, Polysporina cyclocarpa, Pycnora sorophora, Sclerophora peronella* **(16 species)**	***
8. Strathspey		*Alectoria sarmentosa ssp. sarmentosa, Arthonia patellulata, A. subfuscicola, Bacidia igniarii, B. subincompta, B. vermifera, Biatoridium delitescens, Caloplaca ahtii, C. flavorubescens, Candelariella superdistans, Catinaria neuschildii, Chrysothrix chlorina, Cladonia botrytes, Collema nigrescens, Collema occultatum, Diplotomma pharcidium, Lecania dubitans, Lecanora conizaeoides f. variola, L. populicola, L. swartzii, Lecidea antiloga, Lecidella flavosorediata, Leptogium saturninum, Melanohalea septentrionalis (Melanelia septentrionalis), Schismatomma graphidioides* **(25 species)**	***
9. Angus Hills		*Absconditella annexa, A. sphagnorum, Catapyrenium daedaleum, Cyphelium trachylioides, Dermatocarpon leptophyllodes, Lecanora swartzii, Porina mammillosa, Protoparmelia nephaea, Pyrrhospora rubiginans, Rhizocarpon subpostumum, Rinodina mniaracea var. mniaraeiza, Toninia squalida, Usnea chaetophora, Vulpicida pinastri* **(14 species)**	***
10. Dinnet Oakwood		*Arthopyrenia atractospora, Bacidia igniarii, Catillaria globulosa, Catinaria neuschildii, Cliostomum flavidulum, Lecanora horiza, Melanohalea septentrionalis (Melanelia septentrionalis), Rinodina degeliana* **(8 species)**	***
11. Glas Maol - Glen Shee		*Acarospora macrospora, Polyblastia gothica, Rhizocarpon anaperum, R. submodestum, Stereocaulon plicatile* **(5 species)**	***
12. Other Localities		**a. Craigellaiche & b. Creag Dhubh Birchwoods:** *Cetraria sepincola, Melanohalea septentrionalis (Melanelia septentrionalis)*; **c. Creag Ealraich:** *Ramalina polymorpha, Lecanora swartzii*; **d. Kirriemuir:** *Lecanora horiza*; **e. Old Struan:** *Protoparmelia atriseda*; **f. Lochnagar:** *Protoparmelia memnonia*; **g. Dalwhinnie:** *Rhexophiale rhexoblephara*; **h. Cat Law:** *Vulpicida pinastri*; **i. Glencarvie:** *Vulpicida pinastri*	

[2] *Lecania dubitans*: known from Braemar by a dubious 19th Century record

11. *Glas Maol - Glen Shee*. The northern coire of Glas Maol supports an important late snow-lie community that includes the rare crustose species *Stereocaulon plicatile* and *Rhizocarpon anaperum;* two species that are extremely rare in the Eastern Highlands. The rare *Polyblastia gothica* and *Rhizocarpon submodestum* also occur here, while the rare calcicole *Acarospora macrospora* has been reported from Glen Shee, on concrete.

12. *Other localities*. Nine other localities, shown as '12a' to '12i' in Figure 12.1, each hold one or a few notable species. ***a. Craigellaiche*** and ***b. Creag Dhubh Birchwoods***, surveyed by Fryday (1990), are good examples of eastern birchwoods; the principle habitat of a suite of species that are rare in Britain and Ireland. They include *Cetraria sepincola* and *Melanohalea septentrionalis* (*Melanelia septentrionalis*). ***c. Creag Ealraich***, an otherwise unremarkable crag just east of the B9007, north of Carrbridge, is notable for its dense coating of the rare *Ramalina polymorpha*. The only other species of note here is *Lecanora swartzii*. Other isolated occurrences of rare species are *Lecanora horiza* (***d. Kirriemuir***), *Protoparmelia atriseda* (***e. Old Struan***), *P. memnonia* (***f. Lochnagar***), *Rhexophiale rhexoblephara* (***g. Dalwhinnie***) and *Vulpicida pinastri* (***h. Cat Law, i. Glencarvie***) (Figure 12.1).

In the Cairngorms, Vulpicida pinastri *(the yellow lichen, above) has been recorded in the Angus Hills, Cat Law, and at Glencarvie, near Strathdon, where it grows on Juniper.*

Photo: *B. Coppins*

Recent research and survey findings

There are currently no active lichen research programmes at UK universities, and all serious survey work in the Cairngorms (indeed, in the UK) is carried out on contract. Local amateurs play an important role in discovering new records for their area, but tend not to describe habitats or communities, and none of their work (at least in the Cairngorms) is published in peer-reviewed journals. Consequently, for most areas, all that exists are records of the rarest species, reported in the British Lichen Society (BLS) Bulletin. An example of this is the Clova Hills, an exceptionally rich and important area for which the only work in print is a report of five days spent in Caenlochan Glen by Gilbert and Coppins (1992). Although the late R. Munro was extremely active in this area, we have no species lists or habitat descriptions, and only the very rarest species have been reported in the BLS Bulletin (e.g. Munro, 1991, 1993, 1998, 2000). These reports provide only brief notes on autecology and locality.

It is only in the past decade or so that cryptogams have attracted sufficient funding (from SNH and others) to permit comprehensive surveys of the lichen floras of the most important sites to be carried out. Previously, the only surveys were part of the pioneering work of O. Gilbert on the Cairngorm plateau (Gilbert & Fox, 1985) and Caenlochan (Gilbert & Coppins, 1992). In 2000, the RSPB funded a lichen survey of its Abernethy Reserve, while in the same year NTS funded a survey of the native pinewoods of its Mar Lodge Estate. Numerous important areas (e.g. the Angus Hills) and individual sites (e.g. Craig Leek SSSI, Morrone NNR, Glen Feshie and others) have yet to be surveyed properly.

The results of surveys of the high ground within the Cairngorms Area (Cairn Gorm, Cairn Lochan, Braeriach, Beinn a' Bhuird, Ben Avon, Glas Maol and Lochnagar) are presented in Fryday (1997). In particular, much ecological information was gathered on the northern Cairngorms, including the late snow-lie area of Ciste Mhearad (Fryday, 2001a, 2002).

The inclusion of several lichen species on Schedule 8 of the Wildlife and Countryside Act promoted the preparation of reports on these species, funded by SNH and coordinated by the Royal Botanic Gardens Edinburgh. These reports include notes on identification, ecology, threats and species management, along with a report on the status of each species at all of its known British locations. This programme has now been extended to include other endangered lichen species and, so far, has resulted in the production of reports on the following species known from the Cairngorms area (Coppins & Coppins, 1997-2000; Fryday, 1999a,b; Street, 1998; Street & Street, 2000c):

Alectoria ochroleuca	*Cladonia botrytes*	*Jamesiella scotica*
Bellemerea alpina	*C. maxima*	*Halecania rhypodiza*
Brodoa intestiniformis	*C. trassii* (*C. stricta* auct.)	*Ramalina polymorpha*
Caloplaca flavorubescens	*Gyalecta ulmi*	*Schismatomma graphidioides*

In addition, several surveys of important lichen sites have been funded by SNH. Examples include Craigellaiche NNR and Creag Dhubh Birchwoods (Fryday, 1990) in Strathspey, Dinnet Oakwood NNR and Creag Clunie and Lion's Face NNR on Deeside (Coppins & Coppins, 1994, 1999). These have been fundamental in confirming the national significance of the lichen flora of these areas. Most surveys result in the discovery of species not previously reported from Britain or Ireland, and some yield species new to science. This underlines the importance of surveys being carried out by proficient lichenologists, capable of recognizing these important discoveries.

Trends

Trends in the abundance or ranges of lichen species are difficult to assess, due to a lack of baseline data, which are only now being slowly acquired (see above).

It is difficult to assess the validity of many old records, either because they are not supported by herbarium specimens, the locality details are vague (e.g. 'Braemar', 'Clova' etc.), or because there is doubt as to whether the specimens really originated from Scotland (e.g. in the case of some of J. Crombie's records). It appears, however, that at least one species – *Bellemerea alpina* (*Aspicilia alpina*) – has disappeared from its only UK location, at Ciste Mhearad (Cairn Gorm), since it was reported from there by Gilbert (1985). This record is supported by a herbarium specimen, but repeated attempts to re-find the species in recent years have failed.

Monitoring lichens is fraught with problems because many are very small, and not easily identified in the field. For most crustose species there is no practical means of assessing population size without collecting on an unacceptable

The nationally threatened lichen *Catolechia wahlenbergii* can be found in alpine heath on the summit of Beinn a' Bhuird.
Photo: *A. Fryday*

The Critically Endangered *Cladonia botrytes* (left in this picture) is a BAP Priority lichen. It was rediscovered in 1997, not having been recorded for 19 years, and is currently known in Britain from just nine localities, including Abernethy and Mar Lodge Estate.
Photo: *L. Gill*

scale, and so monitoring will have to be based on less direct methods (e.g. monitoring larger, more easily identifiable species that are assumed to have the same ecological requirements). Consequently, estimating trends in the size of populations or stands will continue to be difficult. It is, in any case, probably not practical to attempt to conserve individual lichen taxa. Rather, it is more important to preserve the habitat in which they occur.

Conservation issues

Climate change. This will almost certainly effect the lichen vegetation of the high ground in the Cairngorms area, especially that associated with areas of late snow-lie. There are no long-term lichen monitoring projects within the Cairngorms area, but monitoring on Beinn Eighe (Fryday, 1998) has shown significant changes in the only British population of *Nephroma arcticum* in the space of seven years. These are most probably linked to increased bryophyte growth, with which the lichen could not compete, caused by an increase in

One of the most distinctive of Scottish lichens is the nationally scarce Solorina crocea, *normally found above 850 m.*

Photo: *B. Coppins*

precipitation in recent years, most likely as a consequence of climate change.

Woodland management. Many of the key areas of woodland in the Cairngorms area are owned by conservation agencies, including the RSPB (Abernethy) and NTS (Mar Lodge Estate), which take account of lichens when formulating management plans. However, there are still many areas in private ownership. Efforts should be made to raise the owners' awareness of the lichen flora of these areas and the importance of good management practices to ensure their survival.

Air-borne pollution. There is evidence that long-distance pollution in the atmosphere is concentrated by snow-fall and accumulates in areas of late snow-lie. This concentrated pollution is released as an 'acid-shock' in the early stages of snow-melt and potentially has a devastating effect on the fragile vegetation below the snowbed. This is the habitat of *Bellemerea alpina* (see above), and it is possible that its disappearance from Ciste Mhearad has been due to this effect.

Grazing. Grazing of lichens is probably not a serious issue within the Cairngorms area. Grazing pressure on lichens is generally low on high ground, and at lower altitudes much of the lichen interest is epiphytic.

Access, skiing and erosion. Increased recreational pressure on the northern slopes of the Cairngorms would have an adverse effect on important heathland communities where visitors leave the paths. The area of late snow-lie at Ciste Mhearad is already much used by snow-boarders, with potential damage to the surrounding vegetation, and this may grow with increased access to the summit of Cairn Gorm. Higher numbers of walkers on Cairn Gorm would also affect this area because the same forces that concentrate snow into this hollow will also concentrate litter and other pollutants. It is also probable that increased recreational pressure from hill-walkers causes significant damage to terricolous species, and the boot of a hiker, scrambling up a ridge or over a crag, could cause serious damage to a small lichen population.

Awareness. Very little of the damage done to lichen species and populations is likely to be malicious. If the general public, recreational users, land-owners, managers and others are made aware of the rarity and fragile nature of lichen species and communities, much accidental damage might be avoided. Awareness-raising is probably the single-most important action that could be taken to protect the lichen flora of the Cairngorms area since, although climate change and air-borne pollution are probably greater potential threats, little can be done to reduce their impact at a local level.

References

Church, J.M., Coppins, B.J., Gilbert, O.L., James, P.W. & Stewart, N.F. (1996). *Red Data Books of Britain and Ireland: Lichens. Volume 1: Britain*. 84 pp. Joint Nature Conservation Committee: Peterborough.

Coppins, A.M. & Coppins, B.J. (1994). *Dinnet Oakwood NNR: Lichen Survey*. Report to Scottish Natural Heritage. SNH: Edinburgh.

Coppins, A.M. & Coppins, B.J. (1997a; updated 2000). *Action Plans for Lower Plants in Scotland Project. Lichens*. Schismatomma graphidioides. Report to Scottish Natural Heritage & Royal Botanic Garden Edinburgh. SNH: Edinburgh.

Coppins, A.M. & Coppins, B.J. (1998a). *Action Plans for Lower Plants in Scotland Project. Lichens*. Caloplaca flavorubescens. Report to Scottish Natural Heritage & Royal Botanic Garden Edinburgh. SNH: Edinburgh.

Coppins, A.M. & Coppins, B.J. (1998b). *Action Plans for Lower Plants in Scotland Project. Lichens*. Cladonia botrytes. Report to Scottish Natural Heritage & Royal Botanic Garden Edinburgh. SNH: Edinburgh.

Coppins, A.M. & Coppins, B.J. (1999). *Creag Clunie and the Lion's Face SSSI: Lichen Survey*. Report to Scottish Natural Heritage. SNH: Edinburgh.

Coppins, A.M. & Coppins, B.J. (2000a). *Priority Lower Plants Scotland - Lichens* - Bellemerea alpina. Report to Scottish Natural Heritage & Royal Botanic Garden Edinburgh. SNH: Edinburgh.

Coppins, A.M. & Coppins, B.J. (2000b) *Kindrogan Wood - Monitoring of* Cladonia botrytes. Report to Scottish Natural Heritage & Royal Botanic Garden Edinburgh. SNH: Edinburgh.

Coppins, B.J. (2002). *Checklist of lichens of Great Britain and Ireland*. British Lichen Society Bulletin: London.

Coppins, B.J. & Coppins, A.M. (1997b). *Biodiversity Action Plans for* Catapyrenium psoromoides, Cladonia botrytes, Hypogymnia intestiniformis, Peltigera lepidophora, Pertusaria bryontha *and* Thelenella modesta. SNH: Edinburgh.

Coppins, B.J., Street, L. & Street, S. (2002). Small ecological project report: aspen woods in Strathspey. *British Lichen Society Bulletin* 90: 57.

Coppins, B.J., Street, S. & Street, L. (2001). *Lichens of Aspen Woods in Strathspey*. Report to Scottish Natural Heritage. SNH: Edinburgh.

Fryday, A.M. (1990). *A comparative survey of the lichen flora of four* Betula *woods in North-east Scotland*. Report to the Nature Conservancy Council, Aberdeen. SNH: Edinburgh.

Fryday, A.M. (1997). *Ecology and Taxonomy of Montane Lichen Vegetation in the British Isles*. Ph.D. Thesis, University of Sheffield.

Fryday, A.M. (1998). Re-survey of the *Nephroma arcticum* population on Ruadh-stac Beag, *Beinn Eighe NNR, West-Ross*. Report to Scottish Natural Heritage. SNH: Edinburgh .

Fryday, A.M. (1999a). *Action Plans for Lower Plants in Scotland Project. Lichens*: Alectoria ochroleuca. Report to Scottish Natural Heritage & Royal Botanic Garden Edinburgh. SNH: Edinburgh.

Fryday, A.M. (1999b). *Action Plans for Lower Plants in Scotland Project - Lichens* - Cladonia stricta. Report to Scottish Natural Heritage & Royal Botanic Garden Edinburgh. SNH: Edinburgh.

Fryday, A.M. (2001a). The lichen vegetation associated with areas of late snow-lie in the Scottish Highlands. *Lichenologist* 33: 121-150.

Fryday, A.M. (2001b). Phytosociology of terricolous lichen vegetation in the Cairngorm Mountains, Scotland. *Lichenologist* 33: 331-351.

Fryday, A.M. (2002). Distribution and importance of the lichen vegetation of the Scottish Highlands. *Botanical Journal of Scotland* 54: 133-151.

Gilbert, O.L. & Coppins, B.J. (1992). The lichens of Caenlochan, Angus. *Lichenologist* 24: 143-163.

Gilbert, O.L. & Fox, B.W. (1985). Lichens of high ground in the Cairngorm Mountains, Scotland. *Lichenologist* 17: 51-66.

IUCN (2001). *IUCN Red List Catagories & Criteria. Version 3.1*. IUCN: Gland, Switzerland.

Munro, R.C. (1991). *Protoparmelia nephaea*. *Bulletin of the British Lichen Society* 68: 38.

Munro, R.C. (1993). *Absconditella annexa. Bulletin of the British Lichen Society* 73: 55.

Munro, R.C. (1998). *Rhizocarpon subpostumum. Bulletin of the British Lichen Society* 82: 50.

Munro, R.C. (2000). *Cyphelium trachylioides, Rinodina mniaraea* var. *mniaraeiza. Bulletin of the British Lichen Society* 86: 45-46, 53-54.

Purvis, O.W., Gilbert, O.L. & Coppins, B.J. (1994). Lichens of the Blair Atholl limestone. *Lichenologist* 26: 367-382.

Rose, F. (1976) Lichenological indicators of age and environmental continuity in woodlands. In: Brown, D.H., Hawksworth, D.L., & Bailey, R.H. (eds.). *Lichenology: Progress and Problems*. Academic Press: London. pp. 279-307.

Street, S. (1998). Cladonia botrytes - *Pilot study in Badenoch and Strathspey*. Report to Scottish Natural Heritage. SNH: Edinburgh.

Street, L. & Street, S. (2000c). *Action Plans for Lower Plants in Scotland Project. Lichens*: Alectoria ochroleuca. Report to Scottish Natural Heritage & Royal Botanic Garden Edinburgh - update of earlier species dossier, Fryday 1999. SNH: Edinburgh.

Street, S. & Street, L. (2000a). *Lichen Survey of native pine woods at Mar Lodge Estate*. Report to The National Trust for Scotland.

Street, S. & Street, L. (2000b) *Lichen Report for Abernethy RSPB Reserve*. RSPB: Abernethy.

Woods, R.G. & Coppins, B.J. (2003). *A Conservation Evaluation of British Lichens*. British Lichen Society: London.

Annex 12.1

Additional nationally rare or scarce taxa within the Cairngorms, considered to be of low conservation concern. Those with more than 10% of their UK range within the Cairngorms area are indicated.

More than 10% and nationally rare

Adelolecia pilati
Arthonia mediella
Arthrorhaphis alpina
Buellia arborea
Catillaria scotinodes
Cercidospora decolorella
Chaenothecopsis nigra
Chaenothecopsis pusilla
Chaenothecopsis pusiola
Cladonia symphycarpia
Claurouxia chalybeioides
Collema callopismum
Collema undulatum
Eiglera flavida
Fuscidea arboricola

Gyalidea diaphana
Gyalidea rivularis
Hymenelia cyanocarpa
Ionaspis chrysophana
Ionaspis odora
Lecanactis latebrarum
Lecanographa abscondita
Lecanora cenisia
Lecidea commaculans
Lecidea nylanderi
Lecidea promixta
Lepraria diffusum var. chrysodetoides
Lepraria neglecta
Leptogium intermedium
Lichenomphalia velutina (Omphalina velutina)

Micarea lapillicola
Micarea marginata
Micarea ternaria
Micarea turfosa
Micarea viridiatra
Miriquidica griseoatra
Mycoblastus alpinus
Ochrolechia frigida f. lapuensis
Ochrolechia microstictoides
Pertusaria amarescens
Pertusaria borealis
Placynthium pluriseptatum
Protoparmelia oleagina
Protothelenella sphinctrinoidella
Rhizocarpon badioatrum

Rhizocarpon simillimum
Rhizocarpon sublavatum
Rinodina occulta
Rinodina pityrea
Scoliciosporum intrusum (Carbonea intrusa)
Strigula alpestris
Thelidium papulare f. sorediatum
Thelocarpon pallidum
Thelocarpon strasseri
Thelocarpon superellum
Toninia fusispora
Toninia squalescens
Xanthoria ulophyllodes

More than 10% and nationally scarce

Acarospora glaucocarpa
Ainoa mooreana
Alectoria sarmentosa ssp. vexillifera
Allantoparmelia alpicola
Aspicilia laevata
Bacidia beckhausii
Belonia incarnata
Belonia russula
Biatora chrysantha
Bryophagus gloeocapsa
Bryoria bicolor
Bryoria capillaris
Bryoria chalybeiformis
Bryoria lanestris
Caloplaca cerinella
Caloplaca obliterans
Calvitimela aglaea
Carbonea vorticosa
Catillaria contristans
Catillaria nigroclavata
Cetraria ericetorum
Chaenotheca stemonea

Cladonia carneola
Cladonia zopfii
Diploschistes gypsaceus
Farnoldia jurana
Frutidella caesioatra
Fuscidea gothoburgensis
Fuscidea intercincta
Gyalecta geoica
Hypocenomyce friesii
Immersaria athrocarpa
Ionaspis epulotica
Koerberiella wimmeriana
Lecanactis dilleniana
Lecanora aitema
Lecanora albellula (L. piniperda)
Lecanora cadubriae
Lecanora sambuci
Lecanora subcarnea
Lecidea auriculata
Lecidea berengeriana
Lecidea fuliginosa
Lecidea hypopta

Lecidea plana
Lecidea pycnocarpa f. pycnocarpa
Lecidoma demissum
Lempholemma botryosum
Lepraria elobata
Lithographa tesserata
Melanelia commixta
Melanelia hepatizon
Micarea incrassata
Micarea misella
Micarea tuberculata
Miriquidica nigroleprosa f. nigroleprosa
Mycoblastus affinis
Ochrolechia xanthostoma
Opegrapha dolomitica
Orphniospora moriopsis
Parmelia disjuncta
Peltigera britannica
Peltigera degenii
Pertusaria coronata
Pertusaria dactylina
Pertusaria oculata

Phaeophyscia endophoenicea
Phaeophyscia sciastra
Placynthiella oligotropha
Placynthium flabellosum
Placynthium tantaleum
Polyblastia cruenta
Polyblastia cupularis
Polyblastia melaspora
Polyblastia theleodes
Protoblastenia siebenhariana
Protomicarea limosa
Protoparmelia ochrococca
Protothelenella corrosa
Psora decipiens
Ramonia interjecta
Rhizocarpon alpicola
Rhizocarpon geminatum
Rhizocarpon polycarpum
Rimularia badioatra
Rimularia gyrizans
Rimularia intercedens
Rimularia limborina

More than 10% and nationally scarce

Rimularia mullensis

Solorina crocea

Solorina spongiosa

Staurothele fissa

Staurothele succedens

Stereocaulon condensatum

Stereocaulon leucophaeopsis

Stereocaulon saxatile

Stereocaulon versuvianum var. *nodulosum*

Thelidium pyrenophorum

Thelocarpon epibolum

Thelomma ocellatum

Thrombium epigaeum

Toninia verrucarioides

Trapeliopsis percrenata

Umbilicaria deusta

Verrucaria pinguicula

Xylographa trunciseda

Less than 10% and nationally rare

Amygdalaria consentiens

Bacidia subcircumspecta

Cladonia pleurota

Fuscopannaria ignobilis

Lecidea paupercula

Micarea pseudomarginata

Ochrolechia inaequatula

Porina guentheri var. *lucens*

Protothelenella sphinctrinoides

Ramalina polymorpha

Ramonia dictyospora

Rhizocarpon caesium

Solorina bispora

Strangospora microhaema

Strigula confusa

Thelocarpon lichenicola

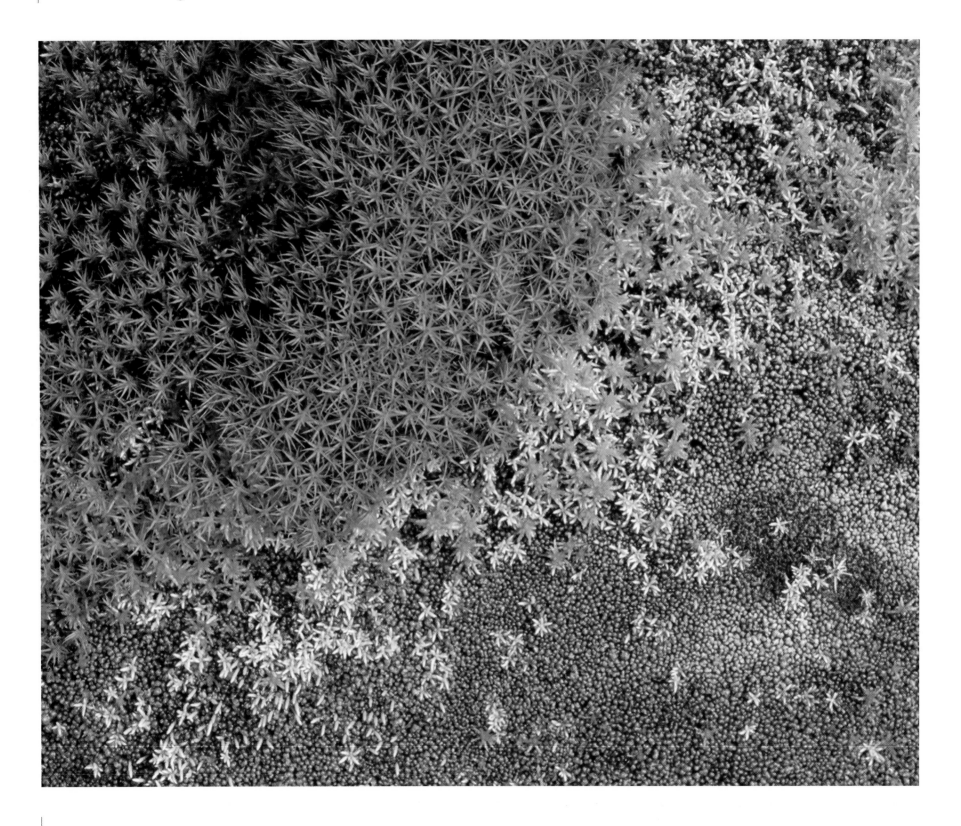

13. BRYOPHYTES

Gordon Rothero

Introduction

The Cairngorms have a large and important bryophyte flora. Their extensive area and diverse habitats provide niches for almost two-thirds of the UK's bryophytes, including some 101 nationally rare species and 154 nationally scarce species[1]. Of these, 56 are considered nationally threatened (Church *et al.*, 2001). A large number of species have the bulk of their UK population within the Cairngorms, and there are bryophyte assemblages of considerable national importance.

The bryophyte flora of the Cairngorms includes species that are internationally important, although there are fewer of these than within Britain's Atlantic or oceanic element, which is best developed in the woods, ravines and mountains along the western seaboard of the UK. Here there are a number of species that are extremely rare in mainland Europe or absent altogether, and some that have a remarkably disjunct global distribution. The Cairngorms, in contrast, are set in one of the most 'continental' parts of the UK and the Atlantic element of the flora, although not absent, is much reduced when compared to that of the western mountains. Most of the rare species and notable communities in the Cairngorms are composed of Arctic-alpine or boreal-montane species, which have a very limited range in the UK, but are often widespread in the mountains and northern forests of mainland Europe.

Important species and habitats

Since a considerable proportion of the bryophytes of interest in the Cairngorms are Arctic-alpine species, most of the important habitats for bryophytes are montane. As with the flowering plants, the longest lists of rare bryophytes come from moderate- or high-altitude exposures of calcareous or base-rich rock, and their associated screes, burns and flushes. The Cairngorm mountains themselves are largely composed of granite and are rather acidic, albeit with local exceptions, and the crags of more basic rocks tend to be scattered around the perimeter of the National Park area. The sites involved differ in character, and so tend to have characteristic assemblages of species. Numerically, the most species-rich areas are those where the underlying rock is some form of schist, notably in Caenlochan Glen, Glen Clova and Glen Shee, but with smaller outcrops in Glen Feshie and the Drumochter Hills. Although many of the species involved here are rare, most of them also occur at a number of sites in the Breadalbane Hills, notably on Ben Lawers. On the eastern side of the Cairngorms the base-rich schist has other minerals, which seem to provide appropriate conditions for a number of species of *Grimmia*, which are otherwise very rare in the UK. Similar rocks in Glen Callater also have metallic elements, giving rise to interesting populations of what are called 'copper mosses'.

Other important base-rich rocks are the outcrops of metamorphosed limestone, again scattered around the perimeter of the National Park. These are probably best developed in the Braemar and Glen Shee areas but there are large exposures near Blair Atholl and in Glen Tilt, around Tomintoul and the River Avon, and in Glen Feshie. Most of these sites are at lower altitudes than the best schist crags, but have a number of the same species. Several bryophyte species have all or most of their UK population on this limestone formation.

The most important bryophyte areas in the Cairngorms, in terms of their share of the UK population and habitat, are those with very late snow-lie. Although there are other mountain areas with large patches of snow-bed vegetation, on Ben Nevis, Ben Alder and Creag Meagaidh for example, the frequency and extent of such vegetation in the Cairngorms is such that it has more bryophyte-dominated snow-beds than all of these other areas combined. The most important factor here is the very large area of ground above 900 m. Also important is the

---

Where competition from vascular plants is less intense bryophytes may grow in profusion, as on this flush on Coire Raibeirt, high up on Cairn Gorm.

Photo: *L. Gill*

Rothero, G. (2006). Bryophytes. In: Shaw, P. & Thompson, D.B.A. (eds.). *The Nature of the Cairngorms: Diversity in a changing environment.* The Stationery Office. pp. 195-213

---

[1] Nationally rare species have been recorded from 15 or fewer 10-km squares, while nationally scarce species have been recorded from 16-100 10-km squares in the UK.

As with the flowering plants, the longest lists of rare bryophytes come from moderate- or high-altitude exposures of calcareous or base-rich rock, and their associated screes, burns and flushes

Photo: *L. Gill*

undulating terrain, providing lee slopes for snow accumulation, and the rock type, consisting of granite, which breaks down readily into a fine gravel. This bryophyte-dominated vegetation will only form in the areas of latest snow-lie, where large patches of snow frequently persist into July, and sometimes last throughout the year. The limited snow-free period in such areas is presumably too short for flowering plants to persist, and so competition is much reduced.

Being near the centre of the Scotland, some way from the sea, the Cairngorms area is relatively dry, with warm summers and cold winters. Its climate probably explains the occurrence of a number of species of dry acid rocks at low altitude, which have most or all of their UK population in the Cairngorms. Favoured localities are large areas of block scree, often with a southerly aspect and with limited tree cover. Here most of the interesting species occur in bryophyte mats that form in the spaces between the rocks. These sites are usually associated with crags, which may be large, but can be areas of broken rock. Although some are low down, as at Creag Dubh near Newtonmore, others are in the main Cairngorm Mountains at over 900 m. For reasons that are unclear, some of the most productive sites for these species are on the very acidic quartzite and flagstones, with outcrops in Strath Nethy, Glen Feshie and the Braemar area.

There are large areas of Scots Pine *Pinus sylvestris* woodland in Strathspey and Deeside, but the ground flora in such woodlands has an abundance – rather than a variety – of bryophytes. The more diverse woodlands are those with a mix of other habitats, including crags, scree and flushes. In the forest itself, old rotting wood also has an interesting flora, which includes the European rarity Green Shield-moss *Buxbaumia viridis* and a number of other scarce species. In Strathspey and Deeside there are frequent stands of Aspen *Populus tremula*. Recent interest in this tree has produced records of many interesting lower plants, including rare species of the moss genus *Orthotrichum*.

The most interesting of the mires in the area also tend to be within woodland, usually as valley mires with a range of *Sphagnum* species. Ombrotrophic mires are widespread on the hills, again with a good range of *Sphagnum* species, particularly where there is some associated flushing, either from calcareous rocks above or from meltwater below snow-beds.

Table 13.1 lists species whose Cairngorms populations are of national or international importance. The list includes all nationally rare species recorded from the Cairngorms and those nationally scarce species that are included in the bryophyte Red Data Book (Church *et al.*, 2001).

Table 13.1. Bryophyte species whose populations in the Cairngorms area are of at least national importance. Those with an internationally important population on at least one site are shown in bold. Notable areas outside of the National Park, but within the wider Cairngorms area, are identified.

Nationally Rare:	Recorded from 1–15 10-km squares in the UK.
RDB:	National Red Data Book status. EX = Extinct; CR = Critically endangered; EN = Endangered; VU = Vulnerable; DD = Data Deficient; NT = Near-threatened; LC = Least Concern (from Church *et al.*, 2001).
BAP:	Biodiversity Action Plan Priority species.
ECCB:	European Committee for Conservation of Bryophytes red list. R = Rare; K = insufficiently known (from ECCB, 1995).
Percentage of UK range:	The percentage of the species' UK range (in 10-km squares) occurring in the Cairngorms area or in the National Park: *** >75%; ** 25-75%; * 10-24%; '-' <10%

Habitat	Species	Common name	Status				Percentage of UK range in:		Notable areas outside of the National Park
			Nationally rare	RDB	BAP	ECCB	Cairngorms area	National Park	
Calcareous montane rocks	*Bryum arcticum*	Arctic Thread-moss	Y	DD			**	*	Gleann Beag
	Bryum dixonii	**Dixon's Thread-moss**	Y	NT		R	*	*	
	Campylophyllum halleri	Haller's Feather-moss	Y	EN			*	*	
	Campylopus schimperi	Schimper's Swan-neck Moss	Y				*	*	
	Didymodon icmadophilus	Slender Beard-moss	Y	NT			*		Beinn a' Ghlo
	Eurhynchium pulchellum var. *diversifolium*	Elegant Feather-moss	Y	EN			**	*	Ben Vrackie
	Gymnomitrion corallioides	Coral Frostwort	Y	NT			*	*	Ben Vrackie
	Heterocladium dimorphum	Dimorphous Tamarisk-moss	Y	VU			*	*	Glas Tulaichean
	Hypnum bambergeri	Golden Plait-moss	Y				*	*	
	Jungermannia polaris	Arctic Flapwort	Y	NT			*	*	Gleann Beag
	Leiocolea gillmanii	Gillman's Notchwort	Y	NT			*	*	
	Mnium ambiguum	Ambiguous Thyme-moss	Y	NT			*	*	
	Mnium spinosum	Spinose Thyme-moss	Y	NT			*	*	
	Myurella tenerrima	Dwarf Mouse-tail Moss	Y	EN			*	*	
	Plagiobryum demissum	Alpine Hump-moss	Y	EN			*	*	
	Plagiothecium piliferum	Hair Silk-moss	Y	CR			**	**	
	Pohlia obtusifolia	Blunt-leaved Thread-moss	Y	EN			*	*	
	Pseudoleskea incurvata	Brown Mountain Leskea	Y	NT			*	*	
	Pseudoleskeella nervosa	Nerved Leskea	Y	VU			***	***	
	Pseudoleskeella rupestris	**Wispy Leskea**	Y	NT		K	*	*	
	Ptychodium plicatum	Plaited Leskea	Y	NT			*	*	
	Scapania gymnostomophila	Narrow-lobed Earwort	Y	NT			*	*	Gleann Beag
	Seligeria diversifolia	Long Rock-bristle	Y	DD	Y		*		Glas Tulaichean
	Syntrichia norvegica	Norway Screw-moss	Y	VU			*	*	
	Timmia austriaca	Sheathed Timmia	Y	EN			**	*	Glas Tulaichean
	Timmia norvegica	Norway Timmia	Y	NT			*	*	
Calcareous flush	*Aongstroemia longipes*	Sprig-moss	Y	NT			*		Atholl
	Barbilophozia quadriloba	Four-fingered Pawwort	Y	NT			*	*	Atholl, Ben Vrackie
	Bryum stirtonii	**Stirton's Thread-moss**	Y	VU		K	*	*	Glas Tulaichean
	Dicranella grevilleana	Greville's Forklet-moss	Y	NT			**		Atholl
	Oncophorus wahlenbergii	Wahlenberg's Spur-moss	Y	NT			*	*	
	Palustriella decipiens	Lesser Curled Hook-moss	Y	NT			*	*	
	Plagiomnium medium	Alpine Thyme-moss	Y	NT			*	*	

Habitat	Species	Common name	Status				Percentage of UK range in:		Notable areas outside of the National Park
			Nationally rare	RDB	BAP	ECCB	Cairngorms area	National Park	
Calcareous flush	*Splachnum vasculosum*	Rugged Collar-moss		NT			*	*	
	Tayloria lingulata	Tongue-leaved Gland-moss	Y	EN			*	*	Glas Tulaichean
Burns: calcareous	*Hygrohypnum smithii*	Arctic Brook-moss	Y	NT			*	*	
	Schistidium agassizii	Water Grimmia		NT					
Base-rich rocks	*Grimmia elatior*	Large Grimmia	Y	EX			***	***	
	Grimmia elongata	Brown Grimmia	Y	NT			*	*	
	Grimmia ovalis	Flat-rock Grimmia		VU			*	*	
	Grimmia unicolor	Dingy Grimmia	Y	VU			***	***	
	Mielichhoferia elongata	**Elongate Copper-moss**	Y	VU		K	**	**	
	Mielichhoferia mielichhoferiana	**Alpine Copper-moss**	Y	VU		K	***	***	
	Saelania glaucescens	Blue Dew-moss	Y	VU			***	***	
Limestone crags	*Athalamia hyalina*		Y	DD			***	***	
	Ctenidium procerrimum	Alpine Comb-moss	Y	VU			**	**	
	Hypnum vaucheri	Vaucher's Plait-moss	Y	VU			**		Beinn a' Ghlo
	Schistidium atrofuscum	Black Mountain Grimmia	Y				**	**	
	Stegonia latifolia	Hood-leaved Screw-moss	Y	NT			***	**	Beinn a' Ghlo, Beinn Vrackie, Gleann Beag
	Tortella fragilis	Brittle Crisp-moss	Y	NT			*	*	
	Tortula leucostoma	**Alpine Pottia**	Y	VU		T	***	**	Gleann Beag
	Weissia controversa var. *wimmeriana*	Wimmer's Stubble-moss	Y				***	***	
Acid flushes	*Lophozia wenzelii*	Wenzel's Notchwort	Y	NT			*	*	
Acid rocks	*Cynodontium tenellum*	Delicate Dog-tooth	Y	NT			***	***	
	Dicranum elongatum	Dense Fork-moss	Y	CR			**	**	
	Paraleucobryum longifolium	Long-leaved Fork-moss	Y	VU			**	**	
	Racomitrium macounii ssp. *alpinum*	Macoun's Fringe-moss	Y	NT			*	*	
Burns: acid	*Bryum muehlenbeckii*	Muehlenbeck's Thread-moss	Y	NT			*	*	
Block scree	*Anastrophyllum saxicola*	Curled Notchwort	Y	NT			***	***	
	Cynodontium fallax	False Dog-tooth	Y	EX			***	***	
	Cynodontium polycarpon	Many-fruited Dog-tooth	Y	DD			*	*	
	Cynodontium strumiferum	Strumose Dog-tooth	Y	NT			***	***	
	Gymnocolea acutiloba	Welsh Notchwort	Y	VU			**	**	
Burns: meltwater	*Hygrohypnum molle*	Soft Brook-moss	Y	VU			**	**	
	Andreaea frigida	**Icy Rock-moss**	Y	NT	Y	R	***	***	
Snow-bed	*Andreaea alpestris*	Slender Rock-moss	Y	DD			***	***	
	Andreaea blyttii	Blytt's Rock-moss	Y	VU			**	**	
	Andreaea nivalis	Snow Rock-moss	Y	NT			**	**	
	Andreaea sinuosa	**Small-spored Rock-moss**	Y			R	**	**	
	Brachythecium glaciale	Snow Feather-moss	Y				**	**	
	Brachythecium reflexum	Reflexed Feather-moss	Y				**	**	
	Brachythecium starkei	Starke's Feather-moss	Y	VU			*	*	
	Cephalozia ambigua	Snow Pincerwort	Y	DD			***	***	
	Gymnomitrion apiculatum	Pointed Frostwort	Y	VU			***	***	

Habitat	Species	Common name	Status				Percentage of UK range in:		Notable areas outside of the National Park
			Nationally rare	RDB	BAP	ECCB	Cairngorms area	National Park	
Snow-bed	*Hygrohypnum styriacum*	**Snow Brook-moss**	Y	CR		R	***	***	
	Kiaeria glacialis	Snow Fork-moss	Y				**	**	
	Marsupella arctica	**Arctic Rustwort**	Y	VU		R	***	***	
	Marsupella boeckii	Boeck's Rustwort	Y	NT			*	*	
	Marsupella condensata	Compact Rustwort	Y	NT			**	**	
	Marsupella sparsifolia	Rounded Rustwort	Y	VU			***	***	
	Nardia breidleri	Book Flapwort	Y				**	**	
	Pseudoleskea patens	Patent Leskea	Y				*	*	
	Rhizomnium magnifolium	Large-leaf Thyme-moss	Y				*	*	
	Scapania paludosa	Floppy Earwort	Y				*	*	
Heath	*Dicranum spurium*	Fuzzy Fork-moss		VU			*	*	
	Philonotis cernua	Swan-necked Apple-moss	Y	CR			*	*	
Hepatic heath	*Anastrophyllum joergensenii*	**Joergensen's Notchwort**	Y	NT		R	*	*	
Carrion	*Aplodon wormskioldii*	Carrion-moss	Y	CR			*	*	
Dung	*Tayloria tenuis*	Slender Gland-moss	Y	CR			*	*	
Mires	*Barbilophozia kunzeana*	Bog Pawwort	Y	NT			*	*	
	Dicranum bergeri	Waved Fork-moss	Y	VU			**	*	Atholl area
	Dicranum leioneuron	Bendy Fork-moss	Y	VU					
	Sphagnum balticum	Baltic Bog-moss	Y	EN	Y		*	*	
	Sphagnum lindbergii	Lindberg's Bog-moss	Y	NT			*	*	
	Sphagnum majus	Olive Bog-moss	Y	VU			*	*	
Serpentine rocks	*Grimmia ungeri*		Y	VU			***	***	
Decaying wood	*Buxbaumia viridis*	**Green Shield-moss**	Y	EN	Y	V	**	**	
	Lophozia longiflora	Reddish Notchwort	Y	DD			***	***	
Trees	*Habrodon perpusillus*	Lesser Squirrel-tail Moss	Y	EN					
	Orthotrichum gymnostomum[1]	**Aspen Bristle-moss**	Y	EX*		RT	***	***	
	Orthotrichum obtusifolium	Blunt-leaved Bristle-moss	Y	EN	Y		**	**	
	Orthotrichum pallens	Pale Bristle-moss	Y	EN	Y		*	*	
	Orthotrichum speciosum	Showy Bristle-moss	Y	NT			**	**	
	Pictus scoticus	**Pict-moss**	Y	DD		K	***		Gleann Beag

[1] *Orthotrichum gymnostomum*: listed as 'Extinct' by Church *et al.* (2001), but recently re-found in Strathspey and at Loch Kinord, on Deeside.

Important areas

Important areas for bryophyte species are listed in Table 13.2 and Figure 13.1, in descending order of international importance. These are areas that are reasonably well defined, and contain important assemblages of bryophytes, populations of rare species, or both.

1. Core Cairngorms. This is a very large area, which encompasses all of the highest tops and the associated plateau and coires, and includes much of the Cairngorms NNR. The most important feature of this area is the amount of bryophyte-dominated snow-bed vegetation both on the plateau and in the deep coires; nowhere else in the UK is there such an expanse of this vegetation type (Rothero, 1990; 1991b). The limited distribution of this kind of vegetation means that many of its constituent species are rare, and that the Cairngorms holds the bulk of the UK population of these bryophytes. Of particular note is the population of *Marsupella arctica* in the Lairig Ghru, first found in 1989 along with a second site on Beinn a' Bhuird, and otherwise not known in Europe other than on Svalbard in the Arctic (Long *et al.*, 1990). Also found in 1989, new to Britain, was a small stand of *Hygrohypnum styriacum* in Coire an t-Sneachda. This species is rare in Europe and this record represents a significant extension of its range (Corley & Rothero, 1992).

The Cairngorms are also of note for their large population of *Andreaea frigida*, found on rocks in burns draining into Loch Avon and Loch Etchachan, on the loch margins, and also in the burn in Garbh Choire on Braeriach. Apart from one old and one recent English locality for this species, all other recent UK sites have been in the Cairngorms (Rothero, 1999d, 2001, 2003a; Rothero & Amphlett, 2001). Other rare species of *Andreaea* also occur here in considerable abundance, including *A. nivalis*, *A. blyttii* and the taxonomically-difficult *A. alpestris* (Murray, 1988). The most important UK populations of other rare snow-bed species are also a feature of the Cairngorms' snow patches, in particular *Gymnomitrion apiculatum*, *Marsupella condensata*, *M. boeckii* and *Kiaeria glacialis*, while the possible UK endemic *M. stableri* is locally abundant (Rothero, 2003a).

Calcicole bryophytes are not common in the Core Cairngorms but Coire an t-Sneachda has *Hygrohypnum smithii*. Flushed ground near the Pools of Dee in the Lairig Ghru has a remarkable collection of rare species in an unlikely setting, including *Plagiomnium medium*, *Syntrichia norvegica*, *Brachythecium starkei*, *B. reflexum*, *Bryum muehlenbeckii*, *Hylocomnium pyrenaicum* and the disjunct oceanic species *Paraleptodontium recurvifolium*. Species of the drier, acidic rocks have a number of sites in the Cairngorms; *Paraleucobryum longifolium* has at least four scattered sites and *Anastrophyllum saxicola* has small populations in the Chalamain Gap and in the huge block scree in upper Strath Nethy. The latter area also has the only Scottish site for *Gymnocolea acutiloba*. The higher hills are sufficiently humid to have the most easterly outposts of the oceanic-montane hepatic heath, usually in heathy scree on north-facing slopes on the bigger mountains. Species here include *Scapania ornithopodioides*, *S. nimbosa*, *Plagiochila carringtonii*, *Anastrophyllum donnianum* and two sites for *Anastrophyllum joergensenii*. All of these species have a very disjunct global distribution (Rothero, 1999c).

2. Glen Clova. The outcrops and screes scattered along the glen, north of Clova village, the calcareous crags around Glen Doll and the diorite crags at Juanjorge, together form a complex and very rich area for bryophytes. The Glen Doll area lies within the Caenlochan SSSI and has some of the rarities of Caenlochan Glen but with the interesting addition of the larger of the only two UK populations of *Saelania glaucescens*, the other being in Glen Feshie

Flushed ground near the Pools of Dee in the Lairig Ghru has a remarkable collection of rare species in an unlikely setting. These include the nationally rare Alpine Thyme-moss Plagiomnium medium, which also occurs in Glen Callater, and on crags at Lochnagar.

Photo: G. Rothero

(Long & Rothero, 1996). At Juanjorge at the head of the main glen, there is an area of slabby diorite crags and screes with an interesting flora, particularly for species of *Grimmia*. There is a very large population of *Grimmia unicolor* here, a species with only one other – recently discovered – site in the UK outside of the Clova area. The endemic *Bryum dixonii* is frequent in places here, as is *G. ovalis*. In the screes, *Cynodontium strumiferum* and *C. tenellum* occur, and there is a 1965 record of *C. polycarpon*. The crags around Loch Brandy also have interesting species of *Grimmia* and *Cynodontium*, and there is a large population of *Paraleucobryum longifolium*. Clova also has the only UK records of *G. elatior* and *C. fallax*, not seen since the 19th century and now considered extinct here – but in such a complex area it is possible that they still survive.

3. Cairnwell, Gleann Beag & Glas Tulaichean. This area includes the limestone outcrops and other calcareous rocks on both the Aberdeenshire side (within the National Park) and Perthshire side of the range, plus an isolated outcrop of similar rocks on Glas Tulaichean. Some of the ground is within the Caenlochan and Cairnwell SSSIs but some interesting areas lie outwith the existing SSSIs. As with nearby Caenlochan, the importance of this area lies in the sheer number of rare calcicole bryophytes. The limestone outcrops in Gleann Beag on the Perthshire side are particularly important, with two stands of *Tortula leucostoma*, usually with the more frequent *Stegonia latifolia* (Long & Rothero, 1996). This is also the area from which *Pictus scoticus*, an endemic Scottish species and genus, was recorded on a single occasion. There remains considerable doubt about the taxonomy of this plant, which may prove to be an odd form of a more common species (Long & Rothero, 1996). Rocks by Loch Vrotachan are the only confirmed UK locality for *Pseudoleskeella nervosa* growing with *P. patens* (Rothero, 1998) and flushes near here have *Tayloria lingulata*. Further southwest, on Glas Tulaichean, there is a very small limestone crag with an astonishing collection of rarities, including *Heterocladium dimorphum*, *Timmia austriaca*, *Tayloria lingulata*, *Ptychodium plicatum* and *Seligeria brevifolia*.

4. Caenlochan Glen. The crags, screes, associated flushes and snow-beds at the upper end of Caenlochan Glen form the richest single area for rare bryophytes in the Cairngorms, and with part of Glen Clova form the Caenlochan SSSI.

Glen Clova has a very large population of Dingy Grimmia Grimmia unicolor; *a species with only one other – recently discovered – British site outside of the Clova area.*
Photo: *G. Rothero*

Flushes in the Caenlochan area support large populations of Lindberg's Bog-moss Sphagnum lindbergii, *here photographed on the plateau east of Glas Maol. This nationally rare species also occurs in flushes in the Drumochter Hills and at the head of the Water of Unich, and has large populations in mires at Coire Kander and Lochanagar.*
Photo: *G. Rothero*

Species like *Plagiothecium piliferum*, *Campylophyllum halleri*, *Plagiobryum demissum* and *Mnium ambiguum* have their only UK sites here and in the Ben Lawers area, and there are important records of *Ptychodium plicatum*, *Heterocladium dimorphum*, *Tayloria lingulata*, *Myurella tenerrima*, *Timmia austriaca*, *Grimmia elongata* and *Eurhynchium pulchellum*. Some of these species have not been seen for a number of years, and give cause for concern. The most enigmatic of these is *Plagiothecium piliferum*, which has been recorded from Ben Lawers (not seen since 1903) and from Caenlochan, where it was seen just once, in 1939 (Long & Rothero, 1996). The endemic Scottish species *Bryum dixonii* also occurs here, while the snow-beds support *Brachythecium starkei* and the flushes have large populations of *Sphagnum lindbergii*, all adding to the floral importance of what is a small area.

5. Eastern Cairngorms. This area comprises the Eastern Cairngorms SSSI and the Inchrory SSSI. As in the main Cairngorm mountains, the major bryophyte interest here is the bryophyte-dominated vegetation of the areas of late snow-lie, but the extensive limestone outcrops at Inchrory and the calcareous rocks on Creag an Dail Bheag provide an additional interest. *Marsupella arctica* has

its second Cairngorm (and UK) site here, on Beinn a' Bhuird. In the same area, there is a small stand of the liverwort *Marsupella sparsifolia* (Rothero, 1990). Also present in the snow-beds here are *Andreaea sinuosa* and *A. alpestris*; both very rare and very difficult to pick out in the field.

The limestone crags at Inchrory have a good list of calcicole bryophytes and important here are *Stegonia latifolia* and *Didymodon icmadophilus*. Creag an Dail Bheag is another isolated area of calcareous rocks, with a relatively recent (1954) record of *Dicranum elongatum* and stands of *Hypnum bambergeri*, *Hygrohypnum smithii*, *Oncophorus wahlenbergii* and *Gymnomitrion corallioides*.

6. Abernethy Forest. This large area of woodland has an abundant but not very diverse bryophyte flora; most of the interest centring on other habitats within the woodland. The exception is the population of *Buxbaumia viridis*, which occurs in two places. Four of only six recent sites for this rare moss in Scotland lie within the Cairngorms area. This is a species of rotting logs, and which is visible only through its fruiting bodies. These are subject to marked fluctuations in number from year-to-year, making the species difficult to monitor. The

Tetraplodon mnioides *(with the taller sporophytes)* and T. angustatus - *a much rarer plant - photographed on a Fox scat in scree at Strath Nethy.*

Photo: *G. Rothero*

Mires in Abernethy Forest provide habitat for the Olive Bog-moss Sphagnum majus, *a nationally vulnerable species.*

Photo: *G. Rothero*

other important bryophyte habitat in Abernethy is its mires, which hold sites for *Sphagnum majus, Dicranum bergeri* and *Barbilophozia kunzeana,* and the only recently-seen Scottish population of *Sphagnum balticum.* At the southern end of the area, near Bynack in An Garbh-choire, there are crags and dry scree with *Anastrophyllum saxicola, Cynodontium strumiferum, C. tenellum* and *Dicranum spurium.*

7. Strathspey. This is a collection of areas along Strathspey, from Newtonmore to Grantown-on-Spey, in which the important habitats are either dry scree and crags, fen or stands of Aspen. The most important crags are at Creag Dubh, Newtonmore, and at Craigellachie. These have significant stands of *Anastrophyllum saxicola, Cynodontium strumiferum* and *C. tenellum.* A mire at the top of Craigellachie also has *Dicranum bergeri.* Insh Marshes, while lacking in rarities, has excellent assemblages of *Sphagnum* species on the fen margins, and a number of species reach their northern limit in the associated willow carr.

Aspen have been somewhat neglected as a substrate for epiphytes, although large stands of *Orthotrichum speciosum* have long been known from Aspens in Strathspey. Survey work in 1999 revealed several stands of *O. obtusifolium* in the Insh area. This moss had been thought to be reduced to just one extant site in the UK (Rothero, 2002). Further work has since revealed two more sites for *O. obtusifolium*; at Kinrara and near Grantown-on-Spey. Growing with *O. obtusifolium* at Kinrara is the very similar *O. gymnostomum,* a moss once thought to be extinct in the UK, having been lost from its only site near Loch an Eilein, but found at Kinrara in 2003 during survey work on Aspens in the Cairngorms. It has since been found in some abundance at New Kinord and at one other site on the River Findhorn; near Dulsie Bridge just outside of the National Park (Amphlett & Rothero, 2003). An interesting older record from this area is of *Buxbaumia viridis,* found on a rotting pine log in the Alvie area in 1951.

8. Rothiemurchus and Glenmore. The woodland in this large area has an abundance of common species, plus one of international importance and three of national importance. Three species are of particular note. *Buxbaumia viridis* has been found on three logs near Loch an Eilein in recent years (Rothero, 2003a,b), at one stage producing more sporophytes than at all other sites in the UK. Rotting logs have also provided a habitat for *Lophozia longiflora* near Loch Morlich. This critical species has not been seen since 1956, but is very similar to the common *Lophozia ventricosa* and is thus easily overlooked. Aspens near Loch an Eilein have *Orthotrichum speciosum,* but numerous attempts to re-find a 1966 site for *O. gymnostomum* (until recently the only UK site) have failed

(Rothero, 2002). The other important habitat in this area is provided by dry, acid crags again near Loch an Eilein and by Lochan Uaine, at Glenmore. Both sites have stands of *Anastrophyllum saxicola.*

9. Lower Deeside. This is an area largely neglected by bryologists, and the few records of species of interest are mostly very old. *Buxbaumia viridis* has recently been found in a woodland near Ballater and it is probable that it occurs elsewhere in the area. There are two 19th century records of *B. viridis* from Craigendinnie above Aboyne and from Pannanich Hill near Ballater, but both sites have changed in character over the intervening years. Recent survey work at Loch Kinord has revealed a strong population of *Orthotrichum gymnostomum* on Aspen; the largest population known in the UK (Amphlett & Rothero, 2003). Here, *Orthotrichum speciosum* is relatively frequent, again in Aspen stands.

10. Braemar area. In the Braemar area there are a number of large outcrops of Dalradian limestone which all have an interesting bryophyte flora. The most important of these are on Craig Leek SSSI and Morrone NNR, but Creag Clunie and the Lion's Face SSSI also have a good flora. Creag Leek is an extremely important site, with one of only two UK populations of the thalloid liverwort *Athalamia hyalina,* first found in 1999 (Long *et al.,* 2003). It also has the largest of the two UK populations of *Tortula leucostoma,* the other being in Glenshee. Added to this are sites for *Stegonia latifolia, Schistidium atrofuscum, Jungermannia polaris, Bryum arcticum* and a number of other scarce species (Rothero, 1999b). In the mire below the crags and just outside of the SSSI is a small stand of *Dicranum bergeri.* The second UK site for *Athalamia hyalina* is in similar habitat close by, on Crathie SSSI.

Morrone Birkwood SSSI also has *Stegonia latifolia* on the crags, while species of interest from its calcareous flushes include *Barbilophozia quadriloba, Leiocolea gillmanii* and *Tayloria lingulata* (Rothero, 2002). Also on Morrone, but possibly outside of the SSSI, is the most recent UK record of *Dicranum elongatum* (in 1964; Long & Rothero, 1996). Recent attempts to re-find this species, however, have not been successful. The Aspens on Morrone also have occasional stands of *Orthotrichum speciosum.* On the Lion's Face the limestone has a small stand of *Pseudoleskeella rupestris* and on the more acid rocks of Creag Clunie there is *Cynodontium strumiferum* and a small stand of *Cynodontium polycarpon* (Rothero, 1999a). Similar acid rocks in Glen Quoich, in Eastern Cairngorms SSSI, have a large population of *Cynodontium strumiferum* growing with *Anastrophyllum saxicola.* In the heath nearby are stands of *Dicranum spurium*

(Rothero, 1999e) and on the opposite side of the Dee, at Corriemulzie, there is an old, unconfirmed record of *Orthotrichum pallens* (Rothero, 2003a).

11. Glen Callater and Coire Kander. The most important areas for bryophytes in this SSSI are the crags around Coire Kander and the mire and flushes on the plateau above the coire. Near the coire lochan there are large stands of the 'copper mosses' *Mielichhoferia elongata* and *Grimmia atrata* on schist, rich in heavy metals. Also recorded here but not seen recently is *Mielichhoferia mielichhoferiana* in its only confirmed UK locality (Long & Rothero, 1996). These rocks also have *Grimmia elongata* in one of only two recent Scottish sites, the other being nearby in Caenlochan Glen. Crags above the lochan have a good collection of calcicole and some snow-bed species. On the plateau above Coire Kander there is an extensive area of mire, with a very large population of *Sphagnum lindbergii* and with lines of flushes supporting *Splachnum vasculosum*, *Sphagnum riparium* and *Pseudobryum cinclidioides*.

12. Lochnagar and Glen Muick. The coires on Lochnagar and the plateau area of White Mounth have large areas of snow-bed vegetation with a similar flora to that of the main Cairngorm mountains, but rather fewer of the rare species. The patches of snow-bed vegetation here provide the main UK sites for the rare liverwort *Marsupella sparsifolia*, which can be locally frequent. Outside of this area there are only tiny populations of this species. *Plagiomnium medium* occurs on Lochanagar crags and mire areas on the plateau can have large stands of *Sphagnum lindbergii*, while *Splachnum vasculosum* occurs in at least one flush. Crags lower down, by the Linn of Muick, have not been well-explored but do have *Cynodontium tenellum*, while *Grimmia ungeri* has one of its two recent UK sites on the serpentine of the Coyles of Muick above. On the south side of Glen Muick, the large mire area at the head of the Black Burn is the site for a 1961 record of *Sphagnum balticum*, but recent determined efforts have failed to re-find this plant (Rothero, 2003a).

13. Blair Atholl, Beinn a' Ghlo, Glen Tilt and Tulach Hill. This is a composite area which includes all of the interesting calcareous ground around Blair Atholl and Beinn a' Ghlo, parts of the Tulach Hill and Beinn a' Ghlo SSSIs, plus a few outlying sites. The bryophyte interest is widely spread over this large area, but of particular importance are the limestone outcrops above Loch Loch and

Ptilium crista-castrensis - *the quintissential plant of pine woodland.*

Photo: *G. Rothero*

Survey work in the Insh area in 1999 revealed several stands of the Blunt-leaved Bristle-moss Orthotrichum obtusifolium; *an Endangered species known from just one other extant site in the UK - near Braemar. Two more sites have since been found: at Kinrara and near Grantown-on-Spey.*

Photo: *A. Amphlett*

near Fealar. At Loch Loch there is the biggest UK population of *Hypnum vaucheri*, in its only site away from Ben Lawers. There is also a good population of *Stegonia latifolia* and some stands of *Didymodon icmadophilus*.

In flushes at Fealar both *Barbilophozia quadriloba* and *Dicranella grevilleana* are present, with much more ground left to explore in this remote site. *Dicranella grevilleana* also occurs in open stony flushes at Tulach and here there are also fine hummocks of *Dicranum bergeri*. Similar ground occurs in Glen Fender with further stands of *D. bergeri*, *Dicranella grevilleana* and *Aongstroemia longipes*. Further east, limestone outcrops near Loch Valigan have *Stegonia latifolia*. The limestone outcrops in the Tilt have no rarities, but a good assemblage of calcicoles, including a number of nationally scarce species of *Seligeria*.

14. *Glen Feshie*. The broken crags and ravines in the main glen, and the extensive area of crags in Coire Garbhlach, have a number of rare bryophytes. The limestone ravines in the southern part of the main glen have an interesting assemblage of species, including the second UK localities for both *Saelania glaucescens* and *Ctenidium procerrimum*, the latter being locally frequent, making

it by far the most important UK population. Also on the limestone, *Schistidium atrofuscum* is locally frequent and there are small populations of *Pseudoleskeella rupestris* and *Weissia controversa* var. *wimmeriana*, the only UK site for the latter taxon. Both *Cynodontium strumiferum* and *Anastrophyllum saxicola* occur in the large areas of more acid scree in the main glen and again in Coire Garbhlach. The calcareous rocks in Coire Garbhlach have a number of nationally scarce species and also a small population of the rare *Timmia norvegica*; the only Cairngorms site for this species.

15. *Tomintoul area*. Most of the interest in this area stems from outcrops of Dalradian limestone near Bridge of Brown and, particularly, the Water of Ailnack. Trees in the area have *Orthotrichum speciosum* and a mire near Bridge of Brown has a record of *Barbilophozia kunzeana*. The ravine on the Water of Ailnack is not easy to explore, but the limestone here has the only Cairngorms record of *Tortella fragilis* and further stands of *Jungermannia polaris* and *Schistidium atrofuscum*. The most recent Scottish record (1983) for *Orthotrichum pallens* comes from an elm in this ravine, but an attempt to re-find this moss in 2001 was not successful (Rothero, 2003a).

The limestone ravines of Glen Feshie hold by far the more important of Britain's only two populations of the Alpine Comb-moss Ctenidium procerrimum, *a vulnerable species.*

Photo: *G. Rothero*

Populations of Curled Notchwort Anastrophyllum saxicola *occur on dry scree in several of the Cairngorms' important bryophyte areas, including Strath Nethy, Abernethy Forest, Glen Feshie, Creag Dubh, Craigellachie, Loch an Eilein, Glenmore and Glen Quoich.*

Photo: *G. Rothero*

Figure 13.1. Important areas for bryophytes. See text for details and Table 13.2 for species lists.

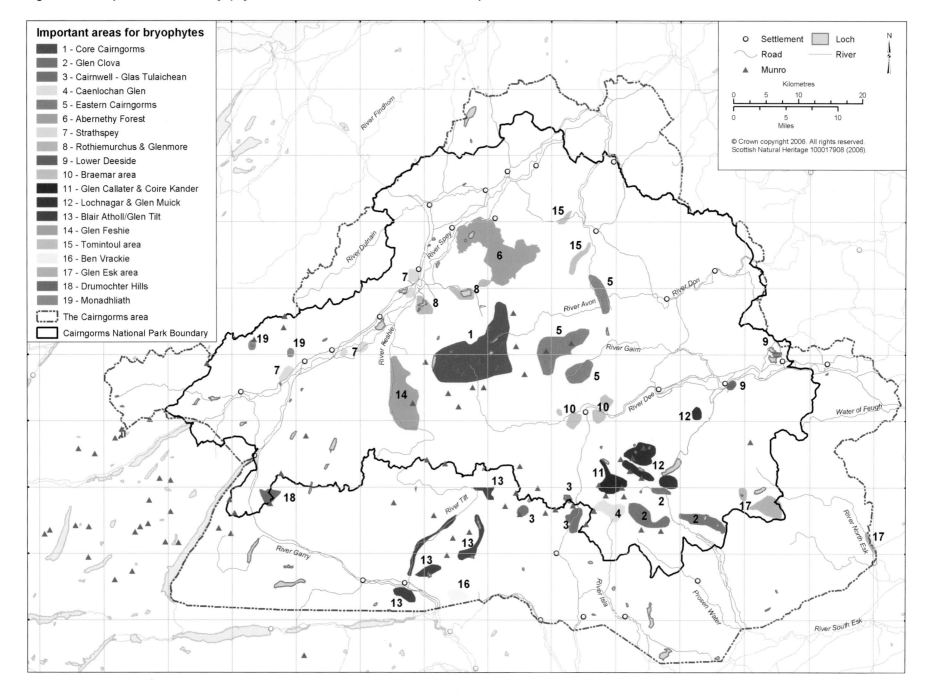

Important areas for bryophytes

1 - Core Cairngorms
2 - Glen Clova
3 - Cairnwell - Glas Tulaichean
4 - Caenlochan Glen
5 - Eastern Cairngorms
6 - Abernethy Forest
7 - Strathspey
8 - Rothiemurchus & Glenmore
9 - Lower Deeside
10 - Braemar area
11 - Glen Callater & Coire Kander
12 - Lochnagar & Glen Muick
13 - Blair Atholl/Glen Tilt
14 - Glen Feshie
15 - Tomintoul area
16 - Ben Vrackie
17 - Glen Esk area
18 - Drumochter Hills
19 - Monadhliath

The Cairngorms area

Cairngorms National Park Boundary

Settlement   Loch
Road   River
Munro

Table 13.2. Important areas for bryophytes in the Cairngorms, listed in descending order of the number of internationally and nationally important species in each area.

Percentage of area occurring within the National Park: *** >75%; ** 25–75%; * 10–24%; '-' <10%

Area	Species of international importance	National importance	% of area within NP
1. Core Cairngorms	*Anastrophyllum joergensenii, Hygrohypnum styriacum, Marsupella arctica*	*Andreaea nivalis, Anastrophyllum joergensenii, A. saxicola, Andreaea alpestris, A. blyttii, A. frigida, Brachythecium glaciale, B. reflexum, B. starkei, Bryum muehlenbeckii, Cynodontium polycarpon, C. strumiferum, Dicranum elongatum, Gymnocolea acutiloba, Gymnomitrion apiculatum, G. corallioides, Hygrohypnum molle, H. smithii, Kiaeria glacialis, Lophozia wenzelii, Marsupella boeckii, M. condensata, Palustriella decipiens, Paraleucobryum longifolium, Plagiomnium medium, Pohlia obtusifolia, Pseudoleskea patens, Racomitrium macounii ssp. alpinum, Rhizomnium magnifolium, Sphagnum lindbergii, Splachnum vasculosum, Syntrichia norvegica* (**31 species**)	***
2. Glen Clova	*Bryum dixonii, B. stirtonii, Philonotis cernua* (pre-1900)	*Brachythecium reflexum, Bryum muehlenbeckii, Campylopus schimperi, Cynodontium fallax, C. polycarpon, C. strumiferum, C. tenellum, Dicranum elongatum, Grimmia elatior, G. elongata, G. ovalis, G. ungeri, G. unicolor, Habrodon perpusillus, Heterocladium dimorphum, Hygrohypnum smithii, Hypnum bambergeri, Lophozia wenzelii, Oncophorus wahlenbergii, Orthotrichum speciosum, Palustriella decipiens, Paraleucobryum longifolium, Pseudoleskea incurvata, P. patens, Racomitrium macounii ssp. alpinum, Saelania glaucescens, Schistidium agassizii, Sphagnum lindbergii, Splachnum vasculosum, Tayloria lingulata, T. tenuis* (**31 species**)	***
3. Cairnwell, Gleann Beag & Glas Tulaichean	*Bryum stirtonii, Pictus scoticus*	*Bryum arcticum, B. subelegans, Dicranella grevilleana, Didymodon icmadophilus, Heterocladium dimorphum, Hygrohypnum smithii, Hypnum bambergeri, Jungermannia polaris, Leiocolea gillmanii, Mnium spinosum, Palustriella decipiens, Pseudoleskea incurvata, P. patens, Pseudoleskeella nervosa, Ptychodium plicatum, Scapania gymnostomophila, Seligeria brevifolia, Sphagnum lindbergii, Splachnum vasculosum, Stegonia latifolia, Tayloria lingulata, Timmia austriaca, Tortula leucostoma* (**23 species**)	**
4. Caenlochan Glen	*Bryum dixonii*	*Andreaea alpestris, Brachythecium glaciale, B. reflexum, B. starkei, Bryum arcticum, Campylophyllum halleri, Campylopus schimperi, Cynodontium strumiferum, Eurhynchium pulchellum, Grimmia elongata, Heterocladium dimorphum, Hygrohypnum smithii, Hypnum bambergeri, Mnium ambiguum, M. spinosum, Myurella tenerrima, Palustriella decipiens, Plagiobryum demissum, Plagiothecium piliferum, Pseudoleskea incurvata, P. patens, Pseudoleskeella rupestris, Ptychodium plicatum, Scapania gymnostomophila, Sphagnum lindbergii, Splachnum vasculosum, Tayloria lingulata, Timmia austriaca* (**28 species**)	***
5. Eastern Cairngorms	*Marsupella arctica*	*Andreaea alpestris, A. blyttii, A. nivalis, A. sinuosa, Bryum muehlenbeckii, Cynodontium strumiferum, Dicranum bergeri, D. elongatum, Didymodon icmadophilus, Gymnomitrion corallioides, Hygrohypnum smithii, Hypnum bambergeri, Lophozia wenzelii, Marsupella condensata, M. sparsifolia, Oncophorus wahlenbergii, Rhizomnium magnifolium, Sphagnum lindbergii, Stegonia latifolia* (**19 species**)	***
6. Abernethy Forest	*Buxbaumia viridis*	*Anastrophyllum saxicola, Barbilophozia kunzeana, Cynodontium strumiferum, C. tenellum, Dicranum bergeri, D. spurium, Orthotrichum speciosum, Sphagnum balticum, S. majus* (**9 species**)	***
7. Strathspey	*Buxbaumia viridis*	*Anastrophyllum saxicola, Cynodontium strumiferum, C. tenellum, Dicranum bergeri, Orthotrichum gymnostomum, O. obtusifolium, O. speciosum, Palustriella decipiens* (**8 species**)	***
8. Rothiemurchus & Glenmore	*Buxbaumia viridis*	*Anastrophyllum saxicola, Lophozia longiflora, Orthotrichum gymnostomum, O. speciosum* (**4 species**)	***
9. Lower Deeside	*Buxbaumia viridis*	*Orthotrichum gymnostomum, O. speciosum* (**2 species**)	**
10. Braemar area		*Anastrophyllum saxicola, Athalamia hyalina, Barbilophozia quadriloba, Bryum arcticum, Cynodontium polycarpon, C. strumiferum, C. tenellum, Dicranum bergeri, D. elongatum, D. spurium, Grimmia elongata, Jungermannia polaris, Leiocolea gillmanii, Orthotrichum obtusifolium, O. pallens, O. speciosum, Pseudoleskeella rupestris, Scapania gymnostomophila, Schistidium atrofuscum, Splachnum vasculosum, Stegonia latifolia, Tayloria lingulata, T. tenuis, Tortula leucostoma* (**24 species**)	***
11. Glen Callater & Coire Kander		*Andreaea nivalis, Brachythecium glaciale, Bryum muehlenbeckii, Cynodontium strumiferum, Grimmia elongata, Gymnomitrion corallioides, Hygrohypnum smithii, Kiaeria glacialis, Leiocolea gillmanii, Mielichhoferia elongata, M. mielichhoferiana, Plagiomnium medium, Pseudoleskea incurvata, Sphagnum lindbergii, Splachnum vasculosum, Tayloria tenuis* (**16 species**)	***

Area	Species of international importance	National importance	% of area within NP
12. Lochnagar & Glen Muick		*Andreaea nivalis, Barbilophozia kunzeana, Brachythecium glaciale, Cynodontium tenellum, Gymnomitrion corallioides, Grimmia ungeri, Hygrohypnum molle, Marsupella condensata, M. sparsifolia, Plagiomnium medium, Rhizomnium magnifolium, Sphagnum balticum, S. lindbergii, Splachnum vasculosum, Tayloria tenuis* (pre-1900) **(15 species)**	***
13. Blair Atholl, Beinn a' Ghlo, Glen Tilt & Tulach Hill		*Aongstroemia longipes, Barbilophozia quadriloba, Cynodontium strumiferum, C. tenellum, Dicranella grevilleana, Dicranum bergeri, Didymodon icmadophilus, Hypnum vaucheri, Leiocolea gillmanii, Oncophorus wahlenbergii, Scapania gymnostomophila, Sphagnum majus, Splachnum vasculosum, Stegonia latifolia* **(14 species)**	
14. Glen Feshie		*Anastrophyllum saxicola, Andreaea nivalis, Barbilophozia kunzeana, Ctenidium procerrimum, Cynodontium strumiferum, Dicranum spurium, Hypnum bambergeri, Mnium spinosum, Palustriella decipiens, Pohlia obtusifolia, Saelania glaucescens, Schistidium atrofuscum, Timmia norvegica, Weissia controversa* var. *wimmeriana* **(14 species)**	***
15. Tomintoul area		*Barbilophozia kunzeana, Jungermannia polaris, Orthotrichum pallens, O. speciosum, Pseudoleskea incurvata, Schistidium atrofuscum, Tortella fragilis* **(7 species)**	***
16. Ben Vrackie		*Barbilophozia quadriloba, Eurhynchium pulchellum* var. *diversifolium, Gymnomitrion corallioides, Leiocolea gillmanii, Stegonia latifolia, Tayloria lingulata* **(6 species)**	
17. Glen Esk		*Cynodontium tenellum Myurella tenerrima, Orthotrichum pumilum, Sphagnum lindbergii, S. majus, Timmia austriaca* **(6 species)**	**
18. Drumochter Hills		*Splachnum vasculosum, Sphagnum lindbergii* **(2 species)**	*
19. Monadhliath		*Aplodon wormskioldii, Bryum muehlenbeckii* **(2 species)**	***

16. *Ben Vrackie*. This hill is well-known for its calcicole vascular plant flora and similarly has a wide range of calcicole bryophytes. Limestone outcrops across the site have small stands of *Stegonia latifolia*. In 2002, a small patch of *Eurhynchium pulchellum* was also found, this being only the third extant site in Britain, the others being on Skye (Church *et al.*, 2001) and in Caenlochan Glen. *Gymnomitrion corallioides* is locally frequent on broken crags, while *Barbilophozia quadriloba, Leiocolea gillmanii* and *Tayloria lingulata* occur in flushes.

17. *Glen Esk area*. This long glen has been neglected by bryologists, so records of more interesting species are all rather old. Calcareous rocks in Glen Effock have old (1916) records of two Ben Lawers and Caenlochan rarities in *Myurella tenerrima* and *Timmia austriaca*. *Sphagnum lindbergii* occurs in flush bogs at the head of the Water of Unich, and there is an old (1947) record of *Sphagnum majus* from Carlochy. *Cynodontium tenellum* is known from the acid rocks in Glen Lee and by The Burn at Edzell.

18. *Drumochter Hills*. These hills are, largely, rather limited in their bryological interest, but do have some calcareous ground in the bigger coires, such as Coire Chuirn and Chama Choire. Nationally rare species are limited to the extensive areas of flushed ground associated with patches of late snow-lie, where there are good stands of *Splachnum vasculosum* and *Sphagnum lindbergii*.

19. *Monadhliath*. These mountains are not very exciting in bryological terms, but *Bryum muehlenbeckii* is recorded from Loch Dubh in Coire na Laogh and, on the southern margins of the hills, in Glen Banchor, is the site of the last UK record of *Aplodon wormskioldii*. This species, which may now be extinct in the UK, was found on a rotting sheep carcase in a mire in 1981, but subsequent searches for suitable habitat in the area have been unsuccessful (Rothero, 2002).

Recent research and survey findings

It is only in recent years that lower plants have attracted the interest and funding that is required for research and survey work. Much of this has consisted of basic survey work, gathering baseline data on the distribution of species of interest, on the distribution of important habitats and species lists for sites of conservation concern.

In 1989 the NCC commissioned a survey of the extent of bryophyte-dominated vegetation in areas of late snow-lie in the Cairngorms NNR and listings of their bryophyte populations (Rothero, 1990). This was carried out in late July and August of 1989, a period too short to cover all of the sites effectively, with the result that a number of remote areas were excluded. The aim of the survey was to produce a list of sites of bryophyte-dominated vegetation, with maps of the extent of this community and a list of constituent species, highlighting those restricted to snow-bed vegetation and ranking sites on that basis. Relevés were made at most sites visited and the quadrat data were used to produce a phytosociological analysis of the vegetation of these extreme sites (Rothero, 1991b).

The product was a brief description of each site, with a map outlining the extent of bryophyte-dominated vegetation and species lists. The survey and analysis showed that bryophyte-dominated sites can be broadly divided into two types: deep coire sites with a large amplitude of relief, large substrate size and rock outcrops; and the 'plateau type', with low amplitude of relief, small substrate size and few rock outcrops. The vegetation analysis produced three basic snow-bed vegetation types: *Marsupella brevissima-Anthelia juratzkana* snow-bed, typical of the drier gravels of the plateau snow-beds; *Polytrichum sexangulare-Kiaeria starkei* snow-beds, typical of damper, more stable gravels and stony ground in the coires; and *Pohlia wahlenbergii* snow-bed on gravels and rocks flushed by meltwater. Although coire sites tend to be the more diverse, having a greater variety of habitats, the plateau type is much more important, in terms of its populations of chionophilous species. As subsequent work elsewhere in Scotland showed (Rothero, 1991a), the Cairngorms has the vast majority of Scottish sites for this snow-bed type.

The 1989 survey also clarified the status of a number of rare species, giving a clearer picture of the distribution of plants like *Gymnomitrion apiculatum*, *Marsupella condensata*, *M. sparsifolia*, *M. boeckii*, *Andreaea frigida* and *A. blyttii*. As a direct result of the survey, two species new to the UK were found: *Marsupella arctica*, a liverwort otherwise unknown in Europe outside of Svalbard (Long *et al.*, 1990), and *Hygrohypnum styriacum*, an Arctic-alpine species rare in Europe (Corley & Rothero, 1992).

Woolgrove & Woodin (1994) examined the relationship between the duration of snow cover and the occurrence of the three major snow-bed communities described by Rothero (1999b), using some sites in the Cairngorms. They concluded that *Polytrichum sexangulare-Kiaeria starkei* snow-beds occur in the areas of longest snow-lie, with *Marsupella brevissima-Anthelia juratzkana* snow-beds in relatively more snow-free areas, and the *Pohlia ludwigii* community

favouring areas kept wet by meltwater. Another paper worthy of mention in the context of snow-bed vegetation is B. Murray's revision of the species of *Andreaea* in Britain (Murray, 1988), which described several new species for the UK, including *Andreaea blyttii*, *A. frigida* and *A. sinuosa*; all snow-bed species.

In 1993, the Royal Botanic Garden Edinburgh was commissioned by SNH to survey known sites for several bryophytes listed under Schedule 8 of the Wildlife and Countryside Act, and to produce a series of reports, or 'species dossiers'. This series has done much to increase our knowledge of the status of rare Scottish bryophytes. Each dossier provides an overview of the species' status in the UK and elsewhere in Europe, describes Scottish sites, the species itself, and its ecology, threats and management. Dossiers have been produced for Schedule 8 species, and for a selection of Red Data species, including a number of species with important Cairngorms populations (Long & Rothero, 1996). More detailed dossiers have also been produced for several BAP Priority species in the Cairngorms (Rothero, 2002).

There have been several basic bryophyte surveys of sites in the Cairngorms for SNH, RSPB and NTS. Craig Leek SSSI and Creag Clunie and Lion's Face SSSI were surveyed in 1999, providing basic information on the rarer species (Rothero, 1999a,b). These surveys confirmed the importance of the limestone outcrops near Braemar, particularly Craig Leek, with the first UK record of *Athalamia hyalina* and the first Scottish record for many years of *Cynodontium polycarpon* from Creag Clunie, as well as a number of other nationally rare species. A similar survey was carried out for the RSPB on the upland part of their Abernethy Reserve (Rothero, 1999c), essentially exploring the Loch Avon basin from Ben Macdui eastwards to Bynack More and the upper part of Strath Nethy. This survey clarified the distribution of snow-bed species in the area and found a number of sites for *Anastrophyllum saxicola*, *A. joergensenii*, *Cynodontium strumiferum*, *C. tenellum*, *Dicranum spurium*, *Hygrohypnum molle*, *Grimmia longirostris* and, notably, *Gymnocolea acutiloba*; new to Scotland, in Strath Nethy (Rothero, 2000). A separate survey at the same time investigated the frequency and abundance of the BAP Priority species *Andreaea frigida* in this area, producing baseline maps of its distribution (Rothero, 1999d; Rothero & Amphlett, 2001). A similar survey for *Andreaea frigida* in Garbh-choire, Braeriach and by Loch Etchachan took place in 2001 (Rothero, 2001).

The National Trust for Scotland have carried out bryophyte survey work on Mar Lodge Estate, the most complete being that of the areas classified as Caledonian Pine woodland. This produced records of interesting species such as *Anastrophyllum saxicola*, *Cynodontium strumiferum*, *Scapania gymnostomophila* and *Dicranum spurium* (Rothero, 1999e). A similar survey of the montane areas of Mar Lodge was more selective, but does provide some useful information (McMullen, 1999). In 2002, as part of SNH's Site Condition Monitoring programme, a survey of the bryophyte species of interest on Morrone Birkwood SSSI resulted in the production of a site dossier and fixed-point photographs of stands of *Barbilophozia quadriloba* and *Stegonia latifolia*, for future monitoring (Rothero, 2002). In 2003, an attempt was made to find more sites for *Buxbaumia viridis* in the Rothiemurchus area and Abernethy, with only limited success. No additional stands to those already recorded near Loch an Eilein were found in Rothiemurchus, or in Glenmore Forest, but a further stand was found in Abernethy (Rothero, 2003a,b).

There has been only a very limited amount of earlier work on bryophytes in the Cairngorms, most of it consisting of reports of meetings of the British Bryological Society in the area, plus a small number of records of interesting species published in the Transactions and Bulletin of the Society. For that part of the Cairngorms that falls within the old county of Angus, there is an excellent account of the bryophyte flora, compiled by Duncan (1966). This is an important area, as it contains the rich sites of Glen Clova and Caenlochan.

The European rarity Green Shield-moss Buxbaumia viridis *grows on rotting logs, and has been recorded recently at four sites in the Cairngorms.*

Photo: *G. Rothero*

Trends

The baseline data required for assessing trends in population or range size are not available for bryophyte species. It is only in the last 10 years that such data have begun to be collected, initially for those species on Schedule 8 of the Wildlife and Countryside Act, and later for BAP priority species (Long & Rothero, 1996; Rothero, 2003a). Setting up schemes for the monitoring of bryophytes is complicated by the plants' small size, by identification problems and by a dearth of skilled bryologists. For some particularly cryptic species, like *Gymnomitrion apiculatum* and *Andreaea sinuosa*, there are no practical means of assessing population size without collecting on an unacceptable scale, and so monitoring will have to be based on less direct methods. This means that observing trends in population or stand size will continue to be difficult, except where stands are relatively small and the plant is easily recognised.

Apart from the small group of species mentioned above, almost all of the data available stem from records made during brief visits by bryologists, usually as a list, backed up by specimens deposited in herbaria, or, more recently, records made on a standard recording card. It is only in the past 50 years that map references, rather than merely site names, have been used as a matter of course. Most of these records (up to 1991) have been entered into the Biological Records Centre database; the source of many of the records given here, other than the most recent. There is no information on population size or frequency in the database and, even if the original record is traced, additional information is usually scant. It is therefore possible to make only tentative suggestions as to trends, using these crude presence-or-absence data.

Several species appear to have been lost from the Cairngorms since the middle part of the 19th century. The most obvious of these is *Tayloria tenuis*, recorded from four areas in the 19th century but not seen for over a hundred years, and now probably extinct there. This is part of a general trend in what has always been a rare species in Scotland and one that has been recorded from only one location (in Caithness) in the last 50 years.

Grimmia elatior has only been recorded in the UK from Glen Clova but has not been seen in this popular area since 1871, and is probably now extinct. The same is likely to be true of *Cynodontium fallax*, last seen in Clova in 1867. Other species are more difficult to assess. *Dicranum elongatum* has been recorded from at least three sites in the Cairngorms, but has not been seen at its most recent site, Morrone, for over 40 years. However, this is not an easy species to find and, with fewer bryologists active in the hills today, a presumption of extinction could be premature. The same may be true of *Plagiothecium piliferum* on Caenlochan and *Mielichhoferia mielichhoferiana* in Coire Kander. It is worthwhile remembering that the 'extinct' *Paraleucobryum longifolium* (Smith, 1978) is now known from at least eight sites in Scotland, including five in the Cairngorms. Also, as noted earlier, *Orthotrichum gymnostomum* has recently been re-found in the Cairngorms after an 'absence' of nearly 40 years.

Other species trends are more transparent. It is important to realise that the distribution pattern of some rare species in the Cairngorms still reflects the pattern of survey effort, rather than their true distribution. Targeted survey work and visits by bryologists to under-worked areas have produced a number of new sites for rare species, as well as confirming the occurrence of others. Targeted surveys have also added at least 10 rare species to the Cairngorms list since 1989, including three species new to the UK. It seems likely that this trend will continue for some time, particularly for poorly documented species.

In the context of concerns over climate change, trends in the size and species composition of the bryophyte-dominated vegetation in areas of late snow-lie would be of considerable interest. The snow-beds on Ben Macdui and Cairngorm, surveyed in 1989 and 1999 (Rothero, 1990, 1999c) showed no evidence of gross change, either in extent or species composition. This time-scale is probably much too short for detecting change, however, particularly since the original survey was not sufficiently detailed to allow small-scale differences to become evident.

Conservation issues

As with most other organisms, loss or significant change in habitats are the major issues, but within this, certain changes could have a considerable affect on bryophyte populations.

Climate change. Most of the important bryophyte species and assemblages in the Cairngorms are montane, and so will presumably be particularly sensitive to climate change. Perhaps the most obvious example is the bryophyte-dominated vegetation in areas of late snow lie, where the link between the persistence of snow and of plant communities seems relatively straightforward.

If summer snow patches become smaller and less predictable, then, over time, plant communities dominated by vascular plants are likely to replace those dominated by bryophytes. As the climate changes, the ability of bryophytes to compete may also change in other habitats. This may lead to 'a perturbation too far' for some species already on the edge of their range.

Grazing. In general, grazing is less of an issue for bryophytes than for vascular plants, and it is not easy to predict the effects of the anticipated reduction in grazing pressure if, or when, deer numbers are reduced. In fact, provided that the intensity of grazing is not so great as to cause erosion, some level of grazing is generally good for bryophytes, keeping some habitats more open and generally reducing competition from larger plants. This is particularly true in woodlands, where interesting bryophytes on low rocks or rotting logs can be overwhelmed by a coarse herb or shrub layer when grazing animals have been excluded. One community that might benefit from a reduction in grazing at higher levels is the dwarf shrub community on sheltered, rocky north and north-east facing slopes. A taller structure to the heath may encourage the growth of the large hepatic species like *Anastrophyllum donnianum* and *Scapania ornithopodioides*,

The Aspen Bristle-moss Orthotrichum gymnostomum *was once thought to be extinct in the UK, but has been re-found after an 'absence' of nearly 40 years: growing on Aspen at Kinrara and Loch Kinord. The latter now has the largest population known in the UK.*

Photo: *A. Amphlett*

that have a very restricted distribution in the Cairngorms at the moment.

Woodland management. While the bryophyte ground flora in most of the woodlands is composed of a few dominant species, certain habitats within woodlands have species of considerable interest. In particular, open areas of scree, low crags, small areas of mire and fallen trees all have a much more diverse flora. In the enthusiasm for regeneration of woodland cover it is possible that the value of such small features may be overlooked. The problem is not just one of trees becoming established on the feature of interest, but a more subtle one of pattern of shade and litter-fall. The bryophyte diversity of the woodlands would be sustained and perhaps increased if such issues could be addressed in management plans. For one of the Cairngorms' woodland rarities, *Buxbaumia viridis*, more positive management steps can be taken by not 'tidying up' fallen timber. It is clear from Swedish studies that the frequency of *Buxbaumia viridis* is related to the amount of habitat available, in the form of large, well-rotted logs (Wiklund, 2002).

Recent work has revealed that stands of Aspen can have an exceptionally rich epiphytic flora of bryophytes and lichens. Current work to raise the profile of such stands – to promote regeneration and to understand the ecology of these assemblages – is to be encouraged.

A number of epiphytic bryophytes and lichens are under some threat in the UK through the loss of parkland and wayside trees, either because of deliberate changes in management policy or through the loss of elms by disease. The Grampian area has always been a stronghold for these species and a policy of sustaining remaining parkland and wayside trees, and of planting replacements within the National Park, would be a welcome measure.

Awareness and education. Appreciation of the richness and diversity of the Scottish lower plant flora is a relatively recent phenomenon. However, there is still a task to be done in enthusing land managers with regard to the bryophytes on their ground. National rarity and international significance still catch the attention and can be used to benefit the generality of bryophytes, provided that information is accurate and accessible. Much more could be done to inform the local community and visitors about the lower plant interest on sites within the Cairngorms area.

Knowledge gaps. Mosses and liverworts are small plants, and can be difficult to identify. Much of the information we have is derived from the work of a small number of bryologists on short, summer visits, mostly to well-known sites. In the last few years, targeted survey work for SNH, RSPB and NTS has produced a large number of new records and some additions to the Cairngorms species list. This indicates that we have an incomplete knowledge of the bryophyte flora, particularly of the more remote sites. The rich areas in Garbh Choire on Braeriach, the head of Glen Einich, and the less obviously attractive sites like Glen Esk, have probably had no more than one or two visits by bryologists in the last 50 years. More survey work is therefore needed.

Particularly important gaps in our knowledge are as follows.

- Nothing is known of the response of the community of snow-bed bryophytes to changes in the pattern of snow accumulation and snow melt; either in the short-term, from year-to-year, or in the much longer-term. At lower elevations, we do not know how areas of dry, acid scree within woodland will respond to changes in the climate or in woodland management.

- There have been few autecological studies of bryophytes, and virtually none of rare species. We know nothing of the population dynamics either of persistent species like *Brachythecium starkei*, where stands seem to change little from year-to-year, or of short-term species like *Tortula leucostoma* or *Stegonia latifolia*, where numbers and the distribution of stems can vary markedly over a short period.

- The taxonomy of several species needs to be resolved. There is considerable doubt as to whether *Pictus scoticus* is a good species or genus, and whether *Bryum stirtonii* and *B. subelegans* are merely forms of other *Bryum* species (Holyoak, 2004). Some critical species like *Andreaea alpestris*, *A. sinuosa*, *Cephalozia ambigua*, *Lophozia wenzelii* and *L. longiflora* are little understood, hampering discussion of their status, frequency or distribution.

A number of rare species are thought to be extinct in the Cairngorms, or have not been seen for many years. For some of these species, the Cairngorms area has provided the only UK records. More work is needed to clarify this situation in the light of the rediscovery in recent years of *Paraleucobryum longifolium*, *Orthotrichum gymnostomum* and *Buxbaumia viridis* in the Cairngorms.

References

Amphlett, A.G. & Rothero, G.P. (2003). Cairngorms *Orthotrichum* survey. An unpublished report for the Cairngorms National Park Authority, Grantown-on-Spey.

Church, J.M., Hodgetts, N.G., Preston, C.D. & Stewart N.F. (2001). *British Red Data Books; Mosses and liverworts*. JNCC: Peterborough.

Corley, M.F.V. & Rothero, G.P. (1992). *Hygrohypnum styriacum* (Limpr.) Broth. in Scotland, new to the British Isles. *Journal of Bryology* 17: 107–110.

Duncan, U.K. (1966). A bryophyte flora of Angus. *Transactions of the British Bryological Society* 5: 1–82.

ECCB (1995). *Red Data Book of European Bryophytes*. University of Trondheim.

Holyoak D.T. (2004). Taxonomic notes on some European species of *Bryum* (Bryopsida: Bryaceae). *Journal of Bryology* 26: 247–264.

Long, D.G. & Rothero, G.P. (1996). *Species dossiers for lower plants; bryophytes*. Unpublished reports for SNH, Edinburgh. (*Bryum dixonii, Dicranum bergeri, Dicranum elongatum, Grimmia unicolor, Mielichhoferia mielichhoferiana, Orthotrichum obtusifolium, Pictus scoticus, Plagiothecium piliferum, Saelania glaucescens, Splachnum vasculosum, Tayloria lingulata, Tayloria tenuis, Tortula leucostoma* [as *Desmatodon leucostoma*]).

Long, D.G., Paton, J.A. & Rothero, G.P. (1990). *Marsupella arctica* (Berrgr.) Bryhn & Kaal. in Scotland, new to the British Isles. *Journal of Bryology* 16: 163–171.

Long, D.G., Rothero, G.P. & Paton, J.A. (2003). *Athalamia hyalina* (Sommerf.) S.Hatt. in Scotland, new to the British Isles. *Journal of Bryology* 25: 253–257.

McMullen, A. (1999). *Mar Lodge Estate; survey of bryophytes in montane areas*. Unpublished report for National Trust for Scotland: Mar Lodge.

Murray, B.M. (1988). The genus *Andreaea* in Britain and Ireland. *Journal of Bryology* 15: 17–82.

Rothero, G.P. (1990). Survey of bryophyte-dominated snow-beds; Part 1, Cairngorms and Aonach Mor. *Scottish Field Unit Survey Report* No. 41. Nature Conservancy Council: Edinburgh.

Rothero, G.P. (1991a). Survey of bryophyte-dominated snow-beds; Part 2, The Highlands other than the main Cairngorms. *Scottish Field Unit Survey Report* No. 51. Nature Conservancy Council: Edinburgh.

Rothero, G.P. (1991b). *Bryophyte-dominated snow-beds in the Scottish Highlands*. MSc Thesis, Glasgow University.

Rothero, G.P. (1998). *Pseudoleskeella nervosa* (Brid.) Nyholm in Scotland. *Journal of Bryology* 20: 505–506.

Rothero, G.P. (1999a). *Survey of bryophytes on the Creag Clunie and Lion's Face SSSI*. Unpublished report for SNH: Perth.

Rothero, G.P. (1999b). *Survey of bryophytes on the Craig Leek SSSI*. Unpublished report for SNH: Perth.

Rothero, G.P. (1999c). *A Survey of the bryophytes of the montane part of RSPB Abernethy Reserve*. Unpublished report for RSPB: Inverness.

Rothero, G.P. (1999d). *Baseline survey of the population of* Andreaea frigida *in the Loch Avon basin*. Unpublished report for RSPB: Inverness.

Rothero, G.P. (1999e). *Mar Lodge Estate; survey of bryophytes in woodland areas*. Unpublished report for NTS: Mar Lodge.

Rothero, G.P. (2000). *Gymnocolea acutiloba* in Scotland. *Bulletin of the British Bryological Society* 75: 31–32.

Rothero, G.P. (2001). *Baseline survey of the population of* Andreaea frigida *in Garbh Coire, Braeriach and the Loch Etchachan area*. Unpublished report for SNH: Perth.

Rothero, G.P. (2002). *Bryophyte Site Dossier for Morrone Birkwood NNR*. Unpublished report for SNH: Perth.

Rothero, G.P. (2003a). *Species dossiers for lower plants; bryophytes*. Unpublished reports for SNH: Perth. (*Andreaea frigida, Aplodon wormskioldii, Buxbaumia viridis, Orthotrichum gymnostomum, Orthotrichum obtusifolium, Orthotrichum pallens, Sphagnum balticum, Tayloria tenuis*).

Rothero, G.P. (2003b). Buxbaumia viridis *on the Cairngorms candidate Special Area of Conservation*. Unpublished report for SNH: Perth.

Rothero, G.P. & Amphlett, A.G. (2001). Survey of *Andreaea frigida* in the Cairngorm Mountains, Scotland. *Bulletin of the British Bryological Society* No. 76.

Smith, A.J.E. (1978). *The Moss Flora of Britain and Ireland*. Cambridge University Press: Cambridge.

Wiklund, K. (2002). Substratum preference, spore output and temporal variation in sporophyte production of the epixylic moss *Buxbaumia viridis*. *Journal of Bryology* 24: 187–195.

Woolgrove, C.E. & Woodin, S.J. (1994). Relationships between the duration of snowlie and the distribution of bryophyte communities within snowbeds in Scotland. *Journal of Bryology* 18: 253–260.

Additional reading

Coker, P.D. (1971). *Mielichhoferia mielichhoferi* (Hook.) Wijk & Marg., new to the British Isles. *Transactions of the British Bryological Society* 6: 317–322.

Paton, J.A. (1999). *The Liverwort Flora of the British Isles*. Harley Books: Colchester.

Perry, A.R. & Dransfield, J. (1967). *Orthotrichum gymnostomum* in Scotland. *Journal of Bryology* 5: 218–221.

Townsend, C.C. (1982). *Pictus scoticus*, a new genus and species of pleurocarpous moss from Scotland. *Journal of Bryology* 12: 1–6.

14. VASCULAR PLANTS

Laszlo Nagy, Chris Sydes, John McKinnell and Andy Amphlett

Introduction

The Cairngorm mountains are the second richest area in Britain (after the Breadalbanes) for mountain plants. These include the Alpine Speedwell *Veronica alpina*, Alpine Saxifrage *Saxifraga nivalis* and the Alpine Foxtail *Alopecurus borealis*, as well as species such as the Alpine Mouse-ear *Cerastium alpinum*, Purple Saxifrage *Saxifraga oppositifolia* and Sibbaldia *Sibbaldia procumbens*, which are characteristic of the Arctic tundra and of alpine regions. Although 21% of the area's vascular plant species are nationally rare, relatively few have their British distribution centred on the Cairngorms. This is because most rare mountain plant species are found not on granite, which forms the bulk of the Cairngorms massif (Chapter 2), but on other rock types, which produce soils with more plant nutrients. Exceptions to this rule include the Curved Wood-rush *Luzula arcuata*, which grows on the nutrient-poor high tops of the Cairngorms, alongside the Three-leaved Rush *Juncus trifidus* and Spiked Woodrush *Luzula spicata*, in a community which appears to have been changed little by the presence of man.

The vegetation of the Cairngorms area strongly reflects its wide altitudinal range (about 150–1,300 m), diversity of landforms and underlying geology. Glacial and peri-glacial landforms dominate the mountains, providing differing degrees of wind exposure and snow accumulation. While glacial corries and troughs shelter a range of grassland and snow-bed types, exposed ridges support wind-clipped prostrate heath, and rock fissures and screes of varying coarseness provide a niche for many specialist plant species. Below the treeline, woodlands and dry heaths grow on well-drained slopes, while wet heaths and blanket bogs occur on flats and gentle slopes.

The underlying geology of the Cairngorms area is responsible for the structure and chemistry of its soils, their moisture-holding properties and their nutrient status (Chapter 3). These, in turn, influence plant species composition (e.g. Ellenberg, 1991; Hill *et al.*, 1999). Although dominated by the acid granitic massifs of the central Cairngorm mountains, the geology of the Cairngorms area has exposures of gneiss, sandstone and schists (Chapter 2). The localised outcrops of mica schist are of particular importance, as these relatively base-rich areas support a greater diversity of plants than more acid soils, a pattern evident at a much larger scale in Europe's alpine regions (e.g. Virtanen *et al.*, 2003).

Historic trends

One legacy of glaciation in Scotland is an impoverished flora, which, after the last major glaciation *c.* 11,000 years ago, formed a boreal vegetation type dominated by Arctic-alpine species (Walker, 1984). The rapid warming that followed enabled forests to expand, up to an altitude of about 850 m[1], but also coincided with a 20% loss in the number of Arctic-alpine taxa (Birks, 1997). The potential natural vegetation of Scotland is now an extreme 'oceanic' variant of the boreal type (Ozenda, 1994), of which the montane vegetation of the Cairngorm mountains and the Angus glens represents a drier variant.

It has been estimated that forest once covered up to 50% of the uplands of Scotland (Birks, 1988). Pollen evidence suggests that the first major woodland clearances in the Grampians and the Cairngorms took place around 3,000 years ago (O'Sullivan, 1974; Huntley, 1981; Birks, 1988). In the mid-18th century, tree felling increased dramatically and this coincided with the introduction of large-scale sheep farming. The latter reached all parts of the Highlands by 1850, raising the stocking level by 40–70%, and undoubtedly contributing to deforestation by suppressing regeneration (Darling, 1955). Felling of timber is likely to have been less important in the ultimate loss of the woodland than the grazing pressure exerted by increasing numbers of Red Deer, sheep and cattle, which prevented the felled forests from regenerating. Before the large-scale

---

Opposite: Purple Saxifrage Saxifraga oppositifolia: *one of the Cairngorm's Arctic and alpine plants. This species is found on damp rocky ground at high altitude, and flowers as soon as the snow melts.*

Photo: *N. Benvie*

Nagy, L., Sydes, C. & McKinnell, J. & Amphlett, A. (2006). Vascular plants. In: Shaw, P. & Thompson, D.B.A. (eds.). *The Nature of the Cairngorms: Diversity in a changing environment.* The Stationery Office. pp. 215-241.

---

[1] The highest natural treeline in the Cairngorms today is at 640 m at Creag Fhiaclach (Chapter 7), although even this is thought to be suppressed by Red Deer *Cervus elaphus* grazing (McConnell, 1996), since dwarfed Scots Pine *Pinus sylvestris* can be found at up to about 850–900 m in Coire Cas.

introduction of improved sheep breeds in the 18th century, smaller numbers of native sheep and cattle grazed around settlements, and on higher ground near shielings in the summer (Walker, 1808).

Red Deer numbers probably reached their nadir early in the 18th century, coinciding with a peak in the human population of the Highlands. However, as human communities were reduced by clearances and constrained from hunting by new laws, deer numbers rebounded (Watson, 1983), and were boosted during the 1870s by the conversion of sheep grazing land to grouse moor or deer forest (Anon., 1944). The latter now occupies an area broadly equivalent to that taken up by all forms of agricultural land combined (Green, 1990). The establishment of deer forests and the earlier elimination of the natural predators of the Red Deer has enabled it to increase in numbers well beyond densities occurring under natural conditions (Watson, 1983; see also Chapter 21).

On higher ground in the central Cairngorms the vegetation on nutrient-poor, acid soils offers poor-quality grazing. This has helped preserve it in a relatively

natural state (Raven & Walters, 1956; Ratcliffe, 1974), in comparison with the more base-rich areas, such as Glen Clova.

Ratcliffe (1974) has provided a comprehensive overview of the vegetation of the Cairngorm mountains. Most rare species populations have since been re-surveyed, and most protected areas have been mapped, using the National Vegetation Classification (NVC) scheme (Chapter 6). Together, these sources have provided much new information on the vascular plants of the Cairngorms, particularly those for which the area is nationally or internationally important.

Important species and habitats

Of 1,117 vascular plant species[2] native to Scotland (Sydes, 1997), 811 (73%) have been recorded in the Cairngorms area (Table 14.1), together with 213 non-native species. The flora of the Cairngorm mountains themselves is numerically poor, comprising about 280 vascular plant species in all (Hill *et al.*, 1996).

Rare plants in the Cairngorms area occur within a wide range of vegetation types, including woodland, mires, heaths, grasslands and, especially, in alpine habitats (Table 14.2). The majority of rare plant species are found above the treeline, where they are usually restricted to small, discrete locations.

About 31% of the Cairngorms area and 49% of the National Park has been mapped using the NVC scheme (Figure 6.1). Most such areas have a relatively high proportion of semi-natural vegetation, are of conservation interest and lie within designated sites. Approximately 25% of the area mapped using the NVC scheme lies above the potential treeline, where most vascular plant rarities occur (Table 14.2).

Species and habitats above the treeline
Alpine vegetation above the treeline ecotone (which extends from the upper edge of the closed forest to the upper limit of tree species growth) consists of various types of prostrate dwarf-shrub heath, grass and moss heaths, rock and scree communities (Chapter 6). Blanket bogs occur on flat areas, while mires are formed where there is soil water seepage. Grasslands, dominated by the Common Bent-grass *Agrostis capillaris*, Sheep's Fescue *Festuca ovina* and Mat-grass *Nardus stricta*, form stands that may be extensive, while most calcareous grasslands occur as small, scattered patches.

The community of vascular plants that occur on the high tops of the Cairngorms appear little modified by human activities. This is in contrast to the vegetation below the treeline, which has been greatly altered by woodland clearances.

Photo: *L. Gill*

[2] Excluding 442 apomictic microspecies of hawkweed (*Hieracium*) and dandelion (*Taraxacum*). Apomictic plants set seed without the normal fertilisation process, and are effectively clones of the mother plant.

Patterns of snow accumulation in the mountains are influenced largely by geomorphology and wind (Jeník, 1998). Since ridges and wind-blown summits have a short period of snow cover, their vegetation is dominated by prostrate *Calluna vulgaris–Cladonia arbuscula* heath (H13)[3], U9 or *Carex bigelowii–Racomitrium lanuginosum* heath (U10), and differs markedly from areas where snow accumulates (McVean & Ratcliffe, 1962). Exposure to frost, windblast and late snow-lie represent extreme conditions, reflected in the low species-richness of such areas across Europe (Virtanen *et al.*, 2003). The same trend is seen in the distribution of alpine rarities in Scotland, with most species occurring in communities that have light- to intermediate snow duration. It is interesting that two of the Cairngorms' rare species – Sibbaldia and the eyebright *Euphrasia frigida* – have been recorded from communities across the full spectrum of conditions, ranging from wind-blasted to snow-protected. Although the Curved Wood-rush occurs largely on wind-blasted ridges in open vegetation (sometimes in U10, but more commonly in U9 (*Juncus trifidus–Racomitrium lanuginosum* heath)), it has also been recorded in U12 (*Salix herbacea–Racomitrium heterostichum* snow-bed), which is found in areas of late snow-lie.

Snow commonly accumulates on the plateaux, in depressions on undulating ground, especially along streamsides. Accumulations of this type also occur in corries, where they may form a cornice along the lip of the slope. The Blue Heath *Phyllodoce caerulea*, which is very rare in Britain, occurs in both types of location. Throughout its world range this species is restricted to long-lasting snow cover, which provides protection from severe frost in winter.

Within corries, snow also builds up on sheltered rock ledges, where it helps to provide a cool, irrigated environment during the growing season. Where the exposed bedrock is of a type that weathers readily, larger ledges may accumulate a layer of soil, in which plant nutrients may be relatively abundant, and which is protected by snow cover in winter. Such ledges carry tall-herb communities and scrub (W20). The Woolly Willow *Salix lanata* has one of its largest populations in Coire Sharroch, above Glen Doll, where it is mixed with Downy Willow *Salix lapponum*. Elsewhere, montane willow populations are now characteristically sparse (see Figure 7.3), having become restricted to locations that are inaccessible to large herbivores.

Several of our rarest plants are also affected in this way. The Alpine Blue-sow-thistle *Cicerbita alpina*, a species endemic to Europe, is restricted in Britain to the Eastern Highlands, where it is found only on a few inaccessible,

The Alpine Blue-sow-thistle Cicerbita alpina *is restricted in Britain to the Eastern Highlands. It belongs to a suite of relatively large, palatable plants in the Cairngorms that are now very rare, having become restricted to sites inaccessible to large grazing animals.*

Photo: *N. Benvie*

[3] For a list of NVC codes and names, see Chapter 6: Annex 6.1.

Table 14.1. The number of vascular plant species recorded in the Cairngorms area.

Taxonomic group	All species	Native species	Introduced species
Anthophyta (flowering plants that produce seeds enclosed in an ovary)	1,024	811	213
Gymnosperms (plants whose seeds are not enclosed within an ovary, e.g. conifers)	15	3	12
Pteridophyta (ferns and fern allies)	32	32	0
Total species	1,071	846	225

Source: National Biodiversity Network. The status of each species (native or introduced) was determined from Stace (1991) and Hill *et al.* (1999).

high-altitude cliff ledges. It became extinct at one of its few remaining locations in about 1975, when deer apparently gained access (Alexander, 2000). Other species in this habitat include the more northerly Highland Cudweed *Gnaphalium norvegicum*, which has five populations surviving in the National Park. It is very restricted, apparently by current densities of large herbivores, and appears to be declining rapidly. Indeed, one of its populations has recently been lost (Payne, 1999).

Crevices in bare rock and narrow ledges with shallow soil may be occupied by common species, but can also provide a niche for rare plants. Small, steep or exposed ledges, or parts of ledges, although possessing little soil, can still provide locations for small species that normally cannot survive alongside more competitive, usually larger, species. These include ferns such as the Mountain Bladder-fern *Cystopteris montana* and Alpine Woodsia *Woodsia alpina*, and a range of uncommon flowering plants, such as Alpine Fleabane *Erigeron borealis*, Alpine Gentian *Gentiana nivalis*, Yellow Oxytropis *Oxytropis campestris*, Highland Saxifrage *S. rivularis* and the Rock Speedwell *Veronica fruticans*. The result is that such areas can resemble a rock garden, with a wealth of flowers visible in late June and early July.

In the corries, late snow maintains open, damp, rocky ground, often dominated mainly by mosses. In those places where higher plants are sparse a number of tiny herbs thrive, including the Starwort Mouse-ear *Cerastium cerastoides*, Arctic Mouse-ear *C. arcticum* and Starry Saxifrage *Saxifraga stellaris*. The Cairngorms area has almost half of all recorded populations of the Highland Saxifrage, and more than half of all British populations of the Alpine Speedwell.

Corries also often have scattered sedges and grasses, including an endemic sub-species of Tufted Hair-grass *Deschampsia cespitosa* ssp. *alpina*. These areas merge with grasslands, irrigated by the late-melting snow. More than half of the populations of two nationally scarce grasses, Alpine Foxtail and Alpine Cat's-tail *Phleum alpinum*, occur in such habitat in the Cairngorms. Two sedges that are even rarer, the Hare's-foot Sedge *Carex lachenalii* and Close-headed Alpine-sedge, also have their main British presence here.

Scree is an accumulation of fragmented rock, which forms a gradient between small particles in the upper part of the slope and larger boulders at its base. The Wavy Meadow-grass *Poa flexuosa* is a notable scree rarity. Block scree hosts tall herbs and, in areas of late snow-lie, snow-tolerant or frost-sensitive ferns are present. These include, for example, the Parsley Fern *Cryptogramma crispa* and the Alpine Lady-fern *Athyrium distentifolium*. The latter is often quite abundant and, where snow lies particularly late in the season, may occur in a stunted form. This form is the result of a recessive gene (or linked genes), and is known as var. *flexile*, which is endemic to Scotland (McHaffie *et al.*, 2001). Because they remain short and spore rapidly, plants of this variety are able to survive conditions that would adversely affect other forms of the same species.

Fell-fields differ from screes in that they occur near summits, where fresh material, from rock fractioning, does not accumulate. Since these sites have little snow protection they are affected by frost-heaving and solifluction. Fell-fields developed over metamorphic ferro-magnesian base rock have such an imbalance of nutrients (low P, low Ca, high Mg and Ni; Nagy & Proctor, 1997a,b; 2001) that even plants able to survive such conditions can scarcely grow, resulting in an open vegetation with a plant cover generally covering less than 5% of the ground (Proctor *et al.*, 1991). Notable plants on such sites are the Scottish endemic form of the Common Mouse-ear *Cerastium fontanum* ssp. *scoticum*, Alpine Penny-cress *Thlaspi caerulescens* and Alpine Catchfly *Lychnis alpina*. The latter has its only Scottish location – and by far the larger of its two British populations – near Meikle Kilrannoch, Caenlochan (Nagy & Proctor, 1996).

High-altitude bogs (M19) reach about 1,000 m asl. Where there is lateral water movement, some localities support the Mountain Bog-sedge *Carex rariflora*, which has the centre of its British range in Cairngorms National Park. It is quite abundant on bogs on high-altitude plateaux in many parts of the area, where it occurs in mires (M7) in hollows and stream sides that are usually snow-filled in winter.

In the higher reaches of the mountains there are numerous wet, flushed areas, with their characteristic vegetation (see e.g. McVean & Ratcliffe, 1962), including a number of rare sedges and rushes (Table 14.2).

Below the treeline

In the past, where topography and hydrology permitted, this zone was occupied largely by Downy Birch *Betula pubescens* and Scots Pine woodland, with some Rowan *Sorbus aucuparia* (see Chapter 7). In the southern parts of the Cairngorms area, such as at Caenlochan, birch-hazel wood appears to have dominated, with pine much less common than elsewhere (Huntley, 1981). Other notable tree species in all wooded areas would have been Alder *Alnus glutinosa*, which grows along watercourses, oak *Quercus* spp., which occurs locally, and Aspen *Populus tremula*, an important tree in the birch woods of Speyside. The understorey of the pine forest is dominated by Heather *Calluna vulgaris* or Blaeberry *Vaccinium myrtillus* heath, or by Juniper *Juniperus communis* (ssp. *communis*) scrub. Dwarf-shrub heath, where it occurs in the forest zone, is likely to be natural only in exposed locations, and to be of secondary origin in sheltered areas. Other treeless vegetation formations in the forest zone include blanket bog and wet heath.

Woodlands. The wet, low-altitude Bay Willow *Salix pentandra* woodlands (W3) of the Cairngorms area host the rare Coralroot Orchid *Corallorhiza trifida* and the nationally scarce Round-leaved Wintergreen *Pyrola rotundifolia*. Another rare orchid species, Creeping Lady's-tresses *Goodyera repens*, is found mostly in the pinewoods (W18), alongside rarities such as the One-flowered Wintergreen *Moneses uniflora* and Twinflower *Linnaea borealis*. The latter also occurs with Intermediate Wintergreen *Pyrola media* in open Juniper woods (W19).

Heaths and grasslands. Where woodland has been cleared, ericaceous dwarf-shrub heaths or grasslands are found today. Dwarf-shrub heaths are characteristic on the acid hillsides in the Cairngorms, whilst in the Caenlochan-Glen Doll area there are extensive grasslands, mostly on mica schist. The Interrupted Clubmoss *Lycopodium annotinum* and Issler's Clubmoss *Diphasiastrum complanatum* grow in heath, or occasionally in open woodland, where snow accumulates and provides local protection from late frosts.

The Alpine Catchfly Lychnis alpina *is known from only two sites in Britain. By far the largest population occurs in an unusual area with toxic soils, near Meikle Kilrannoch.*

Photo: *Niall Benvie*

The beautiful Bog Asphodel Narthecium ossifragum *is a common plant that can easily be seen, especially in the mid- and low-altitude bogs and heaths of Cairngorms National Park.*

Photo: *N. Benvie*

Unimproved hay meadows. Remnant fragments of this habitat are found on riversides and roadsides, particularly on Deeside. They owe their species richness to a long history of traditional management, which includes cutting for hay after flowering, and grazing in the autumn. They can be colourful in high summer, with the blue flowers of Meadow Crane's-bill *Geranium pratense* and Wood Crane's-bill *G. sylvaticum*, the purple flowers of the Melancholy Thistle *Cirsium heterophyllum*, the spectacular yellow Globeflower *Trollius europaeus* and the Spignel *Meum athamanticum*; a rare northern species. For an analysis of the hay meadows of the English, Welsh and Scottish uplands, see Hughes & Huntley (1988).

Arable fields and roadsides. Arable weeds would have played a larger part in the flora of this area when most farms attempted to raise some arable crops. However, in recent decades cereal production has been largely displaced from marginal areas like this. Nevertheless arable weeds still occur where the soil is disturbed in suitable areas. For instance, the rare British endemic Purple Ramping-fumitory *Fumaria purpurea* was recorded near Grantown-on-Spey in 1981.

Cliffs and outcropping rock. In the forest zone this habitat can support a rich mixture of mosses, ferns, woodland and grassland species, which benefit from the gaps created in the canopies of trees and other tall vegetation (Ratcliffe, 1974). It is also home to rarities such as the Forked Spleenwort *Asplenium septentrionale*, which grows in crevices of granitic rock near Deeside, the Wood Cow-wheat *Melampyrum sylvaticum* and the Dark-red Helleborine *Epipactis atrorubens*, which occurs on base-rich rocks.

Fens. This habitat is dominated by sedges which, in the Cairngorms, include the String Sedge *Carex chordorrhiza*; the rarest wetland plant in the area. This species has its largest UK population at Insh Marshes, where it is spreading, probably because of recent reductions in drain maintenance (Cowie & Sydes, 1995).

Ombrogenous mires. In the Cairngorms this habitat is represented by blanket bog (M17–19) and wet heath (M15–16). On the lower, gentler slopes and at the bottom of mountains, ground is mostly too waterlogged to allow trees to grow exceptions, being at Abernethy Forest, Inverness-shire and Ballochbuie. These wet areas are dominated by peat bogs (M17) and wet heath (M15), interrupted by small pools (e.g. M1, M2). The Bog Orchid *Hammarbya paludosa*, rare in Scotland and the rest of Europe, occurs in Glen Doll, on bogs where there is lateral water movement.

Table 14.2. Higher plant species whose populations in the Cairngorms area are of at least national importance. Notable areas outside of the National Park, but within the wider Cairngorms area, are identified.

NVC types: National Vegetation Classification scheme types with which the species is associated. Vegetation types were assigned as follows: regular font – Rodwell (1991-2000); italics – McVean & Ratcliffe (1962); square brackets – Averis *et al.* (2004). The assigned NVC categories of Rodwell (1991-2000) include all records for the species and therefore in some cases list vegetation types which have not been recorded from Scotland.

RDB: National Red Data Book status. EN = Endangered; VU = Vulnerable; NT = Near Threatened; NS = Nationally Scarce (Wigginton, 1999)

BAP: Biodiversity Action Plan Priority species.

Endemic taxon: Species or sub-species endemic to Britain & Ireland ('BI') or to Scotland ('S').

Habitats Directive: Species listed in Annex II of the EC Habitats Directive

Percentage of UK range: The percentage of the species' UK range (in 10-km squares) occurring in the Cairngorms area or in the National Park: *** >75%; ** 25–75%; * 10–24%; '-' <10%

In superscript: Letters in superscript following species' names: A: alpine species, occurring only above the treeline; MA: montane-alpine species, found mainly above the treeline (Ratcliffe, 1991).

Habitat	NVC types	Species			Status				% of UK range in:		Notable areas outside of the NP
				Nationally rare	RDB	BAP	Endemic taxon	Habitats Directive	Cairngorms area	National Park	
Above the treeline											
Rock crevices		*Arabis petraea*MA	Northern Rock-cress		NS				**	*	
	CG12	*Draba norvegica*A	Rock Whitlowgrass		NS				-	-	
		*Woodsia ilvensis*MA (Ca)	Oblong Woodsia	Y	EN	Y			**	**	
Scree	U11, U16, U18, U19, U21	*Athyrium distentifolium*A	Alpine Lady's-fern		NS				**	*	
		*Athyrium flexile*A	Newman's Lady-fern		VU	Y			***	**	
	W8, U15, U17, *U16*	*Cystopteris fragilis*	Brittle Bladder Fern						-	-	Beinn a' Ghlo
		*Poa flexuosa*A	Wavy Meadow-grass	Y	VU				**	**	
Serpentine or ultramafic fell-field		*Cerastium fontanum* ssp. *scoticum*	Common Mouse-ear	Y	NS		S		***	***	
	U10, U13	*Cochlearia micacea*A	Mountain Scurvygrass		NS	Y			**	*	
		*Lychnis alpina*A	Alpine Catchfly	Y	VU				**	**	
Soligenous mires and flushes (base-poor)		*Alopecurus borealis*A	Alpine Foxtail		NS				***	**	
	M7, CG12, U12	*Carex lachenalii*A	Hare's-foot Sedge	Y	NT				**	**	
	M7	*Carex rariflora*A	Mountain Bog-sedge	Y	NT				***	***	
	M33, U11, *U12*	*Cerastium cerastoides*A	Starwort Mouse-ear		NS				***	**	
	U15	*Equisetum pratense*	Shady Horsetail		NS				**	*	Beinn a' Ghlo, Ben Vrackie, Tulach Hill
		*Saxifraga rivularis*A	Highland Saxifrage	Y	NT				**	**	
Soligenous mires and flushes (base-rich)	*M7*, M8, *M11*, M12, *M31*, *M32*, CG12	*Carex saxatilis*A	Russet Sedge		NS				*	*	
	M10, *M11*, M37, CG14	*Equisetum variegatum*	Variegated Horsetail		NS				-	-	Tulach Hill
	[M12]	*Juncus alpinoarticulatus*MA	Alpine Rush		NS				**	-	Beinn a' Ghlo, Tulach Hill
	M12, CG12, U15	*Juncus biglumis*A	Two-flowered Rush		NS				*	-	
	M12	*Juncus castaneus*A	Chestnut Rush		NS				**	*	
	M38	*Sagina nivalis*A	Snow Pearlwort	Y	VU				**	**	
		*Saxifraga hirculus*MA	Marsh Saxifrage	Y	NT	Y		Y	-	-	

Habitat	NVC types	Species		Status					% of UK range in:		Notable areas outside of the NP
				Nationally rare	RDB	BAP	Endemic taxon	Habitats Directive	Cairngorms area	National Park	
Soligenous mires and flushes *(base-poor)*		*Sagina* x *normaniana*^A = *Sagina procumbens* x *saginoides*	Scottish Pearlwort		NS						
	CG10, CG12, U14	*Sagina saginoides*^A	Alpine Pearlwort		NS				**	**	
	U1	*Lychnis viscaria*	Sticky Catchfly		VU				*	-	Tulach Hill
Base-poor rock – cliffs and ledges	*M12, MG3,* CG10, CG11, *CG12, CG14, U5, U15, U17*	*Alchemilla wichurae*	a lady's-mantle		NS				-	-	Beinn a' Ghlo
	CG14	*Cerastium arcticum*^A	Arctic Mouse-ear		NS				*	*	
	U17	*Cicerbita alpina*^A	Alpine Blue-sow-thistle	Y	VU				***	***	
	M32, CG10, CG12, CG14, *U5, U7, U8, U10, U12,* U13, *U14, U18*	*Euphrasia frigida*	an eyebright		NS				**	*	Beinn a' Ghlo
		Euphrasia ostenfeldii	an eyebright		NS				-	-	
		Gnaphalium norvegicum^A	Highland Cudweed		NS				**	*	
		Hieracium carpathicum	a hawkweed		NS				-	*	
		Homogyne alpina^MA	Purple Colt's-foot	Y	EN				***	***	
	CG12, *U12, U15, U17*	*Veronica alpina*^A	Alpine Speedwell		NS				**	**	
Base-rich rock – grasslands on cliffs and ledges	*W20,* CG14, U17	*Carex atrata*^A	Black Alpine-sedge		NS				**	**	
		Carex norvegica^A	Close-headed Alpine-sedge	Y	VU				**	**	
	CG10, CG14	*Carex rupestris*^MA	Rock Sedge		NS				**	*	Beinn a' Ghlo, Ben Vrackie
	CG11, CG12, CG14, U13, U14, *U15,* U17	*Cerastium alpinum*^A	Alpine Mouse-ear		NS				**	*	Ben Vrackie, Sow of Atholl,
	U15	*Cystopteris montana*^A	Mountain Bladder-fern	Y	NT				**	*	
	H10, CG10, CG11, CG12, CG14, U17	*Dryas octopetala*^MA	Mountain Avens		NS				*	*	Beinn a' Ghlo
		Erigeron borealis^A	Alpine Fleabane	Y	VU				***	**	
		Gentiana nivalis^A	Alpine Gentian	Y	VU				**	*	
		Minuartia rubella^A	Mountain Sandwort	Y	NT				*	*	
	CG11, CG12, CG14, U10, U13, U14	*Minuartia sedoides*^MA	Cyphel		NS				*	-	
	CG10	*Oxytropis campestris*^MA	Yellow Oxytropis	Y	VU				**	**	Beinn a' Ghlo
		Oxytropis halleri	Purple Oxytropis	Y	NS				?	?	Ben Vrackie
		Phleum alpinum^A	Alpine Cat's-tail		NS				**	**	
	CG12, *U12, U17*	*Poa alpina*^A	Alpine Meadow-grass		NS				**	*	
	U17	*Poa glauca*^A	Glaucous Meadow-grass		NS				*	*	
	CG10, CG11, CG12, CG14, U17	*Potentilla crantzii*^MA	Alpine Cinquefoil		NS				*	*	Beinn a' Ghlo, Ben Vrackie
	OV39	*Potentilla tabernaemontani*	Spring Cinquefoil		NS				-	-	
	W20, U16	*Salix lanata*^A	Woolly Willow	Y	VU	Y			**	**	

Habitat	NVC types	Species		Status					% of UK range in:		Notable areas outside of the NP
				Nationally rare	RDB	BAP	Endemic taxon	Habitats Directive	Cairngorms area	National Park	
Base-rich rock – grasslands on cliffs and ledges	W20, M11, *CG12*, CG14, *U15*, U17	*Salix reticulata*^A	Net-leaved Willow		NS				**	*	
		Saxifraga cespitosa^A	Tufted Saxifrage	Y	VU				**	*	
	CG12	*Saxifraga nivalis*^A	Alpine Saxifrage		NS				**	*	
	M10	*Schoenus ferrugineus*	Brown Bog-rush	Y	VU				**	-	Beinn a' Ghlo, Tulach Hill
	M38	*Sedum villosum*^MA	Hairy Stonecrop		NS				*	-	
	OV37	*Thlaspi caerulescens*^MA	Alpine Penny-cress		NS				-	-	
	CG14, *U17*	*Veronica fruticans*^A	Rock Speedwell		NT				**	*	Beinn a' Ghlo, Ben Vrackie
		Woodsia alpina^A	Alpine Woodsia	Y	NT				*	*	
Base-poor summits	M10, [M12]	*Kobresia simpliciuscula*^MA	False sedge	Y	NS				**	-?	Beinn a' Ghlo
	U9, U10, U12	*Luzula arcuata*^A	Curved Wood-rush	Y	NT				**	**	
Base-poor grassland	MG3	*Alchemilla glomerulans*	a lady's-mantle		NS				**	*	
	CG10, CG11, CG12, U10, U11, *U12*, U13, U14, *U15*, *U17*, U18	*Sibbaldia procumbens*^A	Sibbaldia		NS				**	*	Beinn a' Ghlo, Sow of Atholl
Base-rich grassland	CG14	*Astragalus alpinus*^A	Alpine Milk-vetch	Y	VU				***	**	Ben Vrackie
	M10, CG10, *CG11*, *CG12*, CG14, U15, *U17*	*Carex capillaris*	Hair Sedge		NS				*	*	Beinne a' Ghlo, Ben Vrackie, Sow of Atholl, Tulach Hill
	M12, *CG12*, CG14, *U6*, U17	*Carex vaginata*^A	Sheathed Sedge		NS				**	**	Ben Vrackie, Sow of Atholl, Tulach Hill
	[W9]	*Crepis mollis*	Northern Hawk's-beard	Y	NS				*	-	
	M10, M38, CG10	*Minuartia verna*^MA	Spring Sandwort		NS				-	-	
Blanket bog	Dwarf-shrub heath H14, M19	*Arctostaphylos alpinus*^MA	Alpine Bearberry		NS				-	-	
	M15, M19	*Betula nana*^MA	Dwarf Birch		NS				**	*	Beinn a' Ghlo, Sow of Atholl
	H12	*Diphasiastrum complanatum*	Issler's Clubmoss	Y	NS				**	**	
	H12, H16, H22	*Lycopodium annotinum*^MA	Interrupted Clubmoss		NS				**	*	Sow of Atholl
	H18	*Phyllodoce caerula*^A	Blue Heath	Y	VU				**	-	Sow of Atholl
		Vaccinium microcarpum^MA	Small Cranberry		NS				**	*	
Upper montane scrub	W20, *CG12*, CG14	*Salix arbuscula*^A	Mountain Willow		NS				**	*	Beinn a' Ghlo, Ben Vrackie, Sow of Atholl,
	W20, CG14, *U15*, U16, *U17*	*Salix lapponum*^A	Downy Willow		NS				**	*	Beinn a' Ghlo, Sow of Atholl,
	W20, CG14	*Salix myrsinites*	Whortle-leaved Willow		NS				**	**	Beinn a' Ghlo, Ben Vrackie, Sow of Atholl,

Habitat	NVC types	Species		Nationally rare	RDB	BAP	Endemic taxon	Habitats Directive	Cairngorms area	National Park	Notable areas outside of the NP
Below the treeline											
Rock crevices, rocky outcrops		*Asplenium septentrionale*	Forked Spleenwort		NS				-	-	
	W8, *W9*, CG8, *CG14*	*Epipactis atrorubens*	Dark-red Helleborine		NS				-	-	
		Melampyrum sylvaticum	Small Cow-wheat		NS	Y			**	-	
Moorland & woodland	W11, W17, W18, W19, W21, H7, *H10*, H12, H14, *H16*, H20, H21, CG7, *U17*	*Juniperus communis*	Juniper			Y			-	-	
Woodland		*Circaea alpina*	Alpine Enchanter's-nightshade		NS				-	-	
		Corallorhiza trifida	Coralroot Orchid		NS				-	-	
	W17, W18	*Goodyera repens*	Creeping Lady's-tresses		NS				*	*	
	W18	*Linnaea borealis*	Twinflower		NS	Y			**	**	
	W18	*Moneses uniflora*	One-flowered Wintergreen	Y	VU				**	-	
	W11, *W17*, W19, H16	*Pyrola media*	Intermediate Wintergreen		NS				**	*	Tulach Hill
	M9, CG14, U17	*Pyrola rotundifolia* ssp. *rotundifolia*	Round-leaved Wintergreen		NS				**	*	Tulach Hill
		Sorbus rupicola	a whitebeam		NS				-	-	
Base-rich woodland		*Ribes spicatum*	Downy Currant		NS				*	*	
Grassland		*Dianthus deltoides*	Maiden Pink		NS				-	-	
		Meum athamanticum	Spignel		NS				**	*	Beinn a' Ghlo,
Mires		*Calamagrostis purpurea*	Scandinavian Small-reed	Y	NT				**	*	
	M4	*Carex chordorrhiza*	String Sedge	Y	VU				**	**	
	M1, M2, M4	*Carex magellanica*	Tall Bog-sedge		NS				-	-	
	W5	*Cicuta virosa*	Cowbane		NS				-	-	
		Deschampsia setacea	Bog Hair-grass		NS				*	-	
	[M1], M21	*Hammarbya paludosa*	Bog Orchid		NS*				-	-	
		Juncus balticus	Baltic Rush		NS				-	-	
	M16	*Lycopodiella inundata*	Marsh Clubmoss		NS	Y			-	-	
	S10, S23	*Rorippa islandica*	Northern Yellow-cress		NS*				-	-	
	M22, S24, S25	*Thelypteris palustris*	Marsh Fern		NS				-	-	
Standing water	A13, A22	*Elatine hexandra*	Six-stamened Waterwort		NS*				-	-	
		Isoetes echinospora	Spring Quillwort		NS*				-	-	
	A7, A13	*Nuphar pumila*	Least Water-lily		NS				*	*	
	M29	*Pilularia globulifera*	Pillwort		NS	Y			-	-	
	A11, A13, A14	*Potamogeton filiformis*	Slender-leaved Pondweed		NS				?	?	Beinn a' Ghlo
Arable		*Fumaria purpurea*	Purple Ramping-fumitory		NS	Y	BI		-	-	

Lochs. There are relatively few water bodies of any size in the Cairngorms area, and fewer still that are mesotrophic and hence support a rich vascular plant community (see Chapter 9). The Marsh Clubmoss *Lycopodiella inundata* is an example of the rare plants that occur occasionally on the shores of some lochs in the Cairngorms. Open water rarities include the Slender Pondweed *Potamogeton filiformis* and the Spring Quillwort *Isoetes echinospora*.

Important areas

Most areas important for rare vascular plant species in the Cairngorms are centred on the higher reaches of mountains (Table 14.3; Figure 14.1). A number of them are dominated by acidic rocks and soils, which support acidophil Arctic-alpine species. The most important (and most species-rich), however, are those areas with base-rich parent material, or with base-rich outcrops or flushes. In the following account, acid-rich and base-rich areas are described separately, and presented in descending order of importance (Table 14.3).

Base-rich areas

Ben Vrackie, Beinn a' Ghlo, Coire Kander, Glas Maol, Glen Callater, Caenlochan and Glen Doll are floristically some of the most important areas in the wider Cairngorms, and are part of the mica-schist mountains of the Central Highlands, extending from Ben Lui on the borders of Argyll to the Angus Glens. Their vegetation contrasts sharply with that of mountains which have an acidic bedrock, and includes a large number of base-loving rare species, particularly above the treeline. The best-known and richest of these sites are Caenlochan Glen and the corries of Glen Doll.

1. Glen Doll. Corrie Sharroch and Corrie Fee are the two richest areas for rare plants in Glen Doll. The habitats harbouring these rarities are rock faces, ledges and steep slopes at the foot of cliffs. Yellow Oxytropis, Alpine Milk-vetch *Astragalus alpinus*, Alpine Fleabane and Rock Speedwell are among the species found here. Larger rocky slopes and ledges support the best examples of willow scrub (W20) in Scotland. Alpine Catchfly has its only Scottish population, and by far its largest British population, near Meikle Kilrannoch, at the head of the glen. Purple Colt's-foot *Homogyne alpina* has its only occurrence within Corrie Sharroch. Corrie Fee supports both Alpine Woodsia and Oblong Woodsia *Woodsia ilvensis*, the latter at one of only three locations in Scotland. Although a relict population of Alpine Blue-sow-thistle

in Canness Glen has been exterminated – apparently by Red Deer grazing – there is still a population thriving in an inaccessible location on Craig Rennet.

2. Caenlochan. Like Glen Doll, Caenlochan Glen and Canness Glen are exceptionally rich botanically. Glen Doll includes the remaining Caenlochan NNR but Caenlochan Glen remains an important SSSI for rare vascular plants. In Britain, this site is second only in montane plant diversity to Ben Lawers, which has some unique species, but the Alpine Gentian is a species not found elsewhere in Britain except on Ben Lawers and Caenlochan. The glen is botanically diverse, and supports a high proportion of the alpine flora of Britain and Ireland (Huntley, 1979). A combination of high altitude, a relatively continental climate and a diversity of rock and soil types has led to the development of a wide range of plant communities, several of which are the most extensive and representative of their type in Britain. Base-rich rock outcrops occur at up to 945 m in the corrie at the head of the glen, which has 67 montane species: more than any other corrie in Britain (Ratcliffe, 1977).

Corrie Fee supports a rich flora, which includes the largest remaining relict population of montane willow scrub in Scotland.

Photo: L. Gill

Mountain Avens Dryas octopetala *is a clear indicator of those rare places in the Cairngorms where there are outcrops of lime-rich rocks.*

Photo: *L. Gill*

Lime-rich rocks support the greatest plant diversity in Britain, but are comparatively rare in the Cairngorms. Limestone outcrops do occur, however, as here on Tulach Hill.

Photo: *L. Gill*

This area has been known for its rare plants since the end of the 18th century. Misguided attempts were made, possibly at this time, to further enrich both Caenlochan and Ben Lawers, by sowing the seeds of alpine plants. Apparently this was unsuccessful at Ben Lawers (Raven & Walters, 1956) but some plants not accepted as natives, such as Pyrenean Columbine *Aquilegia pyrenaica*, still occur on Caenlochan (Stace, 1991) and inevitably raise questions about the status of Purple Colt's-foot. Intense grazing by Red Deer has restricted most of the area's rare plants to the steep scree slopes and rock ledges. Alpine Woodsia, Mountain Bladder-fern, Alpine Speedwell, Rock Speedwell, Highland Cudweed, Alpine Fleabane, Mountain Avens *Dryas octopetala*, Sibbaldia and Alpine Blue-sow-thistle are found here. On the steep slopes at the foot of the cliffs intense grazing has removed the natural species-rich vegetation dominated by tall-herbs and montane shrubs, leaving grassland dominated by Tufted Hair-grass *Deschampsia cespitosa* (McVean & Ratcliffe, 1962).

5. Coire Kander and Glen Callater. A complex of outcropping lime-rich and acid schists of Dalradian age make Coire Kander and Glen Callater among the richest and most diverse botanical sites in the Cairngorms area. Their cliff ledges are home to some of Britain's rarest Arctic-alpine plants, including the Woolly Willow and Close-headed Alpine Sedge *Carex norvegica*. Extensive calcareous flushes occur, and on the plateau of Cairn of Claise there are many high-altitude blanket mires. These support Mountain Bog-sedge; including one population of about 100,000 individuals. Water Sedge *Carex aquatilis* is also found there. Coire Kander has the largest of the four Alpine Blue-sow-thistle populations at present, although population counts for this species are measured as flowering spikes and therefore vary greatly from year to year. There are two Close-headed Alpine Sedge populations on this site; the one in Coire Kander seems to be in decline while a higher, more open population on Tolmount (Glen Callater) appears to be thriving.

8. Coire Garbhlach. This steep corrie is on the base-rich part of Glen Feshie. There is tall herb vegetation, including montane willow scrub, on crumbling rock ledges and steep stony slopes. There are also flushes and flushed grasslands among the crags. The site is particularly well known for large patches of Mountain Avens. This is accompanied by a great variety of ledge and rock herbs such as Alpine Saxifrage, Rock Whitlowgrass *Draba norvegica*, Rock Speedwell, Rock Sedge and Mountain Bladder-fern. The mountain willows are well represented and Woolly Willow occurs at one of its few sites in the central Cairngorms.

9. Beinn a' Ghlo. This is a Dalradian limestone site of outstanding importance for conservation. Its limestone grassland, cliff, flush, wooded gorge and pavement vegetation are all very rare in Scotland and contain many nationally rare species (Table 14.3). Some alpine vegetation types further increase the botanical diversity of the area. The crags above Loch Loch are famous for the large colony of Yellow Oxytropis, which seeds freely into the surrounding area. The species occurs on two other sites in Scotland but this site holds around two-thirds of its Scottish plants. Beinn a' Ghlo is also the only site within the National Park that supports False Sedge *Kobresia simpliciuscula*. Fifteen populations are spread across the limestone in the south of the site, placing it on a par with Ben Lawers. One population has been estimated to contain at least 10,000 flower heads.

11. Glas Maol. This is a conspicuous, domed summit on the eastern side of Glen Beag. The large plateau is clothed with alpine moss heath, sedge heath and blanket bog, and there are grassy flushes with Alpine Cat's-tail, Alpine Foxtail and Mountain Bog-sedge. The slopes of the hill are more markedly base-rich, and there are flushes and mires with such species as Sheathed Sedge *Carex vaginata* and Chestnut Rush *Juncus castaneus*.

12. Ben Vrackie. One of a series of Arctic-alpine plant sites on calcareous schist, Ben Vrackie is of particular importance for its cliff vegetation on both acid and calcareous rocks, which supports a number of nationally rare plant species. These include populations of Alpine Milk-vetch, one estimated at over 10,000 plants in 2002. Purple Oxytropis *Oxytropis halleri* is also found here, in one of only three upland sites in Scotland. Although this is an alpine species in continental Europe, most of the Scottish population is found around the coast. Brown Bog-rush *Schoenus ferrugineus* occurs in a flush very near to the main footpath leading up the mountain. The species was established here from plants moved from Loch Tummel when its water level was raised to support the hydroelectric scheme there.

15. Tulach Hill. Its rare 'sugar limestone' grassland, grass heath, flush and pavement vegetation make this Dalradian limestone site of particular importance. In addition, the east end of the site has acid cliffs covered by relict mixed woodland. These hold the most northerly population of Sticky Catchfly in Scotland. Brown Bog-rush has its stronghold here in flushes at low altitude, having been discovered during re-notification of the SSSI in the early 1980s.

16. Coire Chais. This north-facing corrie is situated at the north-west corner of the Drumochter Hills SSSI. The corrie rises to an altitude of 850 m and the area includes part of the adjacent high plateau at 800–900 m. Outside of the SSSI, it encompasses the high tops of A' Mharconaich (882 m), Meall Odhar Mòr (834 m) and upper escarpment slopes with rock outcrops and scree. The rock is metamorphosed sandstone, moderately base-rich in places. The vegetation in the corries consists of late-lie snow-beds, dominated by Mat-grass *Nardus stricta* or Blaeberry *Vaccinium myrtillus*, while the plateau is covered in blanket bog with acid *Carex–Sphagnum* flushes. Rare species occur on the rock ledges (Downy Willow), in flushes (Mountain Bog-sedge, Russet Sedge *Carex saxatilis*, Alpine Foxtail), in scree with late snow-lie (Alpine Lady-fern) and in flushed grassland (Alpine Cat's-tail).

17. Cairnwell. This is another Dalradian limestone site, with sugar limestone grassland/heath vegetation. Although the sugar limestone outcrops on this site are limited in extent, they support a number of rare vascular plant species. The population of Alpine milk-vetch is relatively small, but the population of Mountain Sandwort *Minuartia rubella*, which thrives on an unstable substratum, is the second largest in the country.

21. Creag an Dail. This site forms part of the Eastern Cairngorms SSSI. It is a low hill (862 m), with outstanding calcicolous flora on its calcareous grassland, flushes and cliffs. Alpine Milk-vetch occurs in the calcareous grassland here; a species known from only four sites in the Eastern Highlands, three of which lie within Cairngorms National Park. Other rare species include Mountain Avens, Rock Sedge, Whortle-leaved Willow *Salix myrsinites* and Alpine Cinquefoil *Potentilla crantzii*.

26. Glen Feshie. This area encompasses part of the upper glen, where it cuts through schists of metamorphosed sandstone and other base-rich rocks. Its slopes ascend to 1,019 m to the north and 849 m to the south. Crags and scree are present, and the vegetation includes both tall and prostrate *Calluna* heaths, blanket bog and *Carex bigelowii–Racomitrium lanuginosum* moss heath. Base-rich grasslands and fens are well developed here – in contrast to areas of the granitic Cairngorms. Species found on the base-rich crags, or in base-rich grassland and flushes, include Black Alpine-sedge *Carex atrata*, Hair Sedge *Carex capillaris*, Sheathed Sedge, Alpine Mouse-ear, Mountain Avens, the eyebright *Euphrasia frigida*, Cyphel *Minuartia sedoides*, Alpine Meadow-grass *Poa alpina*, Glaucous Meadow-grass *Poa glauca*, Alpine Pearlwort *Sagina saginoides*, Whortle-leaved Willow and Alpine Speedwell. Dwarf Birch *Betula nana* occurs in the blanket bog, while Alpine Lady's Fern occurs in scree protected by late-lie snow, and Sibbaldia in snow-beds.

Field Gentian Gentianella campestris. *A substantial population has been found in the Inchrory area, perhaps exceeding 100,000 plants.*

Photo: *L. Gill*

27. Inchrory/Glen Avon. The Glen Builg/Glen Avon area, centred on Inchrory, has a history of botanical exploration dating back to the late 19th century. The botanical interest of this area is centred principally on extensive calcareous grasslands, with their intimately associated flushes, and the limestone outcrops on the east side of the glen. There is also a very small remnant native pinewood. Twenty-nine Red-listed, nationally rare or scarce species have been recorded here. Examples include Field Gentian *Gentianella campestris* which, in 2005, was estimated to have a population in excess of 100,000 plants. The rare Bearded Couch *Elymus caninus* (var. *donianus*) is also present. Nationally scarce species include Dark-red Helleborine, Variegated Horsetail *Equisetum variegatum*, Alpine Cinquefoil, Downy Currant, the whitebeam *Sorbus rupicola*, Hair Sedge *Carex capillaris*, Shady Horsetail *Equisetum pratense* and Twinflower. Blue Fleabane *Erigeron acer* grows on Craig Bhuilg, where it was first recorded in 1906. This is the most northerly and highest altitude site for this species in Britain and Ireland, and the only site within Cairngorms National Park. Although treated as a non-native by Preston *et al.* (2002), its habitat and associated species seem to suggest otherwise.

28. Morrone Birkwood. This is the finest example in Britain of a montane birch wood (with Juniper understorey) on calcareous soils. There is species-rich heath in cleared areas and a series of mires in hollows in morainic ground. In addition, above the wood, there are late snow-beds, blanket bog, wind-clipped prostrate *Calluna* heath and calcareous mires. The flora of this small site, which includes 280 vascular plant species, is as rich as that of the Cairngorm mountains. A number of rare plants, such the Holly Fern, Alpine Cinquefoil, Yellow Saxifrage *Saxifraga aizoides* and Alpine Rush *Juncus alpinus*, occur in the flushes and grassland within the wood and on wooded crags.

29. Creag nan Gamhainn/River Avon. The site consists of areas of calcareous woodland and grassland with limestone outcrops, along with the floodplain of the River Avon. It lies between Bridge of Avon and Delnabo, to the west of Tomintoul, and includes the spectacular gorge of the Water of Ailnack.

Here, limestone outcrops and grassland support the scarce Dark-red Helleborine and Hair Sedge. The calcareous habitats support a rich flora, with perhaps 19 species of regional note, including the rare Bearded Couch *Elymus caninus* var. *donianus* and Scottish Asphodel *Tofieldia pusilla*, which occurs in flushes at an unusually low altitude. Northern Hawk's-beard *Crepis mollis* was recorded here – at its most northerly UK site – in the 19th century, but has not been seen since.

The banks and former channels of the River Avon have very large populations of Baltic Rush *Juncus balticus* (about 8,500 flowering stems in 2005; perhaps the largest inland population of this normally coastal species) and of Variegated Horsetail *Equisetum variegatum*. These two species are often found growing together here. In 2005 a single large stand of the scarce hybrid horsetail *Equisetum* x *trachyodon* was found here; the only site for this taxon in the Cairngorms area. Northern Rock-cress *Arabis petraea* grows on the river shingle.

Areas with acid bedrock

The Cairngorm mountains represent the largest area above the treeline in Britain and Ireland, and include some of Scotland's highest summits. The wind-blasted and frost-shattered ground of the high summits and plateaux provide a stark contrast to the corries below, which are snow-filled in the winter. Although their acid and nutrient-poor soils support a species-poor flora, small, discrete areas with local base-rich flushing or late snow-lie support a number of rare Arctic-alpine species. These acidic areas are discribed below, in descending order of importance.

3. Lochnagar. This area provides acid conditions similar to those of the Cairngorm Mountains, but is remarkably rich. Walters (1956) considered Lochnagar to be 'surely the most rewarding' of all the 'floristically dull' (i.e. acidic) mountains in Britain. Its screes, gullies, north-facing corries and high plateau are home to a number of rare species, making it the third most important area for vascular plants in the Cairngorms, after Glen Doll and Caenlochan Glen (Table 14.3). The north-facing corries are the classic situation for Alpine Blue-sow-thistle, although the current population is relatively low. Highland Cudweed and Highland Saxifrage also find refuge here. The snow-trapping bogs of the higher parts of the granite massif support Mountain Bog-sedge, although the Hare's-foot Sedge, which has similar habitat requirements, has not been relocated recently.

4. Cairn Toul. This area encompasses the high peaks of Sgor an Lochan Uaine (1,258 m), Cairn Toul (1,291 m) and The Devil's Point (1,064 m), and north- and east-facing corries overlooking the Lairig Ghru and the River Dee. The area is rocky, with much rock debris on the high plateau and summits, and extensive scree and cliffs in the corries. The vegetation of the high plateau consists of *Juncus trifidus–Racomitrium lanuginosum* rush-heath, *Nardus stricta– Carex bigelowii* grass-heath, and springs and flushes. The corries hold areas of late-lie mossy snow-beds and snow-bed grasslands. The rock is granite, but

flushing through the rock is sufficient to support those rare species requiring modest base-enrichment.

Many of the rare plant species in this area are associated with rock habitats, especially rock ledges, crevices and gullies, usually with late snow-lie and flushing. They include Highland Saxifrage, Alpine Meadow-grass, Wavy Meadow-grass, Hare's-foot Sedge, Russet Sedge, Black Alpine-sedge, Downy Willow, Mountain Willow *Salix arbuscula*, Whortle-leaved Willow, Mountain Avens and Alpine Speedwell. Curved Wood-rush is found in rock debris on the plateau, while Mountain Bog-sedge occurs in acid flushes. A large population of Alpine Cat's-tail occurs in grassland in Coire an Lochan Uaine. Starwort Mouse-ear occurs on damp, unstable granite scree, where snow lies late.

6. Northern Corries. The varied topography and nearly 800 m altitude range of this area – from Glenmore Forest to the summit of Cairn Lochan – gives rise to a variety of vegetation types, including woodland, grassland, heath, peat bog, flush, snow patch vegetation and fell-field. Some of the best cliff and scree flora in the Cairngorms, including the rare Alpine Saxifrage, Highland Saxifrage, Hare's Foot-sedge and Curved Wood-rush, are found high up on the cliffs and ridges, and in deep gullies. A recent reduction in grazing by Red Deer around the Cairngorm skiing development has resulted in the re-establishment of Scots Pine and Juniper, illustrating the local potential for re-establishing forest cover and scrub at high altitude.

7. Ben Macdui. At 1,309 m, the summit of Ben Macdui is the highest point in the Cairngorms. Above 1,200 m there are large populations of Curved Wood-rush in areas of wind-swept partially-vegetated gravels. The plateau to the north has single, isolated populations of Russet Sedge and Mountain Bog-sedge, while Wavy Meadow-grass grows on nearby Beinn Mheadhoin, amongst Three-leaved Rush. The summit plateau is notable for its extensive snow-bed vegetation, dominated by bryophytes and lichens. Sibbaldia and Hare's-foot Sedge are present – though scarce – at the edges of these late snow-lie areas. Alpine Lady-fern grows amongst the boulder-fields of the plateau and the corrie headwall.

The cliffs around the head of Loch Avon support a rich acidic flora, including Downy Willow, the Lady's-mantle *Alchemilla glomerulans*, Northern Rock-cress *Arabis petraea*, Glaucous Meadow-grass, Arctic Mouse-ear, Black Alpine-sedge, Sheathed Sedge, Starwort Mouse-ear and Alpine Speedwell.

10. Ben Avon. Rising to 1,171 m, Ben Avon has an extensive high-altitude plateau, with summit heaths dominated by Three-leaved Rush. Here, Curved Wood-rush is present on extremely exposed sites, and Sibbaldia in areas of moderate snow accumulation. Most of the vascular plant species interest, however, lies in the north-facing corries overlooking Glen Avon.

On Ben Avon the nationally endangered Tufted Saxifrage has its only extant Cairngorms site; a single population that appears to be in long-term decline. Growing nearby and indicative of local base enrichment are Mountain Avens, Two-flowered Rush *Juncus biglumis* and Alpine Cinquefoil. Elsewhere these corries support an acidic flora, with species such as Northern Rock-cress, Alpine Mouse-ear and Downy Willow, as well as the near-threatened Arctic Mouse-ear, Heath Cudweed *Gnaphalium sylvaticum* and Thyme-leaved Speedwell *Veronica serpyllifolia* (ssp. *hummifusa*). Nationally scarce species include Alpine Lady-fern, Black Alpine-sedge, Hair Sedge, Sheathed Sedge, Starwort Mouse-ear, Alpine Meadow-grass and Alpine Speedwell. On lower ground Dwarf Birch and Interrupted Clubmoss are also found.

Four rare vascular plant species, once present on Ben Avon, have not been recorded there since the 19th century: Alpine Foxtail, Alpine Fleabane, Alpine Cat's-tail and Rock Speedwell. A further three species – the lady's-mantle *Alchemilla glomerulans*, Alpine Saxifrage and Highland Saxifrage – have not been recorded on the site for more than 20 years. This may be indicative of a genuine long-term loss of species with small populations, but may also reflect a reduction in botanical recording on this remote site.

13. Braeriach. Consisting mainly of a high plateau above 1,100 m, this area encompasses several summits of over 1,200 m, including Braeriach (1,296 m) and Einich Cairn (1,237 m). The plateau is ringed by corries facing west, north and east, and with rocky granite slopes overlooking Gleann Einich and the Lairig Ghru. Much of the plateau consists of open granite gravel with scattered mosses and vascular plants, including Curved Wood-rush. Patches of more closed vegetation consist of *Juncus trifidus–Racomitrium lanuginosum* rush-heath, *Nardus stricta–Carex bigelowii* grass-heath and *Carex bigelowii–Polytrichum alpinum* sedge-heath. The corries hold much late-lying snow and are rocky, with cliffs, extensive scree and patches of late-lie moss snow-beds, grasslands and springs.

Rare species here include Hare's-foot Sedge, Highland Saxifrage, Alpine Meadow-grass, Downy Willow and Alpine Speedwell. Very late melting snow-beds dominated by mosses provide habitat for Starwort Mouse-ear and

Sibbaldia. Alpine Lady's Fern and Newman's Lady Fern *Athyrium flexile* occur in the high-altitude boulder fields where snow also lies late.

14. Insh Marshes. The vegetation of this internationally important site consists mainly of sedge-dominated poor-fen communities, with reed bed, herb-rich swamp and willow carr (see Chapter 10). Here, the String Sedge is comparatively abundant; this northern species is only found at one other location in Scotland. Other rare plants include the Least Water-lily *Nuphar pumila*, Awlwort *Subalaria aquatica*, Cowbane *Cicuta virosa* and the Shady Horsetail.

18. East Drumochter. A diverse area of moorland and summit vegetation, the East Drumochter hills have extensive western blanket mire, *Calluna* heath, snow-bed vegetation, cliffs, grasslands, high-level mires and poor fen. Their flora includes a number of nationally scarce montane plants typical of acidic base-rock such as Black Alpine Sedge, Mountain Bog-sedge, and Downy Willow. A few species, such as Hair Sedge, demonstrate that there are some pockets that are slightly more calcareous. The rounded summits are used by very high densities of Red Deer especially in summer.

19. Gaick. Cut through by glaciated steep-sided glens with corries and stream gullies, this area consists mainly of a high plateau, at 750–890 m, with a number of high tops. Its rock is chiefly metamorphosed sandstone and other rocks that are locally base-rich. The vegetation of the plateau consists mainly of blanket bog with *Carex bigelowii–Racomitrium lanuginosum* moss heath on the summits. Crags and scree occur in the corries and stream gullies and on the high slopes of the glens. The vegetation includes late-lie snow-beds, dwarf-shrub heaths and grassland.

Blanket bog on the high plateau has Small Cranberry *Vaccinium microcarpum*, while Mountain Bog-sedge and Alpine Foxtail occur in acid flushes. Rock faces and ledges support the largest assemblages of rare plants in this area, including Black Alpine-sedge, Mountain Avens, Downy Willow, Whortle-leaved Willow, Alpine Saxifrage and Alpine Speedwell. Other rare species occur in its flushed grassland and late-lie snow-beds.

20. Cairn Gorm/Glen Avon. Heaths around Loch Avon and in upper Strath Nethy are notable for locally abundant Juniper, in a form that appears to be intermediate between the subspecies *communis* and *alpina*. Interrupted Clubmoss also forms large stands, especially in north-facing heaths above 750 m. Issler's Clubmoss has a single large population on west-facing slopes in

Strath Nethy, and Alpine Cat's-tail, Alpine Meadow-grass, Scottish Pearlwort *Sagina* x *normaniana*, along with a number of rare *Hieracium* species, are found on calcareous cliffs in Coire Dearg.

22. West Drumochter. Like East Drumochter, this is a range of hills with rounded tops bearing extensive areas of summit heath, with snow-holding communities in depressions and on the slopes. There are also high- and lower altitude blanket bog and heaths. Despite their altitude the tops are visited by very high densities of Red Deer and even sheep, especially in summer. The Sow of Atholl is one of only two sites for Blue Heath in Britain and Ireland. This species is unpalatable to grazing animals in summer and further protected from grazing by snow cover, which lingers on all its locations until June. Blue Heath is known from only single relict sites in the Alps and the eastern Pyrenees (Raven & Walters, 1956; Dendaletche, 1974) but is abundant in Scandinavia, like most of our rare mountain plants.

23. Abernethy Forest. The pinewoods of Strathspey are the most extensive in Britain, and have important peatland sites, dwarf-shrub heaths and Juniper scrub. The forest is not floristically rich, but its flora includes characteristic northern pinewood species, such as One-flowered Wintergreen; one of the rarest plants in Britain. Other rare pinewood species include the orchid Creeping Lady's-tresses, Twinflower and Intermediate Wintergreen. Interrupted Clubmoss occurs in *Calluna* heath and Small Cranberry in blanket bog.

24. Monadhliadh. This area is dominated by low- and high-altitude blanket bogs, with a variety of grasslands, dwarf-shrub and moss heaths and flushes. Late snow-beds support some nationally rare plant species, including Sibbaldia. Additional rare plants found on the heaths and cliffs include Alpine Bearberry *Arctostaphylos alpinus*, Scottish Asphodel and Downy Willow. Where the high altitude bogs hold snow-beds, Mountain Bog-sedge thrives, with one population estimated at 80,000 individuals.

25. Beinn a' Bhuird. The high summit plateau of Beinn a' Bhuird connects South Top (1,177 m), A' Chioch (1,197 m) and North Top (1,197 m). The area includes the upper slopes and corries on the east side of the hill, and is granite-based. The vegetation of the plateau consists of *Juncus trifidus–Racomitrium lanuginosum* rush-heath, *Nardus stricta–Carex bigelowii* grass-heath and springs and flushes. Prostrate *Calluna* heath and other dwarf-shrub heaths

Abernethy Forest and other pinewoods hold some special vascular plants, such as the One-flowered Wintergreen Moneses uniflora; *one of the rarest plants in Britain.*
Photo: *L. Gill*

Figure 14.1. Important areas for vascular plants. See text for further details and Table 14.3 for species lists.

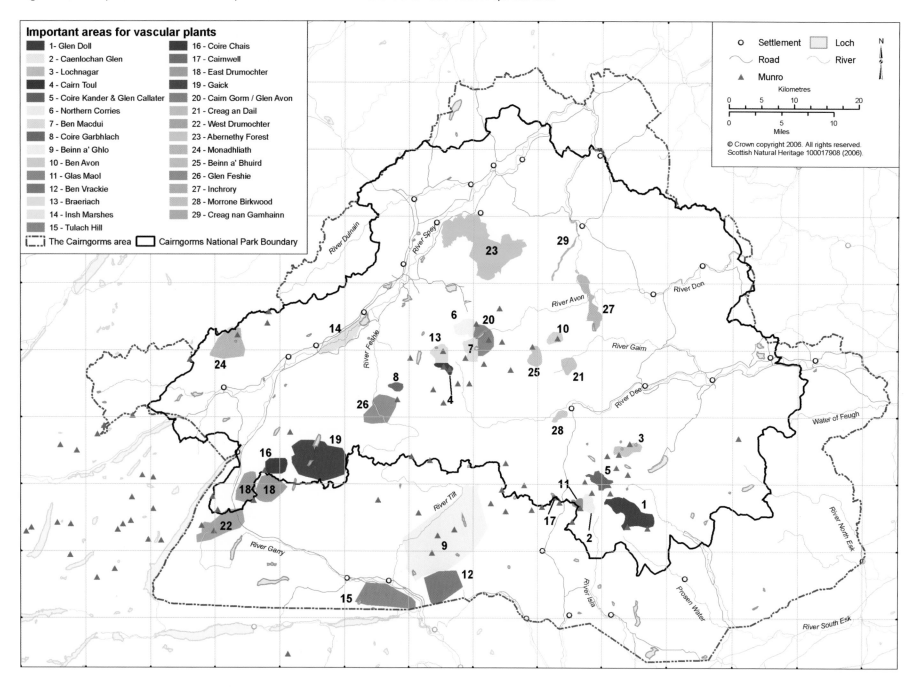

Important areas for vascular plants

1- Glen Doll
2 - Caenlochan Glen
3 - Lochnagar
4 - Cairn Toul
5 - Coire Kander & Glen Callater
6 - Northern Corries
7 - Ben Macdui
8 - Coire Garbhlach
9 - Beinn a' Ghlo
10 - Ben Avon
11 - Glas Maol
12 - Ben Vrackie
13 - Braeriach
14 - Insh Marshes
15 - Tulach Hill
16 - Coire Chais
17 - Cairnwell
18 - East Drumochter
19 - Gaick
20 - Cairn Gorm / Glen Avon
21 - Creag an Dail
22 - West Drumochter
23 - Abernethy Forest
24 - Monadhliath
25 - Beinn a' Bhuird
26 - Glen Feshie
27 - Inchrory
28 - Morrone Birkwood
29 - Creag nan Gamhainn

The Cairngorms area
Cairngorms National Park Boundary

Settlement   Loch
Road   River
Munro   N

Kilometres
0 5 10   20
0   5   10
Miles

© Crown copyright 2006. All rights reserved.
Scottish Natural Heritage 100017908 (2006).

Table 14.3. Important areas for vascular plants in the Cairngorms, listed in descending order of the number of nationally threatened and nationally scarce species.

Percentage of area occurring within the wider Cairngorms or the Cairngorms National Park: *** >75%; ** 25–75%; * 10–25%; '-' <10%;

Area	Nationally threatened species	Nationally scarce species	% of area in:	
			the wider Cairngorms	the National Park
1. Glen Doll	*Astragalus alpinus, Carex norvegica, C. rariflora, Cerastium fontanum* ssp. *scoticum*[1]*, Cicerbita alpina, Erigeron borealis, Homogyne alpina, Lychnis alpina, Oxytropis campestris, Salix lanata, Veronica fruticans, Woodsia alpina, W. ilvensis* (**13 species**)	*Alopecurus borealis, Athyrium distentifolium, A. flexile, Carex atrata, C. capillaris, C. rupestris, C. vaginata, Cochlearia micacea, Cystopteris montana, Deschampsia setacea, Dryas octopetala, Equisetum pratense, Euphrasia frigida, Hammarbya paludosa, Lycopodium annotinum, Meum athamanticum, Minuartia sedoides, Phleum alpinum, Potentilla crantzii, Pyrola rotundifolia* ssp. *rotundifolia, Sagina procumbens x saginoides, S. saginoides, S. x normaniana, Salix arbuscula, S. lapponum, S. myrsinites, S. reticulata, Sibbaldia procumbens, Veronica alpina* (**29 species**)	***	***
2. Caenlochan Glen	*Carex rariflora, Cicerbita alpina, Erigeron borealis, Gentiana nivalis, Salix lanata, Veronica fruticans, Woodsia alpina* (**7 species**)	*Alopecurus borealis, Athyrium distentifolium, Carex atrata, C. capillaris, C. rupestris, C. saxatilis, C. vaginata, Cerastium alpinum, C. cerastoides, Cochlearia micacea, Crepis mollis, Cystopteris montana, Dryas octopetala, Equisetum pratense, Euphrasia frigida, Juncus castaneus, Phleum alpinum, Poa alpina, P. glauca, Potentilla crantzii, Sagina procumbens x saginoides, S. saginoides, S. x normaniana, S. lapponum, S. myrsinites, S. reticulata, Saxifraga nivalis, Sibbaldia procumbens, Thlaspi caerulescens, Veronica alpina* (**30 species**)	***	***
3. Lochnagar	*Carex lachenalii, C. norvegica, C. rariflora, Cicerbita alpina, Poa flexuosa, Saxifraga cespitosa, S. rivularis* (**7 species**)	*Alopecurus borealis, Athyrium distentifolium, Carex vaginata, Cerastium alpinum, Gnaphalium norvegicum, Luzula arcuata, Salix lapponum, Saxifraga nivalis, Sibbaldia procumbens* (**9 species**)	***	***
4. Cairn Toul	*Carex lachenalii, C. rariflora, Poa flexuosa, Saxifraga rivularis* (**4 species**)	*Alopecurus borealis, Athyrium distentifolium, Carex atrata, C. capillaris, C. saxatilis, C. vaginata, Cerastium arcticum, C. cerastoides, Luzula arcuata, Phleum alpinum, Poa alpina, Pyrola media, Salix arbuscula, S. lapponum, S. myrsinites, Veronica alpina* (**16 species**)	***	***
5. Coire Kander & Glen Callater	*Carex norvegica, C. rariflora, Cicerbita alpina, Salix lanata* (**4 species**)	*Alopecurus borealis, Betula nana, Carex atrata, C. capillaris, C. rupestris, C. vaginata, Equisetum pratense, Juncus castaneus, Poa glauca, Sagina procumbens x saginoides, S. x normaniana, Pyrola rotundifolia* ssp. *rotundifolia, Salix lapponum, S. reticulata, Saxifraga nivalis* (**15 species**)	***	***
6. Northern Corries	*Carex lachenalii, Poa flexuosa, Saxifraga rivularis* (**3 species**)	*Alchemilla glomerulans, Alopecurus borealis, Arabis petraea, Athyrium distentifolium, Carex vaginata, Cerastium arcticum, C. cerastoides, Euphrasia frigida, Luzula arcuata, Lycopodium annotinum, Phleum alpinum, Poa alpina, P. glauca, Sibbaldia procumbens, Veronica alpina* (**15 species**)	***	***
7. Ben Macdui	*Carex lachenalii, C. rariflora, Saxifraga rivularis* (**3 species**)	*Arabis petraea, Athyrium distentifolium, Carex capillaris, C. vaginata, Cerastium arcticum, C. cerastoides, Luzula arcuata, Lycopodium annotinum, Phleum alpinum, Poa alpina, Salix lapponum, S. myrsinites, Vaccinium microcarpum, Veronica alpina* (**14 species**)	***	***
8. Coire Garbhlach	*Carex rariflora, Salix lanata*	*Alchemilla glomerulans, Alopecurus borealis, Arabis petraea, Athyrium distentifolium, Carex atrata, C. capillaris, C. rupestris, C. vaginata, Cerastium alpinum, C. arcticum, Cystopteris montana, Draba norvegica, Dryas octopetala, Equisetum pratense, Lycopodium annotinum, Minuartia sedoides, Phleum alpinum, Poa alpina, P. glauca, Potentilla crantzii, Pyrola media, Sagina procumbens x saginoides, S. saginoides, S. x normaniana, Salix lapponum, S. myrsinites, S. reticulata, Saxifraga nivalis, Sibbaldia procumbens, Veronica alpina* (**30 species**)	***	***
9. Beinn a' Ghlo	*Oxytropis campestris, Veronica fruticans*	*Alchemilla wichurae, Betula nana, Carex capillaris, C. rupestris, Cystopteris fragilis, Dryas octopetala, Equisetum pratense, Euphrasia frigida, Juncus alpinoarticulatus, Kobresia simpliciuscula, Meum athamanticum, Potamogeton filiformis, Potentilla crantzii, Salix arbuscula, S. lapponum, S. myrsinites, Schoenus ferrugineus, Sibbaldia procumbens* (**18 species**)	***	
10. Ben Avon	*Saxifraga cespitosa, S. rivularis*	*Arabis petraea, Carex atrata, Carex capillaris, C. vaginata, Cerastium arcticum, C. cerastoides, Luzula arcuata, Lycopodium annotinum, Poa alpina, Sibbaldia procumbens, Veronica alpina* (**11 species**)	***	***
11. Glas Maol	*Carex rariflora, Sagina nivalis*	*Alopecurus borealis, Carex capillaris, C. vaginata, Cochlearia micacea, Juncus castaneus, Phleum alpinum, Sagina procumbens x saginoides, S. saginoides, Sibbaldia procumbens* (**9 species**)	***	***

Area	Nationally threatened species	Nationally scarce species	% of area in:	
			the wider Cairngorms	the National Park
12. Ben Vrackie	*Astragalus alpinus, Veronica fruticans*	*Carex capillaris, C. rupestris, C. vaginata, Cerastium alpinum, Equisetum pratense, Oxytropis halleri, Potentilla crantzii, Salix arbuscula, S. myrsinites* (**9 species**)	***	
13. Braeriach	*Carex lachenalii, Saxifraga rivularis*	*Athyrium distentifolium, A. flexile, Carex vaginata, Cerastium arcticum, C. cerastoides, Dryas octopetala, Luzula arcuata, Sibbaldia procumbens* (**8 species**)	***	***
14. Insh Marshes	*Calamagrostis purpurea, Carex chordorrhiza*	*Cicuta virosa, Deschampsia setacea, Dianthus deltoides, Draba muralis, Nuphar pumila, Pilularia globulifera, Pyrola media, Ribes spicatum* (**8 species**)	***	***
15. Tulach Hill	*Lychnis viscaria, Schoenus ferrugineus*	*Carex capillaris, C. vaginata, Equisetum pratense, E. variegatum, Juncus alpinoarticulatus, Pyrola media, P. rotundifolia* ssp. *rotundifolia* (**7 species**)	***	
16. Coire Chais	*Carex rariflora, Salix lanata*	*Alopecurus borealis, Athyrium distentifolium, Carex saxatilis, Phleum alpinum, Salix lapponum* (**5 species**)	***	***
17. Cairnwell	*Astragalus alpinus, Minuartia rubella*	*Carex capillaris, C. rupestris, Dryas octopetala, Sagina saginoides* (**4 species**)	***	**
18. East Drumochter	*Carex rariflora*	*Alchemilla glomerulans, Alopecurus borealis, Athyrium distentifolium, Carex atrata, C. capillaris, C. magellanica, C. rupestris, C. saxatilis, C. vaginata, Dryas octopetala, Equisetum pratense, Lycopodium annotinum, Phleum alpinum, Pyrola media, Sagina procumbens x saginoides, S. x normaniana, Salix arbuscula, S. lapponum, S. myrsinites, Sibbaldia procumbens, Veronica alpina* (**21 species**)	***	**
19. Gaick	*Carex rariflora*	*Alopecurus borealis, Athyrium distentifolium, Carex atrata, C. vaginata, Dryas octopetala, Equisetum pratense, Euphrasia frigida, E. ostenfeldii, Sagina procumbens x saginoides, Salix lapponum, S. myrsinites, Saxifraga nivalis, Sibbaldia procumbens, Vaccinium microcarpum, Veronica alpina* (**15 species**)	***	***
20. Cairn Gorm/ Glen Avon	*Poa flexuosa*	*Alchemilla glomerulans, Arabis petraea, Athyrium distentifolium, Carex atrata, C. vaginata, Cerastium arcticum, C. cerastoides, Euphrasia frigida, Luzula arcuata, Lycopodium annotinum, Poa glauca, Salix lapponum, Veronica alpina* (**13 species**)	***	***
21. Creag an Dail	*Astragalus alpinus*	*Betula nana, Carex atrata, C. capillaris, C. rupestris, C. vaginata, Dryas octopetala, Lycopodium annotinum, Potentilla crantzii, Salix myrsinites* (**9 species**)	***	***
22. West Drumochter	*Phyllodoce caerulea*	*Betula nana, Carex capillaris, C. vaginata, Cerastium alpinum, Lycopodium annotinum, Salix arbuscula, S. lapponum, S. myrsinites, Sibbaldia procumbens* (**9 species**)	***	-
23. Abernethy Forest	*Moneses uniflora*	*Goodyera repens, Linnaea borealis, Lycopodium annotinum, Pyrola media, Ribes spicatum, Silene gallica, Vaccinium microcarpum* (**7 species**)	***	***
24. Monadhliath	*Carex rariflora*	*Alopecurus borealis, Carex vaginata, Euphrasia ostenfeldii, Lycopodium annotinum, Salix lapponum, S. myrsinites, Veronica alpina* (**7 species**)	***	***
25. Beinn a' Bhuird	*Erigeron borealis*	*Athyrium distentifolium, Cerastium cerastoides, Diphasiastrum complanatum, Phleum alpinum* (**4 species**)	***	***
26. Glen Feshie		*Alchemilla glomerulans, Athyrium distentifolium, Betula nana, Carex atrata, C. capillaris, C. vaginata, Cerastium alpinum, C. arcticum, C. cerastoides, Dryas octopetala, Euphrasia frigida, Lycopodium annotinum, Minuartia sedoides, Poa alpina, P. glauca, Sagina saginoides, Salix myrsinites, Sibbaldia procumbens, Veronica alpina* (**19 species**)	***	***
27. Inchrory/Glen Avon		*Arabis petraea, Carex capillaris, Epipactis atrorubens, Equisetum varigatum, Juncus biglumis, Linnaea borealis, Meum athamanticum, Potentilla crantzii, Ribes spicatum, Sedum villosum, Sorbus rupicola, Vaccinium microcarpum* (**12 species**)	***	***
28. Morrone Birkwood		*Carex capillaris, Cystopteris fragilis, Dianthus deltoides, Diphasiastrum complanatum, Equisetum pratense, Linnaea borealis, Meum athamanticum, Potentilla crantzii, Pyrola media, P. rotundifolia* ssp. *rotundifolia* (**10 species**)	***	***
29. Creag nan Gamhainn/ River Avon		*Arabis petraea, Carex capillaris, Crepis mollis, Epipactis atrorubens, Equisetum varigatum, Juncus balticus, Vaccinium microcarpum* (**7 species**)	***	***

[1] Glen Doll's population of the rare sub-species of Common Mouse-ear *Cerastium fontanum* ssp. *scoticum*, which is endemic to the Cairngorms area, is considered internationally as well as nationally important.

cover the upper slopes. The corries have extensive crags and screes, and the vegetation includes late-lie moss snow-beds and flushed grasslands. Notable species include: the rare Alpine Fleabane, on cliff ledges; Issler's Clubmoss, in prostrate *Calluna* heath; Alpine Lady's Fern, in screes where snow lies late in the corries; Alpine Cat's-tail, in grassland flushed from melting snow; and Starwort Mouse-ear, in late-lie snow-beds.

Recent research and survey findings

Few studies have been conducted specifically on the biology or autecology of plant species in the Cairngorms area. Those published have resulted mainly from wider studies, or from an individual's long-term interest in a particular species or site. Many relate to the Caenlochan Glen–Glen Doll area, where several studies have been published on the population biology, ecology and ecophysiology of the rarities that occur there. They include a description of the endemic sub-species of the Common Mouse-ear *Cerastium fontanum scoticum*, from the ultramafic fell-field near Meikle Kilrannoch, Caenlochan (Jalas & Sell, 1967).

Most botanical work since 1970 has consisted of vegetation surveys, or followed specific ecological or development-related objectives. However the Cairngorms are included in the national 'database' of rare species records, established by the Nature Conservancy, and updated by SNH in 1995–96. Some designated sites have been re-surveyed since.

Work carried out during the 1970s included a description of the status of Alpine Catchfly by Proctor and Johnston (1977). This was followed by a study of the population biology of the species on the ultramafic fell-field near Meikle Kilrannoch, Angus (Nagy & Proctor, 1996). They found that established plants were long-lived, and that the population size in the census areas was stable, despite high rates of clipping of flowering stems by herbivores, and a low count of surviving seeds in the soil.

Rich and Dalby (1996) studied the distribution of Mountain Scurvygrass *Cochlearia micacea* in Scotland, and verified the existence of the species on Glas Maol, Glen Callater and Caenlochan (but not at Meikle Kilrannoch, where Pyrenean Scurvygrass *Cochlearia pyrenaica* ssp. *alpina* occurs).

Marren *et al.* (1986) reported the results of repeated censuses of the Alpine Blue-sow-thistle at Lochnagar and Caenlochan. A study commissioned by SNH assessed the possible re-introduction of the species at sites from where it has been lost, and presented counts from the extant populations (Alexander, 2000). These studies have revealed large fluctuations in population sizes, attributed mainly to variation in late summer weather and to rock falls. In Scotland, grazing pressure has confined Alpine Blue-sow-thistle to rock ledges, but in Scandinavia the species occurs widely in open birch, pinewoods and scrub. Two other studies have independently reported an apparent lack of viable seeds from the Alpine Blue-sow-thistle (Cummins & Miller, 2000; Wilcock, 2002).

Rickard (1972) has described the distribution in Britain of Oblong Woodsia and Alpine Woodsia, species with their main populations in the Caenlochan NNR. Dyer *et al.* (2001) has since considered the environmental and genetic factors causing the decline of Oblong Woodsia in Britain, including its Scottish populations at Glen Doll and the Cairngorm mountains. This study concluded that surviving plants are likely to have been part of a single widespread breeding population in the past.

Cowie and Sydes (1995a) reported on the distribution and management of String Sedge at Insh Marshes. The sedge was present at many more locations than had been reported previously and this apparent expansion could be due to increasing wetness on the site following a decrease in drain maintenance. Seed production in this sedge is very sparse but vegetative regeneration is evidently adequate to maintain the expansion of its populations here. They also reported on the performance of the Brown Bog-rush at its locations on Tulach Hill and Beinn Vrackie (Cowie & Sydes, 1995b). This species occurs on wet moorland grazed by domestic stock. It was found to be surviving and regenerating successfully under a wide range of grazing pressures, including at one site where domestic stock were absent. Its largest population, however, was being suppressed by intensive grazing by sheep and horses.

Cummins and Miller (2000) investigated the role of chilling in seed germination in some high mountain species in Scotland, using material collected from Ben Vrackie, Caenlochan, Cairngorm, Glas Maol, Glen Doll, Lochnagar and elsewhere. Of the 32 species tested, the seeds of four species germinated immediately, without any requirement for chilling, although this exposes their seedlings to the full rigours of the winter climate at high altitude. Only three of the species required chilling before any of their seeds germinated, so ensuring that the seedling germinates as temperatures rise in the spring. But for the majority of the species, chilling increased the number of seeds that germinated. Surprisingly, chilling induced a deep dormancy in four species that could not be broken in the laboratory. The authors suggest that it is possible that the seeds of at least one of the species, Dwarf Willow, may have been killed by the chilling treatment, indicating that the seedlings of this species may have to survive over winter.

Kohn & Ennos (2000) examined Twinflower populations throughout Scotland, but particularly in the Cairngorm area. Their results suggest that tree density and grazing levels are likely to be the two most important factors for the management of Twinflower. This species is eliminated if the tree density is too high. After felling and thinning, the growth rate of Twinflower increases, but competition with dwarf shrubs is also enhanced. The most favourable conditions for persistence and flowering of Twinflower are likely to be where tree density is low, but grazing reduces the competitiveness of dwarf shrubs. They also examined the genetics of Twinflower populations and concluded that there are high levels of polymorphism in most populations, but that special measures may be needed to maintain isolated populations that lie outside of the Cairngorms: the heartland of the species' distribution.

Scott (2001) has conducted an experiment to test the effects of reduced Red Deer grazing on Dwarf Birch growth at Ballochbuie. This showed that Dwarf Birch could successfully recover at sites where Red Deer density does not exceed 3–4 per km².

Welch (1996) described the habitat preferences and status in north-east Scotland of the Marsh Saxifrage *Saxifraga hirculus*, an EC Habitats Directive species. He found that the species grows in *Carex rostrata–Calliergon cuspidatum* mire community (M9) and, during 1968–90, appeared to increase in numbers at Towanreef. Recovery sites for the species have recently been established in the Cairngorms area (Welch, 2002).

Trends

There is no reliable published information on trends in higher plant populations in the Cairngorms. The two national plant atlases (Perring & Walters, 1962; Preston *et al.*, 2002) provide a very valuable picture of national distributions and trends, but are not accurate at the local level because of missing data. Nationally, and on a wide regional scale, the results can be adjusted to take account of this. The lack of data is particularly acute in mountain areas, where

an ageing population of voluntary recorders is most obviously challenged. In many cases it has not been possible to determine whether the absence of recent species records from survey squares reflects a loss of species or merely a reduction in survey effort (see species accounts in Stewart *et al.*, 1994; Preston *et al.*, 2002).

Locations of known populations of nationally rare plants were collated by NC and NCC, and used as the basis for Red Data Book production (Perring & Farrell, 1983; Wigginton, 1999). This approach provides a better basis for recording change in very rare plants. However, the records from many individual sites in Scotland were not repeated for long periods, particularly where the terrain is remote and difficult. SNH instigated a rapid review of all of these known populations during 1995–97. A large number of professional and amateur recorders were asked to visit all populations, and produced a more reliable baseline for establishing future trends. For the first time, recorders were also asked to search suitable habitat in the 1 km square around known populations to discover, for instance, whether new populations had appeared, to replace any that had been lost.

Conservation issues

Grazing has been a major factor in shaping the vegetation below the treeline, particularly over the past 200 years (Table 14.4). Most grasslands and heaths in this zone are of anthropogenic origin and were derived from forest (e.g. McVean & Ratcliffe, 1962; Rodwell, 1991–2000). These landscape-scale changes are related to management and range-use by large grazers such as Red Deer, sheep and cattle (see Chapters 8 and 21).

In these deforested areas a suite of species has undergone historic range-reductions, as inferred from their present-day distributions in similar environments in Scandinavia. These are mostly the large, palatable species that grow along streamsides, and include Globeflower, Melancholy Thistle, Wood Crane's-bill, Alpine Blue-sow-thistle and Wild Angelica *Angelica sylvestris*. Today in the Cairngorms such species have largely been pushed back onto the cliffs, where their requirement for richer soils and more open conditions is met, and where large herbivores are unable to graze.

Scrub formed by willow species at or near the treeline has been all but eliminated by grazing. This vegetation type is likely to have once formed a zone above the altitudinal limit of trees, and would have been prominent in some of the higher ranges of the Cairngorms area. Now willow bushes survive only as scattered relics on cliffs, and can no longer be said to form a habitat. The most visible remnant of this scrub in Scotland is at Coire Sharroch, above Glen Doll (Chapter 7).

The impacts of grazing can be observed at different scales. Open, grazed hillsides are now dominated by a few plant species that are relatively tolerant of grazing. At the patch scale, differences in plant species composition are related to the food preferences and habits of grazers, and to the pattern of dung and urine deposition, seed dispersal and trampling effects (reviewed in Milne *et al.*, 1998).

Individual plant species respond differently to grazing pressure. Grasses grow from their base, so do not lose their meristem (the growth zone) when grazed, and are therefore well able to resist grazing. Some herbs, such as the annual Alpine Gentian, also appear to benefit from the recurrent perturbation caused by current densities of sheep and deer, which creates gaps for seedling establishment (Miller *et al.*, 1999). This probably emulates the disturbance caused by frost heave under more natural conditions. In contrast, the highly artificial exclusion of all grazing by large herbivores could be detrimental for some species. For example, it may explain the disappearance of the last population of the Hawk's-beard *Crepis multicaulis*, a low-stature herb which became extinct in northern Norway following the erection of a protective grazing exclosure around it (Alm & Often, 1997). Fortunately, the total exclusion of all large grazers is difficult to achieve even by fencing, except in very small exclosures. Studies on the Brown Bog-rush (Cowie & Sydes, 1995b) emphasise that it is not grazing *per se* that is inimitable to plants, but that the density of grazing animals in our man-managed systems can be forced above that which vulnerable species are able to tolerate.

The abandonment of grazing causes a change in vegetation, as exemplified by exclosure experiments conducted by, for example, Marrs and Welch (1991). Such changes are not a simple reversal of the effects of grazing on the original, natural vegetation. Nonetheless, woody species have recovered relatively rapidly near to seed sources, even in the montane forest zone in, for example, Austria (Cernusca, 1989), the Spanish Pyrenees (Garcia-Ruiz, 1996) and the Massif Central (André, 1998). In a similar manner, a reduction in the number of deer grazing in the Northern Corries of the Cairngorms has allowed Scots Pine seedlings to appear in the heathland there (French *et al.*, 1997). Regenerating the original herbaceous undergrowth may take much longer.

Woodland management. The pinewoods of the National Park are important for a suite of higher plants, almost entirely restricted to this habitat (Chapter 7). They include Twinflower, Intermediate Wintergreen, Common Wintergreen *Pyrola minor*, Round-leaved Wintergreen, One-flowered Wintergreen and Creeping Lady's-tresses, many populations of which have been lost. One of the greatest threats to these species has been the planting and colonisation of non-native conifers, especially Sitka Spruce *Picea sitchensis* and Norway Spruce *P. abies*. Studies on the Twinflower suggest that tall, dense stands of understorey shrubs, especially Heather, adversely affect this species (Kohn & Ennos, 2000). Management for pinewood birds, such as Black Grouse *Lyrurus tetrix* and Capercaillie *Tetrao urogallus*, has indicated that a particular combination of pine tree height and density helps Blaeberry (one of their food plants) to dominate the forest floor, rather than Heather (Moss & Piccozzi, 1994). Dominance by Blaeberry, rather than by Heather, is also likely to be preferable for rare plants. Grazing by animals at appropriate densities may have a role here in clipping shrubs and reducing their dominance (Kohn & Ennos, 2000). Dense stands of trees created artificially by fencing to encourage natural regeneration tend to shade out most plants, as they mature through the pole stage of growth.

Isolated trees in less accessible areas like this rock outcrop in Glen Doll demonstrate the modification of vegetation that has taken place on our hills below the treeline.
Photo: *N. Benvie*

The nationally scarce Creeping Lady's-tresses Goodyera repens *occurs mostly in pinewoods, including Abernethy Forest.*

Photo: *L. Gill*

Table 14.4. The main effects of grazing and grazing-related impacts on biodiversity.

Initial vegetation	Grazing-derived vegetation	Impact
Above the treeline		
Moss heath	Grass heath, sedge heath	• Loss of cryptogams
Prostrate dwarf-shrub	Bare ground, parent material	• Loss of vegetation cover
		• Erosion of soil
Below the treeline		
Woodland	Scrub, heathland, grassland	• Reduced structural diversity at the landscape and habitat levels
		• Reduced habitat diversity for invertebrates, vertebrates and epiphytes
		• A transient decrease in slope stability
Scrub	Heathland, grassland	• As for woodland
Heathland	Grassland	• As for woodland, but at a reduced rate

Recreation. In the past, the most significant impact of recreational activities on rare higher plants was from those botanists who studied and collected them. Today, this is of negligible concern as botanists have become aware of the potential impact of their hobby on the objects of their affection. More usual recreational impacts have little effect on overall vascular plant populations. Damage to vascular plants from trampling by hill walkers, for instance, is mainly restricted to areas affected by regular footpaths and viewpoints. The resulting soil erosion may be very visible but rarely directly affects threatened plants species. The few populations that are directly threatened might be protected by minor footpath diversions, although the areas concerned are hazardous for remedial work.

One potential area of conflict is rock climbing. In England and Wales, climbing is considered a threat to rare plant populations but there is currently no evidence of it having a significant impact on plant populations in Scotland. Partly this is because vegetated cliffs and base-rich sites consisting of friable rock are less popular. Scottish sites with rare plants that are climbed in winter are covered then by a protective layer of ice and snow which provides protection. However, climate change may weaken the defence provided by snow and ice.

Climate change. The Intergovernmental Panel on Climate Change (IPCC) has predicted a temperature rise in the Cairngorms of 1.5°C, or possibly 2°C, by 2050 (Chapter 20). A rise of approximately 2–4°C is predicted by 2100 (IPCC, 2001), accompanied by increased precipitation and storminess[4]. To date, predicted impacts of climate change on alpine plants have been derived largely from computer models and informed speculation. A model based on a Europe-wide survey of moutain summits in alpine regions, for example, has predicted that a temperature increase of 1.8°C by 2100 would cause all alpine plant species to disappear from the Cairngorms (Gottfried *et al.*, unpublished ms.).

At the moment, such predictions are still based on less than adequate information. The Scots Pine indicates how complex the situation can be, especially with the addition of our own effects on natural habitats. Currently, Scots Pine woodlands are mainly restricted to lower altitudes in the Cairngorms, although this restriction is because it has been eliminated from much of its natural range by felling and deer grazing. Where grazing pressure has been reduced, changes in this restriction are now taking place (French *et al.*, 1997). The loss of Scots Pine from most of Britain prior to human intervention strongly suggests that rising temperatures should soon make low-lying areas in the Cairngorms less suitable for pine. However, when Scots Pine was reintroduced by man to southern England it thrived and spread, although this area was apparently outside the climatic envelope of the species. Presumably this is because the deciduous woodlands that excluded the pine had become modified, fragmented and replaced by heathland as a result of subsequent human management. Thus, our management of pinewoods and the heathlands around them in the Cairngorms might also offset the expected effects of climate change on this species.

This lesson from the Scots Pine may be applicable to our threatened vascular plants. We may be able to modify their vulnerability to change by appropriate management. We could attempt to directly modify their ability to move to new locations. Those species already restricted to locations near the upper part of our mountains, such as Tufted Saxifrage, have almost no potential to move to new locations at higher altitude, although they may have a limited potential to move to new locations on cooler aspects. Other species restricted to a mid-altitude zone, such as Blue Heath, may have the potential to move upwards. In the case of Blue Heath the move would be tosnow-beds that are melting out earlier than in the past, and so providing an adequate growing season, with continuing winter protection fromsevere frost. However, the relatively

low seed rain that existing small populations can produce makes this unassisted move unlikely and the direct management required to enable Blue Heath to colonise new areas would be unpopular with most botanists.

Small populations are likely to have little resilience to survive *in situ* through a period of change. Those species whose populations that have been reduced and fragmented by grazing are more vulnerable than they might otherwise be. Managing the Cairngorms to enable vascular plant populations to attain their maximum potential would give our mountain plants their greatest chance of surviving in the face of change.

References

Alexander, L. (2000). *Feasibility on recovery of Alpine Blue Sow Thistle* Cicerbita alpina *1998–2000*. Report to SNH. SNH: Perth.

Alm, T. & Often, A. (1997). Species conservation and local people in E Finnmark, Norway. *Plant Talk* 11: 30–31.

André, M.-F. (1998). Depopulation, land-use change and landscape transformation in the French Massif Central. *Ambio* 27: 35–353.

Anonymous (1944). *Report of the Committee on Hill Sheep Farming in Scotland*. HMSO: Edinburgh.

Averis, A., Averis, B., Birks, J., Horsfield, D., Thompson, D. & Yeo, M. (2004). *An Illustrated Guide to British Upland Vegetation*. JNCC: Peterborough.

Barber, D.C., Dyke, A., Hillaire-Marcel, C., Jennings, A.E., Andrews, J.T., Kerwin, M.W., Bilodeau, G., Mcneely, R., Southon, J., Morehead M.D. & Gagnon J.-M. (1999). Forcing of the cold event of 8,200 years ago by catastrophic drainage of Laurentide lakes. *Nature* 400: 344–348.

Birks, H.J.B. (1997). Scottish biodiversity in a historical context. In: Fleming, L.V., Newton, A.C., Vickery, J.A. & Usher, M.B. (eds.), *Biodiversity in Scotland: Status, Trends and Initiatives*. The Stationery Office: Edinburgh. pp. 21–35.

Birks, H.J.B. (1988). Long-term ecological change in the British uplands. In: Usher, M.B., Thompson, D.B.A. (eds.), *Ecological Change in the Uplands*. Blackwell: Oxford. pp. 37–56.

Cernusca, A. (1989). Ökosystemforschung in den österreichischen Zentralalpen (Hohe Tauern). In: Cernusca, A. (ed.), *Struktur und Funktion von Graslandökosystemen im Nationalpark Hohe Tauern*. Veröff österr MaB-Programme 13. University of Verlag Wagner, Innsbruck. pp. 549–568.

[4] An alternative scenario suggests that the pattern of warming may be reversed in NW Europe, if increased melt water from the Greenland ice cap causes the North Atlantic Drift to shut down (Barber *et al.*, 1999; Clark *et al.*, 2002).

Clark, P.U., Pisias, N.G., Stocker T.F. & Weaver, A.J. (2002). The role of the thermohaline circulation in abrupt climate change. *Nature* 415: 863–869.

Cowie, N.R & Sydes, C. (1995a). *Status, distribution, ecology & management of String Sedge* Carex chordorrhiza. SNH Review No. 41. SNH: Perth.

Cowie, N.R & Sydes, C. (1995b). *Status, distribution, ecology & management of Brown Bog-rush* Schoenus ferrugineus. SNH Review No. 43. SNH: Perth.

Cummins, R.P. & Miller, G.R. (2000). The role of chilling in the germination of some Scottish montane species. *Botanical Journal of Scotland* 52: 171–185.

Darling, F.F. (1955). *West Highland Survey*. Oxford University Press: Oxford.

Dendaletche, C. (1974). *Guide du Naturaliste dans les Pyrénées occidentales. Hautes Montagnes*. Delachaux & Niestlé: Neuchâtel.

Dyer, A., Lindsay, S. & Lusby, P. (2001). The fall and rise of the Oblong woodsia in Britain. *Botanical Journal of Scotland* 53: 107–120.

Ellenberg, H. (1991). Zeigerwerte von Pflanzen in Mitteleuropa. *Scripta Geobotanica* 18: 1–248.

French, D.D., Miller, G.R. & Cummins, R.P. (1997). Recent development of high-altitude *Pinus sylvestris* scrub in the Northern Cairngorm mountains, Scotland. *Biological Conservation* 79: 133–144.

Garcia-Ruiz, J.M., Lasanta, T., Ruiz-Flano, P., Ortigosa, L., White, S., Gonzalez, C. & Marti, C. (1996). Land-use changes and sustainable development in mountain areas: A case study in the Spanish Pyrenees. *Landscape Ecology* 11: 267–277.

Gottfried, M., Pauli, H., Nagy, L., Hohenwallner, D., Reiter, K., Klettner, C., Akhalkatsi, M., Barancok, P., Bayfield, N., Benito, J-L., Borel, J-L., Brooker, R.W., Coldea, G., Erschbamer, B., Geslin, J., Ghosn, D.R., Holten, J.I., Kanka, R., Kazakis, G., Larsson, P., Merzouki, A., Michelsen, O., Moiseev, P., Molau, U., Molero Mesa, J., Nakhutsrishvili, G., Pelino, G., Puscas, M., Rossi, G., Shiyatov, S., Stanisci, A., Theurillat, J.-P., Tomaselli, M., Unterluggauer, P., Villar, L., Vittoz, P. & Grabherr, G. (unpublished ms). *Quantifying warming-related extinction risks for Europe's mountain plants*. Report of the GLORIA-EUROPE coordination group, Institute of Ecology and Conservation Biology, University of Vienna.

Green, J. (1990). The distribution and management of grasslands in the British Isles. In: Breymeyer, A. (ed.), *Managed Grasslands*. Elsevier: Amsterdam. pp. 15–35.

Hill, M.O., Carey, P.D., French, D.D., Scott, D. & Welch, D. (1996). Low species richness of the Cairngorms site. Final Report, CEC Programme 'Environment' 1991–1994. *Effects of rapid climatic change on plant biodiversity in boreal and montane ecosystems*. ITE: Monks Wood and Banchory.

Hill, M.O., Mountford, J.O., Roy, D.B. & Bunce, R.G.H. (1999). *Ellenberg's indicator values for British plants*. ECOFACT Vol. 2. Technical Index. ITE & DEFRA.

Hughes, J. & Huntley, B. (1988). Upland hay meadows in Britain – their vegetation, management and future. In: Birks, H., Birks, H.J.B. *et al.* (eds.), *The Cultural Landscape. Past, Present and Future*. Cambridge University Press: Cambridge. pp. 91–110.

Huntley, B. (1979). The past and present vegetation of the Caenlochan National Nature Reserve, Scotland. I. Present vegetation. *New Phytologist* 53: 215–283.

Huntley, B. (1981) The past and present vegetation of the Caenlochan National Nature Reserve, Scotland. II. Palaeoecological investigations. *New Phytologist* 87: 189–222.

IPCC (2001). *Climate change 2001: synthesis report. A contribution to Working Group I, II, and III to the Third Assessment Report of the Intergovernmental Panel on Climate Change*. Cambridge University Press: Cambridge.

Jalas, J. & Sell, P.D. (1967). Taxonomic and nomenclatural notes on the British flora. *Watsonia* 6: 292–294.

Jeník, J. (1998). Biodiversity of the Hercynian Mountains in Central Europe. *Pirineos* 151–152: 83–99.

Kohn, D. & Ennos, R. (2000). *Action Plan Research on Twinflower*. Unpublished report to SNH.

Marren, P.R., Payne, A.G. & Randall, R.E. (1986). The past and present status of *Cicerbita alpina* (L.) Wallr. in Britain. *Journal of the Botanical Society of the British Isles* 16: 131–142.

Marrs, R.H. & Welch, D. (1991). *Moorland wilderness: the potential effects of removing domestic livestock, particularly sheep*. ITE: Abbots Ripton.

McHaffie, H.S., Legg, C.J. & Ennos, R.A. (2001). A single gene with pleiotropic effects accounts for the Scottish endemic taxon *Athyrium distentifolium* var. flexile. *New Phytologist* 152: 491–500.

McVean, D.N. & Ratcliffe, D.A. (1962). *Plant Communities of the Scottish Highlands*. Nature Conservancy Monograph No.1. The Stationery Office: Edinburgh.

McConnell, J. (1996). *The history of the* Pinus sylvestris *treeline at Creag Fhiaclach, Inverness-shire*. Ph.D. Thesis, University of Edinburgh.

Miller, G.R., Geddes, C. & Mardon, D.K. (1999). Response of the alpine gentian *Gentiana nivalis* L. to protection from grazing by sheep. *Biological Conservation* 87: 311–318.

Milne, J.A., Birch, C.P.D., Hester, A.J., Armstrong, H.M. & Robertson, A. (1998). The impact of vertebrate herbivores on the natural heritage of the Scottish uplands – a review. MLURI: Aberdeen.

Moss, R. & Picozzi, N. (1994). *Management of forests for capercaillie in Scotland*. Forestry Commission Bulletin 113. HMSO: London.

Nagy, L. & Proctor, J. (1996). The demography of *Lychnis alpina* L. at the Meikle Kilrannoch Ultramafic Outcrops, Angus, Scotland. *Journal of the Botanical Society of Scotland* 48: 155–166.

Nagy, L. & Proctor, J. (1997a). Soil Mg and Ni as causal factors of plant occurrence and distribution at the Meikle Kilrannoch ultramafic site in Scotland. *New Phytologist* 135: 561–566.

Nagy, L. & Proctor, J. (1997b). Plant growth and reproduction on a toxic alpine ultramafic soil: adaptation to nutrient limitation. *New Phytologist* 137: 267–274.

Nagy, L. & Proctor, J. (2001). The effects of different concentrations of available iron and nickel on the growth of *Cochlearia pyrenaica* ssp. *alpina* of ultramafic and non-ultramafic origin and of *C. officinalis*. *South African Journal of Science* 97: 586–590.

O'Sullivan, P.E. (1974). Two Flandrian pollen diagrams for east-central Scotland. *Pollen et Spores* 16: 33–57.

Ozenda, P. (1994). *La végétation du continent européen.* Delachaux et Niestle: Lausanne.

Payne, A.G. (1999). *Gnaphalium norvegicum.* In: Wigginton, M.J. (ed.) (1999), *British Red Data Books. 1. Vascular Plants.* Third edition. JNCC: Peterborough.

Perring, F.H. & Farrell, L. (1983). *British Red Data Books: Vascular Plants, 2nd edition.* RSNC: Lincoln.

Perring, F.H. & Walters, S.M. (1962). *Atlas of the British Flora.* Thomas Nelson: London.

Preston, C.D., Pearman, D.A. & Dines, T.D. (2002). *New Atlas of the British and Irish Flora.* Oxford: Oxford University Press.

Proctor, J. & Johnston, W.R. (1977). *Lychnis alpina* L. in Britain. *Watsonia* 11: 199.

Proctor, J., Bartlem, K., Carter, S.P., Dare, D.A., Jarvis, S.B. & Slingsby, D.R. (1991). Vegetation and soils of the Meikle Kilrannoch ultramafic sites. *Botanical Journal of Scotland* 46: 47–64.

Ratcliffe, R.D. (1974). The vegetation. In: Nethersole-Thomson, D. & Watson, A., *The Cairngorms: Their Natural History and Scenery.* Collins: London. pp. 42–82.

Ratcliffe, R.D. (1991). The mountain flora of Britain and Ireland. *British Wildlife* 3: 1–21.

Raven, J. & Walters, M. (1956). *Mountain Flowers.* Collins: London.

Rich, T.C.G. & Dalby, D.H. (1996). The Status and Distribution of Mountain Scurvy-Grass (*Cochlearia micacea* Marshall) in Scotland, with ecological notes. *Botanical Journal of Scotland* 48: 187–198.

Rickard, M.H. (1972). The distribution of *Woodsia ilvensis* and *Woodsia alpina* in Britain. *British Fern Gazette* 10: 269–280.

Rodwell, J.S. (ed.) (1991–2000). *British Plant Communities. Vols. 1–5.* Cambridge University Press: Cambridge.

Scott, D. (2001). Recovery of dwarf birch (*Betula nana*) population following reduction in grazing by red deer (*Cervus elaphus*). *Botanical Journal of Scotland* 53: 155–167.

Stace, C. (1991). *New Flora of the British Isles.* Cambridge University Press: Cambridge.

Stewart, A., Preston, C.D. & Pearman, D.A. (1994). *Scarce Plants in Britain.* JNCC: Peterborough.

Sydes, C. (1997). Vascular plant biodiversity in Scotland. In: Fleming, L.V., Newton, A.C., Vickery, J.A. & Usher, M.B. (eds.), *Biodiversity in Scotland: Status, Trends and Initiatives.* The Stationery Office: Edinburgh. pp. 89–103.

Virtanen, R., Dirnböck, T., Dullinger, S., Grabherr, G., Pauli, H., Staudinger, M. & Villar, L. (2003). Patterns in the plant species richness of European high mountain vegetation In: Nagy, L., Grabherr, G., Körner, C. & Thompson, D.B.A. *Alpine Biodiversity in Europe.* Ecological Studies 167. Springer Verlag: Heidelberg. pp. 149–172.

Walker, J. (1808). *An economical history of the Hebrides and the Highlands of Scotland.* University Press: Edinburgh.

Walker, M.J.C. (1984). A pollen diagram from St-Kilda, Outer Hebrides, Scotland. *New Phytologist* 97: 99–113.

Watson, A. (1983). Eighteenth century deer numbers and pine regeneration near Braemar, Scotland. *Biological Conservation* 25: 289–305.

Welch, D. (1996). Habitat preferences and status of *Saxifraga hirculus* L. in north-east Scotland. *Botanical Journal of Scotland* 48: 177–186.

Welch, D. (2002). The establishment of recovery sites for *Saxifraga hirculus* L. in NE Scotland. *Botanical Journal of Scotland* 54: 75–88.

Wilcock, C.C. (2002). Maintenance and recovery of rare clonal plants: the case of twinflower (*Linnea borealis* L.). *Botanical Journal of Scotland* 54: 121–131.

Wigginton, M.J. (ed.) (1999). *British Red Data Books. 1. Vascular Plants.* Third edition. JNCC: Peterborough.

15. INVERTEBRATES

Graham E. Rotheray and David Horsfield

Introduction

The Cairngorms area is one of the most important in the UK for invertebrates, with a striking preponderance of northern, boreal and montane species. The area also holds isolated populations of species that have their main population further south in the UK. Although invertebrates are among the least known of all taxa, and current knowledge is biased in favour of insects, over 370 species have been found for which the Cairngorms appear to be at least nationally important[1]. Within the UK, 92 species, mostly true flies (Diptera), are apparently confined to the National Park. In Scotland, no other area is known to hold such a high concentration of rare or threatened species.

Important Species for which the Cairngorms area is considered important include 37 BAP priority species, such as the Aspen hoverfly *Hammerschmidtia ferruginea*, confined to just 12 sites, nine of which occur in Cairngorms National Park. The pine hoverfly *Blera fallax* has an even more restricted range, being confined to just two sites in the UK, both within the National Park (Rotheray & MacGowan, 2000). There are also important populations of the internationally important Freshwater Pearl Mussel *Margaritifera margaritifera*. Scotland's only two sites for the Dark Bordered Beauty moth *Epione vespertaria* occur in Cairngorms National Park, a species of moth also occurring rarely in northern England. The National Park also has the only sites in the UK for the rare leaf-mining moth *Callisto coffeella*, and the only recent record in Scotland of the bee *Andrena marginata*, which is otherwise found only in southern England.

The reasons why so many important species are found in the Cairngorms area are poorly understood, but must reflect the biogeographical pattern of colonisation following the retreat of the ice sheet 10,000 years ago and the quality, quantity and continuity of suitable habitat. For invertebrates, the most important habitats are montane and upland areas, stands of Aspen *Populus tremula*, birch *Betula* and Scots Pine *Pinus sylvestris* woodlands, and freshwater habitats, such as river shingle. In the UK, some of the most extensive examples of these habitats occur within the Cairngorms.

The importance and significance of the Cairngorms for invertebrates must be viewed in context. In comparison with the rest of the UK, invertebrates in Scotland have been relatively neglected (Rotheray, 1996). The reasons for this are diverse, but include the fact that Scottish-based invertebrate biologists have been few in number and are struggling to cope with a fauna of 20,000 or more species. As a result, Scotland has many species and geographical areas for which there is a paucity of records. Furthermore, in many parts of Scotland poor access and climate have deterred entomologists and other invertebrate biologists, who have concentrated mainly on accessible localities and taxa.

These constraints should be borne in mind when assessing records of Scottish invertebrates, including those of the Cairngorms area, which was little-visited until the development of the railway link at the end of the 19th century. With this improvement in accessibility, localities such as Aviemore, Nethy Bridge, Cairn Gorm and certain northern corries became well known for their apparently unique assemblages of northern and montane species, rich in rarities. Welch (1974) provided the first substantial review of the Cairngorms' invertebrate fauna, noting that these localities had become subject to much repeat visiting, while adjacent areas were neglected. In their review of the area's insect fauna, Young and Watt (2002) have compiled a first, provisional list of rare and notable insects of the area, and noted a continued bias in recording effort, such that the hills south of the Feshie and the Geldie Burn had still barely been explored entomologically.

Scottish invertebrates have a particular significance within the UK and elsewhere in Europe. Waves of species have colonised Scotland following

---

The nationally threatened White-faced Darter Leucorrhinia dubia*; one of three important dragonfly species found around lochs and bog pools in the Cairngorms area.*

Photo: *L. Campbell / SNH*

Rotheray, G.E. & Horsfield, D. (2006). Invertebrates. In: Shaw, P. & Thompson, D.B.A. (eds.). *The Nature of the Cairngorms: Diversity in a changing environment.* The Stationery Office. pp. 243-267.

---

[1] Species with at least 10% of their UK range or population occurring in the area; or classed as Nationally Rare (occurring in fewer than 16 10-km squares in the UK); or nationally threatened; or whose presence in the Cairngorms is considered to be of international importance.

changes in climate, topography and vegetation ever since the retreat of the ice sheet (Rotheray, 1996). Given the extent of upland and montane habitats that exist in Scotland, it is not surprising that these areas have been colonised by cold-adapted invertebrates that are essentially boreal in distribution elsewhere in their range. Conversely, such upland areas may have restricted the spread of other types of invertebrates. Crowson (1961), for example, discusses the barrier effect of the Southern Uplands with respect to dispersal by woodland beetles, suggesting that the major dispersal route for such groups is likely to have been along the corridors of the east and west coastlines.

Assuming that invertebrates frequently colonised Scotland via coastlines, river valleys such as those of the Clyde, Dee, Forth, Tay and Spey are particularly important in providing access for dispersing individuals to penetrate inland. Along such valleys a mosaic of climatic conditions, environmental features and habitats often exist, from lowland to highland, nowhere more so in the Cairngorms area than along the Spey. In such areas, invertebrates with widely varying tolerances and environmental preferences can exist in relatively close proximity, reflecting the diversity of circumstances and conditions present. This provides a biogeographical explanation for the Cairngorms being rich in biodiversity, in addition to any bias introduced by the repeated recording noted above.

An additional feature of areas like the Cairngorms is their relative isolation, which has particular consequences for invertebrates. Many populations, being isolated by geography and climate, have evolved into distinctive races and forms. The extent of race formation in Cairngorms' invertebrates has barely been assessed, but it gives them a particular value. Race formation is best known in Lepidoptera (Thompson, 1980). It may involve little more than a change in colour, such that populations can be individually recognised, but can also involve other characteristics, such as the number of generations produced annually, or a dependence on certain food plants. Such differentiation has reached the level of speciation in some groups. This is best known in certain woodland Diptera, in which individual species formerly considered widespread and common in the UK have, on detailed study, been found to consist of different species (Rotheray *et al.*, 2001). There is, for example, a common, widespread species of lance fly, *Lonchaea peregrina* (Diptera, Lonchaeidae), which breeds under the bark of fallen trees and branches. In central and northern Scotland and the Cairngorms it is replaced by a closely related species, *L. hackmani*, which was only discovered in Britain in 2000 and is essentially boreal in its European distribution (MacGowan & Rotheray, 2000). Another example is the fly *Ectaetia clavipes* (Diptera, Scatopsidae), which also breeds in dead wood, and is replaced in the Cairngorms by *E. christii*. This new species has only recently been recognised, and appears to be confined to boreal woodlands (Rotheray & Horsfield, 1997). The extent to which the biodiversity of Cairngorms' invertebrates has been underestimated by such factors is unclear, and the potential for discovering new, unrecognised invertebrate species is probably higher in the Cairngorms than in many other parts of the UK.

Important species and areas

Thirty-seven BAP priority invertebrate species are found in the Cairngorms area, together with 340 other important invertebrate species. Ninety-two species are apparently confined to Cairngorms National Park within the UK (Table 15.1). Many of these species are poorly documented, however. Trend and status data, for example, are missing for the vast majority of the species in Table 15.1, and many are known from fewer than 15 records, which are often more than 20 years old. Lack of relevant data is reflected in the relatively high proportion of species for which basic details, such as specific habitat requirements, are either unknown or questionable. In consequence, more than a third of species in Table 15.1 are considered to be of 'data-deficient' status. Furthermore, the level of recording across invertebrate groups is very uneven. Leaving aside such 'difficult' groups as the microbes, mites and nematode worms, for which techniques of biodiversity assessment have barely been developed, several other groups are also relatively unknown. For example, distribution data for species from the largest group of Hymenoptera, the parasitoids, is rudimentary, both in the Cairngorms and in the UK as a whole. This is because basic species taxonomy is poorly developed (Shaw, 1996). Undoubtedly, many rare, endangered and biologically important parasitic Hymenoptera species await discovery in the Cairngorms area. The same considerations apply to other poorly known groups, such as the cecidomyiids (Diptera) and staphylinids (Coleoptera).

The poor state of knowledge of Cairngorms' invertebrates means that their true status has yet to be determined. Also, the selection of invertebrate species in the BAP process has been somewhat arbitrary, and species in the more 'popular' groups have received greater attention. Thus, in addition to two forest-dependent hoverflies (the pine hoverfly *Blera fallax* and the Aspen hoverfly *Hammerschmidtia ferruginea*), BAP priority species in the Cairngorms area include only five additional species of true fly, six species of beetle, 11 species of moth or butterfly, seven species of bee, wasp and ant, one species each of spider, mayfly and stonefly, and three species of mollusc; two whorl snails and the Freshwater Pearl Mussel (Table 15.1).

Under the EC Habitats Directive, the Freshwater Pearl Mussel is a qualifying interest in three Special Areas of Conservation in the Cairngorms area: the rivers Spey, Dee and South Esk. Recent surveys have found that the River Spey supports one of the largest remaining Freshwater Pearl Mussel populations in the world (Young *et al.,* 2001), while the River Dee also supports a large and important population (Cosgrove *et al.,* 2004). Freshwater Pearl Mussels are also present in reaches of the River South Esk (Young Associates, 2003), and efforts are underway to improve local conditions in Glen Clova for both the mussel and its host salmonid species.

There are 29 Endangered or Critically Endangered invertebrate species apparently confined to the National Park. Of these, only one is currently included in the UK BAP. Nineteen of these species are associated with woodlands, six with river margins and water bodies and three with peatland or montane habitats, while the habitat of one species is unknown. The number of Endangered and Critically Endangered species confined to the National Park is undoubtedly an underestimate, and additional threatened species are likely to be found. Some species have no Red Data Book (RDB) status, but have declined in the UK in recent decades, especially in England and Wales, leaving areas like the Cairngorms as strongholds. Examples are three species of bumble-bee (*Bombus monticola*, *B. muscorum* and *B. soroeensis*), all of which are proposed for inclusion as BAP priority species.

Lack of data also affects consideration of important areas for invertebrates within the Cairngorms. Table 15.2 shows the number of species recorded from 22 such areas. Much of the locality data available are imprecise, however. Collectors often used general locations on labels associated with captured specimens, such as 'Nethy Bridge' or 'Aviemore', even though captures were made over a much broader area. In consequence, 79 important species, of which 24 are BAP priority and/or red-listed (Critically Endangered or Endangered; Table 15.2), have been collected in 'Strathspey', although precise locations seem to be unknown. Data giving precise locations of captures of these species along the strath have not been traced during this assessment, and in some cases may not be available. A search through museum collections, diaries, collectors' notebooks, and consultation with collectors, may help resolve some of this uncertainty. Nonetheless, the data suggest that these 22 areas are particularly important in terms of the number of important, BAP priority or red-listed

species present (Figure 15.1). Note, however, that many of the records used to identify these areas are more than 50 years old, and surveys have not been repeated. This applies particularly to the following areas: Craigellachie to Aviemore and Coylumbridge, Deeside from Linn of Dee to Aboyne, Abernethy, Grantown-on-Spey, and Loch an Eilein to Rothiemurchus.

1. Craigellachie to Aviemore and Coylumbridge. Here, 106 important species have been recorded, of which 32 are BAP priority or RDB species (Table 15.2). Note, however, that the area has undergone a great deal of change over the past 50 years, associated with the growth of Aviemore, so the continued presence of many important species requires confirmation. Many of these are probably associated with woodlands, such as the birch woodland at Craigellachie NNR, to the north of Aviemore. Here, birch is growing in a variety of circumstances, from relatively dry, steep slopes to wet and boggy areas, and dead wood is common. These features undoubtedly add to the invertebrate importance of the area. It is home to the Rannoch Sprawler *Brachionycha nubeculosa*, a moth associated with mature birch trees in long-established birch woodland, as well as the tortrix moth *Ancylis tineana*, associated with low-growing birch

The Bilberry Bumble-bee Bombus monticola *is one of three bumble-bee species in the Cairngorms area proposed for inclusion as BAP priority species. These have declined elsewhere in Britain in recent decades, leaving areas like the Cairngorms a stronghold.*

Photo: *T. Benton*

Table 15.1. Invertebrate species whose populations in the Cairngorms are of at least national importance. Species are listed in order of habitat, and then alphabetically by Order and Family. Notable areas outside of the National Park, but within the wider Cairngorms area, are identified.

Nationally Rare:	Recorded from 1–15 10-km squares in the UK.
RDB:	National Red Data Book status. EX = Extinct; CR = Critically endangered; EN = Endangered; VU = Vulnerable; DD = Data Deficient; LC = Least Concern (from Shirt, 1987; Falk, 1991; Hyman & Parsons, 1992, 1994).
BAP:	Biodiversity Action Plan: P = Priority species; S = Species Statement.
WCA:	Protected under Schedule 8 of the 1981 Wildlife & Countryside Act
Percentage of UK range:	The percentage of the species' UK range (in 10-km squares) occurring in the Cairngorms area or in the National Park: *** >75%; ** 25–75%; * 10–24%; '-' <10%
Habitat:	Doubt over the species' specific habitat indicated by '(?)'.

Habitat	Taxon (Order, Family, Species)		Status				% of UK range in:		Confined to NP?	Notable areas outside of National Park
			Nationally rare	RDB	BAP	WCA	Cairngorms area	National Park		
Wetland:	Soils(?)	Coleoptera, Carabidae		VU			*	*		
	Marshes, rivers: decaying vegetation	Coleoptera, Staphylinidae		VU			*	*		
	Moss	Coleoptera, Staphylinidae	Y	DD			**	**		
	Unknown	Diptera, Hybotidae	Y	EN			**	**		
	Meadows and marshes: leaf litter(?)	Diptera, Lauxaniidae		VU			**	**		
	Eutrophic marsh and fen: decaying vegetation(?)	Diptera, Limonidae	Y	VU			***	***	Y	
	Marshes and bogs: decaying vegetation(?)	Diptera, Limonidae	Y	VU			***	***	Y	
	Marshes and bogs: decaying vegetation(?)	Diptera, Limonidae	Y	DD			**	***	Y	
	Marshes: unknown	Diptera, Mycetophilidae	Y	DD			***	***	Y	
	Marshes, rivers: phytophagous(?)	Diptera, Psilidae		VU			**	**		
	Marshes, rivers: unknown	Diptera, Scathophagidae	Y	DD			***	***	Y	
	Marshes, rivers: unknown	Diptera, Scathophagidae	Y	DD			***	***	Y	
	Marshes, rivers: unknown	Diptera, Scathophagidae	Y	DD			***	***	Y	
	Marshes: parasitoid of snails	Diptera, Sciomyzidae	Y	DD			**	**		
	Marshes: homopteran predator	Diptera, Syrphidae	Y	EN			**	**		
	Fens, damp grassland: stem gall in Sneezewort	Diptera, Tephritidae		DD			**	**		
	Larva in moss and peat	Diptera, Tipulidae		VU			**	**		
		Hemiptera, Aphididae	Y	DD			***	***	Y	
	Plant-feeder	Hemiptera, Delphacidae		DD			**	**		
Water bodies	Lochs: sandy margins	Arachnida, Dictynidae	Y	VU			**	**		
	Banks and margins	Coleoptera, Carabidae	Y	VU	S		**	**		
	Aquatic plants	Coleoptera, Chrysomelidae	Y	VU	P		**	**		
	Rivers and streams: predator of aphids on marginal vegetation	Coleoptera, Coccinellidae		VU			**	**		
	Marginal vegetation/tree holes	Coleoptera, Dytiscidae	Y	DD			***	***	Y	
	Rivers: shingle	Coleoptera, Elateridae	Y	VU			**	**		
	Rivers: shingle	Coleoptera, Elateridae		VU			*	*		
	Rivers(?): shingle(?)	Coleoptera, Staphylinidae		DD			**	**		
	Rivers: sand and mud	Coleoptera, Staphylinidae	Y	DD			***	***	Y	
	Rivers: sand and mud	Coleoptera, Staphylinidae		DD			**	**		

Taxon species names (italic): *Pelophila borealis*, *Aleochara brevipennis*, *Hygropora cunctans*, *Platypalpus pygmaeus*, *Minettia flaviventris*, *Erioptera sordida*, *Limonia consimilis*, *Pilaria decolor*, *Rymosia speyae* n. sp., *Chamaepsila clunalis*, *Cordilura similis*, *Microprosopa pallidicauda*, *Scathophaga pictipennis*, *Anticheta analis*, *Sphaerophoria loewi*, *Campiglossa argyrocephala*, *Prionocera pubescens*, *Macrosiphum scoticum*, *Paraliburnia litoralis*, *Dictyna major*, *Dyschirius angustatus*, *Donacia aquatica*, *Coccinella quinquepunctata*, *Agabus wasastjernae*, *Negastrius pulchellus*, *Negastrius sabulicola*, *Atheta sylvicola*, *Bledius arcticus*, *Bledius terebrans*

Habitat	Taxon (Order, Family, Species)		Status				% of UK range in:		Confined to NP?	Notable areas outside of National Park
			Nationally rare	RDB	BAP	WCA	Cairngorms area	National Park		
Water bodies	Rivers: sand	Coleoptera, Staphylinidae	*Hydrosmecta delicatula*		DD			**	**		
	Rivers: shingle and sand	Coleoptera, Staphylinidae	*Lathrobium dilutum*	Y	VU			**	**		
	Rivers: shingle	Coleoptera, Staphylinidae	*Scopaeus gracilis*	Y	DD			**	**		
	Rivers & streams – sand and shingle	Coleoptera, Staphylinidae	*Stenus incanus*	Y	DD			**	**		
	Rivers & streams – sand and shingle	Coleoptera, Staphylinidae	*Tachyusa scitula*		DD			**	*		
	Rivers & streams – sand and shingle	Coleoptera, Staphylinidae	*Thinobius major*	Y	DD			**	**		
	Rivers & streams – sand and shingle	Coleoptera, Staphylinidae	*Thinobius newberyi*		DD	P		**	**		
	River marshes: phytophagous(?)	Diptera, Chloropidae	*Melanum fumipenne*	Y	DD			***	***	Y	
	Unknown	Diptera, Culicidae	*Culiseta alaskaensis*	Y	DD			**	**		
	Rivers: shingle(?)	Diptera, Dolichopodidae	*Hercostomus sahlbergi*	Y	EN			***	***	Y	
	Rivers: shingle(?)	Diptera, Empididae	*Heleodromia irwini*	Y	EN			***	***	Y	
	Unknown	Diptera, Empididae	*Hilara barbipes*	Y	VU			***	***	Y	
	Unknown	Diptera, Empididae	*Hilara hirta*	Y	DD			***	***	Y	
	River margins: shingle	Diptera, Empididae	*Hilara medeteriformis*	Y	VU			**	**		
	Rivers: shingle	Diptera, Empididae	*Hilara setosa*		LC			**	**		
	Unknown	Diptera, Empididae	*Hilara submaura*	Y	EN			***	***	Y	
	River margins & marshes: unknown	Diptera, Empididae	*Rhamphomyia trigemina*	Y	DD			***	***	Y	
	Unknown	Diptera, Empididae	*Wiedemannia phantasma*	Y	DD			**	**		
	Rivers: shingle	Diptera, Hybotidae	*Platypalpus alter*	Y	VU			**	**		
	Riverside vegetation: unknown	Diptera, Hybotidae	*Tachydromia acklandi*	Y	CR			***	***	Y	
	Rivers: sand & shingle(?)	Diptera, Limonidae	*Erioptera meigeni*	Y	VU			**	**		
	Rivers: marginal soils(?)	Diptera, Limonidae	*Idiocera connexa*	Y	EN			***	***	Y	
	Rivers: sandy river banks – sand & shingle(?)	Diptera, Limonidae	*Limonia omissinervis*	Y	EN			**	**		
	River shingle: predatory larva	Diptera, Limonidae	*Rhabdomastix laeta*	Y	DD	S		**	**	Y	
	Riverside vegetation: decaying vegetation(?)	Diptera, Micropezidae	*Calobata stylifera*	Y	VU			**	**		
	Lochs: larval predator of caddis eggs	Diptera, Scathophagidae	*Ernoneura argus*		VU			**	**		
	Rivers: shingle(?)	Diptera, Therevidae	*Spiriverpa lunulata*	Y	DD	P		**	**		
	Rivers: shingle(?)	Diptera, Therevidae	*Thereva handlirschi*	Y	VU			**	**		
	Rivers: marginal soils(?)	Diptera, Therevidae	*Thereva inornata*	Y	VU			**	**		
	Rivers: marginal soils(?)	Diptera, Therevidae	*Thereva valida*	Y	VU			**	**		
	Rivers: marginal soils(?)	Diptera, Tipulidae	*Nephrotoma aculeata*	Y	DD			**	**		
	Rivers: marginal soils(?)	Diptera, Tipulidae	*Tipula bistilata*	Y	EN			***	***	Y	
	Rivers: shingle	Diptera, Tipulidae	*Tipula nodicornis*	Y	VU			**	**		
	Large rivers: nymph feeding on bottom sediment	Ephemeroptera, Heptaginiidae	*Heptagenia longicauda*	Y	DD	S		**	**		
	Rivers: shingle	Lepidoptera, Nymphalidae	*Cupido minimus*					-	-		
	Rivers: fast-flowing non-calcareous	Mollusca,	*Margaritifera margaritifera*	Y	EN	P	Y	*	*		
	Tufa-depositing springs	Mollusca, Vertiginidae	*Vertigo geyeri*	Y	EN	P		**	-		Glen Fender, Tulach Hill
	In stands of *Juncus* and *Carex* on margins of water bodies	Mollusca, Vertiginidae	*Vertigo lilljeborgi*		VU			*	*		
	Lochs: margins of lochs and bogs: larva predator in bottom debris	Odonata, Coenagridae	*Coenagrion hastulatum*	Y	EN			***	***		
	Rivers: filter-feeders	Plecoptera, Taeniopterygidae	*Brachyptera putata*	Y	VU	P		**	**		

Habitat	Taxon (Order, Family)	Species	Nationally rare	RDB	BAP	WCA	Cairngorms area	National Park	Confined to NP?	Notable areas outside of National Park
Peatland:										
Damp moss: feeding on mites	Coleoptera, Pselaphidae	*Euplectus decipiens*	Y	DD			**	**		
Bogs, coniferous woodland: wet moss	Coleoptera, Staphylinidae	*Neohilara subterranea*		DD			**	**		
Bogs and seepages: decaying vegetation(?)	Diptera, Limonidae	*Limonia rufiventris*	Y	VU			**	**		
Bogs: phytophagous in reeds(?)	Diptera, Psilidae	*Loxocera nigrifrons*		VU			**	**		
Bogs: in damp soil(?)	Diptera, Tabanidae	*Hybomitra lurida*		DD			**	**		
Bogs: peat(?)	Diptera, Tipulidae	*Tipula grisescens*	Y	VU			**	**		
Bogs: soils(?)	Diptera, Tipulidae	*Tipula laetabilis*	Y	EN			***	***	Y	
Bogs: soils(?)	Diptera, Tipulidae	*Tipula marginata*	Y	VU			**	**		
Bog pools and runnels: *Sphagnum* moss	Odonata, Anisoptera	*Somatochlora arctica*	Y				*	*		
Bog pools: submerged *Sphagnum* moss	Odonata, Coenagridae	*Leucorrhinia dubia*		VU			**	**		
Bogs: lochans	Trichoptera, Limnephilidae	*Nemotaulius punctatolineatus*	Y	DD			**	**		
Margins of raised bogs and mires: in water with slight flow	Trichoptera, Phryganeidae	*Hagenella clathrata*	Y	EN			**	**		
Grassland:										
Grassland(?): soil(?)	Coleoptera, Leiodidae	*Catops nigriclavis*	Y	DD			**	**		
Grassland(?): unknown	Coleoptera, Leiodidae	*Colon angulare*	Y	DD			**	**		
Pasture: dung	Coleoptera, Staphylinidae	*Atheta clintoni*	Y	DD			***	***	Y	
Larva in soil(?)	Diptera, Muscidae	*Hydrotaea pandellei*	Y	DD			***	***	Y	
Phytophagous(?)	Diptera, Opomyzidae	*Geomyza angustipennis*	Y	VU			**	**		
Phytophagous(?)	Diptera, Opomyzidae	*Opomyza punctella*	Y	VU			**	**		
Unimproved meadows: decaying vegetation(?)	Diptera, Ulidiidae	*Dorycera graminum*	Y	VU	P		**	**		
Devil's- bit Scabious	Hymenoptera, Apidae	*Andrena marginata*					-	-		
Unknown	Lepidoptera, Elachistidae	*Elachista orstadii*		EN			**	**		Glen Tilt
Herbs	Lepidoptera, Geometridae	*Coenocalpe lapidata*	Y	VU			**	**		
Yarrow	Lepidoptera, Lyonetiidae	*Bucculatrix capreella*	Y	DD			***	***	Y	
Vetch	Lepidoptera, Lyonetiidae	*Leucoptera orobi*		DD			***	**		
Grasses ?	Lepidoptera, Noctuidae	*Xylena exsoleta*		VU	P		**	**		
Yarrow	Lepidoptera, Oecophoridae	*Depressaria silesiaca*	Y	VU			***	***	Y	
Unknown	Lepidoptera, Tortricidae	*Eana argentana*	Y	DD			***	-		Glen Tilt
Grassland & moorland:										
Unknown	Coleoptera, Leiodidae	*Colon viennense*		DD			*	*		
Soil and leaf litter(?)	Coleoptera, Staphylinidae	*Mycetoporus bimaculatus*	Y	DD			**	**		
Soil(?)	Coleoptera, Staphylinidae	*Staphylinus ophthalmicus*		VU			**	**		
Lotus corniculatus and stones to nest under	Hymenoptera, Megachilidae	*Osmia inermis*[2]	Y	VU	P		**	**		
Grassland/heath: Mountain Everlasting	Lepidoptera, Coleophoridae	*Coleophora pappiferella*	Y				***	***	Y	
Grassland/heath: food plant unknown	Lepidoptera, Elachistidae	*Elachista eskoi*					*	*		
Grassland/heath: Mountain Everlasting	Lepidoptera, Gelechiidae	*Scrobipalpa murinella*	Y	DD			*	*		
Grassland/heath: food plant unknown	Lepidoptera, Gelechiidae	*Syncopacma albifrontella*	Y	DD			***	***	Y	
Grassland/moorland: seeds of eyebright	Lepidoptera, Lasiocampidae	*Perizoma minorata ericetata*					*	*		
Grassland/heaths: rock-rose	Lepidoptera, Lycaenidae	*Aricia artaxerxes*	Y	EN	S	Y	**	**		
Grassland/heath: Mountain Everlasting	Lepidoptera, Oecophoridae	*Levipalpus hepatariella*					**	**		Glen Tilt
Grassland/moorland: Devil's-bit Scabious	Lepidoptera, Sphingidae	*Hemaris tityus*			P		-	-		
Heaths:										
Heaths & woodlands: often under bark	Coleoptera, Carabidae	*Agonum quadripunctatum*	Y	DD			**	**		
Soils(?)	Coleoptera, Carabidae	*Leistus montanus*		VU			*	*		

[2] *Osmia inermis*: in Scotland, records of this species and those of *O. uncinata* have been separated only relatively recently. Its current status in the Cairngorms, including the areas listed in Table 15.2 and in the text, requires clarification (M. Macdonald pers. comm. 2006).

Habitat		Taxon (Order, Family, Species)		Status				% of UK range in:		Confined to NP?	Notable areas outside of National Park
				Nationally rare	RDB	BAP	WCA	Cairngorms area	National Park		
Heaths:	Damp heathland & bog: phytophagous(?)	Diptera, Chloropidae	*Chlorops triangularis*	Y	DD			*	**		
	Moorland: carrion(?)	Diptera, Heleomyzidae	*Scoliocentra scutellaris*	Y	VU			**	**		
	Moorland: flowers, soil for nest	Hymenoptera, Apidae	*Bombus distinguendus*[3]		VU	P		**	**		
	Heaths: Blaeberry	Hymenoptera, Apidae	*Bombus monticola*					**	**		
	Heaths: Cross-leaved Heath	Hymenoptera, Apidae	*Bombus muscorum*					-	-		
	Moorland and forest edge	Hymenoptera, Apidae	*Bombus soroeensis*					*	*		
	Moorland & upland forests: parasite of mason wasp nests	Hymenoptera, Chrysididae	*Chrysura hirsuta*	Y	DD	S		**	**		
	Heaths & open woodland: ground layer	Hymenoptera, Formicidae	*Formica exsecta*	Y	EN	P		**	**		
	Young(?) Heather	Lepidoptera, Geometridae	*Dyscia fagaria*		VU			**	**		
	Bog-myrtle and heathers	Lepidoptera, Geometridae	*Lycia lapponaria scotica*	Y	VU			**	**		
	Bearberry	Lepidoptera, Geometridae	*Macaria carbonaria*	Y	VU	P		**	**		
	Wet heaths: Bog-myrtle	Lepidoptera, Geometridae	*Rheumaptera hastata*		VU	P		**	**		
	Bearberry	Lepidoptera, Noctuidae	*Anarta cordigera*		VU			**	**		
	Heaths: Bog-myrtle, Heather	Lepidoptera, Noctuidae	*Acronicta euphorbiae myricae*					**	**		
	Heaths: Bog-myrtle	Lepidoptera, Noctuidae	*Eurois occulta*					*	*		
	Moorland: birch	Lepidoptera, Tortricidae	*Ancylis tineana*	Y				*	*		Glen Fender, Struan Wood
	Heathland: Sweet Gale	Lepidoptera, Tortricidae	*Pammene luerdsiana*	Y				**	**		
Uplands:	Larva in soil(?)	Diptera, Muscidae	*Spilogona septemnotata*	Y	VU			**	**		
	Larva in moss	Diptera, Muscidae	*Thricops hirtulus*		LC			*	*		
	Upland flushes: soil(?)	Diptera, Pediciidae	*Dicranomyia stylifera*		VU			**	**		
	Uplands(?): unknown	Diptera, Phoridae	*Phora praepandens*	Y	DD			**	**		
	Unknown	Hymenoptera, Tenthredinidae	*Dolerus coracinus*	Y	DD			**	**		
	Unknown	Hymenoptera, Tenthredinidae	*Dolerus harwoodi*	Y	DD			**	**		
	Bearberry	Lepidoptera, Coleophoridae	*Coleophora arctostaphyli*	Y	VU			***	***	Y	
	Calcareous wet flushes	Mollusca, Vertiginidae	*Vertigo genesii*	Y	EN	P		**			Glen Fender, Ben Vrackie
Montane:	Grassland: snow-beds	Arachnida, Lycosidae	*Tricca alpigena*	Y	VU			**	**		
	Heath: under rocks and in litter	Arachnida, Lynyphidae	*Lepthyphantes antroniensis*	Y	EN			***	***	Y	
	Under rocks and in litter	Arachnida, Lynyphidae	*Rhaebothorax paetulus*	Y	EN			**	**		
	Grassland, wet heath	Coleoptera, Carabidae	*Amara alpina*	Y	VU			**	**		
	Wetlands: springs and flushes	Coleoptera, Carabidae	*Elaphrus lapponicus*		VU			**	**		
	Phytophagous on *Salix*	Coleoptera, Chrysomelidae	*Phyllodecta polaris*	Y	VU			**	**		
	Roots and soil	Coleoptera, Staphylinidae	*Eudectus whitei*		VU			**	**		
	Moss	Coleoptera, Staphylinidae	*Gabrius scoticus*		DD			**	**		
	Moss, leaf litter	Coleoptera, Staphylinidae	*Olophrum assimile*		DD			**	**		
	Moss	Coleoptera, Staphylinidae	*Stenus glacialis*	Y	DD			*	*		
	Unknown	Diptera, Anthomyiidae	*Alliopsis albipennis*	Y	DD			***	***	Y	
	Moss-heath	Diptera, Anthomyiidae	*Alliopsis atronitens*		LC			**	**		
	Unknown	Diptera, Anthomyiidae	*Alliopsis similaris*	Y	DD			***	***	Y	
	Unknown	Diptera, Anthomyiidae	*Botanophila apicseta*	Y	DD			**	**		

[3] *Bombus distinguendus*: the occurrence and habitat associations of this species in the Cairngorms require confirmation. The record providing the basis for its inclusion here is thought likely to prove erroneous.

Habitat	Taxon (Order, Family, Species)		Status				% of UK range in:		Confined to NP?	Notable areas outside of National Park
			Nationally rare	RDB	BAP	WCA	Cairngorms area	National Park		
Montane	Unknown	Diptera, Anthomyiidae	*Botanophila flavisquama*	Y	DD			**	**		Killiecrankie
	Unknown	Diptera, Anthomyiidae	*Botanophila moriens*	Y	VU			**	**		
	Unknown	Diptera, Anthomyiidae	*Delia pilifemur*	Y	DD			***	***	Y	
	Unknown	Diptera, Anthomyiidae	*Zaphne spiniclunis*	Y	DD			**	**		
	Carrion(?)	Diptera, Calliphoridae	*Calliphora stelviana*		LC			*	*		
	Pools and lochans	Diptera, Chironomidae	*Pseudorthocladius pilosipennis*	Y	DD			***	***	Y	
	Unknown	Diptera, Cyclindrotomidae	*Triogma trisulcata*	Y	DD			**	**		
	By water bodies	Diptera, Dolichopodidae	*Dolichopus maculipennis*		VU			**	**		
	Pools	Diptera, Dolichopodidae	*Hydrophorus rufibarbis*	Y	VU			**	**		
	Moss, water flushes	Diptera, Empididae	*Clinocera nivalis*	Y	VU			**	**		
	Unknown	Diptera, Empididae	*Rhamphomyia hirtula*	Y	EN			**	**		
	By water bodies	Diptera, Empididae	*Wiedemannia simplex*	Y	EN			***	***	Y	
	Seepages(?)	Diptera, Limonidae	*Limonia caledonica*		VU			**	**		
	Decaying vegetation(?)	Diptera, Limonidae	*Ormosia fascipennis*	Y	DD			**	**		
	Larva in soil(?)	Diptera, Muscidae	*Phaonia colbrani*	Y	DD			***	***	Y	
	Larva in soil(?)	Diptera, Muscidae	*Phaonia lugubris*	Y	VU			**	**		
	Larva in soil(?)	Diptera, Muscidae	*Phaonia meigeni*		LC			**	**		
	Larva in soil(?)	Diptera, Muscidae	*Phaonia subfuscinervis*		VU			**	*		
	Larva in soil(?)	Diptera, Muscidae	*Spilogona triangulifera*		LC			**	**		
	Mycophagous(?)	Diptera, Mycetophilidae	*Macrocera zetterstedti*	Y	EN			**	**		
	In soil	Diptera, Pediciidae	*Dicranota simulans*		VU			**	**		
	Montane(?): carrion(?)	Diptera, Phoridae	*Triphleba excisa*	Y	DD			**	**		
	Montane(?): unknown	Diptera, Scathophagidae	*Gonatherus planiceps*	Y	VU			**	**		
	Phytophagous, host plant uncertain	Diptera, Syrphidae	*Cheilosia sahlbergi*		VU			**	**		
	Homopteran predator	Diptera, Syrphidae	*Platycheirus melanopsis*	Y	VU			**	**		
	Soils(?)	Diptera, Tipulidae	*Tipula montana*		DD			*	*		
	Grassland	Hemiptera, Cicadellidae	*Ebarrius cognatus*	Y	DD			**	**		
	Rock-rose	Hemiptera, Cicadellidae	*Emelyanoviana contraria*		VU			**	**		
	Unknown	Hymenoptera, Tenthredinidae	*Allantus basalis caledonicus*	Y	DD			***	***	Y	
	Willows	Hymenoptera, Tenthredinidae	*Amauronematus abnormis*	Y	DD			***	***	Y	
	Willows	Hymenoptera, Tenthredinidae	*Amauronematus arcticola*	Y	DD			***	***	Y	
	Willows	Hymenoptera, Tenthredinidae	*Nematus reticulatus*		DD			**	**		
	Alpine Meadow-rue	Lepidoptera, Ethemiidae	*Ethmia pyrausta*	Y	DD			***	***	Y	
	Crowberry	Lepidoptera, Geometridae	*Psodos coracina*		VU			**	**		
	Crowberry	Lepidoptera, Noctuidae	*Anarta melanopa*	Y	VU			**	**		
	Blaeberry/Crowberry	Lepidoptera, Noctuidae	*Xestia alpicola*		VU	S		**	**		
	Montane heaths: Cloudberry	Lepidoptera, Nepticulidae	*Stigmella poterii* f. *tengstroemi*	Y				*	*		
	Montane heaths: Crowberry	Lepidoptera, Zygaenidae	*Zygaena exulans subochracea*	Y	VU			***	***	Y	
	Montane zone: *Salix* spp.	Lepidoptera, Gracillariidae	*Callisto coffeella*	Y				***	***	Y	
	Grassland/heath: food plant unknown	Lepidoptera, Tortricidae	*Olethreutes obsoletana*					*	*		
	Grassland: moss	Lepidoptera, Pyralidae	*Eudonia alpina*					*	*		

Habitat	Taxon (Order, Family, Species)		Status				% of UK range in:		Confined to NP?	Notable areas outside of National Park
			Nationally rare	RDB	BAP	WCA	Cairngorms area	National Park		
Woodland:	Coniferous: leaf litter	Arachnida, Clubionidae	*Clubiona subsultans*	Y	VU	S		**	**		
	Coniferous: leaf litter	Arachnida, Gnaphosidae	*Haplodrassus soerenseni*	Y	VU			**	**		
	Coniferous: heathery ground flora	Arachnidae, Lycosidae	*Pardosa lugubris*	Y				***	***	Y	
	Coniferous: leaf litter	Arachnida, Lynyphidae	*Pelecopsis elongata*	Y	VU			**	**		
	Coniferous: on bark, eats wood ants	Arachnida, Theridiidae	*Dipoena torva*	Y	EN			**	**		
	Coniferous: in dead wood	Coleoptera, Cerambycidae	*Leptura sanguinolenta*	Y	VU			***	***	Y	
	Coniferous: in tops of pine trees	Coleoptera, Cleridae	*Thanasimus rufipes*	Y	VU			***	***	Y	
	Coniferous: in dead wood	Coleoptera, Cryptophagidae	*Atomaria badia*	Y	CR			***	***	Y	
	Coniferous: under bark	Coleoptera, Cryptophagidae	*Atomaria bella*	Y	CR			**	**		
	Coniferous: in dung	Coleoptera, Cryptophagidae	*Atomaria hislopi*		DD			*	*		
	Coniferous: in woody debris	Coleoptera, Cryptophagidae	*Atomaria ornata*	Y	DD			**	**		
	Coniferous: pine cones and shoots	Coleoptera, Curculionidae	*Pissodes validirostris*	Y	VU			**	**		
	Coniferous: in dead wood	Coleoptera, Elateridae	*Ampedus tristis*	Y	VU			**	**		
	Coniferous: unknown	Coleoptera, Lathridiidae	*Corticaria latipennis*	Y	DD			***	***	Y	
	Coniferous: in dead wood	Coleoptera, Oedemeridae	*Chrysanthia nigricornis*	Y	EN			***	***	Y	
	Coniferous: in dead wood	Coleoptera, Peltidae	*Ostoma ferrugineum*	Y	EN			***	***	Y	
	Coniferous: fallen twigs	Coleoptera, Scolytidae	*Pityophthorus lichtensteini*	Y	VU			**	**		
	Coniferous: fallen twigs	Coleoptera, Scolytidae	*Tomicus minor*	Y	VU			**	**		
	Coniferous: fallen wood	Coleoptera, Scraptiidae	*Anapis bohemica*	Y	DD			***	***	Y	
	Coniferous: fallen wood	Coleoptera, Scraptiidae	*Anaspis septentrionalis*	Y	EX?			***	***	Y	
	Coniferous: under bark	Coleoptera, Staphylinidae	*Paranoplecta inhabilis*		DD			**	**		
	Coniferous: moss	Coleoptera, Staphylinidae	*Schistoglossa benicki*	Y	DD			***	***	Y	
	Coniferous: wet decay under bark	Diptera, Anisopodidae	*Mycetobia gemella*	Y	DD			***	***	Y	
	Coniferous: wood-boring beetle predator	Diptera, Asilidae	*Laphria flava*		VU			**	**		
	Coniferous: decaying wood	Diptera, Clusiidae	*Clusiodes geomyzinus*	Y	CR			***	***	Y	
	Coniferous: under bark	Diptera, Dolichopodidae	*Medetera excellens*		VU			**	**		
	Coniferous: under bark	Diptera, Dolichopodidae	*Medetera fasciata*	Y	DD			**	**		
	Coniferous: under bark(?)	Diptera, Dolichopodidae	*Medetera setiventris*	Y	DD			***	***	Y	
	Coniferous: carrion(?)	Diptera, Heleomyzidae	*Borboropsis puberula*	Y	CR			***	***	Y	
	Coniferous: under bark of fallen wood	Diptera, Lonchaeidae	*Lonchaea caledonica*	Y	DD			**	**		
	Coniferous: under bark of fallen wood	Diptera, Lonchaeidae	*Lonchaea zetterstedti*	Y	DD			**	**		
	Coniferous: larva in soil(?)	Diptera, Muscidae	*Thricops separ*	Y	EN			**	**		
	Coniferous: mycophagous	Diptera, Mycetophilidae	*Bolitophila fumida*	Y	CR			***	***	Y	
	Coniferous: mycophagous(?)	Diptera, Mycetophilidae	*Cordyla insons*	Y	DD			***	***	Y	
	Coniferous: fallen wood	Diptera, Mycetophilidae	*Creagdhubhia mallochorum*	Y	DD			***	***	Y	
	Coniferous: mycophagous(?)	Diptera, Mycetophilidae	*Mycetophila schnablii*	Y	EN			**	**		
	Coniferous: mycophagous(?)	Diptera, Mycetophilidae	*Syntemna stylata*	Y	EN			***	***	Y	
	Coniferous: parasitoid of leafhoppers	Diptera, Pipunculidae	*Eudorylas terminalis*	Y	EN			**	**		
	Coniferous: exuding sap	Diptera, Psilidae	*Chyliza annulipes*		VU			**	**		
	Coniferous: parasitoid of snails	Diptera, Sciomyzidae	*Ectinocera borealis*		VU			**	**		Ben Vrackie
	Coniferous: holes in stumps	Diptera, Syrphidae	*Blera fallax*	Y	CR	P		***	***	Y	

251

Habitat		Taxon (Order, Family, Species)		Status				% of UK range in:		Confined to NP?	Notable areas outside of National Park
				Nationally rare	RDB	BAP	WCA	Cairngorms area	National Park		
Woodland:	Coniferous: tree holes	Diptera, Syrphidae	*Callicera rufa*		LC			**	**		
	Coniferous: ground flora, unknown	Diptera, Syrphidae	*Chamaesyrphus caledonicus*	Y	CR			**	**		
	Coniferous: ground flora, unknown	Diptera, Syrphidae	*Chamaesyrphus scaevoides*	Y	EN			**	**		
	Coniferous: aphid predator	Diptera, Syrphidae	*Eupeodes lapponicus*	Y	DD			**	**		
	Coniferous: predatory larva under bark	Diptera, Xylophagidae	*Xylophagus cinctus*		VU			**	**		
	Coniferous: predatory larva under bark	Diptera, Xylophagidae	*Xylophagus junki*	Y	DD			***	***	Y	
	Coniferous: leaf feeder	Hymenoptera, Diprionidae	*Gilpinia frutetorum*	Y	DD			**	**		
	Coniferous: leaf feeder	Hymenoptera, Diprionidae	*Gilpinia pallida*	Y	DD			**	**		
	Coniferous: leaf feeder	Hymenoptera, Diprionidae	*Microdiprion pallipes*	Y	DD			**	**		
	Coniferous: glades and clearings	Hymenoptera, Megachilidae	*Osmia uncinata*	Y	VU	P		**	**		
	Coniferous: holes – stocked with aphid prey	Hymenoptera, Sphecidae	*Pemphredon wesmaeli*	Y	VU			***	***	Y	
	Coniferous: pine cones	Hymenoptera, Xyelidae	*Xyela longula*	Y	DD			**	**		
	Coniferous: Stitchwort	Lepidoptera, Gelechiidae	*Caryocolum junctella*	Y	DD			**	**		
	Coniferous: Cowberry	Lepidoptera, Coleophoridae	*Coleophora idaeela*	Y				***	***		
	Coniferous: Cowberry	Lepidoptera, Coleophoridae	*Coleophora glitzella*					**	**		
	Coniferous: Blaeberry	Lepidoptera, Tortricidae	*Olethreutes metallicana*	Y				*	*		
	Deciduous: leaf feeder	Coleoptera, Chrysomelidae	*Cryptocephalus coryli*	Y	CR	P		**	**		
	Deciduous: leaf feeder	Coleoptera, Chrysomelidae	*Cryptocephalus decemmaculatus*	Y	EN	S		**	**		
	Deciduous: fungi or under bark	Coleoptera, Cisidae	*Cis coluber*	Y	VU			**	**		
	Deciduous: exuding sap, fungi	Coleoptera, Rhizophagidae	*Rhizophagus parvulus*	Y	VU			***	***	Y	
	Deciduous: wet decay under bark	Diptera, Anisopodidae	*Mycetobia obscura*	Y	DD			***	***		
	Deciduous: decaying wood	Diptera, Clusiidae	*Clusiodes apicialis*	Y	VU			**	**		
	Deciduous: under bark	Diptera, Dolichopodidae	*Medetera inspissata*	Y	VU			**	**		
	Deciduous: dead wood or fungi(?)	Diptera, Drosophilidae	*Stegana hypoleuca*	Y	DD			***	***	Y	
	Deciduous: birchwood ground flora(?)	Diptera, Empididae	*Rhamphomyia ignobilis*	Y	CR			***	***	Y	
	Deciduous: birchwood ground flora(?)	Diptera, Empididae	*Rhamphomyia vesiculosa*	Y	EN			***	***	Y	
	Deciduous: unknown	Diptera, Fanniidae	*Fannia hirticeps*	Y	DD			**	**		
	Deciduous: unknown	Diptera, Fanniidae	*Fannia umbratica*	Y	DD			**	**		
	Deciduous: under bark of Aspen and birch	Diptera, Hybotidae	*Tachypeza heeri*	Y	EN			**	**		
	Deciduous: under bark(?)	Diptera, Hybotidae	*Tachypeza truncorum*		VU			**	**		
	Deciduous: under bark of fallen wood	Diptera, Lonchaeidae	*Lonchaea hackmani*	Y	DD			**	**		
	Deciduous: in soft decayed fallen wood	Diptera, Lonchaeidae	*Lonchaea ragnari*	Y	DD			**	**		
	Deciduous: unknown	Diptera, Muscidae	*Phaonia amabilis*	Y	DD			***	***	Y	
	Deciduous: exuding sap	Diptera, Periscelididae	*Periscelis nigra*	Y				**	**		
	Deciduous: decaying tree roots	Diptera, Syrphidae	*Criorhina ranunculi*		LC			**	**		
	Deciduous: leaf beetle predator	Diptera, Syrphidae	*Parasyrphus nigritarsis*	Y	VU			**	**		
	Deciduous: under bark(?)	Diptera, Syrphidae	*Sphegina sibirica*	Y	DD			*	*		
	Deciduous: under bark of fallen wood	Diptera, Ulidiidae	*Homalocephala biumbrata*	Y	EN			**	**		
	Under bark of pine and birch	Coleoptera, Cisidae	*Cis dentatus*	Y	VU			**	**		
	In dead wood	Coleoptera, Cryptophagidae	*Atomaria procerula*	Y	DD			**	**		
	Nests and dead wood	Coleoptera, Cryptophagidae	*Cryptophagus badius*	Y	DD			***	***	Y	
	Nests and fungi	Coleoptera, Cryptophagidae	*Cryptophagus lapponicus*	Y	DD			***	***	Y	

Habitat		Taxon (Order, Family, Species)		Status				% of UK range in:		Confined to NP?	Notable areas outside of National Park
				Nationally rare	RDB	BAP	WCA	Cairngorms area	National Park		
Woodland:	In dead wood	Coleoptera, Cryptophagidae	*Micrambe bimaculatus*		DD			**	**		
	Under bark	Coleoptera, Cucujidae	*Uleiota planata*		DD			**	**		
	Alder carr: unknown	Coleoptera, Curculionidae	*Rhynchaenus testaceus*	Y	EN	P		**	**		
	Deer dung	Coleoptera, Hydrophilidae	*Cercyon alpinus*	Y	DD			***	***	Y	
	Unknown	Coleoptera, Lathridiidae	*Corticaria longicollis*	Y	DD			**	**		
	Under bark	Coleoptera, Lathridiidae	*Enicmus rugosus*	Y	VU			**	**		
	Under bark	Coleoptera, Leiodidae	*Agathidium arcticum*		DD			**	**		
	Margins of burns: subterranean fungi	Coleoptera, Leiodidae	*Leiodes picea*		DD			*	*		
	Margins of burns: subterranean fungi	Coleoptera, Leiodidae	*Leiodes silesiaca*	Y	DD			***	***	Y	
	Exuding sap	Coleoptera, Nitidulidae	*Epuraea terminalis*	Y	DD			**	**		
	Fungi	Coleoptera, Nitidulidae	*Epuraea variegata*	Y	DD			**	**		
	In dead wood	Coleoptera, Pselaphidae	*Euplectus bescidicus*	Y	DD			**	**		
	In dead wood	Coleoptera, Pselaphidae	*Euplectus punctatus*	Y	VU			**	**		
	In dead wood	Coleoptera, Ptiliidae	*Ptiliolum caledonicum*	Y	DD			***	***	Y	
	Fungi	Coleoptera, Ptiliidae	*Ptiliolum schwarzi*		DD			**	**		
	Under bark	Coleoptera, Ptiliidae	*Ptinella limbata*		DD			**	**		
	Decaying wood, dung etc.	Coleoptera, Sphaeritidae	*Sphaerites glabratus*		VU			**	**		
	Fungi	Coleoptera, Staphylinidae	*Atheta boletophila*	Y	DD			***	***	Y	
	Carrion	Coleoptera, Staphylinidae	*Atheta procera*	Y	DD			***	***	Y	
	Carrion	Coleoptera, Staphylinidae	*Atheta spatuloides*		DD			*	*		
	Fungi	Coleoptera, Staphylinidae	*Gyrophaena pulchella*	Y	DD			**	**		
	Carrion	Coleoptera, Staphylinidae	*Phyllodrepa salicis*		DD			**	**		
	Decaying wood(?)	Diptera, Asteiidae	*Asteia elegantula*	Y	VU			**	**		
	Mycophagous	Diptera, Bolitophilidae	*Bolitophila bimaculata*	Y	EN			***	***	Y	
	Carrion(?)	Diptera, Heleomyzidae	*Oldenbergiella brumalis*	Y	CR			***	***	Y	
	Unknown	Diptera, Heleomyzidae	*Suillia oxyphora*		VU			*	*		
	Woodland(?): unknown	Diptera, Hybotidae	*Symballophthalmus pictipes*		VU			*	*		
	Leaf litter(?)	Diptera, Lauxaniidae	*Lyciella laeta*		VU			**	**		
	Dead wood: under bark of wet wood	Diptera, Limonidae	*Lipsothrix ecucullata*	Y	VU	P		**	**		
	Predatory larva in streams and seepages	Diptera, Limonidae	*Rhabdomastix inclinata*		VU			**	**		
	Unknown	Diptera, Mycetophilidae	*Anatella pseudogibba*	Y	EN			***	***	Y	
	Mycophagous(?)	Diptera, Mycetophilidae	*Boletina digitata*	Y	EN			**	**		
	Liverworts	Diptera, Mycetophilidae	*Boletina silvatica*	Y	EN			**	**		Killiecrankie
	Mycophagous(?)	Diptera, Mycetophilidae	*Brevicornu fennicum*	Y	EN			**	**		
	Mycophagous(?)	Diptera, Mycetophilidae	*Diadocidia valida*	Y	EN			**	**		
	Mycophagous(?)	Diptera, Mycetophilidae	*Dynatosoma abdominale*	Y	VU			**	**		
	Mycophagous(?)	Diptera, Mycetophilidae	*Dynatosoma cochleare*	Y	EN			***	***	Y	
	Mycophagous(?)	Diptera, Mycetophilidae	*Ectrepesthoneura pubescens*	Y	CR			***	***	Y	
	Mycophagous(?)	Diptera, Mycetophilidae	*Eudicrana nigriceps*	Y	CR			***	***	Y	
	Mycophagous(?)	Diptera, Mycetophilidae	*Mycetophila bohemica*	Y	EN			***	***	Y	
	Mycophagous(?)	Diptera, Mycetophilidae	*Mycetophila caudata*	Y	EN			**	**		
	Mycophagous(?)	Diptera, Mycetophilidae	*Mycetophila mohilevensis*	Y	EN			**	**		

Habitat	Taxon (Order, Family, Species)		Status				% of UK range in:		Confined to NP?	Notable areas outside of National Park
			Nationally rare	RDB	BAP	WCA	Cairngorms area	National Park		
Woodland:	Mycophagous(?)	Diptera, Mycetophilidae	*Mycetophila morosa*	Y	EN			**	**		
	Mycophagous(?)	Diptera, Mycetophilidae	*Mycetophila scotica*	Y	EN			**	**		
	Mycophagous(?)	Diptera, Mycetophilidae	*Mycetophila v-nigrum*	Y	EN			**	**		
	Predatory under bark(?)	Diptera, Mycetophilidae	*Mycomya shermani*	Y	VU			**	**		
	Mycophagous(?)	Diptera, Mycetophilidae	*Phronia persimilis*		VU			**	**		
	Unknown	Diptera, Mycetophilidae	*Rymosia britteni*	Y	EN			**	**		
	Mycophagous(?)	Diptera, Mycetophilidae	*Urtalpa macrocera*	Y	EN			**	**		
	Wet woodland, seepages: unknown	Diptera, Piophilidae	*Pseudoseps signata*	Y	EN			***	***	Y	
	Leaf litter	Hemiptera, Lygaeidae	*Eremocoris abietis*		VU			**	**		
	Ground layer	Hymenoptera, Formicidae	*Formica aquilonia*	Y	VU	P		**	**		
	Ground layer	Hymenoptera, Formicidae	*Formica lugubris*	Y	VU	S		**	**		
	Willows	Hymenoptera, Tenthredinidae	*Amauronematus semilacteus*	Y	DD			**	**		
	Damp woodlands: larva on horsetails	Hymenoptera, Tenthredinidae	*Dolerus bimaculatus*		DD			**	**		
	Open woodland: Broom	Lepidoptera, Geometridae	*Chesias rufata*	Y	VU			**	**		
	Open woodland: fine leaved grasses	Lepidoptera, Noctuidae	*Noctua orbona*		VU	P		**	**		
	Bilberry and Heather	Lepidoptera, Noctuidae	*Protolampra sobrina*	Y	VU	S		**	**		
	Deciduous: low plants?	Lepidoptera, Noctuidae	*Xestia rhomboidea*			P		-	-		
	Open woodland: violets	Lepidoptera, Nymphalidae	*Boloria euphrosyne*		VU	P	Y	**	**		
	Wall Lettuce	Lepidoptera, Pterophoridae	*Pselnophorus heterodactyla*		EN			**			Glen Tilt
	Open woodland: grasses	Lepidoptera, Pyralidae	*Catoptria permutatella*		VU			**	**		
	Bracket fungi	Lepidoptera, Tineidae	*Archinemapogon yildizae*	Y	DD			***	***	Y	
	Bracket fungi *Piptoporus betulinus*	Lepidoptera, Tineidae	*Nemapogon picarella*		DD			**	**		Killiecrankie
	Dame's violet	Lepidoptera, Yponomeutidae	*Rhigognostis incarnatella*		EN			***	**		
	Gooseberry *Ribes*	Lepidoptera, Incurvariidae	*Lampronia capitella*					*	*		
	Burnet Rose	Lepidoptera, Incurvariidae	*Lampronia pubicornis*					*	*		
	Deciduous: birch	Lepidoptera, Oecophoridae	*Exaeretia ciniflonella*					**	**		
	Aspen: under bark	Diptera, Scatopsidae	*Ectaetia christii*	Y	DD			***	***	Y	
	Aspen trees: under bark of fallen wood	Diptera, Strongylophthalmyiidae	*Strongylophthalmyia ustulata*	Y	CR			**	**		Dulsie Bridge
	Aspen trees: under bark of fallen wood	Diptera, Syrphidae	*Hammerschmidtia ferruginea*	Y	CR	P		**	**		
	Aspen trees: under bark of fallen wood	Diptera, Ulidiidae	*Homalocephala albitarsis*	Y	EN			**	**		
	Aspen: young trees	Lepidoptera, Geometridae	*Epione vespertaria*	Y	VU	P		**	**		
	Aspen	Lepidoptera, Lyonetiidae	*Paraleucoptera sinuella*	Y	EX?			***	***	Y	
	Aspen	Lepidoptera, Tortricidae	*Gypsonoma nitidulana*	Y	EX?			***	***	Y	
	Birch: fungi	Coleoptera, Cisidae	*Ropalodontus perforatus*	Y	VU			**	**		
	Birch: fungi	Coleoptera, Melandryidae	*Abdera affnis*	Y	EN			**	**		
	Birch: exuding sap	Coleoptera, Nitidulidae	*Epuraea silacea*	Y	EN			**	**		
	Birch: fungi	Coleoptera, Tenebrionidae	*Bolitophagus reticulatus*		VU			**	**		
	Birch: unknown	Diptera, Hybotidae	*Oedalea hybotina*	Y	EN			***	***	Y	
	Birch: *Fomes* fungus	Diptera, Mycetophilidae	*Sciophila rufa*	Y	LC			**	**		
	Birch: bark	Hemiptera, Aradidae	*Aradus betulae*		VU			**	**		
	Birch: young trees	Lepidoptera, Endromidae	*Endromis versicolora*	Y	VU			**	**		

Habitat		Taxon (Order, Family, Species)		Status				% of UK range in:		Confined to NP?	Notable areas outside of National Park
				Nationally rare	RDB	BAP	WCA	Cairngorms area	National Park		
Woodland:	Birch : mature trees	Lepidoptera, Noctuidae	*Brachionycha nubeculosa*	Y	VU			**	**		
Woodland & moorland	Leaf litter and moss	Coleoptera, Staphylinidae	*Euryporus picipes*		DD			**	**		
	Woodland, uplands: leaf litter, carrion, fungi	Coleoptera, Staphylinidae	*Tachinus rufipennis*		VU			**	**		
	Woodland and coasts: in dead wood	Coleoptera, Cryptophagidae	*Micrambe lindbergorum*		DD			**	**		
	Leaf litter/moss	Hemiptera, Lygaeidae	*Eremocoris plebejus*		VU			**	**		
	Juniper	Hemiptera, Miridae	*Zygimus nigriceps*	Y	VU			**	***	Y	
	Juniper	Hymenoptera, Diprionidae	*Monoctenus juniperi*	Y	DD			**	**		
	Wood ant nests	Lepidoptera, Tineidae	*Myrmecozela ochraceella*	Y	VU			**	**		
	Moorland and woodland	Lepidoptera, Incurvariidae	*Nematopogon magna*	Y	DD			*	*		
	Open woodland: Juniper	Lepidoptera, Gelechiidae	*Dichomeris juniperella*					**	**		
Other:	Sandy soils: subterranean fungi	Coleoptera, Leiodidae	*Leiodes flavescens*	Y	DD			**	**		
	Leaf litter: subterranean(?)	Coleoptera, Staphylinidae	*Atheta puberula*		DD			**	**		
	Sandy soils: predator	Diptera, Asilidae	*Pamponerus germanicus*		VU			**	**		
	Sandy soils: predator	Diptera, Asilidae	*Rhadiurgus variabilis*		VU			**	**		
	Shingle banks: algal grazing	Diptera, Ephydridae	*Scatella callosicosta*	Y	VU			**	**		
	Dune slacks: larva in soil(?)	Diptera, Muscidae	*Lispocephala rubricornis*		VU			**	**		
	Ant nests: predator	Hemiptera, Cimicidae	*Xylocoris formicetorum*	Y	DD			***	***	Y	
	Nests in cavities in walls, banks etc.: preys on caterpillars	Hymenoptera, Eumenidae	*Ancistrocerus antilope*[4]		VU			**	**		
Unknown:	Decaying vegetation	Coleoptera, Scydmaenidae	*Scydmoraphes sparshalli*		DD			**	**		
	Unknown	Diptera, Anthomyiidae	*Delia hirtitibia*	Y	DD			***	***	Y	
	Parasitoid(?)	Diptera, Tachinidae	*Hemimacquartia paradoxa*	Y	CR			***	***	Y	

trees. Other important locations are the pinewoods between Aviemore and Coylumbridge. The many stumps from previous fellings and clearances are important in this area of woodland, providing breeding sites for many beetles and flies, including the rare clusiid fly, *Clusiodes geomyzinus*, which has been recorded from this area in the past. River margins, shingle and associated boggy and marshy areas along the Spey and the Druie are also important for species such as the stiletto fly *Thereva inornata*, although recent records are lacking.

2. Deeside from Linn of Dee to Aboyne.
In this area 92 important species have been recorded (Table 15.2), of which 21 are BAP priority or RDB. The pine and birch woodlands and the river margins are important for woodland specialists like the BAP hoverfly *Hammerschmidtia ferruginea*, which breeds under the bark of recently fallen Aspen. Open spaces in pinewoods are important for the Narrow-headed Ant *Formica exsecta*, also a BAP priority species. River shingle and sandy

margins hold populations of stiletto flies belonging to the genus *Thereva* (Diptera, Therevidae). The moth *Lampronia capitella* feeds on Gooseberry *Ribes uva-crispa* along the river bank at its only known site in Scotland, although the species also occurs (rarely) in England. *Callisto coffeella* is another rare moth occurring on montane willows near Braemar. This species was first found in the UK in Glen Callater in 1983, and is also known from glens Clova and Doll but not from outside the Cairngorms. The moth *Elachista orstadii* occurs in grassland, but its breeding site has yet to be discovered. Base-rich grassland is important for the rare moth *Coleophora pappiferella*, which feeds on Mountain Everlasting *Antennaria dioica*, and in the UK is known only from Deeside.

3. Strathspey.
Running along the valley of the Spey from Kingussie to Grantown-on-Spey, this area encompasses a wide range of characteristic lowland Cairngorms habitats, from woodlands to wetlands, river margins,

[4] *Ancistrocerus antilope*: the occurrence of this species in the Cairngorms area requires confirmation. The record providing the basis for its inclusion here is thought likely to prove erroneous.

Craigellachie's combination of dry, steep slopes, wet, boggy areas and an abundance of dead wood help support a remarkable invertebrate fauna. Craigellachie and Coylumbridge together form the richest area for important invertebrates in the Cairngorms.

Photo: *L. Gill*

The threatened beetle Bolitophagus reticulatus *is associated mainly with birch, and has been recorded from two of the Cairngorms important areas for invertebrates.*

Photo: *R. Key*

heaths and grassland. Seventy-nine important species are known, of which 25 are BAP priority or RDB. However, in most cases the location of captures is unrecorded, and further work is needed to ascertain whether populations persist in this locality. Nonetheless, from the known requirements and records of these species, the main habitats of importance are pine and birch woodlands, river margins, shingle and sandbars, bogs, heaths and grasslands. The internationally important Freshwater Pearl Mussel, which is found throughout the Spey, is most common from Grantown-on-Spey down to Fochabers (Hastie, 2001a,b). All three important dragonfly species in the Cairngorms area (Northern Damselfly *Coenagrion hastulatum*, White-faced Darter *Leucorrhinia dubia* and Northern Emerald *Somatochlora arctica*) also occur. Habitats of these species include lochs, bog pools and *Sphagnum* moss; all well represented in the area.

4. Abernethy. Seventy-seven important species have been recorded from this area, which includes Boat of Garten, Loch Garten and Abernethy Forest to the Dorback Burn and Tulloch. Of these, 28 are BAP priority or RDB species. Woodlands are the most important habitats for invertebrates in the area, particularly the native pine woodland from Garten to Abernethy, and the Aspen stand at Tomnagowhan near Tulloch. Both are the most extensive of their type in the UK, and a good range of species breed and otherwise depend on these trees. Some species feed on the foliage of living trees while others depend on dead, fallen wood. Examples include the scolytid beetle *Pityophthorus lichtensteini*, which breeds in fallen pine twigs, and the hoverfly *Chamaesyrphus scaevoides*, whose requirements have yet to be ascertained. The UK stronghold for the latter species appears to be in the vicinity of Loch Garten. Cousin German *Protolampra sobrina*, a BAP priority moth of open upland birch woodland with an understorey of Blaeberry *Vaccinium myrtillus*, is widespread in this area.

Abernethy is one of the best localities for one of the rarest dragonfly species in UK; the Northern Damselfly, an Endangered species (Smith & Smith, 1996). Its main UK populations are in the Cairngorms, and only two sites are known outside of the area. Two species are known in the UK only from Abernethy: the water beetle *Agabus wasastjernae*, recorded at Loch Garten, and the wolf-spider *Pardosa lugubris*, which was discovered in Abernethy Forest in 2005. Although the latter is currently only known from this area it seems likely to occur elsewhere in the UK.

5. Nethy Bridge. Centred on the village of Nethy Bridge, this area includes the surrounding fields and margins of River Nethy, to where it meets the Spey to the north and Dell Lodge in the south. Fifty-eight important species are known, of which 12 are BAP priority or RDB. Unfortunately, this is another locality for which the precise locations of captures are often missing from the records. From the known requirements of these species, the main areas of importance are the (mainly) pine and birch woodlands surrounding the village. This woodland also forms a margin along both sides of the River Nethy, from where it joins the Spey in the north, to Dell Lodge in the south. In the village itself, the banks of the Nethy and the more mixed wooded areas are also important, particularly where large, old trees and stumps remain in close proximity to a variety of flowers, providing additional habitats and sources of food. Bogs, heaths and small areas of grassland are frequent throughout these woodlands, adding to their invertebrate importance.

6. *Cairngorm Mountains.* This area lies mainly between Cairn Gorm, Ben Macdui, Braeriach, Cairn Toul, Beinn a' Chaorainn and Derry Cairngorm. Fifty-four important species are known, of which 11 are BAP priority or RDB. A wide variety of characteristic upland and montane habitats occur here, including some of the most extensive of their type. They include habitats that are largely confined to the Cairngorms, such as Bearberry heath (*Calluna-Arctostaphylos* heath; H16 in the NVC) (see Chapter 6), which is important for several scarce Lepidoptera, including the two BAP priority species Netted Mountain Moth *Macaria carbonaria* and Northern Dart *Xestia alpicola*, as well as the Small Dark Yellow Underwing *Anarta cordigera*. The area is probably the most important in Scotland for upland and montane invertebrates, supporting 22 of a group of 24 species of montane Higher Diptera, most of whose habitat requirements are uncertain or unknown. In this area, snow-bed grasslands are important for the rare wolf-spider *Tricca alpigena*, dwarf-shrub heath is important for the spider *Lepthyphantes antroniensis*, while wet heath is important for the ground beetle *Amara alpina* (Horsfield, 1997). Little is known of their precise requirements or distributions. Other habitats of importance include moss beds, flushes, pools and lochans, but the extent to which invertebrates depend on these habitats is unknown.

7. *Grantown-on-Spey.* Centred on Grantown-on-Spey, from Glen Beg and Castle Grant in the north, to Speybridge and Anagach in the south, 40 important species are known from this area, of which 16 are BAP priority or RDB. The main habitats for invertebrates include the pinewoods in and around Grantown-on-Spey, and the Aspen stands at Speybridge and Dulicht. The pinewoods include trees of a wide range of ages and sizes, areas of previous fellings and many large stumps, important for saproxylic species such as the BAP priority hoverfly *Blera fallax* and the clusiid fly *Clusiodes geomyzinus*, both of whose UK

populations appear to be centred on this locality. The Aspen stands at Speybridge and Dulicht are important for the hoverfly *Hammerschmidtia ferruginea* and for other important members of the saproxylic community, such as the fly species *Strongylophthalmyia ustulata* and *Homalocephala albitarsis*. Sandbars and shingle beds of the Spey, between Speybridge and Grantown-on-Spey, are important for RDB flies such as the stiletto fly *Thereva valida*. Other important species probably occur in this area, but detailed surveys are lacking.

8. *Loch an Eilein to Rothiemurchus.* Thirty-five important species have been recorded from the area between Loch an Eilein and Rothiemurchus. Of these, 12 are BAP priority or RDB species (Table 15.2). Pinewood is believed to be the main habitat of these species, including areas of large, old trees with open canopies, plantations and areas of younger trees with closed or partially closed canopies. Many of the area's important invertebrates are saproxylic on dead wood of pine. These include the robber fly *Laphria flava* and the RDB cryptophagid beetle *Atomaria bella*. In many places the heathy understorey contains areas of stumps, and fallen wood is frequent. Two BAP priority ants – the Narrow-headed Ant and Hairy Wood Ant *Formica lugubris* – occur here, in places where the understorey is more open.

Twenty-seven important invertebrate species have been recorded from Glen Feshie, of which nine are BAP Priority or nationally threatened. Most are associated with the River Feshie's sand, shingle and adjacent vegetation.

Photo: *L. Gill*

9. Glen Feshie. This area extends from the shingle beds of the Spey, south of Kincraig and Speybank at the point where the Feshie joins the Spey, and follows the Feshie south to Slochd Beag. Twenty-seven important species are known, of which nine are BAP priority or RDB. From their known requirements, the main habitats of importance are those associated with sand, shingle and vegetated areas on the margins of the Feshie, including boggy and other wetlands near the northern edge of the area above Balnascriten. Along the Feshie, these habitats are some of the most extensive and varied of their type in the UK. Important invertebrate species dependent on these habitats include the click beetle *Negastrius pulchellus*, which is associated with shingle beds, and the BAP priority crane fly *Lipsothrix ecucullata*, which breeds in wet, fallen branches lying partially submerged in slow-flowing, shaded streams, flushes and boggy areas. The Small Blue butterfly *Cupido minimus* continues to survive on and adjacent to the river shingles, in what are probably its only inland colonies left in Scotland.

10. Kingussie to Insh and Speybank. Extending from Kingussie and Inverton in the west, to Speybank and Insh Marshes in the east, 25 important species are known from this area, of which eight are BAP priority or RDB. From the known requirements and records of these species the main habitats of importance are the Aspen stands at Inverton, Insh and Speybank, the grasslands at Insh and Speybank, and the wetlands at Insh. The BAP hoverfly *Hammerschmidtia ferruginea* occurs at Inverton, Insh and Speybank in Aspen stands. The BAP priority solitary bees *Osmia inermis* and *O. uncinata* are also known from the locality, the latter breeding in the grassland understorey of pinewoods.

11. Glenmore. Consisting mainly of pine and birch forest around Loch Morlich, this area holds at least 14 important species, of which five are BAP priority or RDB. They include species dependent on conifers, such as the dipteran *Xylophagus cinctus*, which breeds under the bark of fallen pine trees and cut stumps. Also present are the BAP priority Narrow-headed Ant, which prefers relatively open spaces within the forest, and the solitary bee *Osmia inermis*, which occurs in open grassland and moorland.

12. Beinn a' Ghlo to Ben Vrackie, Blair Atholl and Killiecrankie. There is a mix of deciduous and coniferous woodland in this area, which includes steep, wooded valleys with rivers and burns. The area also has open moorland where seepages and flushes are frequent. Eleven important species are known, of which four are BAP priority species (Table 15.2). They include the Round-mouthed Whorl Snail *Vertigo genesii*, which occurs in calcareous wet flushes, and *Vertigo geyeri*, which depends on tufa-depositing

The stiletto fly Spiriverpa lunulata *is a BAP priority species, associated mainly with sand- and shingle areas, and recorded from parts of Deeside and Strathspey, including Nethy Bridge, Newtonmore and Glen Feshie.*

Photo: *R. Key*

In Britain the BAP Aspen hoverfly Hammerschmidtia ferruginea *is known from just 12 sites, nine of which occur in Cairngorms National Park.*

Photo: *I. MacGowan*

The pine hoverfly Blera fallax *has an even more restricted range, being known from just two sites in Britain: at Curr Wood and near to Grantown-on-Spey. Like* Hammerschmidtia ferruginea, Blera fallax *is classed as Critically Endangered in Britain.*

Photo: *I. MacGowan*

springs. Pearl-bordered Fritillaries *Boloria euphrosyne* are present in the clearings, glades and edges of many of the woodlands, while larva of the Cousin German moth feed on dwarf-shrubs and birch in the birchwoods and pine forest.

13. *Struan.* Eight important species are known from this area, which is predominantly a birchwood with a heath and grass understorey. Two of its species are BAP priority lepidoptera: the Northern Brown Argus *Aricia artaxerxes* and Argent & Sable *Rheumaptera hastata,* which breed in upland grassland and birch woodland, and in moorland, respectively. Rannoch Brindled Beauty *Lycia lapponaria scotica* is another rare moth that occurs on boggy moorland here. Several rare species are dependent on dead birchwood for breeding, such as the lonchaeid *Lonchaea ragnari,* first discovered in Scotland in 1998. It is also the only known site in Scotland for the drosophilid *Stegana hypoleuca,* whose breeding requirements are unclear, but are likely to be saproxylic, like other members of the genus.

14. *Bridge of Brown to Tomintoul.* This area includes the pine and birchwoods along the margins of the A939 road and the River Avon, between Bridge of Brown and Tomintoul. It also includes the shingle and sandy margins of the river. Six important species are known, of which three are listed as Endangered in the RDB (Table 15.2). In riverside habitats the RDB predatory fly *Heleodromia irwini* and the stiletto fly *Thereva inornata* have been recorded, while the RDB predatory fly *Rhamphomyia vesiculosa* occurs in the understorey of birchwoods.

15. *Glen Tanar.* Based around the Water of Tanar and the surrounding pinewood, this area extends from Aboyne in the north to the edge of the woodland near Clachan Yell, in the south. Six important species have been recorded, four of which are BAP priority or RDB. Forest-dependent species include the saproxylic beetles *Chrysanthia nigricornis* and *Tomicus minor.* The hemipteran bug *Eremocoris plebejus* is known from the leaf litter of the forest floor, while the Scottish Wood Ant *Formica aquilonia* and Hairy Wood Ant (both BAP priority species) occur in more open parts of the forest.

16. *Carrbridge.* This area includes the predominantly pine and birchwoods surrounding Carrbridge. Eight important species are known, of which three are BAP priority: the wood ants *Formica exsecta* and *F. aquilonia,* and Sword-grass *Xylena exsoleta*; a moth of upland woodland and moorland whose larval food plants and early stages are unknown in the wild.

The Northern Brown Argus Aricia artaxerxes *is nationally endangered, and is associated mainly with upland grassland sites. In the Cairngorms these include Craigellachie and Struan.*
Photo: *L. Gill*

The Hairy Wood Ant Formica lugubris *is a nationally threatened species occurring at a number of sites in the Cairngorms, sometimes together with the BAP Priority Narrow-headed Ant* F. exsecta; *as at Abernethy, Carrbridge, Rothiemurchus and Glenmore.*
Photo: *L. Gill*

Figure 15.1. Important areas for invertebrate species. See text for details and Table 15.2 for species lists.

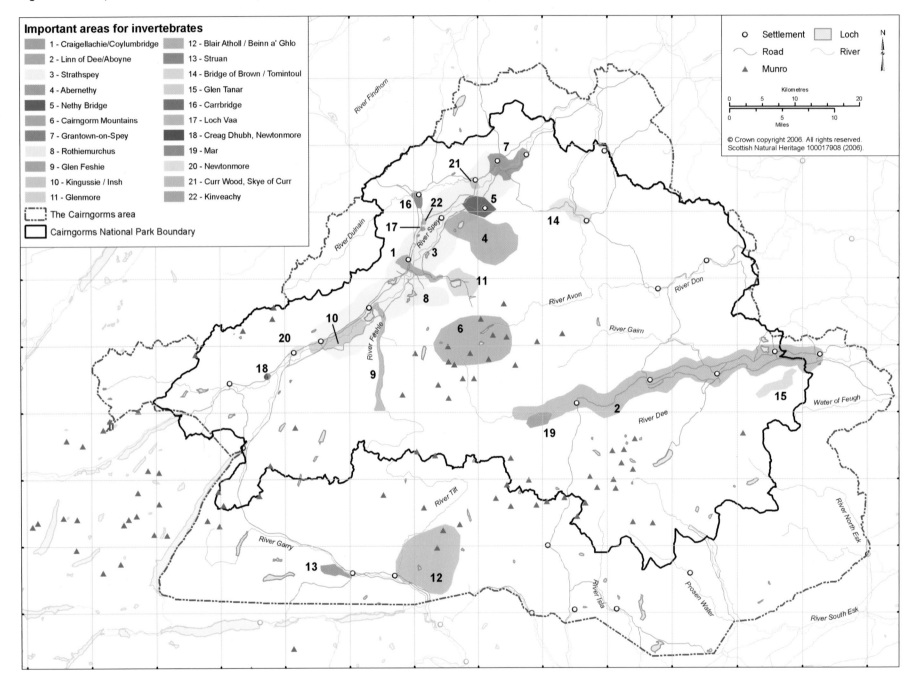

Important areas for invertebrates

1 - Craigellachie/Coylumbridge
2 - Linn of Dee/Aboyne
3 - Strathspey
4 - Abernethy
5 - Nethy Bridge
6 - Cairngorm Mountains
7 - Grantown-on-Spey
8 - Rothiemurchus
9 - Glen Feshie
10 - Kingussie / Insh
11 - Glenmore
12 - Blair Atholl / Beinn a' Ghlo
13 - Struan
14 - Bridge of Brown / Tomintoul
15 - Glen Tanar
16 - Carrbridge
17 - Loch Vaa
18 - Creag Dhubh, Newtonmore
19 - Mar
20 - Newtonmore
21 - Curr Wood, Skye of Curr
22 - Kinveachy

The Cairngorms area
Cairngorms National Park Boundary

Settlement   Loch
Road   River
Munro

Kilometres
0   5   10   20
0   5   10
Miles

© Crown copyright 2006. All rights reserved.
Scottish Natural Heritage 100017908 (2006).

Table 15.2. Important areas for invertebrates in the Cairngorms, listed in descending order of the number of nationally important species.

Percentage of area occurring within the National Park: *** 75–100%; ** 25–75%; * 10–25%; '-' <10%.

Area	Species of national importance	Percentage of area within NP
1. **Craigellachie to Aviemore and Coylumbridge**	*Alliopsis similaris, Boletina digitata, Bolitophila fumida, B. bimaculata, Borboropsis puberula, Botanophila apicseta, Callicera rufa, Chlorops triangularis, Clusiodes geomyzinus, Culiseta alaskaensis, Dynatosoma abdominale, Erioptera meigeni, Eudorylas terminalis, Eupeodes lapponicus, Fannia umbratica, Hilara barbipes, H. submaura, Hydrotaea pandellei, Laphria flava, Limonia consimilis, L. omissinervis, Lyciella laeta, Macrocera zetterstedti, Medetera fasciata, Minettia flaviventris, Mycetobia obscura, Mycetophila bohemica, Oldenbergiella brumalis, Pamponerus germanicus, Phaonia amabilis, Platypalpus pygmaeus, Prionocera pubescens, Pseudoseps signata, Rhabdomastix laeta, Rhadiurgus variabilis, Rhamphomyia ignobilis, R. trigemina, R. vesiculosa, Scatella callosicosta, Scathophaga pictipennis, Scoliocentra scutellaris, Sphaerophoria loewi, Symballophthalmus pictipes, Tachypeza heeri, Thereva inornata, Thricops hirtulus, Tipula bistilata, T. nodicornis, Wiedemannia phantasma, Xylophagus cinctus* **50 Diptera species**; *Amara alpina, Anapis bohemica, A. septentrionalis, Atheta clintoni, A. procera, Atomaria bella, Bolitophagus reticulatus, Cis dentatus, Cryptophagus lapponicus, Dyschirius angustatus, Enicmus rugosus, Epuraea terminalis, E. variegata, Hygropora cunctans, Leiodes silesiaca, Leptura sanguinolenta, Ropalodontus perforatus, Sphaerites glabratus, Stenus incanus, Thanasimus rufipes, Thinobius newberyi* **21 Coleoptera species**; *Aradus betulae, Ebarrius cognatus, Eremocoris abietis, E. plebejus, Paraliburnia litoralis, Xylocoris formicetorum, Zygimus nigriceps* **7 Hemiptera species**; *Amauronematus semilacteus, Dolerus coracinus, D. harwoodi, Gilpinia frutetorum, G. pallida, Osmia uncinata, Xyela longula* **7 Hymenoptera species**; *Anarta cordigera, A. melanopa, Ancylis tineana, Aricia artaxerxes, Brachionycha nubeculosa, Depressaria silesiaca, Dichomeris juniperella, Dyscia fagaria, Endromis versicolora, Epione vespertaria, Leucoptera orobi, Macaria carbonaria, Protolampra sobrina, Psodos coracina, Rhigognostis incarnatella, Xestia alpicola, Xylena exsoleta.* **17 Lepidoptera species**; *Hagenella clathrata, Nemotaulius punctatolineatus* **2 Trichoptera species**; *Vertigo lilljeborgi* **1 Mollusca species**; *Clubiona subsultans* **1 Arachnida species. (Total: 106 species)**	***
2. **Deeside from Linn of Dee to Aboyne**	*Boletina silvatica, Callicera rufa, Dicranomyia stylifera, Hammerschmidtia ferruginea, Hydrophorus rufibarbis, Idiocera connexa, Medetera fasciata, Mycetobia obscura, Oedalea hybotina, Opomyza punctella, Platycheirus melanopsis, Rhabdomastix inclinata, Scathophaga pictipennis, Spiriverpa lunulata, Tachydromia acklandi, Tachypeza truncorum, Thereva handlirschi, T. inornata, T. valida, Thricops hirtulus, T. separ, Xylophagus cinctus* **22 Diptera species**; *Amara alpina, Ampedus tristis, Atomaria badia, A. hislopi, Cercyon alpinus, Colon angulare, Corticaria latipennis, Cryptocephalus decemmaculatus, Elaphrus lapponicus, Gabrius scoticus, Leistus montanus, Mycetoporus bimaculatus, Ostoma ferrugineum, Pissodes validirostris, Pityophthorus lichtensteini, Ptiliolum schwarzi, Ptinella limbata, Scopaeus gracilis, Sphaerites glabratus, Stenus glacialis, Thanasimus rufipes, Uleiota planata* **22 Coleoptera species**; *Ebarrius cognatus, Emelyanoviana contraria, Eremocoris abietis, E. plebejus, Zygimus nigriceps* **5 Hemiptera species**; *Allantus basalis caledonicus, Formica aquilonia, F. exsecta, F. lugubris, Microdiprion pallipes, Monoctenus juniperi* **6 Hymenoptera species**; *Anarta cordigera, A. melanopa, Brachionycha nubeculosa, Bucculatrix capreella, Callisto coffeella, Catoptria permutatella, Chesias rufata, Coenocalpe lapidata, Coleophora pappiferella, C. pappiferella, Depressaria silesiaca, Dichomeris juniperella, Dyscia fagaria, Elachista orstadii, Endromis versicolora, Epione vespertaria, Eudonia alpina, Exaeretia ciniflorella, Lampronia capitella, L. pubicornis, Levipalpus hepatariella, Macaria carbonaria, Myrmecozela ochraceella, Nemapogon picarella, Olethreutes obsoletana, Protolampra sobrina, Psodos coracina, Scrobipalpa murinella, Syncopacma albifrontella, Xestia alpicola, Xylena exsoleta, Zygaena exulans subochracea* **32 Lepidoptera species**; *Coenagrion hastulatum, Leucorrhinia dubia* **2 Odonata species**; *Brachyptera putata* **1 Plecoptera species**; *Tricca alpigena* **1 Arachnida species**; *Vertigo lilljeborgi* **1 Mollusca species. (Total: 92 species)**	***
3. **Strathspey**	*Anatella pseudogibba, Bolitophila bimaculata, Brevicornu fennicum, Chyliza annulipes, Diadocidia valida, Dicranota simulans, Dorycera graminum, Ectrepesthoneura pubescens, Eudicrana nigriceps, Limonia caledonica, L. rufiventris, Microprosopa pallidicauda, Mycetophila caudata, M. mohilevensis, M. morosa, M. scotica, M. v-nigrum, Mycomya shermani, Pilaria decolor, Rymosia britteni, Sciophila rufa, Spilogona septemnotata, Spiriverpa lunulata, Thricops separ* **24 Diptera species**; *Aleochara brevipennis, Ampedus tristis, Atheta puberula, A. spatuloides, Catops nigriclavis, Cis coluber, Coccinella quinquepunctata, Cryptocephalus coryli, Cryptophagus badius, Epuraea silacea, Euplectus bescidicus, E. punctatus, Gabrius scoticus, Gyrophaena pulchella, Hydrosmecta delicatula, Leiodes flavescens, Micrambe bimaculatus, Micrambe lindbergorum, Negastrius sabulicola, Pelophila borealis, Phyllodecta polaris, Ptiliolum schwarzi, Ptinella limbata, Rhizophagus parvulus, Rhynchaenus testaceus, Scydmorapes sparshalli, Tachinus rufipennis* **27 Coleoptera species**; *Allantus basalis caledonicus, Bombus distinguendus[5]; Dolerus bimaculatus, Microdiprion pallipes, Monoctenus juniperi* **5 Hymenoptera species**; *Archinemapogon yildizae, Boloria euphrosyne, Brachionycha nubeculosa, Coenocalpe lapidata, Coleophora glitzella, C. idaeella, Elachista eskoi, Endromis versicolora, Eudonia alpina, Exaeretia ciniflorella, Gypsonoma nitidulana, Hemaris tityus, Levipalpus hepatariella, Nemapogon picarella, Olethreutes obsoletana, Pammene luerdsiane, Paraleucoptera sinuella, Xestia rhomboidea* **18 Lepidoptera species**; *Coenagrion hastulatum, Leucorrhinia dubia, Somatochlora arctica* **3 Odonata species**; *Brachyptera putata* **1 Plecoptera species**; *Maragaritifera maragaritifera* **1 Mollusca species. (Total: 79 species)**	***

---

[5] *Bombus distinguendus*: see Table 15.1. The occurrence of this species in the Cairngorms area requires confirmation.

Area	Species of national importance	Percentage of area within NP
4. Abernethy	*Bolitophila bimaculata, Borboropsis puberula, Callicera rufa, Chamaesyrphus scaevoides, Chlorops triangularis, Clusiodes geomyzinus, Cordyla insons, Dynatosoma cochleare, Eudorylas terminalis, Eupeodes lapponicus, Fannia umbratica, Hammerschmidtia ferruginea, Heleodromia irwini, Hemimacquartia paradoxa, Hilara submaura, Hybomitra lurida, Laphria flava, Lipsothrix ecucullata, Lonchaea caledonica, L. zetterstedti, Mycetobia gemella, Oldenbergiella brumalis, Platypalpus alter, Suillia oxyphora, Syntemna stylata, Xylophagus cinctus* **26 Diptera species;** *Ancylis tineana, Brachionycha nubeculosa, Caryocolum junctella, Chesias rufata, Coleophora arctostaphyli, C. glitzella, Endromis versicolora, Leucoptera orobi, Macaria carbonaria, Myrmecozela ochraceella, Pammene luerdsiane, Protolampra sobrina, Xylena exsoleta* **13 Lepidoptera species;** *Coenagrion hastulatum, Leucorrhinia dubia* **2 Odonata species;** *Clubiona subsultans, Dipoena torva, Haplodrassus soerenseni, Pardosa lugubris, Pelecopsis elongata* **5 Arachnida species;** *Agabus wasastjernae, Amara alpina, Atomaria badia, A. bella, A. hislopi, A. ornata, Cercyon alpinus, Cis dentatus, Donacia aquatica, Enicmus rugosus, Euryporus picipes, Leiodes picea, Leistus montanus, Leptura sanguinolenta, Neohilara subterranea, Paranoplecta inhabilis, Phyllodrepa salicis, Schistoglossa benicki, Sphaerites glabratus, Staphylinus ophthalmicus, Thanasimus rufipes* **21 Coleoptera species;** *Aradus betulae* **1 Hemiptera species;** *Ancisatrocerus antilope[6], Chrysura hirsuta, Formica aquilonia, F. exsecta, F. lugubris, Gilpinia pallida, Osmia inermis, O. uncinata, Pemphredon wesmaeli* **9 Hymenoptera species. (Total: 77 species)**	***
5. Nethy Bridge	*Bolitophila bimaculata, Callicera rufa, Clusiodes geomyzinus, Culiseta alaskaensis, Delia hirtitibia, Ectinocera borealis, Erioptera sordida, Fannia hirticeps, Hilara barbipes, H. hirta, H. setosa, Homalocephala albitarsis, Laphria flava, Limonia consimilis, Lispocephala rubricornis, Loxocera nigrifrons, Medetera fasciata, M. inspissata, Melanum fumipenne, Periscelis nigra, Platypalpus pygmaeus, Pseudoseps signata, Rhadiurgus variabilis, Scatella callosicosta, Spiriverpa lunulata, Symballophthalmus pictipes, Tachypeza truncorum, Thereva inornata, Tipula bistilata, T. nodicornis, Wiedemannia phantasma* **31 Diptera species;** *Abdera affnis, Agonum quadripunctatum, Anapis bohemica, Atheta sylvicola, Bledius arcticus, B. terebrans, Colon viennense, Corticaria longicollis, Dyschirius angustatus, Epuraea terminalis, Lathrobium dilutum, Leiodes picea, L. silesiaca, Leptura sanguinolenta, Negastrius pulchellus, Olophrum assimile, Ptiliolum caledonicum, Stenus incanus, Tachyusa scitula, Thanasimus rufipes, Thinobius major* **21 Coleoptera species;** *Ebarrius cognatus, Zygimus nigriceps* **2 Hemiptera species;** *Formica exsecta, Gilpinia pallida, Osmia inermis, O. uncinata* **4 Hymenoptera species. (Total: 58 species)**	***
6. Cairngorm Mountains	*Alliopsis albipennis, A. atronitens, A. similaris, Botanophila apicseta, B. moriens, Calliphora stelviana, Campiglossa argyrocephala, Chamaesyrphus scaevoides, Cheilosia sahlbergi, Chlorops triangularis, Clinocera nivalis, Delia pilifemur, Dolichopus maculipennis, Ernoneura argus, Fannia hirticeps, Gonatherus planiceps, Loxocera nigrifrons, Macrocera zetterstedti, Minettia flaviventris, Ormosia fascipennis, Phaonia lugubris, P. subfuscinervis, Platycheirus melanopsis, Pseudorthocladius pilosipennis, Rhamphomyia hirtula, Spilogona triangulifera, Tipula grisescens, T. montana, Triogma trisulcata, Triphleba excisa, Wiedemannia simplex, Zaphne spiniclunis* **32 Diptera species;** *Amara alpina, Elaphrus lapponicus, Eudectus whitei, Leistus montanus* **4 Coleoptera species;** *Eremocoris abietis* **1 Hemiptera species;** *Amauronematus abnormis, A. arcticola, Formica aquilonia, F. exsecta, Nematus reticulatus* **5 Hymenoptera species;** *Chesias rufata, Coleophora arctostaphyli, Leucoptera orobi, Psodos coracina, Macaria carbonaria, Xestia alpicola, Xylena exsoleta* **7 Lepidoptera species;** *Leucorrhinia dubia* **1 Odonata species;** *Dictyna major, Lepthyphantes antroniensis, Rhaebothorax paetulus, Tricca alpigena* **4 Arachnida species. (Total: 54 species)**	***
7. Grantown-on-Spey	*Asteia elegantula, Blera fallax, Callicera rufa, Chamaepsila clunalis, Clusiodes geomyzinus, Ectaetia christii, Eudorylas terminalis, Geomyza angustipennis, Hammerschmidtia ferruginea, Hemimacquartia paradoxa, Hercostomus sahlbergi, Hilara hirta, H. medeteriformis, H. setosa, Homalocephala albitarsis, Hydrotaea pandellei, Lonchaea hackmani, Medetera inspissata, Melanum fumipenne, Mycetophila schnablii, Parasyrphus nigritarsis, Periscelis nigra, Phaonia colbrani, Scatella callosicosta, Strongylophthalmyia ustulata, Tachypeza heeri, Thereva inornata, T. valida, Wiedemannia phantasma* **29 Diptera species;** *Atomaria bella, Enicmus rugosus, Leptura sanguinolenta, Staphylinus ophthalmicus* **4 Coleoptera species;** *Aradus betulae* **1 Hemiptera species;** *Epione vespertaria, Hemaris tityus, Rhigognostis incarnatella* **3 Lepidoptera species;** *Coenagrion hastulatum, Leucorrhinia dubia, Somatochlora arctica* **3 Odonata species. (Total: 40 species)**	***
8. Loch an Eilein to Rothiemurchus	*Callicera rufa, Chamaesyrphus caledonicus, Cordyla insons, Dynatosoma abdominale, Eudorylas terminalis, Laphria flava, Medetera fasciata, Mycetobia gemella, Mycetophila bohemica, Oldenbergiella brumalis, Rhadiurgus variabilis, Scoliocentra scutellaris, Xylophagus cinctus* **13 Diptera species;** *Agathidium arcticum, Atheta boletophila, Atomaria bella, Cis dentatus, Leptura sanguinolenta, Pissodes validirostris* **6 Coleoptera species;** *Ebarrius cognatus, Macrosiphum scoticum, Zygimus nigriceps* **3 Hemiptera species;** *Formica exsecta, F. lugubris, Osmia uncinata* **3 Hymenoptera species;** *Brachionycha nubeculosa, Dichomeris juniperella, Elachista eskoi, Levipalpus hepatariella, Myrmecozela ochraceella, Protolampra sobrina, Xylena exsoleta* **7 Lepidoptera species;** *Coenagrion hastulatum* **1 Odonata species;** *Dipoena torva, Pelecopsis elongata* **2 Arachnida species. (Total: 35 species)**	***
9. Glen Feshie	*Anticheta analis, Bolitophila bimaculata, Cheilosia sahlbergi, Lipsothrix ecucullata, Medetera setiventris, Nephrotoma aculeata, Phaonia amabilis, Rhabdomastix inclinata, Suillia oxyphora, Thereva handlirschi, Spiriverpa lunulata, Tipula laetabilis, Tipula marginata* **13 Diptera species;** *Bledius terebrans, Coccinella quinquepunctata, Dyschirius angustatus, Lathrobium dilutum, Leiodes picea, Negastrius pulchellus, Stenus incanus, Tachyusa scitula, Thinobius major* **9 Coleoptera species;** *Osmia inermis, Osmia uncinata* **2 Hymenoptera species,** *Cupido minimus, Protolampra sobrina, Xylena exsoleta* **3 Lepidoptera species. (Total: 27 species)**	***

[6] *Ancistrocerus antilope*: see Table 15.1. The occurrence of this species in the Cairngorms area requires confirmation.

Area	Species of national importance	Percentage of area within NP
10. Kingussie to Insh & Speybank	*Calobata stylifera, Cheilosia sahlbergi, Chlorops triangularis, Cordilura similis, Ectaetia christii, Hammerschmidtia ferruginea, Homalocephala albitarsis, Lispocephala rubricornis, Lonchaea hackmani, Phora praepandens, Rymosia speyae* **n. sp.**, *Scatella callosicosta, Tipula grisescens* **13 Diptera species;** *Atomaria procerula, Bolitophagus reticulatus, Donacia aquatica, Epuraea variegata* **4 Coleoptera species;** *Brachionycha nubeculosa, Dyscia fagaria, Protolampra sobrina, Xestia rhomboidea, Xylena exsoleta* **5 Lepidoptera species;** *Eremocoris plebejus* **1 Hemiptera species;** *Osmia inermis, Osmia uncinata* **2 Hymenoptera species. (Total: 25 species)**	***
11. Glenmore	*Callicera rufa, Chlorops triangularis, Eupeodes lapponicus, Lonchaea zetterstedti, Sphegina sibirica, Xylophagus cinctus, Xylophagus junki* **7 Diptera species;** *Zygimus nigriceps* **1 Hemiptera species;** *Formica aquilonia, Formica exsecta, Formica lugubris, Osmia inermis* **4 Hymenoptera species;** *Boloria euphrosyne, Eudonia alpina* **2 Lepidoptera species (Total: 14 species)**	***
12. Beinn a' Ghlo to Ben Vrackie, Blair Atholl & Killiecrankie	*Botanophila flavisquama, Ectinocera borealis* **2 Diptera species;** *Ancylis tineana, Boloria euphrosyne, Eana argentana, Elachista orstadii, Levipalpus hepatariella, Protolampra sobrina, Pselnophorus heterodactyla* **7 Lepidoptera species;** *Vertigo genesii, Vertigo geyeri* **2 Mollusca species. (Total: 11 species)**	-
13. Struan	*Lonchaea ragnari, Stegana hypoleuca* **2 Diptera species;** *Ancylis tineana, Aricia artaxerxes, Chesias rufata, Dyscia fagaria, Lycia lapponaria scotica, Rheumaptera hastata* **6 Lepidoptera species. (Total: 8 species)**	-
14. Bridge of Brown to Tomintoul	*Heleodromia irwini, Nephrotoma aculeata, Rhamphomyia vesiculosa, Thereva inornata, Urtalpa macrocera* **5 Diptera species;** *Zygimus nigriceps* **1 Hemiptera species. (Total: 6 species)**	***
15. Glen Tanar	*Chrysanthia nigricornis, Tomicus minor* **2 Coleoptera species;** *Eremocoris plebejus* **1 Hemiptera species;** *Formica aquilonia, Formica lugubris* **2 Hymenoptera species;** *Coenagrion hastulatum* **1 Odonata species. (Total: 6 species)**	***
16. Carrbridge	*Euplectus decipiens* **1 Coleoptera species;** *Formica aquilonia, F. exsecta, F. lugubris* **3 Hymenoptera species;** *Noctua orbona, Protolampra sobrina, Rhigognostis incarnatella, Xylena exsoleta* **4 Lepidoptera species (Total: 8 species)**	***
17. Loch Vaa	*Hygropora cunctans* **1 Coleoptera species;** *Endromis versicolora, Macaria carbonaria, Protolampra sobrina* **3 Lepidoptera species;** *Coenagrion hastulatum* **1 Odonata species. (Total: 5 species)**	***
18. Creag Dhubh	*Creagdhubhia mallochorum* **1 Diptera species;** *Boloria euphrosyne, Lycia lapponaria scotica, Rheumaptera hastata, Xylena exsoleta* **4 Lepidoptera species. (Total: 5 species)**	***
19. Mar	*Creagdhubhia mallochorum* **1 Diptera species;** *Ampedus tristis, Cercyon alpinus* **2 Coleoptera species;** *Formica exsecta* **1 Hymenoptera species. (Total: 4 species)**	***
20. Newtonmore	*Spiriverpa lunulata* **1 Diptera species;** *Bledius terebrans* **1 Coleoptera species;** *Psodos coracina* **1 Lepidoptera species. (Total: 3 species)**	***
21. Curr Wood, Skye of Curr	*Blera fallax, Callicera rufa* **2 Diptera species (Total: 2 species)**	***
22. Kinveachy	*Hammerschmidtia ferruginea* **1 Diptera species**	***

17. Loch Vaa. This area includes the pinewoods and heaths surrounding Loch Vaa. Five important species are known, of which two are BAP priority species. These include the Bearberry-dependent Netted Mountain Moth, a BAP priority species found commonly on the *Arctostaphylos* heath adjacent to the lochs. The Kentish Glory moth *Endromis versicola*, which is associated with young birch trees, occurs in the more open areas where birch regeneration is common. The Northern Damselfly, which breeds in lochs and bogs, is also known from this locality.

18. Creag Dhubh. This area, with five important species, consists of upland habitats and an old pine plantation on the northern hills between Newtonmore and Kingussie. Upland heaths at this locality support the RDB species Rannoch Brindled Beauty moth, which breeds on Bog-myrtle *Myrica gale* and Heather *Calluna vulgaris*, as well as two BAP priority species: Pearl-bordered Fritillary and Argent & Sable. The area is also the type locality for *Creagdhubhia mallochorum*; a saproxylic pine-dependent, fungus-gnat, first described in 1999.

19. Mar. The pine forest at Mar and its associated habitats are the main interest for invertebrates in this area. Four important species are known, of which one is a BAP priority: the Narrow-headed Ant. The RDB saproxylic click beetle *Ampedes tristis* also occurs here. Mar is also the second site for the pine-dependent fungus gnat *Creagdhubhia mallochorum*. Results of a survey of the invertebrates of Mar Lodge Estate are given in Godfrey (2000).

20. Newtonmore. The main invertebrate interests of this area are the upland habitats surrounding Newtonmore and the marginal habitats along the rivers Calder and Spey. Three important species are known, of which one is a BAP priority species: the sand- and shingle-dependent stiletto fly *Spiriverpa lunulata*. The sand/mud burrowing beetle *Bledius terebrans* is also known from riverside habitat, while the Black Mountain Moth *Psodos coracina*, which breeds on Crowberry *Empetrum nigrum*, is known from upland parts of the area.

21. Curr Wood, Skye of Curr. This area consists of an old pine plantation south of Dulnain Bridge. Two important species of Diptera are known: *Callicera rufa* and the BAP priority hoverfly *Blera fallax*. The latter breeds in holes in pine stumps, and is known from only one other site in Britain and Ireland: at Grantown-on-Spey. A species recovery programme for this hoverfly is underway at both localities.

22. Kinveachy. The interest of this locality centres on the scattered stands of Aspen near to the junction between the B9153 and A95, south of Carrbridge. One important species is known: the BAP priority hoverfly *Hammerschmidtia ferruginea*, which breeds under the bark of recently fallen Aspen branches and trees.

Recent research and survey findings

Welch (1974) and Young and Watt (2002) comment on how few studies have been conducted on the invertebrates of the Cairngorms. Most of the information available has been the result of opportunistic collecting by amateur invertebrate biologists during visits to the area, rather than systematic or long-term collecting. As noted above, the lack of data has presented difficulties for the current assessment. Over the past decade, a few detailed studies have been made, however, as follows.

Saproxylic Diptera. This group was surveyed in Scottish forests between 1988 and 1998, with over 300 woodlands visited, including those of the Cairngorms (Rotheray & MacGowan, 2000; Rotheray *et al.*, 2001). The survey concentrated on discovering breeding sites and rearing larval stages. Throughout Scotland, over 250 species in 32 families were encountered, of which 53 were red-listed, nine were new to Britain and 10 were new to science. The most important area for these Diptera was the Cairngorms, where 37 red-listed species, six species new to Britain and five species new to science were found. Most were associated with native boreal trees such as Downy Birch *Betula pubescens*, Scots

Pine and Aspen. Survey results enabled recovery programmes for the BAP hoverflies *Blera fallax* and *Hammerschmidtia ferruginea* to be initiated.

Shingle and riverside species. A survey of insects from river shingle and riverside habitats was undertaken in the Cairngorms area in 1993 (Rotheray & Robertson, 1993). Since the emphasis in this survey was on adult captures, little investigation of breeding requirements was made. Of 514 species collected, 405 were flies and 109 were beetles. Sixty-nine species were red-listed. Species were collected from six Cairngorm sites, from Glen Feshie to the Spey at Nethy Bridge. The data confirmed the continued presence of these species in historical localities and yielded new distribution records.

Upland and montane Higher Diptera (Brachycera and Cyclorrhapha). Horsfield and MacGowan (1998) have investigated this group by using hand searching, netting, and pitfall and water traps. These methods proved more successful than anticipated, yielding 422 Higher Diptera records. A further 135 records were obtained from the literature. Trapping was carried out from 1985 to 1995 at 176 localities, including 38 Scottish hill ranges and the Cairngorms. The results enabled a group of 24 Higher Diptera to be characterised as 'montane' on the basis that all, or nearly all, of their records occurred above the potential climatic treeline. The results also clarified the distribution and status of these Diptera, most of which are red-listed. Twenty-two of the 24 species occur within the Cairngorms; more than in any other area in Scotland.

Butterflies and moths. Since 2002, Butterfly Conservation Scotland has significantly raised the level of recording of the distribution of UK BAP priority and other butterflies and moths in the Cairngorms area, through a series of projects funded by SNH, the Heritage Lottery Fund and Cairngorms National Park Authority. Target species have included the Pearl-bordered Fritillary (dependent on violets growing in warm micro-climates), the Kentish Glory (dependent on young birch), Netted Mountain Moth and the Dark Bordered Beauty (dependent on young Aspen).

These projects have clarified the status of several species, notably the Dark Bordered Beauty (Young, 2002), which has also had its ecology and behaviour studied, and has benefited from habitat management and the establishment of annual monitoring (T. Prescott, pers. comm.).

Loch Garten Coleoptera. The beetles of Loch Garten have also been studied in detail (Owen, 1989a–c). Over a 10-year period (1978–1988), 807 species (*c.* 20% of the UK beetle fauna; Owen 1989a,b) were recorded, using a variety of trapping techniques. Only 20 beetle species had been known from the site previously; a clear indication of how poorly surveyed the Cairngorms area is. Of the 807 species recorded, 15 were red-listed in Shirt (1987). As part of this work, the 'Owen Emergence Trap' was developed to sample insects breeding in dead wood (Owen, 1989c).

Trends

Studies revealing changes in the status of invertebrates in the Cairngorms are few indeed, and exist for only a handful of species. In the UK as a whole, the best-studied group is the butterflies. From UK-wide surveys, distribution data for 23 butterflies in the Cairngorms area may be compared over two periods: 1970–82 (Pollard *et al.*, 1986) and 1995–99 (Asher *et al.*, 2001). Some species, like the Large Heath *Coenonympha tullia* and Small Mountain Ringlet *Erebia epiphron,* showed apparent range decreases. Others, like the Small Pearl-bordered Fritillary *Boloria selene* showed an increase, while species like the Small Blue and the Pearl-bordered Fritillary showed little change, although recent records imply that the numbers of colonies may have declined. It is notable that two upland species, which are adapted to cold conditions, showed a decrease in range, due, perhaps, to warmer climatic conditions. However, it is difficult to know whether variation in survey effort has influenced the results. The work of Horsfield and MacGowan (1998), who used pitfall and water traps to survey upland and montane Diptera, provides a viable methodology and baseline data by which to assess trends in this important group.

The Malloch Society[7] studied saproxylic Diptera and, in particular, analysed records for three RDB saproxylic hoverflies in Cairngorms National Park (Rotheray & MacGowan, 2000). Since one of these hoverflies – *Callicera rufa* – is found commonly throughout northern Scotland, its status has been changed to 'Notable'. The two other species – *Blera fallax* and *Hammerschmidtia ferruginea* – had their RDB status confirmed. Other RDB Diptera occurring in the National Park have been re-assessed by comparing previous records with recent survey results based on breeding sites and early stages, prompting proposals to change their threat status. For example, the dolichopid fly *Medetera excellens*, which is dependent on dead wood and classed as Vulnerable, was re-assessed as Rare (Rotheray *et al.*, 2001). Based on these surveys, other species discovered in Britain for the first time, and several entirely new species, were given provisional RDB status. *Mycetobia gemella*, for example, was new to

Britain and classed as 'Rare', while *Ectaetia christii*, a species new to science, was given Endangered status, based on the number of 10-km squares occupied. In Britain, both species appear to be confined to Cairngorms National Park.

These surveys were based on new techniques, in particular on the identification of breeding sites and on searches for larvae and puparia, since adult stages are too rare and elusive to be surveyed cost-effectively. Many other poorly known invertebrates in the Cairngorms would likewise benefit from the development of more effective survey techniques.

Conservation issues

The overwhelming issue affecting the conservation of invertebrates in the Cairngorms is a lack of knowledge. The main gaps in our knowledge are as follows.

Working in partnership with land owners, members of the Malloch Society have created artificial breeding sites for the hoverfly Blera fallax *at its two British localities, both in Strathspey. These modified tree stumps were used as breeding sites within 12 months of their creation, suggesting that the technique could help increase the population size.*

Photo: D. Horsfield

[7] For further details of the Malloch Society and its work on Scottish Diptera, see: www.mallochsociety.org.uk.

- *Inventory*. Species lists for many invertebrate groups in the Cairngorms, such as parasitic Hymenoptera, Cecidomyidae and others, are incomplete.

- *Status*. The status and distribution of most of the area's 377 important species are known from under 15 records each. Some areas of the Cairngorms have barely been studied for invertebrates, while other parts of Scotland require surveying to help place Cairngorms' records in context.

- *Requirements*. Basic life-history data, without which potential threats cannot be recognised or recovery programmes carried out, are missing.

A strategic approach to assessing Cairngorms invertebrates is required, as is a rationale for dealing with groups not presently covered at any level.

Climate change. The most serious threat to upland and montane habitats is probably climate change (Chapter 20). The effect of warming on essentially cold-adapted species may restrict them to higher altitudes, and some populations, if not entire species, are likely to disappear. Monitoring is required to properly assess the effects of climate warming. For Diptera, MacGowan and Horsfield (1998) showed that this could be achieved using pitfall and water traps.

Habitat management. As discussed above, three habitats are particularly important for most of the invertebrate species for which the Cairngorms area is important: upland and montane areas; river and water body margins, including bogs and shingle beds; and forests, particularly stands of Aspen, birch and pine. Strategies to survey and monitor specialist species in these habitats are required. This is particularly the case for habitats largely or wholly restricted to the Cairngorms. For example, one upland microhabitat, Bearberry heath (H16 in the NVC), is important for several scarce Lepidoptera, including the BAP priority species Netted Mountain Moth and the Small Dark Yellow Underwing, which are essentially confined to the Cairngorms. Within Cairngorms' forests, the importance of stands of Aspen has been recognised only recently, not only for their dependent invertebrates, which include over a dozen RDB species and two BAP priority species (the hoverfly *Hammerschmidtia ferruginea* and the Dark Bordered Beauty), but also for lower plants (see Chapters 11–13) (Cosgrove & Amphlett, 2002).

The most severe threat to invertebrates in the Cairngorms' woodlands appears to be unsympathetic management, e.g. the removal of fallen wood or under-planting with non-native species. The needs of many species are unknown, however, and further investigation is required. For example, the life histories of all but one of the 22 endangered species of woodland fungus gnat (Mycetophilidae) occurring in the Cairngorms are completely unknown (Table 15.1).

Built development. Although fairly limited in extent, housing and other developments continue to pose a threat. For example, Aspen stands important for BAP priority and RDB species at Speybank, Speybridge and Dulicht have been damaged in the past 10 years by clear-felling, house building, the extension of a local authority rubbish tip and the building of a sewage farm. Agricultural improvements can also threaten Cairngorms' invertebrates where they involve drainage of wetland areas or the conversion of meadows and grasslands.

Sources

The Scottish Insects Records Index (SIRI) – a compilation of all citations to Scottish Insects maintained by the National Museum of Scotland – is a major source of published data on Cairngorms insects. An electronic version of SIRI was recently produced with funding from SNH. SIRI enables literature on individual insect species to be consulted, providing a list of published distribution records. Major sources of unpublished records, used in the preparation of this review, included the following.

Ismay, J. (unpublished). *A review of the scarce and threatened acalypterate Diptera of Great Britain*. Draft version, unpublished.

Phillips, D. (1996). *Unpublished list of RDB and BAP Scottish invertebrates*. SNH: Perth.

Ravenscroft, N. (1994). *A Strategy for the Conservation of Invertebrates in Scotland*. Report prepared for SNH: Perth.

Sivell, D, & Phillips, D. (1999). *Local Biodiversity Action Plans – Technical Information on Species: III. Invertebrate Animals*. Review No 5. SNH: Perth.

In addition, members of the Initiative for Scottish Insects, which is part of the Edinburgh Entomological Club, provided data. K. Bland and S. Pye, in particular, assisted with the Lepidoptera and Molluscs, respectively.

References

Asher, J., Warren, M., Fox, R., Harding, P., Jeffcoate, G. & Jeffcoate, S. (2001). *The Millennium Atlas of Butterflies in Britain and Ireland*. Oxford University Press: Oxford.

Cosgrove, P. & Amphlett, A. (2002). *The Biodiversity and Management of Aspen Woodlands*. Cairngorms Partnership: Grantown-on-Spey.

Cosgrove P.J., Hastie L. & Farquhar J.E. (2004). *Freshwater Pearl Mussel Survey of the River Dee candidate Special Area of Conservation*. Scottish Natural Heritage Research Report F02PA04a (Unpublished, confidential report). SNH: Perth.

Crowson, R. (1961). Observations on Coleoptera in Scottish oak woods. *Glasgow Naturalist* 18: 177–195.

Falk, S. (1991). *A review of the scarce and threatened flies of Great Britain (Part 1)*. Research and Survey in Nature Conservation, No. 39. NCC: Peterborough.

Godfrey, A. (2000). *Invertebrate Survey of the Mar Lodge Estate*. Unpublished report to the National Trust for Scotland.

Harvey, P.R., Nellist, D.R. & Telfer, M.G. (2002). *Provisional Atlas of British Spiders*. Biological Records Centre, CEH: Monks Wood.

Hastie, L. (2001a). *Freshwater pearl mussel survey and river habitat survey of the River Spey. Volume 1 – main report*. SNH Commissioned Report (F99PA02). SNH: Perth.

Hastie, L. (2001b). *Freshwater pearl mussel survey and river habitat survey of the River Spey. Volume 2 – data and photographs*. SNH Commissioned Report (F99PA02). SNH: Perth.

Horsfield, D. (1997). Beetles from pitfall-trapping at high altitude in the Scottish Highlands. *Entomologist's Record and Journal of Variation* 109: 81–88.

Horsfield, D. & MacGowan, I. (1998). An assessment of the distribution and status of montane Brachycera (Diptera) in Scotland. *Malloch Society Research Report* No. 3.

Hyman, P.S. & Parsons, M.S. (1992). *A review of the scarce and threatened Coleoptera of Great Britain (Part 1)*. UK Nature Conservation, No. 3. JNCC: Peterborough.

Hyman, P.S. & Parsons, M.S. (1994). *A review of the scarce and threatened Coleoptera of Great Britain (Part 2)*. UK Nature Conservation, No. 12. JNCC: Peterborough.

MacGowan, I. & Rotheray, G.E. (2000). New species, additions and possible deletions to British *Lonchaea* (Diptera, Lonchaeidae). *Dipterists Digest* 7: 37–49.

Owen, J.A. (1989a). The 1987 Presidential Address Part 2. A preliminary account of the beetles of the RSPB Loch Garten Reserve. *British Journal of the Entomological & Natural History Society* 2: 17–28.

Owen, J.A. (1989b). Beetles from pitfall-trapping in a Caledonian pinewood at Loch Garten, Inverness-shire. *British Journal of the Entomological & Natural History Society* 2: 107–113.

Owen, J.A. (1989c). An emergence trap for insects breeding in dead wood. *British Journal of the Entomological & Natural History Society* 2: 65–67.

Pollard, E., Hall, M.L. & Bibby, T.J. (1986). Monitoring the Abundance of Butterflies 1976–1985. *Research and Survey in Nature Conservation* No. 2. NCC: Peterborough.

Rotheray, G.E. (1996). Why Conserve Scottish Insects? In: Rotheray, G.E. & MacGowan, I. (eds.), *Conserving Scottish Insects*. Edinburgh Entomological Club: Edinburgh. pp 11–16.

Rotheray, G.E. & Horsfield, D. (1997). *Ectaetia christii* sp. n. a Scottish species similar to *Ectaetia clavipes* (Diptera, Scatopsidae). *Dipterists Digest* 4: 41–44.

Rotheray, G.E. & Robertson, D. (1993). Insects from Shingle Banks and Riverside Habitats in Strathspey. *Malloch Society Research Report* No. 2.

Rotheray, G.E. & MacGowan, I. (2000). Status and breeding sites of three presumed endangered Scottish saproxylic syrphids (Diptera, Syrphidae). *Journal of Insect Conservation* 4: 215–223.

Rotheray, G.E. Hancock, G., Hewitt, S., Horsfield, D., MacGowan, I., Robertson, D. & Watt, K. (2001). The biodiversity and conservation of saproxylic Diptera in Scotland. *Journal of Insect Conservation* 5: 77–85.

Shaw, M. (1996). Hymenoptera in relation to insect conservation in Scotland. In: Rotheray, G.E. & MacGowan, I. (eds.), *Conserving Scottish Insects*. Edinburgh Entomological Club: Edinburgh. pp 55–64.

Shirt, D.B. (ed.) (1987). *British Red Data Books: 2 Insects*. NCC: Peterborough.

Smith, R.W.J. & Smith, E.M. (1996). Review of sites and preliminary action plan for *Coenagrion hastulatum*. Scottish Natural Heritage Commissioned Report F96AC304. Unpublished report. SNH: Perth.

Thompson, G. (1980). *Butterflies of Scotland*. Croom Helm: London.

Welch, R.C. (1974). Insects and other Invertebrates. In: Nethersole-Thompson, D. & Watson, A., *The Cairngorms: Their Natural History and Scenery*. Collins: London. pp. 237–245.

Young Associates (2003). *Freshwater Pearl Mussel and River Habitat Survey of a candidate Special Area of Conservation: River South Esk*. Scottish Natural Heritage Research Report F02PA04b (Unpublished, report). SNH: Perth.

Young, M. (2002). The importance of Aspen for Lepidoptera. In: Cosgrove, P. & Amphlett, A. (eds.), *The Biodiversity and Management of Aspen Woodlands: Proceedings of a one-day conference held in Kingussie, Scotland, on 25th May 2001*. Published by The Cairngorms Local Biodiversity Action Plan 2002: Granton-on-Spey. pp. 29–31.

Young, M. & Watt, K.R. (2002). Insects of the Cairngorms. In: Gimingham, C.H. (ed.), *The Ecology, Land Use and Conservation of the Cairngorms*. Packard Publishing Limited: Chichester. pp 54–66.

Young, M.L., Hastie, L.C., Cooksley, S.L., Scougall, F. & Hawkins, C. (2001). *Freshwater Pearl Mussel Survey and River Habitat Survey of the River Spey*. Unpublished and confidential research report for Scottish Natural Heritage.

16. FISH

Colin Bean

Introduction

Of the 57 species of fish currently found in Britain and Ireland (Maitland, 2004), 23 have been recorded from the Cairngorms area. The European Eel *Anguilla anguilla* and a range of euryhaline species[1], such as River Lamprey *Lampetra fluviatilis*, Sea Lamprey *Petromyzon marinus*, Atlantic Salmon *Salmo salar*, Brown or Sea Trout *Salmo trutta*, Arctic Charr *Salvelinus alpinus*, sticklebacks *Gasterosteus aculeatus* and *Pungitius pungitius*, colonised Scottish freshwater habitats from the sea when the ice cap, which covered most of Britain 13,000–15,000 years ago, receded. Brook lamprey *Lampetra planeri* is also present, although it has no known marine affinities. Other freshwater species colonised the UK via water courses that flowed through the land bridge connecting southern Britain with continental Europe about 10,000 years ago. Four of these freshwater species (Pike *Esox lucius*, Perch *Perca fluviatilis*, Minnow *Phoxinus phoxinus* and Stone Loach *Barbatula barbatula*) have been present in Scotland since at least 1790, and have been recorded in the Cairngorms area. Nine other species native to the UK have been introduced into the Cairngorms area in recent times for ornamental or recreational angling purposes. These are: the Common Carp *Cyprinus carpio*, Crucian Carp *Carassius carassius*, Tench *Tinca tinca*, Common Bream *Abramis brama*, Rudd *Scardinius erythrophthalmus*, Roach *Rutilus rutilus*, Orfe *Leuciscus idus* and Dace *Leuciscus leuciscus*. Mirror Carp, a variety of Common Carp not previously recorded in the Cairngorms area, is also reported to be present (Redgewell *et al.*, 2004).

Two fish species not native to Britain (Rainbow Trout *Oncorhynchus mykiss* and Brook Charr (also known as Brook Trout) *Salvelinus fontinalis*) have also been introduced into the Cairngorms area and are present within the National Park. Both are native to the Pacific coast of North America, but, in Britain, are deliberately introduced for angling purposes (SEERAD, 2003a; Maitland, 2004). It is not known whether either species has established self-maintaining populations in the Cairngorms area.

Arctic Charr are present in a number of lochs in the Cairngorms area, mainly those of glacial origin. Together they account for about 5-6% of the known Scottish populations.

Photo: *S. Scott*

[1] Species capable of tolerating a wide range of salinity levels.
[2] A large fish-eating form that may be genetically distinct from other forms of Brown Trout.

Important species and areas

Gardiner and MacKay (2002) provided the first authoritative review of the fish populations of the Cairngorms area, although a previous account was provided by Maitland (1997). Those of particular conservation value in the area include Atlantic Salmon, Brook Lamprey, River Lamprey, Sea Lamprey and Arctic Charr. Post-glacial relict (ancestral) populations of the ferox[2] form of Brown Trout, which may be present in headwater streams and lochs in the Cairngorms area, may also be of conservation value. Table 16.1 lists those species considered to be of national or international importance in the Cairngorms area, and indicates the level of protection afforded to each.

Six of the Cairngorms' protected areas have been designated at least in part for their important fish populations (Table 16.2, Figure 16.1). These include four SACs, one of which – the River Tay – holds internationally important populations of all three lamprey species, as well as Atlantic Salmon. In addition, two SSSIs hold nationally important populations of Arctic Charr: River Spey Insh Marshes SSSI (at Loch Insh) and Eastern Cairngorms SSSI (at Loch Builg).

Atlantic Salmon

Atlantic Salmon are relatively widespread in the Cairngorms, being present in all of the river systems that drain the area (Gardiner & Egglishaw, 1986; Gardiner & Mackay, 2002). Salmon utilise rivers and streams both for their reproduction and nursery stages, and the marine environment during their adult growth phase. They spawn during November and December in excavated depressions in the river substrate, known as 'redds'. To reach suitable spawning areas, adult fish may enter rivers as early as January, and this may continue throughout the year.

Atlantic Salmon pass through a range of life history types or stages. As adults,

Bean, C. (2006). Fish. In: Shaw, P. & Thompson, D.B.A. (eds.). *The Nature of the Cairngorms: Diversity in a changing environment.* The Stationery Office. pp. 269-283.

Table 16.1. Fish species whose populations in the Cairngorms are of national or international importance. Those that qualify on at least one candidate Special Area of Conservation in the Cairngorms area are shown in bold. None of those listed is a BAP Priority species.

Species	EC Habitats Directive[1]	Bern Convention[2]	Percentage of UK population[3]	Sources
Atlantic Salmon	II, V +	Yes	**	SEERAD (2003b)
Brook Lamprey	II	Yes	U	Ecological Research Associates (2004, 2005)
River Lamprey	II,V	Yes	U	Ecological Research Associates (2004, 2005)
Sea Lamprey	II	Yes	U	Ecological Research Associates (2004, 2005)
Arctic Charr	No		-	Davies et al. (2004); Maitland (2004)

[1] Annexes of the EC Habitats Directive on which the species is listed (+ denotes Annex II species protected when in freshwater only).

[2] Listed on Annex III of the Convention on the Conservation of European Wildlife and Natural Habitats. (Annex III species are those whose exploitation is subject to regulation.)

[3] Percentage of the UK population occurring in the Cairngorms area: ** 25–75%; '-' <10%, U, Unknown.

Table 16.2. Important areas for fish in the Cairngorms, listed in descending order of the number of species with populations meeting SAC or SSSI selection criteria.

Area	Species meeting SAC selection criteria	Species meeting SSSI selection criteria only	% of site[1] within: the Cairngorms area	% of site[1] within: the National Park
1. River Tay SAC	Atlantic Salmon, Sea Lamprey, River Lamprey, Brook Lamprey		-	
2. River Spey SAC	Atlantic Salmon, Sea Lamprey		***	**
3. River Dee SAC	Atlantic Salmon		**	**
4. River South Esk SAC	Atlantic Salmon		**	*
5. Loch Builg		Arctic Charr	***	***
6. Loch Insh		Arctic Charr	***	***

[1] Percentage of site occurring within the Cairngorms area or Cairngorms National Park: *** >75%; ** 25–75%; * 10-24%; '-' <10%

they may occur as 'grilse' or as 'salmon', depending on how long they have spent in the marine environment. Grilse are fish that have returned to spawn after spending only one winter at sea, while 'salmon' are fish that have wintered at sea for 2–3 years before returning to their natal rivers to spawn. These are also known as Multi-Sea Winter (MSW) fish.

MSW fish are usually the first fish to enter river systems in any given year. They are generally thought to spawn in the upper catchment areas of rivers, and can be relatively large (3–12 kg). Grilse, by virtue of the fact that they have spent only one winter at sea, are generally smaller than MSW fish, and usually weigh 2–3 kg. Although some fish may enter river systems at other times, they tend to appear in greatest numbers during the summer months (June–August). These fish are thought to spawn in the lower areas of river catchments. Eggs of grilse and MSW fish may occasionally be fertilised by 'precocious parr' – young Atlantic Salmon that have not yet gone to sea, but have become sexually mature while in fresh water. The importance of precocious parr in maintaining genetic diversity in Atlantic Salmon populations is not fully known, but may be significant.

In the Cairngorms, as elsewhere, Atlantic Salmon movements within most of the main streams and major tributaries are generally free from obstructions that might inhibit their movement (Gardiner & Mackay, 2002). However, some man-made obstacles, such as weirs and even some fish passes, may not be navigable at all times. Natural obstacles, such as waterfalls, are present in some tributaries, and these may restrict access to the upper catchments. Stream width and depth are also important, and Atlantic Salmon rarely spawn in streams less than 2 m wide. Low flows and shallowness determine the suitability of such habitats. Gardiner and MacKay (op. cit.) provide a map showing the location of the main spawning streams for Atlantic Salmon in the Cairngorms area, and report that spawning can take place at altitudes of 450–500 m, although some limited spawning may occur as high as 550 m. Examples of high altitude spawning sites in the Cairngorms include the rivers Feshie and Avon.

Once spawning has taken place in suitable habitats, juvenile fish (parr) may spend several years in fresh water before migrating to sea as smolts. The time taken by individual fish to reach the size required to smolt depends on a number of factors, including genetically-based traits, density-dependant

Figure 16.1. Important areas for fish species. Species with nationally or internationally important populations in these areas are listed in Table 16.2.

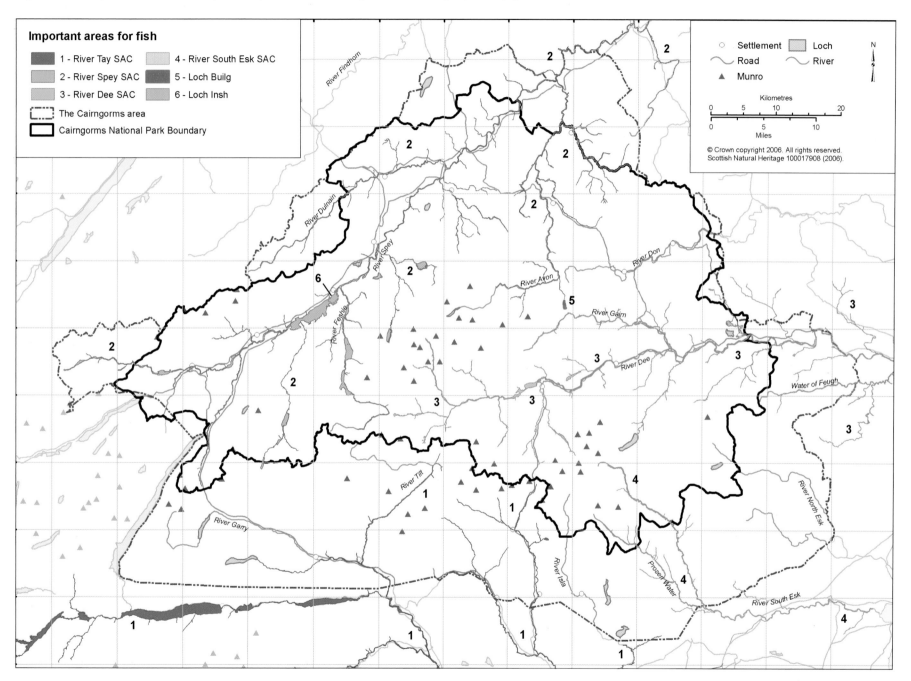

competition for food and space, and water temperature. During the freshwater phase of their life cycle juvenile fish become imprinted on the chemical cues that enable them to navigate back to their natal rivers and streams. The time taken for juvenile fish to pass through to the smolt stage is determined by a number of internal (genetic) and external (environmental) factors, and fish from different sub-catchments in a single river system may migrate at slightly different times, depending on population-specific adaptive traits and prevailing environmental conditions.

A number of rivers whose catchments lie within the Cairngorms area, either in full or in part, are notable for the size and diversity of their Atlantic Salmon populations. They include the Spey, Tay, Dee, Don, North Esk, South Esk, Deveron and Findhorn. Based on summary data provided by SEERAD (2003b) and by CEFAS and the Environment Agency (2003), these rivers accounted for 61% of the Scottish Atlantic Salmon rod-catch and 50% of the UK total during 2002. Of the eight river systems listed above, the River Spey (and its tributaries) is the dominant riverine feature in the National Park, followed by the Dee and Don catchments. Whilst the Findhorn and Deveron catchments lie entirely outside of the National Park, sub-catchments of the River Tay (River Isla), North Esk (Water of Mark and Water of Unich) and South Esk (upper reaches to Loch Esk) lie within its boundaries.

Significant lengths of the rivers Spey, Dee, Don, North Esk and South Esk occur inside the Cairngorms area. Together, these contributed 44% of the Scottish Atlantic Salmon rod-catch and 36% of the UK total during 2002[3]. Although not all of the fish produced by these rivers originate from within the Cairngorms area, it is clear that drainage from those parts of the river catchments that lie within the Cairngorms contribute to Atlantic Salmon production outside of the area.

The dominant river system within the Cairngorms area, the River Spey, contributed 11% of the Scottish rod catch of Atlantic Salmon during 2002. Grilse accounted for more of the catch (14%) than MSW fish (9%). In terms of its contribution to the UK rod-catch, the River Spey contributed 7% of the UK total, 9% of the UK grilse catch and 7% of the UK MSW salmon catch. Although the main stem of the River Spey is an important spawning site in its own right, many of its tributaries are also of high importance, including the rivers Avon, Livet, Nethy, Dulnain, Einich, Feshie, Tromie and Truim. Spawning also takes place in smaller sub-catchments, such as Allt Mór,

Raitts Burn and the River Calder. The Spey's Atlantic Salmon population is a qualifying feature in the River Spey Special Area of Conservation (SAC), reflecting its importance on a European scale.

The River Dee is the next largest river catchment in the Cairngorms area. In 2002, it contributed 6% of the Scottish rod catch of Atlantic Salmon, including 5% of the grilse and MSW fish caught by rod The Dee also contributed 5% of the UK total catch, 4% of the UK grilse catch and 6% of the UK MSW salmon catch. As well as spawning throughout the length of the Dee, Atlantic Salmon spawn in extensive reaches of a number of its sub-catchments, including the Muick, Gairn, Baddoch/Clunie, Ey and Geldie sub-catchments. Spawning also occurs in the Girnock Burn, Feadar Burn, Pollagach Burn, Bynack Burn, and in lower reaches of the Upper Dee, Lui and Quoich sub-catchments. Like the Spey, the River Dee has also been afforded SAC status on account of its Atlantic Salmon, reflecting the species' abundance and the range of life-history types represented.

The River Don is the third largest of the major river catchments in the Cairngorms area. The smaller size of this catchment is reflected in its overall rod-catch. During 2002, the Don contributed 4% of the total Scottish Atlantic Salmon rod catch. In contrast to the Spey and in common with the Dee, the grilse catch was lower (3%) than that achieved for MSW fish (4%). In terms of its contribution to the UK rod-catch, the Don accounted for 3% of the UK total catch, the grilse catch and of the MSW salmon catch. Atlantic Salmon spawn throughout the length of the River Don and also extensively throughout the Water of Nochty, Water of Buchat, Deskry Water and Ernan Water.

The headwaters of the River North Esk are located within the drainage basin of Loch Lee. Tributaries of the North Esk that lie within the Cairngorms area include the Water of Mark and the Water of Unich. While the main stem of the River North Esk does not fall within the National Park, these tributaries are two of the largest sub-catchments in the North Esk system. Atlantic Salmon are present in both sub-catchments, which Gardiner and Egglishaw (1986) consider to be major spawning areas for this species. The River North Esk contributed 14% of the Scottish rod-catch during 2002 and 11% of the UK total. Grilse were dominant in the North Esk Atlantic Salmon catches, accounting for 22% of the Scottish rod-catch and 20% of the UK total. MSW fish accounted for 8% and 7% of the Scottish and UK totals, respectively.

---

[3] Data for the River Tay are not included in this estimate since although the River Isla sub-catchment of the Tay system lies partly within the Cairngorms area, Atlantic Salmon are prevented from accessing this catchment upstream of Airlie.

The River South Esk extends into the Cairngorms area as far as Loch Esk, which Atlantic Salmon are unable to reach. This river contributed 9% of the Scottish rod catch of Atlantic Salmon during 2002. Like the rivers North Esk and Spey, the grilse catch was higher (14%) than the MSW fish catch (6%). In terms of its contribution to the UK rod-catch, the River South Esk contributed 7% of the UK total, 12% of the UK grilse catch and 4% of the UK MSW salmon catch. Like the Spey and Dee, the river's Atlantic Salmon population is a qualifying feature on the River South Esk SAC, the boundary of which extends into Cairngorms National Park.

Atlantic Salmon are not restricted to rivers and streams, occurring in a number of lochs in the Cairngorms area as they pass through onto spawning streams. Within the Spey catchment, these include lochs Bhrodainn, an t-Seilich, Cuaich, Crunachdan, Einich, Builg, Morlich, Insh and Loch an Eilean. Atlantic Salmon are also present in Loch Muick on the Dee catchment and in Loch Lee on the River North Esk catchment.

In addition to being a species of conservation interest in its own right, juvenile Atlantic Salmon play an important role in the ecology of the Freshwater Pearl Mussel *Margaritifera margaritifera*, a BAP Priority species whose larvae parasitise juvenile salmon (Chapter 15). The Freshwater Pearl Mussel is undergoing a general decline throughout its holarctic range, and Scotland is now considered to be a global stronghold for the species, supporting approximately half of the world's known remaining viable populations (Young *et al*, 2001a). Even within Scotland, a range of factors, including pearl fishing and river engineering, have resulted in a loss of some populations (Cosgrove *et al.*, 2000) and declines in Atlantic Salmon numbers may pose a threat to the long-term survival of the mussel (Cosgrove & Hastie, 2001).

Lamprey species

Three species of lamprey exist in Scottish freshwaters: the Brook, River and Sea Lamprey. Although they have much in common, there are significant ecological differences between the three.

The life cycle of River and Sea Lampreys involves the migration of adults between freshwater and marine habitats. In contrast, Brook Lamprey remain in freshwater throughout their life cycle, although some upstream migration may occur during the spawning period. Spawning usually takes place on stony or gravelly stretches of running water (Maitland & Campbell, 1992). Once there, lamprey spawn either in pairs or in groups, and lay their fertilised eggs in

shallow depressions, or nests, previously created by clearing away small stones with their suckers. Gravel with a diameter of 9.5–50.8 mm and small amounts of sand must be present for successful nest construction either by Brook or River Lamprey. The larger Sea Lamprey requires gravel with a diameter of 15–115 mm to construct its nests, which are typically located in open, shallow water, but may also occur under large stones, logs or clumps of vegetation.

Adults are very vulnerable to predators when nest building. The timing of spawning varies between species, with Brook and River Lamprey spawning earlier (March–April) than Sea Lamprey (late May–June). The larger size of Sea Lamprey, and their choice of substrate, may mean that spawning sites are spatially separated from those of Brook and River Lamprey. Empirical evidence for this is lacking, however. Spawning sites are typically at a depth of 10–50 cm (Entec, 2000), but can occur in shallower water.

After hatching, lamprey larvae, known as ammocoetes, either swim or are washed downstream by the current, to areas of sandy silt in still or slow-moving water. The optimum particle size of sediment beds in which they occur is thought to be 0.18–0.38 mm, and should include clay, silt and sand fractions. Once a suitable area has been located, the ammocoetes burrow into the substrate and may spend up to five years there, feeding on organic particles (coated with bacteria), minute plants and algae, such as diatoms. Suitable sites may only occur in some reaches of each river system, and in some rivers habitat suitable for spawning or for juveniles may be absent. In British streams, most populations occur where the average stream gradients are 1.9–5.7 m per km, and lampreys are rarely found where gradients exceed 7.8 m per km (Maitland, 2003). Within stretches of a suitable gradient, adequate sites are often found in conditions of slowing current, where there is active deposition of sand and silt. Ammocoetes have been known to inhabit substrates in rivers up to 2.2 m deep, and in lakes up to 16 m deep.

The metamorphosis from ammocoete to adult is a dramatic change, which takes place over a few weeks, usually between July–September. The transformation involves changes to skin pigmentation, the development of eyes and of adult, disk-like, mouthparts. The size at which ammocoetes transform into adults differs between species. River Lamprey transform at a length of 9–12 cm and Sea Lamprey at 12–14.5 cm. Interestingly, Brook Lamprey, the smallest of the three lamprey species in Scotland, transform at a larger size (12–15 cm) than anadromous[4] forms (Maitland, 2003; Ecological Research Associates, 2004, 2005).

[4] Species or forms that spawn in freshwater but spend part of their life cycle in the sea.

Following metamorphosis lampreys migrate, usually downstream, away from their nursery areas. Brook Lamprey never feed as adults, and spawn, then die having spent their entire life in freshwater. River and Sea Lamprey, by contrast, prey on other fish, either in large freshwater lakes and rivers or in the sea, where most of their adult life is spent. On reaching sexual maturity, adult lamprey stop feeding and return to their spawning streams. Like the Brook Lamprey, River and Sea Lamprey die after spawning.

Brook Lamprey

The Brook Lamprey is the smallest of the British lampreys. Its larvae are virtually indistinguishable from those of the River Lamprey, except when nearing metamorphosis (Gardiner, 2003). It has been suggested that the Brook Lamprey may be a non-anadromous form of the River Lamprey, rather than a separate species (Gardiner & MacKay, 2002).

The Brook Lamprey is the most abundant and widespread of the British lampreys, but has declined in parts of the UK. It is often found in the absence of the other two species, for example above a barrier that excludes its (migratory)

The Brook Lamprey is the smallest and most abundant of the British lampreys, but has declined in parts of the UK.

Photo: *A. MacEwan/OSF*

congeners. It was previously thought that Brook Lamprey were absent from much of Scotland north of the Great Glen, including Orkney, Shetland and all but a few of the Western Isles. The recent, SNH-funded National Lamprey Survey confirmed that Brook Lamprey are indeed absent from the Northern Isles, but found them to be present as far north as Loch Carron, with populations in east Sutherland, Caithness, Easter Ross and, notably, an isolated population on the Isle of Lewis. The study confirmed that Brook Lamprey were more prevalent in rivers south of the Great Glen.

Brook Lamprey are common and widespread in the rivers and lower reaches of tributary streams in the Cairngorms area (Gardiner & MacKay, 2002) and are known to occur in all of the major rivers. Within the National Park, Brook Lamprey are present in the River Don and its tributaries (Deskry Water and Water of Buchat), rivers North Esk and South Esk, River Spey and its tributaries (rivers Dulnain, Nethy, Avon and Livet), as well as many smaller burns (e.g. Crom Allt and Allt Lorgy). Although no lampreys have been recorded from the rivers Druie, Feshie, Truim, Tromie or Calder (Cairngorms Partnership, 1999), the National Lamprey Survey may yet find evidence of their existence in these sites. Only one tributary of the River Tay lies within the National Park; the River Isla. At least two records of Sea Lamprey exist for this site, and it is highly likely that Brook Lamprey is also present. Elsewhere in the Cairngorms area, Brook Lamprey have been recorded in the Burn of Cattie, River Garry and the River Tilt. It is likely that Brook Lamprey also exist in other Tay tributaries that extend into the Cairngorms area (e.g. Errochty Water, Bruar Water, Fender Burn and Black Water).

River Lamprey

The River Lamprey is also widespread in the UK, occurring in many rivers from the Great Glen in Scotland southwards, and has many strong populations. River Lamprey populations have been recorded in 42 mainland rivers, but are absent from the Northern and Western Isles (Ecological Research Associates, 2004, 2005). There is little information relating to the distribution of River Lamprey north of the Great Glen, although populations are known to exist in the rivers Shiel (Lochaber) and Conon (Ecological Research Associates *op. cit.*). Several sites with healthy populations of River Lamprey, clear water and suitable areas of gravel, silt or sand for spawning, have been selected as SACs. River Lamprey are qualifying interests in four freshwater SACs: the rivers Tay, Teith, Tweed and the Endrick Water. Marine sites considered to be important migration routes or feeding grounds for the species have also been selected, usually where they abut onto a freshwater site, as, for example, at the Solway Firth.

River Lamprey have been recorded in almost all of the major river systems in the Cairngorms area (rivers Spey, Don, North Esk, South Esk and Tay) but are absent from the River Dee (Ecological Research Associates, 2004, 2005). In the Spey, River Lamprey have been recorded as far upstream as Spey Dam. They have also been recorded in the Water of Buchat, a tributary of the Don that lies within the National Park. Some records exist for the rivers North and South Esk, and it is possible that River Lampreys could be present on stretches of these rivers within the National Park boundary. The species' inability to ascend physical obstacles, such as waterfalls, may restrict their distribution to the lower reaches of these catchments. One possible record exists for the River Isla, the only tributary of the River Tay that extends into the National Park.

Sea Lamprey

The Sea Lamprey is considered to be the rarest of the three lamprey species in Scotland. Sea Lamprey have been recorded from 35 rivers around Scotland (Ecological Research Associates, 2004, 2005). It occurs in estuaries and easily accessible rivers, and is an anadromous species. Like Brook and River Lamprey, Sea Lampreys require clean gravel for spawning, and marginal silt or sand for the burrowing juvenile ammocoetes. Features such as weirs, dams and polluted sections of river may impede migration to spawning grounds. In comparison with River Lamprey, Sea Lampreys appear to be even less capable of ascending obstacles to migrate, and are frequently restricted to the lower reaches of rivers.

The Sea Lamprey occurs over much of the Atlantic coastal area of western and northern Europe, from northern Norway to the western Mediterranean, and in eastern North America. It is also found in estuaries and easily accessible rivers in these regions. The Sea Lamprey is reasonably widespread in UK rivers, and is common in places, but has declined or become extinct in a number of rivers. It appears to reach its northern limit of distribution in Scotland and no records exist from north of the Great Glen.

Several sites with reliable records of Sea Lamprey, and which contain the necessary habitat requirements for spawning and survival of juveniles, have been selected as SACs. In Scotland, these waters include the rivers Spey, Tay, Tweed and Teith. As for River Lamprey, marine sites considered to be important migration routes or feeding grounds for Sea Lamprey species have also been selected, usually where they abut onto a freshwater site (e.g. the Solway Firth).

The River Lamprey is a qualifying feature on four SACs in Scotland, one of which - the Tay - lies partly within the Cairngorms area.
Photo: *J. Paling/OSF*

The Sea Lamprey is the rarest of our three species. Like the Brook and River Lamprey it requires clean gravel for spawning. It appears to be less capable of ascending obstacles to migrate, and so is usually restricted to the lower reaches of rivers.
Photo: *NHPA*

Sea Lamprey are known to ascend the rivers Spey, Don, North Esk, South Esk and Tay, although the distance travelled upstream is strongly limited by the presence of physical barriers, such as waterfalls. Gardiner and Mackay (2002) suggest that adult Sea Lamprey are unlikely to be able to penetrate the rivers Don and Tay as far inland as the Cairngorms area. The same is possibly true of the rivers North and South Esk, although Sea Lamprey in the Spey are known to occur as far upstream as Kingussie. SNH's Site Condition Monitoring Programme (APEM, 2002, 2004; Laughton & Burns, 2003) has shown that Sea Lamprey ammocoetes occur as far north as Boat of Garten. One record exists for juvenile Sea Lamprey in the River Isla, within the Park boundary.

Arctic Charr

As its name suggests, the Arctic Charr *Salvelinus alpinus* is a stenothermic[5], holarctic species, which occurs in lakes and rivers throughout the northern hemisphere. In the northern parts of its range, Arctic Charr may form mixed anadromous and non-anadromous populations. Populations at above 65°N exhibit anadromous behaviour patterns where they have access to marine habitats, while those south of 65°N almost certainly originated from anadromous ancestors, but became non-anadromous or 'land-locked' during post-glacial times.

Most of the Arctic Charr populations that currently exist in Scotland are natural, although some are of anthropogenic origin. Hydroelectric and water storage schemes have been responsible for the majority of these transplantations. Examples include the incidental movement of Arctic Charr from Loch Awe to the Cruachan Reservoir in Argyll, and from Loch Garry to Loch Errochty in Tayside, when water is passed from one body to another for hydroelectricity generation. Maitland *et al.* (1984) calculated that less than 3% of the 3,788 lochs in Scotland with a surface area greater than 5 ha are known to contain Arctic Charr. Occupied lochs are usually of glacial origin and characterised by their moderate altitude, depth, oligotrophic nutrient status and acid to neutral pH. Although there appear to be no native anadromous Arctic Charr populations in Scotland, some fish have been captured in riverine environments. Maitland *et al.* (*op. cit.*) provide a review of such captures and suggest that these fish have either been displaced by power station entrainments, are spawning individuals, or are the resulting juveniles, which migrate back into their original parental loch habitat.

In keeping with their environmental requirements, the distribution of Arctic Charr in Britain and Ireland is polarised towards northern upland areas. In Scotland, Arctic Charr are generally regarded as being unimportant in economic or sporting terms, and this has meant that many isolated populations may remain unreported. Of the approximately 250 known Arctic Charr populations in Britain and Ireland (Davies *et al.*, 2004; Maitland, 2004), the majority are located in the Scottish Highlands, where 200 populations may exist (Greer, 1995).

Three ecologically and morphologically distinct forms of Arctic Charr have been described in Loch Rannoch (Gardner *et al.*, 1988; Walker *et al.*, 1988; Adams *et al.*, 1998), of which two also show significant genetic differences (Hartley *et al.*, 1992), suggesting that they are reproductively isolated. Data regarding the extent of polymorphism in other Scottish lochs are few, possibly reflecting the level of scientific interest in this species and the geographical isolation of some populations. However, more recent surveys in Perthshire lochs have suggested that polymorphism may also occur at a number of other sites in the area (Fraser *et al.*, 1998), and it is likely that considerably more exist throughout Scotland (Alexander & Adams, 2000).

Few data are available regarding the spawning behaviour of Arctic Charr in Scotland, which is generally considered to occur from late September to early December, over gravel and stone substrates, either in shallow, littoral habitats or on submerged reefs (Maitland & Campbell, 1992). While it is likely that most Scottish Arctic Charr populations spawn in lochs, a small number of populations utilise streams or rivers. Maitland *et al.* (1984) provide a list of populations known to spawn in riverine environments, including lochs Insh, na Sealga and Tarff. Further work on this species may yield more examples of this behaviour.

Arctic Charr are known to be present in a number of lochs in the Cairngorms area, including Loch an t-Seilich, lochs Bhrodainn, Einich, Builg, Avon, Lee, Callater, Cuaich and Insh. Two of these populations (at Loch Insh and Loch Builg) are notified features of the River Spey Insh Marshes and East Cairngorms SSSIs, respectively. Outwith the Cairngorms National Park, but within the Cairngorms area, Arctic Charr are present in Loch an Duin, Loch Loch, Loch Garry and Loch Errochty. Approximately 5.6% of known Scottish populations occur within the Cairngorms area; 4% within the National Park. Additional, unsurveyed Arctic Charr sites may yet be found in the Cairngorms area.

Brown/Sea Trout

Brown Trout are almost ubiquitous throughout the Cairngorms area, and are present in almost every stream and loch up to an altitude of 450 m (Gardiner & Mackay, 2002). Brown Trout are also present in some lochs at higher

---

[5] Capable of living or growing only within a narrow range of temperatures.

altitudes, including Dubh Lochan on Beinn a' Bhuird (at 843 m). This is possibly the highest altitude in Britain at which a self-sustaining fish population exists (Campbell, 1970). Brown Trout present in streams and lochs above impassable waterfalls may be reproductively isolated from other populations, and may constitute a unique genetic resource. At least two populations are thought to have become extinct within Cairngorms National Park – at lochs Etchachan and nan Stuirteag – for reasons that are currently unclear (Morrison & Harriman, 1992). 'Ferox' trout are known to be present in one loch within the Cairngorms area (Loch Garry), but have not been recorded in the National Park. Ferox trout are commonly associated with Arctic Charr, and it is possible that other populations exist in the Cairngorms, where the two species coincide.

In areas of a river catchment where productivity is low and access to the sea is assured, Brown Trout may have retained their ability to smolt and become Sea Trout. Quite apart from their value as a component of fish biodiversity in the Cairngorms area, Sea Trout production in rivers that drain the area constitute a major fisheries resource. The rivers North Esk and South Esk are particularly well known for their Sea Trout populations, and in 2002 accounted for 10% and 9%, respectively, of the Scottish rod-caught Sea Trout total.

Recent research, surveys and trends

Most of the fish survey work undertaken in the Cairngorms area has involved the study of **_Atlantic Salmon_** populations. Historical catch records, available since 1952, have shown an increase in the number of Atlantic Salmon caught annually up to the 1960s, and a steady decline since the mid-1970s. While declines have been most severe on the west coast, they have also been reported in east coast systems.

A number of radio-tracking studies in Scottish rivers over the last two decades (Laughton, 1989; Webb & Hawkins, 1989; Webb, 1992) have demonstrated a strong association between the timing of Atlantic Salmon runs and the subsequent location of the fish at spawning time. Early-running (spring) fish tend to penetrate further into catchments and spawn at higher altitudes than later-running fish. In rivers originating in the Cairngorms area, declines in spring Atlantic Salmon catches have caused the most concern, and have focussed attention on the status of populations in the higher reaches of river catchments.

Although juvenile survey data are available for a large number of sites in the Cairngorms area, from the Scottish Fisheries Co-ordination Centre (SFCC), few data have been published in a format allowing a detailed examination of population trends. The catchments of the rivers Spey, Dee and Tay, in particular, are large, and although a number of core sites are sampled every year by the Spey Research Trust and the Dee and Tay District Salmon Fishery Boards, they are often undertaken on a rotational basis. Juvenile monitoring is also undertaken by the Esk District Salmon Fishery Board. This means that annual data for specific areas, outwith the core sampling sites, are relatively few. The District Salmon Fishery Board and Fisheries Trusts (pers. comm.) have suggested that while juvenile numbers appear to have remained relatively constant, the number of returning adults has given cause for concern.

Historical records show that the River Spey has supported an Atlantic Salmon fishery for many years. Despite noted declines elsewhere in Scotland, the River Spey maintained an average catch of approximately 10,000 fish per annum during the 1950s–1990s, but with lower catches during 1996–2001. Although fish numbers remained reasonably constant over that time, an increase in the number of grilse in the river (which normally run between July and September) and a decrease in spring salmon (which run between February and June) has been noted.

The Pitlochry fish counter provides the best estimate of Atlantic Salmon abundance in the Tay system. Eatherley _et al._ (2004) demonstrated that counter data from Pitlochry Dam and rod catch data are positively correlated. Data available for the Pitlochry counter suggests that while fish numbers are lower than those observed during the 1970s, catches have not shown the catastrophic decline evident elsewhere. Few reliable historical data are available from the Logie design fish counter located on the River North Esk. However, rod catch data suggest that fish numbers have risen significantly since 1980. Independent fish counter data are not available for the River South Esk, although a total catch of 5,108 grilse and MSW salmon during 2002 suggest that the number of returning adults remains acceptably high.

Data from those rivers in which Atlantic Salmon is a qualifying SAC interest (the Spey, Dee, South Esk and Tay) are currently being analysed by SFCC and SEERAD Fisheries Research Services, as part of SNH's Site Condition Monitoring programme. This evaluation, which includes an assessment of both juvenile and adult population trends against historical data, will be used to judge whether Atlantic Salmon populations in these sites are in 'favourable condition'.

Lamprey have been largely ignored by fishery biologists in many areas of the UK, partly because they have no commercial or recreational angling value. They are also difficult to sample adequately with conventional techniques used for assessing salmon and trout populations. Despite their lack of value as a sporting quarry, academic researchers have produced a considerable volume of data relating to the distribution and biology of this species within some areas of the UK, (reviewed in Maitland, 2003).

The inclusion of the UK's three lamprey species on Annex II of the EC Habitats Directive has led to renewed interest in this species by the UK Conservation Agencies and fisheries biologists, and this has led, in turn, to a dramatic increase in the volume of lamprey survey work being undertaken (e.g. APEM, 2002, 2004; Laughton & Burns, 2003). The SNH-funded National Lamprey Survey spanned 2003–04, and analyses were completed during 2005. This study, carried out by Ecological Research Associates (ERA) aimed at assessing the distribution of each of the three lamprey species in Scotland. Although it is clear that lamprey species are much more widely distributed than was first thought (Ecological Research Associates, 2004, 2005), no fully quantitative data are available for areas outwith the SACs designated for these species. Semi-quantitative data gathered as part of the National Lamprey Survey should provide a baseline for further work.

Arctic Charr. With the exception of two populations identified as notified features on SSSIs (lochs Insh and Builg), no quantitative data are available to assess the current status of existing populations. Both sites were surveyed as part of SNH's Site Condition Monitoring programme during 2003–04 (Winfield *et al.*, 2003, 2004). These surveys confirmed that both populations were in favourable condition and that no habitat problems were apparent. Data obtained for the Loch Insh Arctic Charr population suggest that from a demographic viewpoint, it was in good condition. Similar information has been gathered for the Arctic Charr population at Loch Builg. These data will serve as a baseline for future assessment of Arctic Charr populations at these sites.

Conservation issues

Maitland (1994) provides a generic list of the main pressures facing freshwater fish and their habitats in Scotland, many of which apply to the Cairngorms area. They include: industrial and domestic pollution; acid deposition; land use practices; industrial development (including roads); warm water discharge; river obstruction (dams); infilling, drainage and canalisation; water abstraction; fluctuating water levels (reservoirs); fish farming; angling and fishery management; commercial fishing; the introduction of new species; and climate change.

Gardiner and MacKay (2002) considered those issues that have particular relevance to fish species in the Cairngorms area, and suggest that acidification, forestry, land use, industrial/domestic pollution, hydroelectric development, obstruction of fish migration routes, the introduction of new species, the spread of existing species, predator control and over-fishing are key issues. Many of these issues apply to freshwater habitats generally, and are described in Chapter 9. The following remarks relate more specifically to fish populations.

Industrial and domestic pollution. Localised, nutrient enrichment problems may occasionally occur in the Cairngorms area, as a result of industrial or domestic discharges (Davidson *et al.*, 2002) (see Chapter 9). Warm water discharges, relating to whisky production, also occur. Temperature gradients may occur in relatively short stretches of some watercourses, with slight or moderate impacts on fish populations.

Land Use. Point- and diffuse pollutants can lead to an increased risk of acidification and eutrophication. Erosion and siltation can also occur, in streams and rivers bisecting or abutting with forestry plantations or agricultural land. Although negative impacts may be associated with older forestry plantations, the development of the Cairngorms Forestry Framework and the new *Forest and Water Guidelines* (Forestry Commission, 2003), mean that forestry operations should not impact negatively on freshwater habitats, or the fish species they support, in future years.

Acid deposition. Fish populations throughout much of Europe have been seriously affected by atmospheric pollutants over much of the last century. Due to a range of factors, including topography, underlying base-poor geology, high rainfall levels and snow melt, freshwater habitats in the Highlands and Southern Uplands of Scotland are particularly sensitive to acidification and the occurrence of short-duration low pH episodes. Rapid and longer-term pH reduction can result in the mortality of Atlantic Salmon and Brown/Sea Trout. This is particularly true during sensitive stages of their life cycles, most notably during hatching and smoltification (Harriman *et al.*, 1990). Aluminium compounds may also be mobilised by low pH conditions and these may, in turn, reach levels that damage the gill structure of fish and affect their ability to osmoregulate.

Acidification can also affect fish by reducing the diversity and biomass of invertebrate prey in affected streams (Hildrew & Ormerod, 1995). Acid conditions are not uncommon in running and standing waters in the Cairngorms area. Although acidification has occurred in the area over much of the last century (Patrick *et al.*, 1989; Jones *et al.*, 1993), it should be noted that some habitats may be naturally acidic as a result of decomposing organic matter, such as peat.

Hydro-electric development. The impoundment of the upper reaches of the River Spey at Spey Dam to provide energy for British Alcan is perhaps the biggest example of this type of development within the boundary of the National Park. Scottish and Southern Energy also extract water from within the National Park, at the rivers Tromie, Truim and Allt Cuaich, to supply the Tummel-Garry scheme. Although a large number of fish passes have been installed at affected sites, Atlantic Salmon are prevented from reaching the upper reaches of the Allt Cuaich. Impoundment above the Spey Dam has also led to the 'flooding out' and loss of some spawning and juvenile holding habitat in this area.

Species introductions and colonisation. A number non-native fish species have been introduced into the Cairngorms area in recent years. Some of these, including Pike, Perch, Minnow and Stone Loach, have been present for many decades or even hundreds of years. Others, such as the Common Carp, Crucian Carp, Tench, Common Bream, Rudd, Roach, Orfe, Dace and Mirror Carp, are more recent arrivals, and are thought to be less widespread. Pike have been present in Scotland for many centuries and are widespread in lochs in the Cairngorms area. As predators of other fish species, the translocation of Pike, or any other species, to waters where they do not currently exist should be actively discouraged. Salmonid species, such as Rainbow Trout and Brook Charr, are also present in the Cairngorms, and are used for sporting purposes. Care must be taken to ensure that they do not escape into the wild, where they can compete with native salmonids for food or space. The recent discovery of North American Signal Crayfish *Pacifasticus leniusculus* in the nearby River Nairn and in two ponds within the catchments of the rivers North Esk and Tay, also give cause for concern.

Translocating fish that are indigenous to the Cairngorms area, such as Arctic Charr, Atlantic Salmon and Brown Trout, should also be avoided. Since little is known of the level of sympatry between existing Arctic Charr populations in the Cairngorms, the ecological impact of translocating of this species to lochs in which it already occurs should be avoided. The impacts of moving Atlantic Salmon or Brown Trout within the Cairngorms area are considered below.

Fisheries management. Sport fisheries exist for Atlantic Salmon and Brown/Sea Trout in most or all of the river systems of the Cairngorms area. Atlantic Salmon stocks are generally regarded as being the most important fishery in economic terms, although Brown/Sea Trout and, to a more limited extent, Pike fishing, also contribute to the angling economy.

All of the major catchments in the Cairngorms area support significant Atlantic Salmon fisheries. Grilse make up a large proportion of the catch in these rivers, but a decline in the number of MSW fish gives cause for concern. Although one of the primary reasons for this decline is low marine survival, it is clear that fisheries management must play a major role in the conservation of MSW fish stocks. Conservation policies, such as catch-and-release, now exist for MSW Atlantic Salmon originating in the Cairngorms area. The Esk District Salmon Fishery Board has asked the Scottish Executive to introduce a range of statutory measures to assist in the conservation of salmon under the Salmon Act 1986 (as amended by the Salmon Conservation (Scotland) Act 2001) to ban the capture or retention of all MSW Atlantic Salmon during periods when they are most vulnerable to capture in the Esk system.

Supplementary fish stocking is widely practiced throughout the Cairngorms area. In the past, stocking has been used to restore or enhance fish stocks, to compensate for habitat loss and to re-establish fish stocks in waters where they no longer occur. Some stocking also occurs in areas that are naturally inaccessible to Atlantic Salmon, giving cause for concern. Recent research (e.g. McGinnity *et al.*, 2003) has shown that the genetic integrity of Atlantic Salmon populations can undergo irreversible damage or loss if the population is subjected to repeated stocking events. In addition to the deliberate release of fish, the constant 'drip-feeding' of hatchery or fish farm escapees may cause significantly more damage than one-off stocking events.

The impact of trout stocking on natural trout populations is likely to be similar to that postulated for Atlantic Salmon. Trout fisheries are less well developed in the Cairngorms area, and populations located in small upland lochs may be subjected to unsustainable levels of angling pressure. Few data are available to assess the current impact of angling on these populations, and active management is virtually absent.

One other area of concern from a fisheries management perspective is the increased risk of parasite or disease transfer to Atlantic Salmon from rivers outwith Scotland. The advent of cheap air travel has meant that anglers have an increased potential to fish abroad, and for contaminated angling equipment to act as a vector for parasite or disease transfer from one area of Europe to another. Recent attention has focussed on the potential transfer of the parasitic fluke *Gyrodactylus salaris* into Scottish waters. This parasite, which would have a catastrophic impact on native Atlantic Salmon stocks, as well as other aquatic species of conservation concern, is more likely to be transferred into those rivers that are regularly fished by anglers specialising in this species. All of the major systems that drain the Cairngorms area can be considered to be key Atlantic salmon angling venues in Scotland. Equipment disinfection procedures should be applied by all individuals or groups who use rivers for recreation in the National Park.

In addition to sport fishing for salmonids and a (more limited) potential for coarse angling, for species such as Pike or Perch, some commercial exploitation of European Eel populations took place in Loch Insh during the 1980s. Data presented by Pullan (1986), Bloor (1988) and Witcamp (1989) suggest that eel fisheries within the National Park could be considered to be small-scale when compared to similar fisheries elsewhere in Europe. European Eel populations are declining rapidly throughout their former range and ICES has now produced an emergency plan to try to tackle this. Given the panmictic nature of the species, it may be that a better case could be made for general controls and protection measures, rather than for protection through particular local sites. However, it may in future be possible to set up a network of sites throughout the UK to offer some protection if populations continue to decline at the current rate.

Legal predator control. The control of fish-eating birds and mammals, and their impact on fish species of commercial or sporting value, continues to be an issue throughout Scotland, including the Cairngorms area. Some level of control is exercised through the granting of licences to shoot piscivorous birds, such as Cormorant *Phalacrocorax carbo* and sawbill ducks, although licence applications must demonstrate that the birds are causing '... *serious damage to fisheries'* and that '... *no other satisfactory solution can be found'*. The control of seals is more complex. While seals have the potential to predate Atlantic Salmon and Sea Trout from the Cairngorms during their marine phase, the magnitude of this threat is unclear. Recent attention has focussed on assessing the impact of seals entering freshwater habitats and predating salmonids, especially in rivers or estuaries. While the Conservation of Seals Act 1970 allows for the provision of licences to control seals for the protection of fisheries, outbreaks of Phocine Distemper Virus in 1998 and 2002 resulted in the passing of additional legislation, in the form of the Conservation of Seals (Scotland) Order 2002. This prohibited the killing, injuring or taking of Common Seals anywhere in Scotland during September 2002–04. A new Seal Management Plan, which may influence the way in which seals are controlled within the environs of the River Spey, is currently under development.

In some cases conflict may arise between the need to control predator numbers and the requirement to protect sites or species within the SSSI, SAC or SPA series. For example, birds that forage within the Cairngorms area may be a notified feature of a site that lies outwith it. Clearly, more research is required before such conflicts can be resolved.

Habitat loss. Access to spawning and holding areas is regarded as a major issue in many catchments and sub-catchments in the Cairngorms area. The need for Atlantic Salmon, particularly MSW fish, to access the upper catchment areas of rivers to spawn has long been recognised and The Salmon (Fish Passes and Screens) (Scotland) Regulations 1994 were designed to ensure that fish access is maintained. Despite this, a large number of man-made obstacles to Atlantic Salmon and Sea Trout migration exist. Thirteen of these obstacles in the River Spey will be removed or modified, as part of the EC LIFE Salmon project, and additional fish access and habitat rehabilitation works will be carried out on the rivers South Esk, Dee and Tay as part of the same project. In future, river engineering works and water abstraction will be subject to licensing procedures as part of The Water Environment (Controlled Activities) (Scotland) Regulations 2004.

Lamprey species (particularly River and Sea Lamprey) and European Eel also require free access between freshwater and marine environments, and their requirements are often neglected. Sea Lamprey are restricted to the main stem of the River Spey, and access may not be an issue for this species in this locality. Little is known about the movement of lamprey species in other catchments in the Cairngorms area. Although the situation regarding the European Eel is also unclear, it is suggested that small in-river obstacles may not present a serious problem for them.

Climate change. Climate change was identified by Maitland (1991, 1994) as a factor likely to impact on fish populations in the UK and elsewhere in Europe. The frequency of severe flooding and drought events can have a damaging impact on the recruitment and survival of salmonids in rivers and streams draining the Cairngorms area. Temperature variations in running and standing water habitats may impact both on fish and on the invertebrates on which they feed, leading to reduced individual growth rates and recruitment potential, as well as access to suitable spawning habitat.

References

Adams, C.E., Fraser, D., Huntingford, F.A, Greer, R.B., Askew, C.M. & Walker, A.F. (1998).. Trophic polymorphism amongst Arctic charr from Loch Rannoch, Scotland. *Journal of Fish Biology* 52: 1259–1271.

Alexander, G.D. & Adams, C.E. (2000). The phenotypic diversity of Arctic charr, *Salvelinus alpinus*, (Salmonidae) in Scotland and Ireland. *Journal of Ichthyology and Aquatic Biology* 4: 77–88.

APEM (2002). *Distribution of Sea, Brook and River Lampreys on the River Tay*. Scottish Natural Heritage Commissioned Report F01AC610. SNH: Perth.

APEM (2004). *Assessment of sea lamprey distribution and abundance in the River Spey: Phase II*. Scottish Natural Heritage Commissioned Report F01AC608. SNH: Perth.

Bloor, P.D. (1988). Eel Fishing in the River Spey and Loch Insh. Report to the Nature Conservancy Council, North East Scotland Region.

Campbell, R.N. (1970). The growth of brown trout, *Salmo trutta* L., in northern Scotland with special reference to the improvement of fisheries. *Journal of Fish Biology* 3: 1–28.

CEFAS & Environment Agency (2003). *Salmon Stocks and Fisheries in England and Wales, 2002*. Preliminary assessment prepared for ICES, April 2003.

Cosgrove, P.J. & Hastie, L. (2001). River management, translocation and conflict resolution in the conservation of threatened freshwater pearl mussels. *Biological Conservation* 99: 183–190.

Cosgrove, P.J., Young, M.R., Hastie, L. & Boon, P.J. (2000). The status of freshwater pearl mussel *Margeratifera margeratifera* (L.) in Scotland. *Aquatic Conservation: Marine and Freshwater Ecosystems* 10: 197–208.

Davidson, M.B., Owen, R.P. & MacKay, D.W. (2002). Ecology of Aquatic and Sub-aquatic Habitats. In: Gimingham, C.H. (ed.), *The Ecology, Land Use and Conservation of the Cairngorms*. Packard Publishing Ltd.: Chichester. pp. 67–84.

Davies, C.E., Shelley, J. Harding, P.T., McLean, I.F.G., Gardiner, R. & Peirson, G. (2004). *Freshwater Fishes in Britain – the species and their distribution*. Harley Books: Colchester. 184 pp.

Eatherley, D., Thorley, J.L., Stephen, A., Simpson, I., MacLean, J., Youngson, A. & Burns, C. (2004). *Natural Heritage Trends – Fish Counter Data*. Scottish Natural Heritage Commissioned Report AB(01NB02)030468. SNH: Perth.

Ecological Research Associates (2004). *National Lamprey Survey: Phase I Report*. Scottish Natural Heritage Commissioned Report F02AC602a. SNH: Perth.

Ecological Research Associates (2005). *National Lamprey Survey: Phase II Report*. Scottish Natural Heritage Commissioned Report F02AC602b. SNH: Perth.

Entec (2000). *Generically acceptable flows for British lamprey*. Environment Agency: Penrith.

Forestry Commission (2003). *Forests and Water Guidelines*. 4th Edition. Forestry Commission: Edinburgh.

Fraser, D., Adams, C.E. & Huntingford, F.A. (1998). Trophic polymorphism among Arctic charr *Salvelinus alpinus* L., from Loch Ericht, Scotland. *Ecology of Freshwater Fish* 7: 184–191.

Gardiner, R. (2003). *Identifying Lamprey. A Field Key for Sea, River and Brook Lamprey*. Conserving Natura 2000 Rivers Conservation Techniques Series No. 4. English Nature, Peterborough.

Gardiner, R. & Egglishaw, H. (1986). *A Map of the Distribution in Scottish Rivers of the Atlantic Salmon* Salmo salar *L*. DAFS Freshwater Fisheries Laboratory: Pitlochry.

Gardiner, R. & Mackay, D.W. (2002). Fish Populations. In: Gimingham, C.H. (ed.), *The Ecology, Land Use and Conservation of the Cairngorms*. Packard Publishing Ltd.: Chichester. pp. 148–159.

Gardner, A.S., Walker, A.F. & Greer, R.B. (1988). Morphometric analysis of two ecologically distinct forms of Arctic charr, *Salvelinus alpinus* (L.), in Loch Rannoch, Scotland. *Journal of Fish Biology* 32: 901–910.

Greer, R. (1995). *Ferox Trout and Arctic Charr*. Swan Hill Press: Shrewsbury.

Harriman, R., Gillespie, E. & Morrison, B.R.S. (1990). Factors affecting fish survival in Scottish catchments. In: Mason, B.J. (ed.), *The Surface Waters Acidification Programme*. Cambridge University Press: Cambridge. pp. 343–355.

Hartley, S.E., Bartlett, S.E. & Davidson, W.S. (1992). Mitochondrial DNA analysis of Scottish populations of Arctic charr, *Salvelinus alpinus* (L.). *Journal of Fish Biology* 40: 219–224.

Hildrew, A.G. & Ormerod, S.J. (1995). Acidification, Causes, Consequences and Solutions. In: Harper, D.M. & Ferguson, J.D. (eds.), *The Ecological Basis for River Management*. John Wiley & Sons: Chichester. pp147–160.

Jones, V.J., Flower, R.J., Appleby, P.G., Natkanski, J., Richardson, N., Rippey, B., Stevenson, A.C. & Battarbee, R.W. (1993). Paleolimnological evidence for the acidification and atmospheric contamination of lochs in the Cairngorm and Lochnagar areas of Scotland. *Journal of Ecology* 81: 3–24.

Laughton, R. (1989). *The movements of adult salmon within the River Spey*. Scottish Fisheries Research Report, No 41.

Laughton, R. & Burns, S. (2003). *Assessment of sea lamprey distribution and abundance in the River Spey: Phase III*. SNH Commissioned Report F02AC604. SNH: Perth.

Maitland, P.S. (1991). Climate change and fish in northern Europe: some possible scenarios. *Proceedings of the Institute of Fishery Management Annual Study Course* 22: 97–110.

Maitland, P.S. (1994). Fish In: Maitland, P.S., Boon, P.J. & McLusky, D.S. (eds.), *The Fresh Waters of Scotland: A National Resource of International Significance*. Wiley & Sons: Chichester. pp. 191–208.

Maitland, P.S. (1997). Freshwater Fish In: Omand, D (ed.), *Grampian Book*. Northern Times. pp. 113–115.

Maitland, P.S. (2003). *Ecology of the River, Brook and Sea Lamprey*. Conserving Natura 2000 Rivers Ecology Series No. 5. English Nature, Peterborough.

Maitland, P.S. (2004). *Keys to the freshwater fish of Britain and Ireland with notes on their distribution and ecology*. Freshwater Biological Association (Scientific Publication No.62).

Maitland, P.S. & Campbell, R.N. (1992). *Freshwater Fishes*. HarperCollins: London.

Maitland, P.S., Greer, R.B., Campbell, R.N. & Friend, G.F. (1984). The status and biology of the Arctic charr *Salvelinus alpinus* L. in Scotland. In: Johnson, L. & Burns, B. (eds.), *Biology of the Arctic Charr: Proceeding of the International Symposium on Arctic charr*. University of Manitoba Press: Winnipeg. pp. 193–215.

Maitland, P.S., May, L., Jones, D.H. & Doughty, C.R. (1991). Ecology and conservation of Arctic charr, *Salvelinus alpinus* (L.), in Loch Doon, an acidifying Loch in southwest Scotland. *Biological Conservation* 55: 167–197.

McGinnity, P., Prodohl, P., Ferguson, A., Hynes, R., O´Maoileidigh, N., Baker, N., Cotter, D., O'Hea, B., Cooke, D., Rogan, G., Taggart, J. & Cross, T. (2003). Fitness reduction and potential extinction of wild populations of Atlantic salmon, *Salmo salar*, as a result of interactions with escaped farm salmon. *Proceedings of the Royal Society of London B.* 270: 2443–2450.

Morrison, B.R.S. & Harriman, R. (1992). Fish populations and invertebrates in some headwaters of the Rivers Dee and Spey. *Scottish Fisheries Research Report* No. 53. Patrick, S.T., Flower, R.J., Appleby, P.G., Oldfield, F., Rippey, B., Stevenson, A.C., Darley, J. & Battarbee, R.W. (1989). *Palaeoecological evaluation of the recent acidification of Lochnagar, Scotland*. Palaeoecology Research Unit, University College London, Research Paper, No. 34.

Pullan, D. (1986). *Monitoring of the Eel Fishery within the River Spey/Insh Marshes SSSI*. Report to the Nature Conservancy Council, North East Scotland Region.

Redgewell, K.J., Laughton, R. & Hudson, A. (2004). *Survey of Lochs in the Spey and Dee Catchments for Non-Native Fish Species*. Report Prepared for Cairngorms National Park Authority, December 2004.

SEERAD (2003a). *Status of Rainbow Trout in Scotland: Results from a Questionnaire Survey*. SEERAD FRS Scottish Fisheries Information Pamphlet No. 23 2003. 28pp.

SEERAD (2003b). *Statistical Bulletin: Scottish Salmon and Sea Trout Catches, 2002*. SEERAD FRS Fisheries Series Fis/2003/1.

Young, M.L., Cosgrove, P.J. & Hastie, L.C.. (2001a). The extent of, and causes for, the decline of a highly threatened naiad: *Margaritifera margaritifera*. In: Bauer, G. & Wachtler, K. (eds.), *Ecology and Evolutionary Biology of the Freshwater Mussels Unionoidea*. Springer-Verlag, Berlin. pp. 337–357.

Walker, A.F., Greer, R.B. & Gardiner, A.S. (1988). Two ecologically distinct forms of Arctic charr (*Salvelinus alpinus* (L.)) in Loch Rannoch, Scotland. *Biological Conservation* 33: 43–61.

Webb, J. (1992). *The behaviour of adult salmon (Salmo salar L.) in the River Tay as determined by radio telemetry*. Scottish Fisheries Research Report, No 52.

Webb, J. & Hawkins, A.D. (1989). *The movements and spawning behaviour of adult salmon in the Girnock Burn, a tributary of the Aberdeenshire Dee, 1986*. Scottish Fisheries Research Report, No 40.

Winfield, I.J., Fletcher, J.M. & James, B. (2003). *Site Condition Monitoring of Fish in Standing Waters (Phase I)*. Report to Scottish Natural Heritage F03AC610a. SNH: Perth.

Winfield, I.J., Fletcher, J.M. & James, B. (2004). *Site Condition Monitoring of Fish in Standing Waters (Phase II)*. Report to Scottish Natural Heritage F03AC610b. SNH: Perth.

Witkamp, J.H. (1989). *Eel Fishing in the River Spey and Loch Insh Area*. Report to the Nature Conservancy Council, North East Scotland Region.

Additional reading

Ballentyne, C.K. (1991). Holocene geomorphic activity in the Scottish Highlands. *Scottish Geographical Magazine* 107: 84–98.

Campbell, R.N. (1979). Ferox trout (*Salmo trutta* L.) and Charr (*Salvelinus alpinus* (L.)) in Scottish lochs. *Journal of Fish Biology* 14: 1–29.

Charter, E. (1988). *Survey of Spey Valley Lochs, 1985*. Contract Surveys No. 16. Nature Conservancy Council. Peterborough.

Cosgrove, P.J., Hastie, L. & Farquhar, J.E. (2004). *Freshwater Pearl Mussel Survey of the River Dee candidate Special Area of Conservation*. Scottish Natural Heritage Research Report F02PA04a (Unpublished, confidential report).

Gimingham, C.H. (2002). *The Ecology, Land Use and Conservation of the Cairngorms*. Packard Publishing Ltd.: Chichester.

Leaper, G. (1999). *Biodiversity in the Cairngorms: an assessment of priority habitats and species*. Report to the Cairngorms Partnership.

Lyle, A.A. & Maitland, P.S. (1992). Conservation of freshwater fish in the British Isles: the status of fish in National Nature Reserves. *Aquatic Conservation* 2: 19–34.

Thomson, K.J. (2002). Agriculture. In: Gimingham, C.H. (ed.), *The Ecology, Land Use and Conservation of the Cairngorms*. Packard Publishing Ltd.: Chichester. pp. 97–106.

Young, M.L., Hastie, L.C., Cooksley, S.L., Scougall, F. & Hawkins, C. (2001b). *Freshwater Pearl Mussel Survey and River Habitat Survey of the River Spey*. Unpublished and confidential research report for Scottish Natural Heritage.

Young Associates (2003). *Freshwater Pearl Mussel and River Habitat Survey of a candidate Special Area of Conservation: River South Esk*. Scottish Natural Heritage Research Report F02PA04b. SNH: Perth.

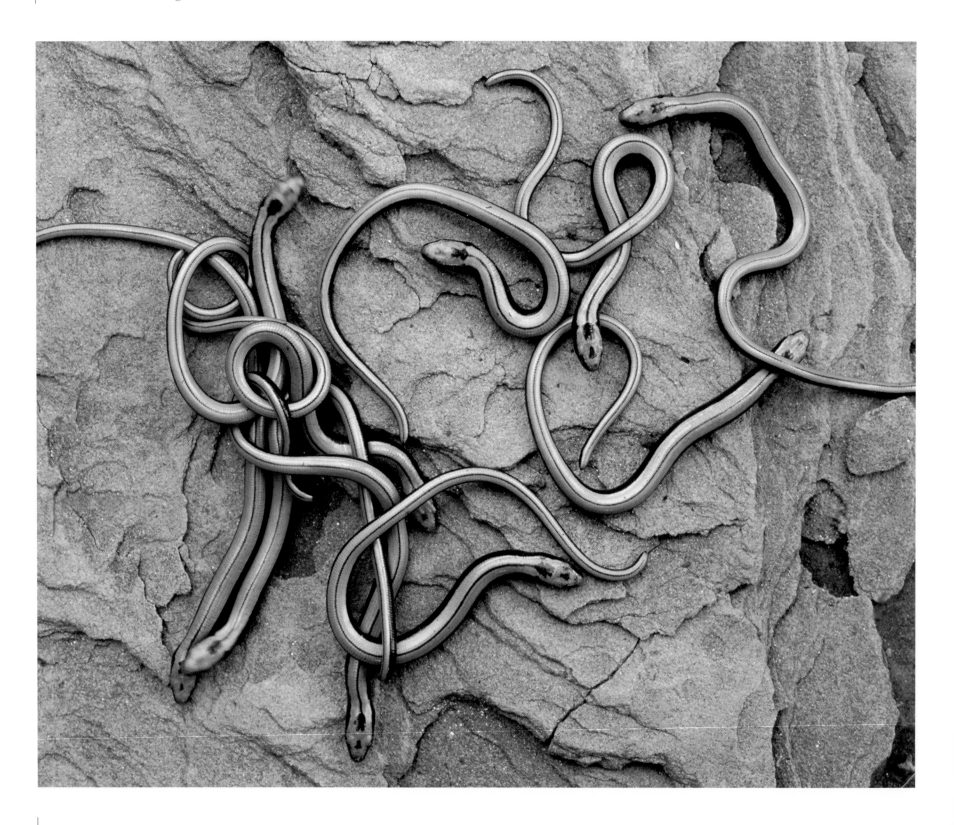

17. AMPHIBIANS AND REPTILES

Frank Bowles, Mairi Cole and Robert Raynor

Introduction

The British amphibian and reptile fauna is much smaller than that of most other European countries, reflecting Britain's island status and cool, damp climate. There are currently 12 species of native amphibian and reptile recorded in the UK, of which nine are native to Scotland. Seven have been recorded in the Cairngorms, comprising four amphibian and three reptile species.

The Cairngorms provide good quality habitats for reptiles and amphibians. South-east facing slopes, well-drained soils in many areas and undisturbed habitat provide appropriate basking and hibernaculum sites for reptiles, while amphibians benefit from the relatively low pollution levels in much of the area. The remoteness of much of the environment, the variety of habitats present (spanning altitudes of about 150–1,200 m) and the comparative lack of human interference are ideal for species such as the Adder[1]. The Cairngorms area thus has the capacity to support important amphibian and reptile populations.

Species accounts

Amphibians

All of the amphibian and reptile species recorded in the Cairngorms (Table 17.1) are protected under the Wildlife & Countryside Act 1981 (as amended). The Great Crested Newt is also a Biodiversity Action Plan Priority species, and is protected under the EC Habitats Directive, which is implemented in domestic law through the Conservation (Natural Habitats & c.) Regulations 1994 (as amended). The Common Frog, Common Toad and Palmate Newt are widespread in the Cairngorms (Arnold, 1983), while the Great Crested Newt has been recorded at only two sites in the area.

Although a fifth amphibian species – Smooth Newt *Triturus vulgaris* – was reported from Deeside in the 1950s, these records are thought likely to have been of female or juvenile Palmate Newts, which are similar to Smooth Newts (Leaper, 1999). The Smooth Newt is generally rare in north-east Scotland, perhaps reflecting its preference for deep, stable and well-vegetated water bodies at lower altitudes.

Common Frog. Being capable of spawning in a wide variety of situations, including small, shallow puddles and ditches, the Common Frog is widely distributed throughout the Cairngorms, and is found up to about 1,000 m, particularly on south-facing slopes. Common Frog populations from north-east Scotland are of particular interest in that they include several unusual morphs, regarded by earlier authors as full species (Smith, 1951). In Angus, striped morphs, similar in markings to the Moor Frog *Rana arvalis*, are sometimes seen (Bowles, 2002).

Most frog records originate from between the Dee Valley and North Angus. They are also well-recorded between Carrbridge and Farr in Strathspey, and in the vicinity of Glenmore, but are less well-recorded in the north-eastern part of the Cairngorms, around Cock Bridge. This probably reflects the level of survey effort in this area.

Common Toad. This species requires deep, persistent ponds with clumps of aquatic vegetation suitable for anchoring their strings of eggs. Although widespread in the Cairngorms, the species is sparse or absent from mountainous areas. Common Toads are rarely found above 300 m, but have been recorded above 400 m in Glen Muick and Glen Gairn, and at 500 m in Glen Callater (Leaper, 1999).

Most records are from the Rothiemurchus Forest area, in the vicinity of Kincraig, Clunie Water and along the Dee Valley. There are virtually no

---

A young brood of Slow-worms: the rarest of Scotland's three reptile species.
Photo: *L. Campbell*

[1] Scientific names of species recorded from the Cairngorms are given in Table 17.1.

Bowles, F., Cole, M. & Raynor, R. (2006). Amphibians and reptiles. In: Shaw, P. & Thompson, D.B.A. (eds.). *The Nature of the Cairngorms: Diversity in a changing environment*. The Stationery Office. pp. 285-291.

Common Toad records from the north-eastern part of the Cairngorms; in the triangle between the peak of Ben Avon, Tomintoul and Logie Coldstone. This does not necessarily indicate that they are absent from the area, but may reflect the unevenness of survey effort within the Cairngorms.

Great Crested Newt. This species requires deep, persistent, nutrient-rich ponds to reproduce successfully. In the Cairngorms such habitats are confined to Strathspey, where there are two authenticated sites, and old records from a third site (Abernethy Forest; Leaper, 1999). The Cairngorms thus hold a small proportion of the 100+ known Great Crested Newt sites in Scotland.

Ponds are, generally, at risk from drainage, pollution and changes in acidity (Beebee, 1996), and protection afforded the species under the Wildlife & Countryside Act 1981 (as amended) are in place to help counteract these pressures.

Palmate Newt. Capable of surviving in a variety of aquatic habitats, including puddles and ditches with relatively low pH levels, Palmate Newts are generally recorded up to around 700 m, and occasionally higher. Although common in some areas, the Cairngorms' population is not large enough to be of national significance. The species is, however, locally abundant in the splash pools, ponds and water bodies found alongside the upper reaches of the River Esk, north-west of Auchronie, the Water of Tanar, and at several locations along the Dee valley.

Reptiles

Unlike amphibians, reptiles do not have discrete breeding sites. Even at regularly monitored sites, numbers can fluctuate considerably between seasons, making it difficult to monitor their distribution and abundance with any accuracy.

Slow-worm. The Slow-worm is the rarest of Scotland's three reptile species. It has a lower altitude range than the Common Lizard or the Adder and prefers areas where it can conceal itself, including woods, deserted gardens, churchyards and undisturbed stone heaps. Because of their legless appearance, Slow-worms may be mistaken for snakes.

Prior to 1969 the Slow-worm was reported frequently from Deeside (Arnold 1995), but increased building, disturbance of habitat and persecution may have reduced its numbers considerably. Although there are few recent distribution records, there are still sites in the area where Slow-worms are locally abundant,

including the vicinity of Ballindalloch Castle, Rothiemurchus Forest and North Glen Esk.

Common or Viviparous Lizard. Like many amphibian and reptile species, Common Lizards are sensitive to disturbance and are probably under-recorded. From the records available, it appears to be relatively common along the Dee Valley, Glen Avon between The Bruach and the Water of Ailnack, and in Glen Doll and Glen Esk. Common Lizards have also been recorded as far west as Newtonmore and Dalwhinnie, and occur at up to 900 m.

Adder or Northern Viper. Adders have been recorded throughout most of the Cairngorms area, and are relatively common on suitable slopes in upper Glen Esk, Deeside, Glen Avon and in the south-east of the Cairngorms area. Along the Dee Valley, Adder habitat has been lost to building and development, but many good localities remain, for example, around Dinnet.

Cairngorms National Park encompasses some of the most favourable habitats for Adder and Common Lizard in Britain. Up to the 1950s, both were common throughout most of Britain (Frazer, 1983), but have declined, possibly due to hedgerow removal, the increased utilisation of suitable ground for building, and the use of chemical pesticides and herbicides (Frazer, 1983; Beebee, 1996). The Cairngorms, however, have retained both species at several sites, including the north bank of the Dee at Aboyne, and at Invercauld Bridge, where Common Lizards and Adders can both occasionally be seen basking in Blaeberry *Vaccinium myrtillus* and Heather *Calluna vulgaris* amongst ancient Scots Pine *Pinus sylvestris*. Common Lizards prefer Blaeberry to stands of Heather and, unlike Adders, avoid long Couch Grass *Elytrigia repens* and Bracken *Pteridium aquilinum*.

Notable areas

There are insufficient data with which to identify areas that may be nationally important for amphibian or reptile species, most of which are widespread or only sparsely distributed in the Cairngorms area. However, based on distribution maps (Swan & Oldham, 1993; Arnold, 1995; Dundee Museum Biological Records, 2000) and fieldwork by F. Bowles during 1975–2003, the following areas are thought to hold notable amphibian or reptile populations or assemblages. There are no statutory sites in the Cairngorms designated for their amphibian or reptile interest.

Table 17.1. Amphibian and reptile species recorded from the Cairngorms. In all cases, the Cairngorms encompass less than 10% of the species' UK range. Notable areas outside of the National Park, but within the Cairngorms area, are identified.

RDB:	National Red Data Book status. LR = Lower Risk
BAP:	Biodiversity Action Plan Priority species.
WCA:	Schedule(s) on which the species is listed under the Wildlife & Countryside Act 1981
Habitats Directive:	Listed in Annex II of the EC Habitats Directive

Habitat	Species	Status				Notable locations outside of National Park
		RDB	BAP	WCA	Habitats Directive	
Moist pasture, gardens, moorland, ponds	Common Frog *Rana temporaria*			Sc.5, 9(5)		(Ubiquitous)
Fields, moorland, ponds	Common Toad *Bufo bufo*			Sc.5, 9(5)		SE part of the Cairngorms area, between Glen Clova and Glen Esk.
Ponds, lochans, moist ground	Great Crested Newt *Triturus cristatus*	LR	Y	Sc.5	Y	None
Small water bodies, moist ground	Palmate Newt *Triturus helvetica*			Sc.5, 9(5)		(Ubiquitous)
Moorland, undisturbed road verges, sunny banks	Common or Viviparous Lizard *Zootoca vivipara*			Sc.5, 9(1) 9(5)		Ballindalloch Castle, Glen Clova, Glen Prosen, Glen Esk and Glen Garry
Undisturbed rough ground, stone piles.	Slow-worm *Anguis fragilis*			Sc.5, 9(1) 9(5)		Ballindalloch Castle, Glen Esk and Glen Garry
Moorland, rough grazing, bracken, scrub	Adder or Northern Viper *Vipera berus*			Sc.5, 9(1) 9(5)		Glen Esk, Glen Garry and the Forest of Atholl

Glen Esk. Common Frog, Common Toad, Palmate Newt, Slow-worm, Common Lizard and Adder are all found in this area, the bulk of which lies within the National Park.

Glen Avon. Common Lizard and Adder have frequently been reported from this area.

Ballindalloch Castle, near Cragganmore, falls partly outside of the National Park, and contains all three Scottish reptile species.

The Dee (*Invercauld Bridge to Banchory*). The Dee west of Banchory, particularly between Invercauld Bridge and Inver, holds good populations of Common Lizard and Adder.

Cambus O'May to Muir of Dinnet. This area holds good populations of all three Scottish reptile species.

Glen Tanar. The forest and Water of Tanar support good populations of amphibians, including Palmate Newt. Common Lizard and Adder are also present.

Apparent trends

Recent declines in amphibian populations in Britain have been attributed to the effects of insecticides, herbicides, drainage of water-bodies, low pH levels in breeding ponds and a loss of feeding sites (Beebee, 1996). British reptile species have also declined, mainly as a result of habitat loss, a reduction in their invertebrate food supply (as a result of insecticides and pollution), and increased human disturbance and persecution.

It is difficult to build an accurate picture of status or trends in amphibians and reptiles in the Cairngorms. Because of its mountainous terrain, much of the area is difficult to access, and records may tend to reflect the distribution of recorders rather than the abundance of the species being surveyed. Variation in the weather can also influence amphibian and (particularly) reptile sightings. For example, warm spring weather encourages early emergence from hibernation and frequent basking, raising the number of sightings made. Cold weather, in contrast, can prevent the animals from appearing in the open at all.

There has been no systematic research or survey work on amphibians or reptiles in the Cairngorms. Consequently, the following is based largely on informal or

The Cairngorms area encompasses some of Britain's most favourable habitats for Adder, which are relatively common on suitable slopes in upper Glen Esk, Deeside, Glen Avon and in the south-east of the area.

Photo: *L. Campbell*

local observations.

- A note on the occurrence of the Common Lizard in Perthshire (Leighton, 1901) suggests that this species may have been less common there in the early 1900s than in recent years.

- An expansion in forestry since the 1950s (Chapter 7) may have had a positive impact on amphibian and reptile populations. On south-facing slopes the ecotone between mature woodland and moorland can provide food-rich habitats for reptiles. Some of the most extensive colonies of Common Lizard recorded recently in the Cairngorms have been found in such situations (Bowles, 2002). During 1997–2003, Adders were also found to have been colonising mature plantations following recent thinning (F. Bowles, pers. obs.). It is possible that reptile populations may have benefited from recent warmer weather in the spring and summer.

- Recent research in Angus has demonstrated annual fluctuations in the number of Common Lizards present at one site (Bowles, 2002), and suggests a possible increase in populations in Glen Doll, on the boundary between mature forestry plantations and moorland on south-facing slopes. Bowles (2002) has also recently recorded Common Lizard at Dalwhinnie and Newtonmore; an area for which few reptile records are available (Arnold, 1995).

- In 1996, a questionnaire survey suggested that while Adder sightings in Scotland as a whole declined slightly during 1983–92, those in the Cairngorms area had remained approximately constant (Reading *et al.*, 1996). Research is required on the impact on Adder populations of mountain biking and other recreational activities.

- A survey of Slow-worms in the Scottish Highlands during 1997 suggested that its abundance in the Cairngorms had remained approximately steady during 1960–97 (Highland Biological Recording Group, pers. comm.).

Conservation issues

Amphibian and reptile populations in the Cairngorms are generally subject to the same risks as populations elsewhere in the UK. These are as follows.

Disturbance. Increased use of the rural environment, housing development and changes in the rural access policy have raised pressure on otherwise undisturbed areas. Increased public access has the potential to impact significantly on the amphibian and reptile populations in the Cairngorms, through direct effects on their habitats.

Water sports. The release of fish into ponds and lochans for leisure purposes has presented significant risks to amphibian populations across the UK, through predation of eggs and tadpoles. This can effectively reduce the number of sites at which amphibians are able to breed successfully.

Road casualties. A recent survey of Adder sightings in Scotland noted significant numbers of amphibian and reptile deaths on paths and tracks in Aberdeenshire (SEPA, 1999). Although there is no information with which to quantify the risks more widely, increased access and traffic pose a potential threat, particularly to reptiles, which use such areas for basking.

Persecution. A fear of reptiles, particularly snakes and snake-like lizards, has, in the past, led to the illegal persecution of Adders and, to a lesser extent, Slow-worms (Corbett, 1989). Educational leaflets for climbers, walkers and grouse beaters may reduce threats to reptiles.

Environmental deterioration. Acidification of ground water by atmospheric pollutants, such as sulphur dioxide, is thought to cause more damage to amphibian populations than pesticides, particularly in upland areas. Amphibians are also threatened by damage to stratospheric ozone (e.g. by CFCs), allowing increased levels of UV-B to enter the atmosphere, endangering spawn and tadpoles (Beebee, 1996)

Spring muirburn (i.e. after February) on heather moorland coincides with the time when reptiles are emerging from hibernation, and are often less mobile, due to the low temperatures. Given that Adders and Common Lizards frequently occur in heather-rich areas, extensive burning during this time is likely to be harmful to their populations. Heathland fires in southern England are known to result in reptile casualties.

Legislation. The Wildlife & Countryside Act 1981 has recently been amended by the Nature Conservation (Scotland) Act 2004, which introduced a new offence of 'reckless' killing, to protect all of the species listed in the original Act.

References

Arnold, H.R. (1983). *Distribution Maps of the Amphibians of the British Isles.* Biological Records Centre: Huntingdon.

Arnold, H.R. (1995). *Atlas of Amphibians and Reptiles in Britain.* HMSO: London.

Beebee, T.J.C. (1996). *Ecology and Conservation of Amphibians.* Chapman & Hall: London.

Bowles, F.D. (2002). Are Common Lizards increasing their range in Scotland? *Herpetological Bulletin* 80: 4–6.

Corbett, K. (1989). *Conservation of European Reptiles & Amphibians.* Helm: London

Dundee Museum Biological Records Centre (2000). *Angus Reptiles 1989–2000.* Dundee Museums: Dundee.

Frazer, J.F.D. (1983). *Reptiles and Amphibians in Britain.* Collins: London.

Leaper, G. (1999). *Biodiversity of the Cairngorms. An Assessment of Priority Habitats and Species.* Cairngorms Partnership: Grantown-on-Spey.

Extensive muirburn after February is likely to be harmful to reptiles which, having just emerged from hibernation, are often less mobile due to the low temperatures.

Photo: *L. Gill*

Leighton, G. (1901). *The Life History of British Serpents and their Local Distribution in the British Isles.* Blackwood: London.

Reading, C.J., Buckland, S.T., McGowan, G.M., Gorzula, S., Jayasinghe, G., Staines, B.W., Elston, D.A. & Ahmadi, S. (1996). *Status of the Adder in Scotland.* Report to Scottish Natural Heritage, Part 2. SNH: Perth.

Scottish Environment Protection Agency (1999). *Records of Adders in Scotland.* Unpublished report to Froglife (Scotland). Froglife.

Smith, M.A. (1951). *The British Amphibians and Reptiles.* Collins: London.

Swan, M.J.S. & Oldham, R.S. (1993). *Herptile Sites Volume 1: National Common Reptile Survey Final Report.* English Nature Research Reports No. 39. EN: Peterborough.

Additional reading

Arnold, E.N. & Burton, C.J.A. (1973). *A Field Guide to the Reptiles and Amphibians of Britain and Europe.* Collins: London.

Bowles, F.D. (1995). Observations on the Distribution of the Common Lizard, (*Lacerta vivipara*) in Scotland. *British Herpetological Society Bulletin* 54: 32–33.

Joyce, A. (1997). *Adders, Slow-worms and Lizards.* Highland Biological Group Newsletter: Caithness.

Leighton, G. (1903). *The Life History of British Lizards and their Local Distribution in the British Isles.* Blackwood: London.

Perth Museum Biological Records Centre (2003). *Distribution Maps of Reptiles & Amphibians in Perthshire.* Perth Museum: Perth.

Sage, J. (1975). *The Status of Reptiles and Amphibians in Angus 1974–1975.* Wildlife Review: Rochdale.

Slater, F. (1992). *The Common Toad.* Shire Natural History: Haverfordwest.

Stafford, P. (1987). *The Adder.* Shire Natural History: Haverfordwest.

Stafford, P. (1989). *Lizards of the British Isles.* Shire Natural History: Haverfordwest.

Wisniewski, P.J. (1989). *Newts of the British Isles.* Shire Natural History: Haverfordwest.

18. BIRDS

Philip Shaw, Des B.A. Thompson, Keith Duncan and Nigel Buxton

Introduction

The Cairngorms are exceptional for birds, especially those associated with Arctic tundra, boreal pine forests, moorland, northern lakes and wetlands. Since these habitats are widespread at high northern latitudes many of the species they support have extensive global ranges, stretching across Scandinavia, Siberia and sometimes into the New World. A few of these northern bird species have maintained a tenuous hold in Britain since the last glaciation, their populations doubtless expanding and contracting down the ages as the climate has changed.

By virtue of their wide distributions and large populations, few northern bird species are globally threatened (Stattersfield *et al.*, 1998; BirdLife International, 2000), although many are of European or national conservation concern (Heath & Evans, 2000; Stroud *et al.*, 2001). One species of global conservation concern is Britain's sole endemic bird, the Scottish Crossbill[1], which is closely associated with the forests of Strathspey and Deeside. The Cairngorms also hold internationally important sites for species such as the Dotterel, Capercaillie and Golden Eagle, as well as small numbers of high Arctic birds, including the Purple Sandpiper and Snow Bunting. The Osprey, a conservation 'flagship' species restricted to the Cairngorms in the 1950s (Brown & Waterston, 1962) has expanded throughout Scotland and into England and Wales, but is still strongly associated with Strathspey, providing an economic boost through tourism. Goldeneye have shown a similarly impressive rise in numbers, greatly facilitated by the provision of nestboxes throughout Badenoch & Strathspey.

Small populations on the edge of their range, often in habitat 'islands', are more prone to extinction and, by virtue of their partial isolation, to speciation. In Britain, some of our range-edge species are probably dependent on frequent or occasional immigration from their source populations. They include our few pairs of Purple, Wood and Green Sandpiper, and, arguably the Snow Bunting. These are migratory species, whose Scottish populations are supplemented by passage or wintering birds, some of which stay to breed. While their numbers have remained relatively stable in recent years, those of Wryneck, Redwing and Lapland Bunting have declined, following peaks during the late 1970s or early 1980s. Although their rarity and origins excite interest in the UK, such populations are too small to be numerically important on a European or global scale. In contrast, a few of Britain's more abundant range-edge species are of real significance, having evolved into distinctive forms, adding to the genetic diversity of Europe's bird fauna. Two such species are the Ptarmigan and Crested Tit, which have their UK strongholds in the Cairngorms. Both are widespread elsewhere in Europe, but are isolated and sedentary in Britain, where they have evolved into endemic sub-species: *Lagopus mutus millaisi* and *Parus cristatus scoticus*, respectively (Hartert, 1910; Prazák, 1897, in McGowan *et al.*, 2003). A third sub-species, the Red Grouse *L. lagopus scoticus*, is abundant in the Cairngorms area, but appears to reach its highest densities in northern England (Hudson, 1986).

The Cairngorms have a great range and extent of moorland habitats, supporting a characteristic bird community which includes high breeding densities of species such as Golden Plover *Pluvialis apricaria* and Merlin (Ratcliffe, 1990). Also of note are Strathspey's farmland wader population (RSPB, 2000) and, in past decades, its forest-nesting Greenshanks, whose numbers have declined since the 1930s. The area also holds internationally important sites for wintering Greylag and Pink-footed Goose, Whooper Swan and Hen Harrier, all of which roost on its lochs or wetlands, and feed on surrounding moorland and farmland. Recent research has highlighted the importance of upland farmland for wintering bird communities, including several species of conservation concern, such as the Black Grouse, Linnet and Reed Bunting; the latter having become very rare in the Cairngorms (R. Dennis, pers. comm.).

A winter-plumage Ptarmigan, its feathers puffed out to help beat the cold. The species' range and population size may decline substantially in the coming century, as climate change impacts become more pronounced.
Photo: *N. Mcintyre*

Shaw, P., Thompson, D.B.A., Duncan, K. & Buxton, N. (2006). Birds. In: Shaw, P. & Thompson, D.B.A. (eds.). *The Nature of the Cairngorms: Diversity in a changing environment*. The Stationery Office. pp. 293-339.

[1] Scientific names are given in Tables 1 & 2.

While many of the Cairngorms' bird species are individually of interest or concern, the area is especially important for the diversity of its species assemblages (Ratcliffe & Thompson, 1988); nowhere else in the world supports the same mix of breeding assemblages in such a confined area.

This chapter describes the status of bird species for which the Cairngorms are of national importance, and summarises recent trends, research findings and conservation issues.

Important species and habitats

The Cairngorms area is nationally or internationally important for 26 bird species (Table 18.1), whose status is described below in order of their main habitat. A number of rare or scarce species, many of them of Scandinavian origin, have also bred occasionally in the area, or have occurred in suitable habitat during the breeding season (Table 18.2). Although many are represented only by vagrant or late passage individuals, there is a possibility that some of these may eventually attempt to breed.

Lochs and rivers

In western Europe the **Slavonian Grebe** occurs mainly in Fennoscandia, with small numbers in Iceland, Britain and the Baltic States (Hagemeijer & Blair, 1997). It breeds on lochs with extensive marginal sedge beds and good water clarity, enabling it to feed more efficiently on its main prey, the Three-spined Stickleback *Gasterosteus aculeatus* and Minnow *Phoxinus phoxinus* (Summers & Mavor, 1995, 1999).

The European population of the Slavonian Grebe was stable during 1970-90, but showed a moderate decline during 1990-2000, and is now considered to be of European conservation concern (BirdLife International, 2004b). A broadly similar trend has occurred in the UK, where, following a rise in numbers during the 1970s, the Slavonian Grebe population showed little change between the late 1970s and early 1990s (Benn, 2003; Benn pers. comm., 2005). By 2000, however, it had dropped to just 31 pairs, recovering slightly during 2001–05 (Figure 18.1a). Its decline during the 1990s coincided with a reduction in the number of young reared; from 57 in 1988 to just 12 in 1999 (Figure 18.1b). In a recent study, most nest failures in Scotland were attributed to natural causes, including flooding and wave action (Hancock *et al.*, 2002). Although some clutches were lost to predators,

the predation rate was not found to be high compared with other parts of its range, and was not considered to be a cause for conservation concern (Perkins *et al.*, 2005).

Almost all breeding attempts in the Cairngorms area have occurred in Strathspey, with up to 11 pairs recorded on six lochs in Badenoch & Strathspey in 1991 (Dennis, 1995). During the early 1990s one of the species' main sites was Loch Vaa; the Cairngorms' only Special Protection Area (SPA) designated for Slavonian Grebe. On Deeside, Slavonian Grebes have been recorded only occasionally, for example at Loch Davan (Buckland *et al.*, 1990) and on artificial lochs near Logie Coldstone (A. Watson pers. comm.).

Trends in the Cairngorms' small breeding population have broadly reflected the national picture, although with slight differences in timing. During 1984–93 an average of 8.1 pairs bred, accounting for about 11% of the UK population. This dropped to about 6% of the UK population during 2000–05. Productivity at Cairngorms sites was relatively high during the 1980s–90s, peaking in 1991, when 13 young were reared. The Cairngorms' population and

The number of pairs of Slavonian Grebe breeding in the Cairngorms peaked during the early 1990s, and remained low during the early 2000s, despite signs of recovery elsewhere in Scotland.
Photo: *M. Hamblin*

Figure 18.1. The number and productivity of Slavonian Grebes in the Cairngorms area, compared with trends in the UK population as a whole.

a. Population size: the number of breeding pairs recorded in each year.

▩ UK ▪ Cairngorms area

Following a rise in numbers during the 1970s, the UK Slavonian Grebe population varied between 63 and 80 breeding pairs in the late 1970s and early 1990s, dropping to a low of 31 pairs by 2000. A similar decline has occurred in the Cairngorms: from 6-10 pairs in 1984-93, to 1-4 pairs annually during 2000-05.

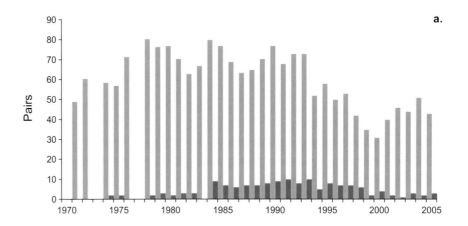

b. Breeding output: the number of young birds recorded in each year.

▩ UK ▪ Cairngorms area

The Slavonian Grebe's decline during the 1990s coincided with a reduction in breeding output; from 57 young reared in 1988, to just 12 in 1999. Productivity in the Cairngorms area peaked in 1991, when 13 young were reared (25% of the national total).

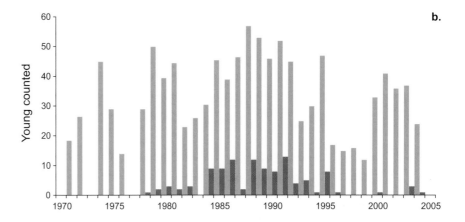

c. Relative importance: the mean number of pairs and young recorded in the Cairngorms area in successive 5-year periods, as a percentage of the UK total.

▩ Pairs ▪ Young reared

The abundance and breeding output of Slavonian Grebes in the Cairngorms area have declined, both in absolute terms and in comparison with the rest of the UK. As a percentage of UK figures, productivity in the Cairngorms peaked during the late 1980s, while abundance peaked in the late 1990s.

[Note: no data were available for 1970, 1973 and 1977.]

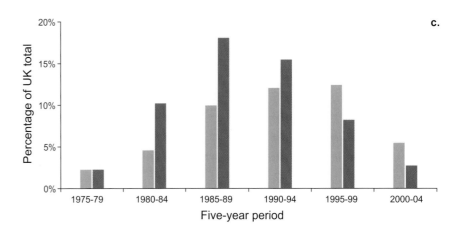

Source: S. Benn, RSPB, pers. comm. (2005).

Table 18.1. Bird species for which the Cairngorms area is considered nationally or internationally important[1]. See opposite for key to status.

Habitat	Species		Status								% of UK range or population in:		NP nationally important
			Small UK breeding range or population	Red Listed	BAP	SPEC	Endemic	IBA	SPA	Notable population	Cairngorms area	National Park	
Lochs/ rivers	Podiceps auritus	Slavonian Grebe	Y			3			Y		-	-	Y
	Cygnus cygnus	Whooper Swan	Y					Y	Y		-	-	Y
	Anas penelope	Wigeon							Y		-	-	Y
	Bucephala glangula	Goldeneye	Y								***	***	Y
	Pandion haliaetus	Osprey	Y			3		Y	Y		*	-	Y
Lochs/ farmland	Anser brachyrhynchus	Pink-footed Goose						Y	Y		-	-	
	Anser anser	Greylag Goose[2]						Y	Y		**	**	Y
Wetland	Porzana porzana	Spotted Crake	Y						Y		*	*	Y
	Tringa ochropus	Green Sandpiper	Y								***	***	Y
	Tringa glareola	Wood Sandpiper	Y			3		Y	Y		**	**	Y
	Larus canus	Common Gull				2		Y			*	-	
Pine forest	Tetrao urogallus	Capercaillie		Y	Y			Y	Y		**	**	Y
	Tringa nebularia	Greenshank[3]								Y	-	-	
	Parus cristatus	Crested Tit				2	Y				**	**	Y
	Loxia scotica	Scottish Crossbill	Y	Y	Y	1	Y	Y	Y		*	*	Y
	Loxia pytyopsittacus	Parrot Crossbill[4]	Y								**	**	Y
Pine forest edge/ scrub	Tetrao tetrix	Black Grouse		Y	Y	3		Y			*	-	Y
Moorland	Circus cyaneus	Hen Harrier		Y		3		Y	Y		-	-	Y
	Aquila chrysaetos	Golden Eagle				3		Y	Y		*	-	Y
	Falco columbarius	Merlin						Y	Y		-	-	Y
	Falco peregrinus	Peregrine						Y	Y		-	-	Y
	Asio flammeus	Short-eared Owl				3		Y	Y		-	-	
	Turdus torquatus	Ring Ouzel		Y							*	-	Y
Montane	Lagopus mutus	Ptarmigan					Y				*	*	Y
	Calidris maritima	Purple Sandpiper	Y								***	***	Y
	Charadrius morinellus	Dotterel						Y	Y		**	**	Y
	Plectrophenax nivalis	Snow Bunting	Y								**	**	Y

[1] Selection criteria: a qualifying species on an SPA or IBA in the Cairngorms, or ≥25% of UK range or population occurs in the Cairngorms area, or 10–24% of UK range or population occurs in the Cairngorms area and at least one of the following: small UK breeding range (recorded breeding in <16 10-km squares) or population (1–300 pairs); Red listed; BAP Priority species; nationally important population on at least one IBA or SPA; or an endemic taxon.

[2] Greylag Goose: recent counts at Loch of Kinnordy and Loch of Lintrathen suggest that the combined wintering population within the Cairngorms area may have dropped below 25% of the species' biogeographical population.

[3] The Greenshank is included here as a notable species only, on the basis of its unusual occurrence in semi-forested habitats. Its Cairngorms population does not meet the selection criteria listed above.

[4] The Parrot Crossbill's range in Britain is poorly known, but it seems likely that at least 25% of the breeding population occurs within the Cairngorms.

Key to Table 18.1.

Small breeding range	Evidence of breeding in only 1–15 10-km squares in the UK during 1988-91 (Gibbons *et al.*, 1993).
Small breeding population	Species with a mean of between one and 300 pairs during 1995–99 (Gregory *et al.*, 2002).
Red Listed	Red listed in *Birds of Conservation Concern* (Gregory *et al.*, 2002).
BAP	Biodiversity Action Plan Priority species.
SPEC	Species of European Conservation Concern. 1: European species of global conservation concern; 2: Species concentrated in Europe, with an unfavourable conservation status; 3: Species not concentrated in Europe, with an unfavourable conservation status (BirdLife International, 2004a).
Endemic	Species or sub-species endemic to the UK.
IBA	Qualifying species on at least one Important Bird Area (Fisher *et al.*, 2000)
SPA	Qualifying species on at least one Special Protection Area (Stroud *et al.*, 2001)
Percentage of UK range or population	The percentage of the species' UK range (in 10-km squares) or population size (where available) occurring in the Cairngorms area or in the National Park: *** >75%; ** 25–75%; * 10–24%; '-' <10%
NP nationally important	Occurs in nationally important numbers in Cairngorms National Park

breeding output have thus declined in absolute terms since the 1980s–90s, and in relation to the UK population, having been relatively high during the late 1990s (in terms of breeding pairs) and in the late 1980s (in terms of breeding output) (Figure 18.1c).

Black-necked Grebes have also bred in the Cairngorms area in nationally important numbers, but no longer do so (see Loch of Kinnordy account).

The **Whooper Swan** breeds in Iceland, Scandinavia and northern Russia, east as far as the Bering Sea. A mean of 5,720 birds were thought to have wintered in Britain during 1994/95–98/99 (Kershaw & Cranswick, 2003). Notable sites in the Cairngorms include Insh Marshes, which has held up to 208 birds (in 1992/93; C. Mitchell, pers. comm.), Loch Garten, with up to 134 (in 1975; Dennis 1995) and Loch of Lintrathen, with a mean of 71 birds during 1995/96–1999/2000 (Robinson *et al.*, 2004). On Deeside, peaks of 350 and 157 have been recorded on lochs Davan and Kinord (Buckland *et al.*, 1990).

Most sites are used primarily as roosts, with birds dispersing to feed on farmland by day. An exception is the Insh Marshes, where Whooper Swans have tended to feed mainly in extensive reedbeds; one of a very few wintering groups in Britain still to do so (C. Mitchell, pers. comm. 2005).

Figure 18.2. Trends in the number of wintering Whooper Swans counted at Insh Marshes, and in Scotland as a whole.

Peak counts of Whooper Swans at Insh Marshes during 1972/73–2004/05. During 1991/92–95/96 Insh Marshes held about 3.5% of the British population.

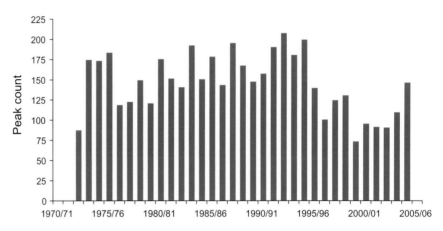

Source: RSPB, Insh Marshes

An index of the number of Whooper Swans counted at Wetland Bird Survey sites throughout Scotland during 1970/71–2003/04.

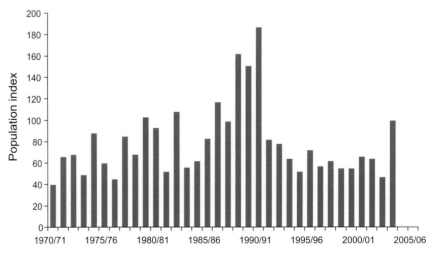

Source: BTO

Designated as an SPA for Whooper Swan, Insh Marshes held an average peak of 190 birds during the winters of 1991/92–95/96 (Stroud *et al.*, 2001), but an average of only 93 birds during 1999/00–03/04. This follows a marked decline since the winter of 1992/93, and a more pronounced decline in the Scottish population, which began in 1990/91 (Figure 18.2). A few birds have summered in the Cairngorms, and may have bred occasionally (Dennis, 1995).

Britain has a breeding population of about 300 pairs of **Wigeon**, which nest mainly in dense cover close to wetlands, preferring shallow, open, mesotrophic waters, with ample submerged or floating vegetation (Stroud *et al.*, 2001). Breeding pairs are probably widely scattered, with small numbers at each of a handful of sites. They include the River Truim and Glen Clunie, the latter having an estimated population of about 10-15 breeding pairs during 1989-92 (Duncan & Duncan, in litt.). Although most females at this site nested in tall heather, leading their ducklings to feed in rich pasture nearby, more open nest sites have been recorded elsewhere (Duncan & Foster, 1998). Breeding success at Glen Clunie was strongly influenced by June weather and by predation (Duncan & Duncan, in litt.). Re-sightings of females ringed as ducklings indicate that at least some individuals returned to breed at their natal site (Duncan *et al.*, 1992).

Wigeon also breed at lochs Davan and Kinord, which were thought to hold 15–30 pairs during the 1980s (Buckland *et al.*, 1990), but appeared to produce only a single brood in 2004 and 2005 (H. Scott, pers. comm. 2005). Declines have also been recorded at River Spey – Insh Marshes SPA, where Wigeon is a qualifying species, with up to 39 males or pairs recorded during the 1990s. Annual counts at Insh Marshes suggest that the breeding density fell by 43% between 1993-97 and 2001-05; from a mean of 4.7 to 2.7 males or pairs per km² (C. Mitchell pers. comm.).

Goldeneye first began breeding in Scotland at Loch an Eilein in 1970 (Dennis, 1995). A northern, hole-nesting duck, the species responded well to the widespread provision of nestboxes in Strathspey, begun by the RSPB in the 1960s. As a result, its breeding population climbed fairly steadily during the 1970s and 1980s, reaching a maximum of 101 occupied boxes in 1991 (Figure 18.3). The maximum number of breeding females present is likely to have been higher than this, however, since a high proportion of females may 'dump' their eggs in occupied boxes. Overall, productivity in Strathspey is thought to be low, due mainly to low duckling survival.

The number of occupied nestboxes in Strathspey has declined since 1991 (Figure 18.3). This may partially reflect a reduction in observer effort during the 1990s and the fact that, although the number of boxes available has changed little, some have fallen into disrepair. These two factors do not appear to fully explain the decrease in numbers, however. At Insh Marshes, for example, observer effort has remained relatively constant, yet the number of occupied boxes has declined since 1998 (C. Mitchell, pers. comm.).

By 2002 the UK population was thought to include about 150 breeding females. While Strathspey still holds the bulk of these, with 83 occupied nestboxes in 2004, small numbers of Goldeneye breed on Deeside. Breeding was first confirmed on the River Dee (near Aberdeen) in 1992, and the first occupied nestbox was found in 2002, near Dinnet. At least 12 clutches were found in 2005, four being at lochs Davan and Kinord (H. Scott pers. comm., 2005). Breeding has also been confirmed in central Scotland and as far north as Golspie, and summering birds have been recorded recently as far south as Wales (Ogilvie & RBBP, 2004).

Despite declines during the 1990s, Strathspey continues to hold the bulk of Britain's breeding Goldeneye, which began colonising Deeside in 1992.

Photo: *L. Campbell*

Figure 18.3. The minimum number of nestboxes occupied by Goldeneye in Strathspey during 1975-2004. Figures for Insh Marshes, where observer effort has remained relatively constant, are shown separately.

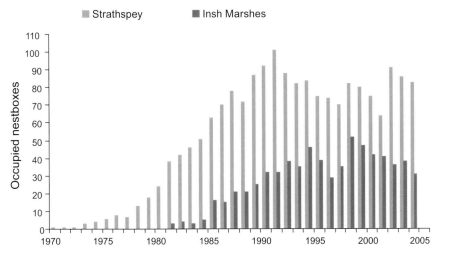

Source: RSPB

Figure 18.4. Change in the number of pairs of Osprey recorded in Badenoch & Strathspey and in Scotland as a whole (to 2004).

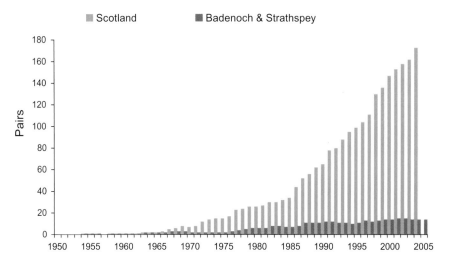

Source: R. Dennis, pers. comm., 2005

A cosmopolitan species with a wide global distribution, over 90% of Europe's **Ospreys** breed in Sweden, Finland or Russia (Hagemeijer & Blair, 1997). Despite having increased throughout most of its European range during 1970-2000, the Osprey is considered to be of European conservation concern, on the basis of its small breeding population (about 7,600 pairs; BirdLife International, 2004b).

The Osprey is thought to have become extinct as a British breeding species after 1916, returning to breed in Strathspey in 1954. A recent re-examination of the records, however, suggests that it may have bred sporadically in Strathspey during the 1930s and 1940s (R. Dennis, pers. comm., 2005). Its Scottish population increased moderately during 1954–85, but more rapidly thereafter (Figure 18.4). Not surprisingly, the number of pairs in Badenoch & Strathspey – which accounts for the bulk of the Cairngorms' population – has increased more slowly, with a median of 8 pairs in the 1980s, 12 in the 1990s and 14 during 2000–05. Most of Britain's Osprey pairs breed north of the Central Highlands, with small numbers in England, Wales and southern Scotland. The species is a qualifying interest on five SPAs that lie wholly or partly within the Cairngorms area. Together, these were thought to hold 17 pairs during the 1990s (Stroud *et al.*, 2001).

Like their counterparts elsewhere in western Europe, British Ospreys winter in Africa, returning to breed in late March or early April. At Loch Garten, where breeding activity has been monitored annually since 1958, spring return dates have varied markedly. While the median return date for both sexes during 1958–2005 was the 7th of April[2], there has been a trend towards earlier return dates since the mid-1980s, resulting in a median return date of 30th March (for females) and 31st March (for males) during 1996-2005 (from RSPB, 1989-2003; S. Taylor, per. comm., 2005). It is possible that this trend has been influenced by climate change, although patterns of pair formation and disruption are also known to have an influence; older, established pairs tending to return earlier to breed.

Britain supports a substantial wintering population of **Pink-footed Goose**, which peaked at about 250,000 during the mid-1990s, but stabilised during 1995/96–1999/2000, when the mean census total was 222,436 (Mitchell & Hearn, 2004). A high proportion of those visiting Britain from Iceland and Greenland winter in Scotland, mainly in lowland areas in Aberdeenshire, Perth & Kinross, Stirling and the Lothians. Although the main concentration of Pink-footed Geese thus lies outside of the Cairngorms area, large numbers were recorded at Loch of Kinnordy during the early 1990s. Counts at Loch of

---

[2] Excluding years in which established breeders have failed to arrive, and have later been replaced by new individuals.

Table 18.2. Species with few or no breeding records elsewhere in the UK, and that have: bred or been in present in the Cairngorms during the breeding season on a small number of occasions; or have bred since the 1970s, but no longer do so regularly. Species represented by individuals that were almost certainly on passage, or vagrant, are indicated.

Status: C: Confirmed breeder (eggs or young recorded); P: present during the breeding season in suitable habitat, but probably vagrant or migrant; V: definitely vagrant or migrant (R. Dennis, pers. comm., 2005).

Species		Status	Notes
Podiceps nigricollis	Black-necked Grebe	C	Confirmed breeding at Loch of Kinnordy in 1986 and subsequently, with a peak of 11 pairs in 1994, declining to one pair by 1999. No young fledged since 1997 and no pairs present since 2001 (A. Leitch, pers. comm., 2005).
Falco vespertinus	Red-footed Falcon	V	Single birds present, May – June, 1961, 1992 (Dennis, 1995) and 2002 (RSPB, pers. comm.).
Falco rusticolus	Gyr Falcon	P	Single birds in March – May, 1950s-90s (Dennis, 1995).
Grus grus	Crane	P	Single birds: unidentified crane species, June-July 1971; single bird, April 1976, Insh Marshes (Dennis, 1995).
Charadrius hiaticula tundrae	Ringed Plover	P	1-6 birds thought to be of the northern race seen at three sites, May-August, 1966-79 (Dennis, 1995).
Calidris alba	Sanderling	V	Two birds in summer plumage, displaying, June 1974, but absent the following day. Also recorded as prey at a Peregrine eyrie (Dennis, 1995).
Calidris temminckii	Temminck's Stint	C	First bred in 1934 (Dennis, 2002). 1-8 birds present during 1974–86, with young hatched in at least six years (Dennis, 1995).
Tringa erythropus	Spotted Redshank	P	1-2 birds recorded during April–August in at least six years since the 1950s (Dennis, 1995).
Arenaria interpres	Turnstone	V	Recorded as food items at Peregrine eyries (Payne & Watson, 1990).
Phalaropus lobatus	Red-necked Phalarope	C	Bred at Boat of Garten in 1977. Up to five birds present during 1978-84, with breeding likely during most of these years (Dennis, 1995).
Stercorarius longicaudus	Long-tailed Skua	P	Single birds recorded in June 1974, 1975, 1984, and two possibles in June 1988. (Oliver, 1975; Dennis, 1995).
Larus minutus	Little Gull	V	One bird, Insh Marshes, May 1975 (Dennis, 1995)
Chlidonias niger	Black Tern	V	Recorded in April-September, 1962, 1969, 1978 and 1987 (Dennis, 1995)
Nyctea scandiaca	Snowy Owl	P	1-2 birds during summer months in at least 15 years since 1952 (Dennis, 1995).
Upupa epops	Hoopoe	P	Single birds have been recorded in May or June 1972, 1973 and 1983 (Dennis, 1995).
Jynx torquilla	Wryneck	C	First bred in 1969 (three pairs). Recorded annually in Badenoch & Strathspey during 1968–71 and 1972–2004 (Dennis (1995), Highland Bird Report (HBR), RSPB pers. comm.). Peak of 14 individuals and three pairs, Badenoch & Strathspey, 1978 (Dennis, 1995). Previously recorded in Deeside (A. Watson, pers. comm.).
Bombycilla garrulus	Waxwing	P	Recorded as late as May in 1968, 1976 and 1989, and as late as 30 June in 1975 (Dennis, 1995).
Eremophila alpestris	Shore Lark	C	A singing male was present in 1973 and 1976, and breeding was confirmed in 1977, when four males and a female were recorded (Campbell *et al.*, 1974; Dennis, 1995), and in 2002-03 (HBR).
Oriolus oriolus	Golden Oriole	V	Single males recorded in May or June in 1977, 1981, 1982, 1991, 1992 (Dennis, 1995) and 2002.
Luscinia svecica	Bluethroat	C	A single female laid six eggs in 1968; no male was found (Greenwood, 1968; Dennis 1995). A singing male was recorded in June 1980 and 1982. Two birds taken by Merlin, May 1981 & 1984 (Rebecca *et al.*, 1987). One pair bred successfully in 1985 (Murray, 1987). One male seen and another found dead in May 1987 (Dennis, 1995). Male singing in Strathspey, May 2003 (HBR).
Turdus pilaris	Fieldfare	C	Breeding confirmed in 1970. Singles and pairs recorded in 1973, July 1976, June 1986 and 1989. Bred in Deeside (Nethersole-Thompson & Watson, 1981), Newtonmore and Laggan in the 1980s, and at Insh Marshes in 1993 (Dennis, 1995).
Turdus iliacus	Redwing	C	First recorded nesting in 1968. Small numbers of pairs and individuals in Strathspey during the 1970s-80s, with five pairs and 12 males in 1982, and one pair plus 20 singles in 1983. Five pairs and six males were recorded in 1990 (Dennis, 1995). One pair bred in Strathspey, 2003 (HBR).

Species		Status	Notes
Acrocephalus arundinaceus	Great Reed Warbler	V	One in song, June 1964 (Dennis, 1995).
Hippolais icterina	Icterine Warbler	C	One pair bred at Creag Meagaidh in July 1992 (Dennis, 1995).
Lanius collurio	Red-backed Shrike	C	First confirmed breeding in 1977 (Dennis, 2002). 1-3 birds recorded annually in Strathspey during 1977-82, and single males only in 1985, 1987-89. Two birds in 1992 (Dennis, 1995). Up to three birds recorded in Scotland during 2000–03. Two males in Strathspey, May 2003 (HBR). Confirmed breeding in Badenoch & Strathspey in 2005 (Butterfield, 2005).
Fringilla montifringilla	Brambling	C	First bred in Scotland in 1979 (Buckland & Knox, 1980), and again in 1982 (Bucknall, 1983). Single males have been recorded in May-July, 1951, 1969, 1975, 1981 and a pair plus three males in 1982. A pair with two young was recorded in July 1983 (Dennis, 1995).
Loxia leucoptera	Two-barred Crossbill	V	One male found dead, Newtonmore, August 1959 (Dennis, 1995).
Carpodacus erythrinus	Common Rosefinch	C	Bred in 1992. Single males were recorded in song in May or June 1978, 1983, 1987–90 (Dennis, 1995, 2002).
Calcarius lapponicus	Lapland Bunting	C	One pair bred in 1977 and up to seven males and two females were recorded in suitable habitat. One male in 1978, and 1–2 pairs, plus one male in 1979 (Cumming, 1979; Dennis, 1995).

Kinnordy declined substantially during the late 1990s (see Important Areas), coinciding with an increase in numbers at nearby Loch of Lintrathen (Mitchell & Hearn, 2004).

About three-quarters of Iceland's **Greylag Geese** travel to Scotland each autumn. In the winter of 2000/01 almost 80,000 birds from this population were counted at Scottish sites, mainly on lowland farmland in the east. The Cairngorms thus lies outside of the species' main wintering area, but include three SPAs on which Greylag Goose is a qualifying species: Loch of Kinnordy, Loch of Lintrathen and Muir of Dinnet. Large numbers have also been recorded at Loch Garten, with over 2,000 birds present during November–December in some years. In recent years, increasing numbers of Greylag Geese have bred in Badenoch & Strathspey, where almost 1,000 birds now summer (R. Dennis, pers. comm., 2005).

Wetlands

The **Spotted Crake** breeds in lowland fen-like habitats, where shallow water is interspersed with extensive stands of low plant cover (Cramp & Simmons, 1980). It has a wide but patchy distribution, stretching from western Europe to central Russia, and is thought to be declining in half of the countries in Europe, due to continued large-scale drainage of wetlands and agricultural intensification (Koskimies & Dvorak, 1997). Being highly secretive and difficult to survey, counts of singing males during May to mid–July (the standard method used) may underestimate the true population size in some years, and are particularly sensitive to variation in survey effort.

During the only systematic national survey of Spotted Crake, in 1999, 73 singing males were recorded at 29 sites in Britain[3], as far apart as Shetland and Cornwall (Stroud, in litt., 2004). They include 14 males (19% of the national population) at two sites in the Cairngorms. One of these was Insh Marshes SPA, where Spotted Crake is a qualifying species. Despite the extensive area of apparently suitable habitat there, site occupancy has been sporadic, varying between eight singing males in 1999 and none in 2003-05 (Figure 18.5). During 1969-71 singing males were recorded at three other Strathspey sites (Dennis, 1995).

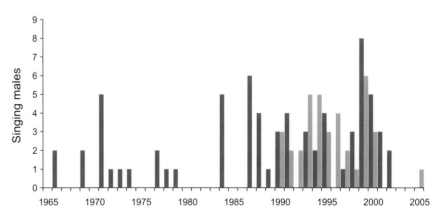

Figure 18.5. Male Spotted Crakes heard singing at Insh Marshes during 1966–2005 (■), and at Muir of Dinnet during 1990-2005 (■).

Sources: Dennis (1995) (Insh Marshes, 1966-93); C. Mitchell, RSPB (2005) (Insh Marshes, 1994-2005); Stroud, in litt. (2004) (Dinnet, 1990-2000); I. Francis, pers comm. (2005) (Dinnet, 2001-05).

[3] Excluding seven males detected outside of the survey period, and three further sites at which juveniles were recorded (Stroud in litt., 2004).

Spotted Crakes have also been recorded breeding regularly on Deeside, in wetland habitats around the Muir of Dinnet. An average of 3.3 singing males were recorded during the 1990s, with a peak of six males during the 1999 national survey (D. Stroud, in litt., 2004) (Figure 18.5). There were no records during 2001-04, however, and only a single bird on one occasion in 2005 (I. Francis, pers. comm.).

The **Green Sandpiper** breeds in boreal forest, ranging from Scandinavia into Russia. Unusually for a wader species, it often uses old nests of songbirds, such as the Song Thrush *Turdus philomelos*, and is easily overlooked. Singing males and pairs were recorded near Rothiemurchus during the 1930s and '40s, and a pair was seen with a single chick near Loch an Eilein in 1959 (Dennis, 1995).

Since the mid–1990s pairs and displaying males have been seen at up to four sites in the Highlands, including two sites in the Cairngorms area. Singing or alarming birds were recorded at one Cairngorms site in 1995, 1996 and 1998, and at two sites (in Strathspey and Deeside) in 1999. Breeding was confirmed annually at one Cairngorms site during 2000-05, and involved two pairs in 2004. At least one out of two pairs present in 2005 also bred (Ogilvie & RBBP, 2004; RSPB pers. comm., 2005).

In Europe, the **Wood Sandpiper** breed mainly in the boreal and sub-Arctic zones of Scandinavia, the Baltic States and northern Russia. Its European population underwent a moderate decline during 1970–90 and, in 2004, was considered to be of conservation concern (BirdLife International, 2004b).

Small numbers have bred every year in Scotland since 1959, mainly in marshy areas and boggy moorland with scattered pools (Nethersole-Thompson & Nethersole-Thompson, 1986; Thom, 1986). Pairs have been recorded at approximately 50 sites in total, with a maximum of 21 pairs in any given year (K. Chisholm, pers. comm.). Breeding was first confirmed in the Cairngorms in 1968, and has been recorded at four sites, all within the National Park. Two of these have held 1–2 pairs each in most years since the 1980s at least, with a maximum of 5–7 pairs at one site. Both sites have been less active in recent years. At a third site, 2–6 pairs were recorded in every year between 1998 and 2004. Over the past 15 years, Badenoch & Strathspey has held 30–53% of the British breeding population in each season (K. Chisholm pers. comm., 2004).

Europe holds over 50% of the global population of the **Common Gull**, which declined during 1970–90, and is considered to be of European conservation concern (BirdLife International, 2004). Scotland, in turn, holds 97% of the British and Irish breeding population (about 3–8% of the European population). Most of the population tends to nest in small, scattered colonies on river shingles, loch shores and moorland, from which birds may forage widely. During 1998–2002 over 5,400 pairs were counted at colonies within the Cairngorms area, accounting for 11% of the UK total (M. Parsons, JNCC, pers. comm.). The bulk of these were found at Bluemill IBA, near Strathdon; the third largest colony in Britain (Mitchell & Thompson, 1989). Loch Etchachan, at about 930 m asl, has what is probably the highest breeding colony in the UK.

Pine forest

The **Capercaillie** became extinct in Britain during the 18th century, and was reintroduced from 1837–38 onwards, since when its population has, in turn, flourished, faltered and collapsed. Similar declines – and some local extinctions – have been recorded elsewhere in western Europe, and have been attributed mainly to the deterioration and fragmentation of its forest habitat (Batten *et al.*, 1990).

National trends

In the 1970s the British Capercaillie population was thought to have numbered some 20,000 birds (Kortland, 2000). This had fallen to about 2,200 birds by 1992–94 (Catt *et al.*, 1998) and to about 1,070 by the winter of 1998–99 (Wilkinson *et al.*, 2002). Although a repeat survey in 2003–04 suggested a rise in numbers, to about 1,980 birds, confidence limits around these estimates overlapped substantially (Figure 18.6), and the apparent increase was not statistically significant. Nevertheless, these findings, coupled with a rise in the number of males counted at a sample of leks (Figure 18.7), suggest that the Capercaillie's rapid decline has at least been arrested, and may have been reversed.

Trends within the Cairngorms

Based on extrapolations from lek counts and on patterns of habitat occupancy, the Cairngorms area was thought to hold at least 50% of the British Capercaillie population in 2004, mainly within the National Park (K. Kortland, pers. comm., 2005). There is some evidence that the species' decline during the 1970s and 1980s was less severe in the Cairngorms than elsewhere in Scotland, perhaps reflecting the relative abundance of semi-natural pine forest in Strathspey and Deeside (Chapter 7), and the efforts of conservation bodies and local estates. One indication of this is that the number of 10-km squares occupied by

Capercaillie in the Cairngorms during *c.* 1970–90 fell by 39%, compared with a drop of 64% in Scotland as a whole (Sharrock, 1976; Gibbons *et al.*, 1993).

Trends within the Cairngorms have varied between sites, reflecting differences in local pressures and management practices. At Kinveachy Estate, Strathspey, Capercaillie winter densities dropped by about 60% between the mid–1970s and mid–1980s (Figure 18.8), reflecting a decline in the number of young birds recruited into the population each year. The recruitment rate itself was found to be unrelated to breeding success, however, suggesting that winter densities were more strongly influenced by mortality and/or emigration rates of young birds during the preceding summer and autumn (Moss & Weir, 1987).

Counts of lekking males at Glen Tanar Estate rose slightly during the 1980s, but dropped by about 80% between the early 1990s and early 2000s (Figure 18.9). In contrast, Capercaillie numbers at Abernethy Forest fluctuated markedly over the same period but showed little evidence of a sustained decline (Figure 18.10), perhaps as a result of the RSPB's intensive and varied programme of habitat management, embracing predator control, deer culling, Blaeberry *Vaccinium myrtillus* enhancement trials and fence removal.

There are signs that the Capercaillie's rapid decline since the 1970s has been arrested, and may have been reversed. This follows the introduction of a package of measures aimed at improving its habitat, and reducing mortality associated with deer fencing.

Photo: *L. Campbell*

Figure 18.6. National Capercaillie population estimates. The British population was thought to be of the order of 20,000 individuals in the 1970s. 95% confidence limits are shown for the three national surveys (1992–94, 1998-99 and 2003-04).

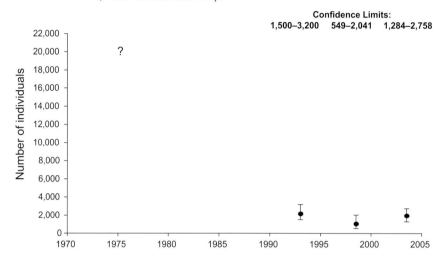

Sources: Figures derived from Kortland (2000), Catt *et al.*, (1998), Wilkinson *et al.* (2002), K. Kortland, pers. comm. (2004).

Figure 18.7 The mean number of cock Capercaillie counted at a sample of leks during 2002–05.

■ Cairngorms National Park   ■ Cairngorms area   ■ Scotland as a whole

Note that apparent changes may reflect variation in the sample of leks surveyed in each year. Sample sizes were as follows. Cairngorms National Park: 33–44 leks; Cairngorms area: 37–49; Scotland: 67–81.

The number of hens present increased throughout 2002-05, and several new leks were located (K. Kortland, pers. comm. 2005).

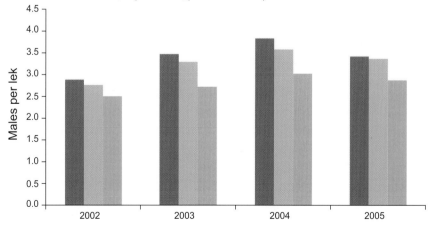

Source: K. Kortland, RSPB (from fieldwork co-funded by the RSPB, FCS, SNH and the Capercaillie EC LIFE project).

Figure 18.8. The mean density of Capercaillie detected in parts of Kinveachy Estate during November-January, 1975/76 – 1984/85.

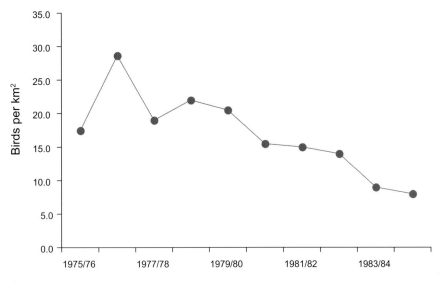

Source: based on figures presented in Moss & Weir (1987).

Figure 18.9. The median number of male Capercaillie counted at lek sites on Glen Tanar Estate in successive 5–year periods. Minimum and maximum counts in each period are indicated (-).

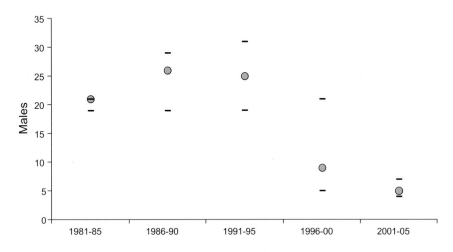

Source: R. Moss pers. comm. (2005), from counts made mainly by J. Oswald (Glen Tanar Estate), R. Moss (CEH) & A. Stolte (Capercaillie EC LIFE Project).

In addition to habitat loss, deterioration and fragmentation, factors limiting the breeding performance and survival of Britain's Capercaillie population have included the effects of cold spring and wet summer weather on chick survival, and egg and chick predation (Moss, 1986; Moss *et al.*, 2001). As a result, the number of chicks fledged has often fallen well below that required to maintain the population. At Abernethy Forest, for example, the ratio of chicks: hens in July–August varied between 0 and 2.9 over a 15 year period, and was negatively correlated both with rainfall levels in June and with a measure of egg predation by crows. Chick survival was particularly high during 1994–96, when drier summer weather coincided with relatively low levels of predation pressure (Figure 18.11) (Summers *et al.*, 2004).

Low breeding success has been the main proximate cause of the Capercaillie's national decline (Moss *et al.*, 2001), but has been exacerbated by the deaths of juveniles and adults flying into deer fences (Baines & Summers, 1997; Moss *et al.*, 2000). Indeed, Moss (2001) has estimated that the number of hen Capercaillies in Britain declined by about 18% (± 5% S.E.) per annum during the 1990s, but might otherwise have changed by about +6% (± 10% S.E.) per annum, were it not for the mortality caused by collisions with deer fences. To address this problem, a programme of fence removal and marking was begun in 2001, funded by the Scottish Executive and managed by the Forestry Commission. This has led to the removal or marking of about 300 km of deer fencing throughout the species' current and recent range in Scotland, and likely to have contributed to the recent increase in the number of cocks (Figure 18.7) and hens counted at lek sites (K. Kortland pers. comm., 2005). Other conservation measures proposed include the trial introduction of Highland and Luing cattle at Abernethy, to investigate the effects of grazing and trampling on excessive heather growth (Beaumont *et al.*, 2005).

The Cairngorms area encompasses six SPAs designated for Capercaillie, and one proposed SPA. In addition, an EC LIFE Project was launched in 2002[4], with the aim of improving breeding success and halting the Capercaillie's decline at 43 localities in Scotland, thereby helping towards the Biodiversity Action Plan target of 5,000 Capercaillie by 2010. At Kinveachy SPA, for example, several measures have been undertaken with the aim of improving survival and breeding success. They include the removal or marking of about 18 km of deer fencing; targeted predator control (foxes and crows) within *c.* 6,200 ha of the SPA; and the establishment in 2005 of a programme to reduce Red Deer *Cervus elephas* numbers from approximately 18 per km^2 to 4 per km^2 by 2008.

[4] *Capercaillie LIFE Project: Urgent Conservation Management for Scottish Capercaillie.* See: http://www.capercaillie-life.info.

Figure 18.10. Trends in the number of Capercaillie counted at Abernethy Forest, a.) during winter drive counts; and b). at six lek sites. In each case, only those sites counted in all years have been included. Note that the areas selected for drive counts may not have been representative of the whole forest. Also, changes between years may reflect movements of birds between counted and uncounted leks, as well as real changes in abundance.

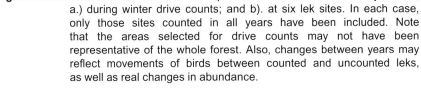

● males   ○ females.

a. Winter drive counts

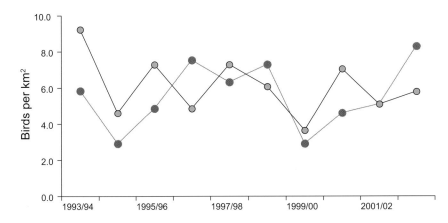

b. Lek counts

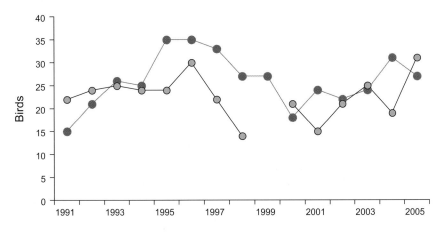

Source: RSPB, Abernethy.

Figure 18.11. The ratio of Capercaillie chicks:hens recorded during summer brood counts at Abernethy Forest.

June rainfall levels and a measure of crow predation pressure were monitored during 1989–99. Counts of Capercaillie hens and chicks were made in all years shown, and were based on a sample of at least 10 hens in each year. Breeding success was relatively high in 1994–96, when low rainfall in June coincided with a low index of crow predation (Summers *et al.*, 2004).

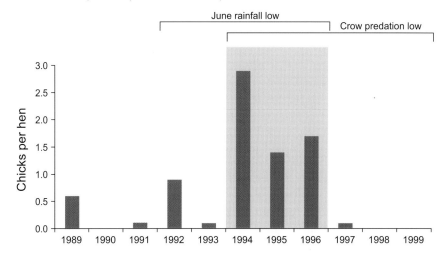

Sources: Summers *et al.* (2004); RSPB, Abernethy.

Together, these varied initiatives, applied throughout the Capercaillie's Scottish range, may help secure a sustained recovery for this charismatic bird.

Britain's **Greenshank** population lies on the extreme western edge of its breeding range, which extends across the boreal region of Eurasia. Its British population was estimated at 1,100–1,790 summering pairs in 1995 (Hancock *et al.*, 1997), concentrated mainly north and west of the Great Glen (Nethersole-Thompson & Nethersole-Thompson, 1979; Gibbons *et al.*, 1993). Greenshanks are relatively scarce in the Cairngorms area, which held just 6% of the species' Scottish breeding range in 1988–91 (Gibbons *et al.*, 1993). The Cairngorms' Greenshank population is therefore not considered to be of national importance, but is notable for its tendency to breed in semi-forested habitats.

During the 1980s–90s Greenshanks bred in small numbers in parts of Strathspey and upper Deeside (Buckland *et al.*, 1990; Dennis, 1995), but were formerly more common, 11 pairs being recorded between Loch Morlich and Inshriach in the 1930s, dropping to six pairs in the vicinity of Loch Morlich in 1962 (Dennis, 1995). A similar decline has occurred in the number of birds recorded annually during June counts along the shores of Loch Morlich: from 2–7 birds in the 1930s and early 1940s, to none by the mid–1970s (Watson *et al.*, 1988). Nethersole-Thompson and Watson (1981) attributed the Greenshank's decline at Loch Morlich to a drying out of forest bogs in Rothiemurchus, and to an increase in the amount of tall heather and tree cover there. Other factors thought likely to have influenced the number of shore waders at Loch Morlich were: human disturbance, habitat impoverishment (through trampling), habitat destruction, and gull and crow predation (Watson *et al.*, 1988).

The extent of the Greenshank's decline in the Cairngorms area is illustrated by changes in the number of 10-km squares occupied during two breeding atlas surveys; from 30 squares in *c.* 1970 to 15 in *c.* 1990. This 50% decline in occupied squares contrasts with a 4% decline in Scotland as a whole (Sharrock, 1976; Gibbons *et al.*, 1993).

The **Crested Tit** is widespread in Europe, its range extending from the southern tip of Spain to the Arctic Circle, and east as far as the Urals. While its population throughout most of Europe has remained stable over the past 30 years, its large Russian population declined during 1990–2000, suggesting

Figure 18.12. The number of Crested Tit territories recorded in a survey area at Loch Garten, 1977-88.

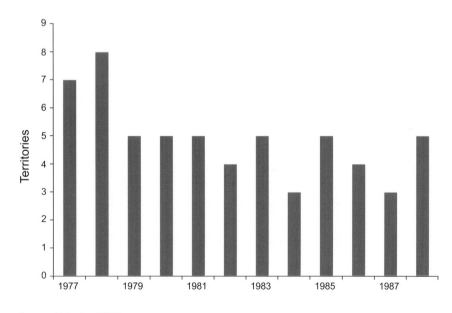

Source: S. Taylor, RSPB

[5] A proposed Special Protection Area.

that its European population has suffered a moderate decline overall (BirdLife International, 2004b). As a result, the Crested Tit was considered to have an Unfavourable status in Europe in 2004, having been classed as Favourable 10 years earlier (BirdLife International, 2004a).

In Britain, the Crested Tit is not considered threatened, but is included here partly because of its taxonomic importance (as an endemic sub-species; *Parus cristatus scoticus*) and because of the relative importance of its Cairngorms' population. The Crested Tit also has a potential role as a 'flagship species', whose habitat requirements are shared by a range of other pine forest specialists.

On the Continent, the Crested Tit is found mainly in pine and spruce, particularly in northern Europe, and in mixed woodland, beech *Fagus* forest and Cork Oak *Quercus suber*. Only in Britain is it restricted mainly to old, open stands of native pine, where it favours structurally diverse, ancient forests (Moss, 1978) with an abundance of broad, rotting stumps and standing dead trees (Hill *et al.*, 1990). The latter provide it with nest sites, particularly where the diameter of the stump exceeds 30 cm and the sapwood has begun to rot, leaving a cavity between the bark and the inner heartwood (Baker, 1991; Denny, 1995; Denny & Summers, 1996; Summers, 2004). Where there is little deadwood available nesboxes are sometimes used, notably at Culbin Forest, and in a plantation in Badenoch and Strathspey.

The Crested Tit's distribution in Britain thus largely reflects that of ancient semi-natural pine forest and mature pine plantations, and includes Strathspey, the Beauly catchment, parts of the Great Glen, east Ross-shire and the coasts of Nairn, Moray and Banffshire (Summers *et al.*, 1999). Throughout much of its Scottish range the Crested Tit tends to be more thinly dispersed than most temperate tits, achieving a mean winter density of about 30 birds per km² in ancient native pinewood (Summers *et al.*, 1999). At Abernethy Forest a winter survey yielded an estimated 10.6 birds per km² (Stewart, 2003), broadly similar to densities estimated during a spring survey of North Rothiemurchus Pinewood (4 territories per km²; Calladine, 2005) and during an early spring survey of Cairngorms pSPA[5] (about 6 or 10 birds per km²; Marquiss *et al.*, 1997). Even in optimal habitat, encounter rates thus tend to be low, averaging one group per 1.4 km walked in ancient native pinewood (Summers *et al.*, 1999) and one group per 2 km in the pinewoods of Cairngorms SPA (Marquiss *et al.*, 1997). Densities are much lower still in poorer quality habitat, showing a ten-fold difference between the prime habitat of ancient native woodland and other coniferous woodlands (Summers *et al.*, 1999).

Curiously, the Crested Tit is all but absent from Deeside, where there have been sporadic sightings of individuals and small groups as far east as Glen Dye, but no confirmed breeding attempts, despite the availability of apparently suitable habitat (Knox, 1983). Most records are from upper Deeside, indicating that birds may occasionally disperse through the Cairngorms, perhaps via Glen Feshie or the Lairig Ghru. In 1996, for example, three birds were recorded at Morrone, near Braemar, and in 1998 and 1999 single birds were seen at the Linn of Dee. These birds had perhaps moved through the southern part of the Cairngorms, the nearest occupied wood in Glen Feshie being 20 km away (Summers & Canham, 2001). Cook (1982) has suggested that its absence as a breeding species in Deeside may be linked to lower winter temperatures on upper Deeside (at Braemar), although this does not explain its absence from forests at lower altitudes further east (Knox, 1983). Moreover, minimum temperatures at Braemar and Abernethy are often similar (S. Taylor, pers. comm.).

During 1992–99 Crested Tits were recorded from 79 10-km squares in Scotland (Summers & Canham, 2001), of which 20 (25%) lay at least partly within the Cairngorms area and 17 (22%) within the National Park. Its winter population has been estimated at 5,600–7,900 birds, which, allowing for the effects of winter mortality, may occupy some 2,400 territories in spring (Summers *et al.*, 1999). These figures are considerably higher than earlier estimates by Sharrock (1976; 1,000 pairs) and Cook (1982; 900 pairs), which were based on less rigorous methods and smaller sample areas.

The Cairngorms holds about half of Scotland's semi-natural pinewood. Although much of this lies in Deeside (Figure 7.2), where Crested Tits are absent, the area nonetheless holds a substantial share of the national population. Indeed, some of Strathspey's main Crested Tit forests are individually important on a national scale. Cairngorms SPA was thought to hold about 183 or 286 breeding pairs in late winter/early spring 1997, representing about 8–12% of the British population (Marquiss *et al.*, 1997). More recent surveys of Abernethy Forest and North Rothiemurchus Pinewood[6] suggest that they may hold about 5–6% and 2%, respectively, of the British population. Levels of uncertainty associated with Crested Tit estimates tend to be high, however, as indicated by their wide confidence limits (Table 18.3).

Crested Tits are highly sedentary, juveniles normally moving only a few km from their natal site (Deadman, 1973). The species is therefore vulnerable

The endemic British race of the Crested Tit Parus cristatus scoticus *is more thinly dispersed than most temperate tits, and more specific in its habitat requirements than Continental races. Even in Caledonian pine forest you may encounter few Crested Tits, compared with the more ubiquitous Coal Tit.*

Photo: *N. Mcintyre*

---

[6] North Rothiemurchus Pinewood lies within the Cairngorms SPA

Table 18.3. Recent estimates of Crested Tit abundance in Strathspey forests

Location	Area surveyed (km²)	Period		Estimate	Confidence Limits	% of UK population[1]	Source
Kinveachy Forest	14.9	February	1994	80 birds	30–221	1.0–1.4% (W)	Summers & Ellis (1994)
Cairngorms SPA[2]	58.8	Feb–April	1997	286 pairs	165–498	11.9% (S)	Marquiss et al. (1997)
		March–April	1997	183 pairs	99–356	7.6% (S)	
Abernethy Forest	33.5	Winter	2001/02	356 birds	286–445	4.5–6.4% (W)	Summers & Proctor (2002)
North Rothiemurchus Pinewood SSSI	14.0	March	2005	56 territories	-	2.3% (S)	Calladine (2005)

[1] Expressed as a percentage of the UK Winter population (W) (5,600–7,900 birds) or of the Spring population (S) (2,400 territories), as appropriate (based on national estimates given in Summers et al., 1999).

[2] The area surveyed comprised Cairngorms pSPA and Glenmore Forest SSSI.

to harsh winter weather (Lens & Dhondt, 1992) and, like most temperate songbirds, its abundance can fluctuate substantially between years. At a study site at Loch Garten the number of breeding pairs varied between 29 in 1978 and 18 in 1981 (S. Taylor, RSPB, pers. comm.; Dennis, 1995), while territory numbers at a smaller survey area, also near Loch Garten, varied between eight and three over a 12–year period, (S. Taylor, RSPB, pers. comm.) (Figure 18.12).

While there are no national population trend data for the Crested Tit, its distribution has been mapped on five occasions since c. 1970. These include a winter atlas survey (Lack, 1986) and the two national breeding atlases. The latter suggested that the species' Scottish range expanded by 11% during c. 1970–90, but was unchanged within the Cairngorms (Sharrock, 1976; Gibbons et al., 1993). These two breeding surveys, and a third by Cook (1982), yielded broadly similar range estimates: of 46, 51 and 45 10-km squares, respectively. In contrast, Summers and Canham (2001) reported Crested Tits from 79 squares during the 1990s, but attributed much of this apparent expansion to variation in observer effort during earlier surveys. They noted that the three earlier breeding surveys had, in combination, recorded Crested Tits in 75 squares, and suggested that each of the previous surveys had underestimated its true range.

The recent expansion of semi-natural pine forest (Chapter 7) may enable the Crested Tit to extend its range in Scotland. In the longer-term, however, the Scottish Crested Tit's conservative, sedentary nature may leave it vulnerable to the impacts of climate change, should this have an adverse effect on its restricted habitat.

The Cairngorms support breeding populations of three crossbill species: the widespread **Common Crossbill** Loxia curvirostra; the endemic **Scottish Crossbill**; and the **Parrot Crossbill**, which is scarce in Britain but, like the Common Crossbill, is widespread and abundant in Fennoscandia. These three species differ in terms of body size, bill size and voice, but show no diagnostic physical characters that enable them to be separated with confidence in the field (Marquiss & Rae, 2002; Summers et al., 2002a).

Crossbills use their crossed bill tips to extract seeds from the cones of larch, spruce or pine. Differences in the size, shape and hardness of cone types are reflected in the average bill depth of each crossbill species, with Parrot Crossbill having the deepest and Common Crossbill the shallowest bill. Bill depths of Scottish Crossbill overlap with those of Common and Parrot Crossbill (Knox, 1976), however, making it difficult to identify some individuals, even in the hand. Not surprisingly, given their similarity, the Scottish Crossbill has at times been regarded as a sub-species of the Common Crossbill and of Parrot Crossbill (see Knox, 1975), and was only recognised as a full species in 1978 (Voous, 1978; Cramp & Perrins, 1994). Although Scottish Crossbills were initially thought to predominate in ancient semi-natural pine forests, studies during the 1990s revealed that many of the birds caught in such habitats were Parrot Crossbills. Indeed, of 62 crossbills caught at Abernethy during 1995-2001, 46 were Parrot Crossbill, and only five were Scottish Crossbill (Summers, 2002). In the Cairngorms area, Parrot Crossbill has also been recorded at Glenmore, Rothiemurchus, Curr Wood, Mar Lodge, Glen Tanar and Ballochbuie, and is now considered to be the main crossbill species in Caledonian forest during winter and early spring (Summers & Piertney, 2003; R. Rae & M. Marquiss pers. comm.; see also Nethersole-Thompson, 1975).

Table 18.4. Locations at which Scottish Crossbills were recorded during 1995–2003 (Summers *et al.*, 2003), in 10-km grid squares lying at least partly within the Cairngorms area.

Location	10-km square(s)	National Park[1]	Location	10-km square(s)	National Park[1]	Location	10-km square(s)	National Park[1]
Abernethy Forest	NJ01, NH91, NH92	Y	Fordbridge Hill	NJ31	Y	Hill of Dalnapot	NJ13	
Alltcailleach Forest	NO39	Y	Gairnshiel	NJ20	Y	Inshriach Forest	NN89	Y
Blackhall	NO69		Glen Feshie	NN89	Y	Loch Davan	NJ40	Y
Bogieshiel Lodge	NO59		Glen Quoich	NO19	Y	Morinsh Wood	NJ23	
Bridge of Brown	NJ12	Y	Glen Tanar	NO49	Y	Rothiemurchus Forest	NH90	Y
Carrbridge Woods	NH92	Y	Glenmore Forest	NH90, NH91	Y	Sluggan	NH82	Y
Craigmore Wood	NJ02	Y	Glenmullie, Tomintoul	NJ11	Y	Tomvaich	NJ03	Y
Curr Wood	NH92	Y	Grantown-on-Spey	NJ02	Y			

[1] 10-km squares that lie at least partly (≥ 20%) within Cairngorms National Park boundary.

Since bill depth and shape are linked to diet, the three species show different – but overlapping – habitat preferences, and different patterns of movement. On Deeside, Common Crossbills are more itinerant and migratory than the other two species, switching seasonally between the (softer) cones of spruce and larch, and those of Scots Pine *Pinus sylvestris*, once its cones have opened (Marquiss & Rae, 2002). The larger-billed Parrot Crossbill is more sedentary, feeding throughout the year on pine seed in semi-natural Scots Pine forest. Scottish Crossbills, with their intermediate bill size, are also more sedentary than Common Crossbills, but switch seasonally between conifer species (Marquiss & Rae, 2002), and are common in pure- and mixed plantations of Lodgepole Pine *Pinus contorta*, Sitka Spruce *Picea sitchensis*, larch *Larix* spp. and Scots Pine (Summers *et al.*, 2002a). One explanation for the Scottish Crossbill's current distribution and intermediate bill size is that it has largely been displaced from Caledonian forest through competition with Parrot Crossbill, and has adapted to exploit the spread of non-native conifer plantations over the past 150 years (Marquiss & Rae, 2002).

The lack of diagnostic physical characters, clearly visible in the field, has hampered efforts to establish the status of Scottish Crossbill, and to determine whether its range or abundance are changing. Its movements are also poorly known. Although Nethersole-Thompson (1975) suggested that Scottish Crossbills were likely to move between Deeside and Strathspey, this remained unproven until 1994, when a bird colour-ringed near Ballater was sighted in Abernethy (Marquiss *et al.*, 1995). A movement from Strathspey to Deeside has also been noted (Summers & Piertney, 2003).

This female Parrot Crossbill continued to sit tight while her nestlings were weighed, as part of a study at Abernethy Forest. Colour ringing has helped researchers to trace local crossbill movements, and even movements between Deeside and Strathspey.

Photo: *R. Summers*

Given the lack of diagnostic physical characters, survey methods have focussed on differences in excitement calls used by the three species. During 1995–2003 Scottish Crossbills, identified by call type, were recorded in 83 10-km squares, centred on the eastern Highlands, with outlying records in Caithness and Sutherland, Glen Garry, Stirlingshire and Fettereso Forest, near Stonehaven (Summers *et al.*, 2003). Twenty of these squares lay mainly within the Cairngorms area, and 16 mainly within the National Park (Table 18.4), representing 24% and 19%, respectively, of the species' global range. Since there are currently no reliable population estimates for Scottish Crossbill, it is classed as globally Data Deficient and is of European conservation concern (BirdLife International, 2004b). In the Cairngorms, it is a qualifying species on five SPAs, all of which fall within the National Park, and meets IBA selection criteria on a further seven sites in the Cairngorms area (Table 18.9). Based on its distribution (Summers *et al.*, 2003) and the amount of mature coniferous forest present, the Cairngorms area seems likely to support at least 25% of the species' global population.

Figure 18.13. The number of Wryneck recorded in Badenoch & Strathspey (■) and in Scotland as a whole (■).

The number of pairs and single birds (combined) recorded in Badenoch and Strathspey during 1968-94 (from Dennis, 1995), and the number of pairs and singing males recorded in Scotland during 1969-2003 (M.A. Ogilvie: Rare Breeding Birds Panel).

Since the total number of birds involved often cannot be established, these figures should be taken as indicative only.

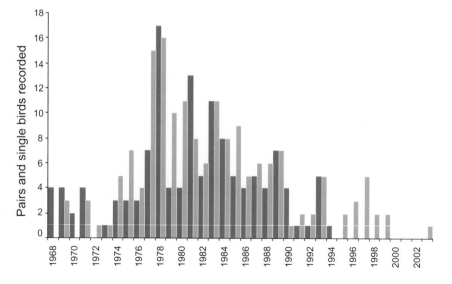

7 Including Piciforms.

Scandinavian songbirds and allied species. Several scarce songbirds and allied species[7], mainly of Scandinavian origin, bred more regularly in the Cairngorms area during the 1970s and 1980s than since. They include the Wryneck, which was first recorded breeding in Scotland in 1969, reaching a peak of 14 singles and three pairs in Badenoch & Strathspey in 1978 (Figure 18.13) (Dennis, 1995). Red-backed Shrike breeding records also peaked in 1978, with seven pairs or single males in Scotland, while the Lapland Bunting peaked briefly in 1977, when up to seven males and two females were present in Badenoch & Strathspey (Dennis, 1995). Brambling numbers peaked in 1982, with eight pairs or singing males in Scotland, while one pair and 20 singing male Redwing were reported in Badenoch & Strathspey in the following year (Dennis, 1995). Breeding records for Fieldfare, Common Rosefinch and Shore Lark have remained low, however, the latter breeding in 1977 and in 2002–03.

Factors precipitating these peaks during the 1970s–80s are unknown. One possibility is that spring conditions during that period more often encouraged Scandinavian migrants to drift from their normal migration routes, and to remain in Scotland to breed. R. Dennis (pers. comm.) has speculated that while individuals that have bred in Scotland may return to breed again in successive years, their offspring may be genetically programmed to migrate between the species' normal breeding range (e.g. Scandinavia) and wintering area, in which case they would be unlikely to return to Scotland. The Scottish breeding population would then become extinct following the death of its founding members, unless suitable spring conditions deliver further waves of prospective colonisers. An alternative explanation is that breeding conditions in Scotland are normally sub-optimal for these species, and that the number of young reared in most years is too low to offset mortality, with the same eventual result.

Pine forest edge and scrub
The **Black Grouse** is associated mainly with forest edge, young conifer plantations and clear-felled areas with a well-developed field- and shrub layer, comprising heather and Blaeberry, with rushes and cotton-grasses. Following a decline throughout most of its European range in 1970–2000, the Black Grouse has been classed as a species of European conservation concern (BirdLife International, 2004b).

In Britain the Black Grouse is red-listed and a BAP Priority species, its breeding range having declined by 28% during *c.* 1970–90 (Gibbons *et al.*, 1993). Its UK population was thought to include about 25,000 lekking males in 1990, but only 6,510 in 1995–96, of which 4,719 were in Scotland (Baines & Hudson, 1995; Hancock *et al.,* 1999). By 2005 the UK estimate had dropped to 5,078 displaying males, while the Scottish estimate was of 3,344, representing a 29% decline in Scotland over the 10-year period (RSPB, 2005). The number of displaying males present in a small sample of survey squares within Cairngorms National Park declined by 10% over the same period (I. Sim, pers. comm., 2006).

The species' decline has been attributed mainly to agricultural intensification, particularly the effects of burning and grazing. Overgrazing reduces the availability of invertebrate prey for Black Grouse chicks, of cover for nesting birds, and of nutritionally rich flower heads and cottongrass shoots, taken by females prior to laying (Hudson & Baines, 1993). Like the Capercaillie, the breeding success of Black Grouse at Abernethy Forest during the 1990s was negatively related to a measure of nest predation by crows, and to June rainfall (Summers *et al.,* 2004). Evidence from grouse bags suggests that climate change may have also played a part in its national decline since, for much of

the 20th century, all four British grouse species having fluctuated together and in step with the North Atlantic Oscillation (R. Moss, unpublished data).

During the 1988–91 breeding bird atlas survey the Cairngorms area encompassed about 11% of the species' UK range and about 15% of its Scottish range (from Sharrock, 1976; Gibbons *et al.,* 1993), but probably supported rather more of its national population than these figures suggest. Tayside, especially, has become a stronghold for Black Grouse, which may partly explain a disparity between trends evident in the National Park and in the Cairngorms area as a whole. During *c.* 1970–90 the number of 10-km squares occupied by Black Grouse declined by 21% within the area now encompassed by Cairngorms National Park, but by only 6% within the Cairngorms area, due partly to gains made in Perthshire.

Notable areas for Black Grouse in the Cairngorms include Glen Tanar, the Forest of Clunie (thought to hold about 400 birds in 1996; Fisher *et al.,* 2000) and Mar Lodge (over 150 males in 2005; I. Francis, pers. comm.). Abernethy

Figure 18.14. The number of Blackcock counted at lek sites in Abernethy Forest during 1991-2005.

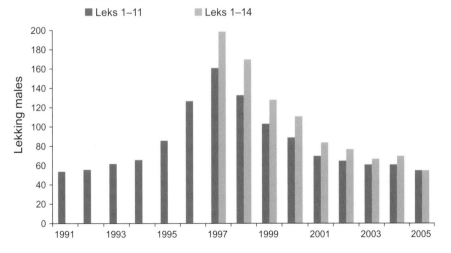

Counts were made at 11 lek sites during 1991–2005, and at an additional three leks from 1997 onwards.

No data were available for four of the lek sites in 1–2 years. In three cases, no birds had been present for several years prior to the missing count. In the remaining case, the mean value from the preceding and subsequent two years was used.

Source: S. Taylor, RSPB

The number of lekking blackcock in Scotland is estimated to have fallen by 29% during 1995-2005. A high proportion of Scotland's remaining population are found in the Cairngorms area, particularly in parts of Perthshire, Strathspey and upper Deeside.

Photo: M. Hamblin

Forest is also particularly important, supporting 1–3% of the British population (RSPB, 1989–2003). The number of males counted at a sample of leks at Abernethy has varied markedly over the past 15 years, however, almost trebling during 1991–97, since when the population has shown a steady decline (Figure 18.14). This pattern may reflect an improvement and subsequent decline in the condition of the field layer, due to a reduction in grazing pressure (R. Moss, pers. comm. 2005), as a result of regulated deer culling. At Abernethy the Red Deer density fell below 5 per km[2] in 1994 (Beaumont et al., 2005), enabling field layer shrubs, particularly heather and Blaeberry, to flourish in the following years.

Moorland

The Cairngorms area supports important numbers of five raptor species associated mainly with heather moorland: **Hen Harrier, Golden Eagle, Merlin, Peregrine** and **Short-eared Owl** (Table 18.5). Three of these are classed as species of European conservation concern, on account of recent, widespread population declines (Hen Harrier, Short-eared Owl) or small population size (Golden Eagle) (BirdLife International, 2004b). Populations of all five species are subject to constrants associated with grouse moor management, illegal disturbance or killing (Table 18.6).

In the Cairngorms, areas of Deeside and Perthshire managed for grouse shooting are particularly important for Hen Harrier and Merlin, which require moorland with a high proportion of heather cover, and patches of tall,

rank heather for nesting in. Indeed, the southern and eastern fringes of the Cairngorm and Grampian mountains support some of the highest breeding concentrations of Hen Harrier, Merlin and Short-eared Owl in Britain (Glue, 1993; Rebecca & Bainbridge, 1998; Sim et al., 2001). In contrast, population densities of Golden Eagle are generally lower in the East Highlands than in the West Highlands and Islands, despite the fact that live prey is more abundant and breeding success is higher in the east (Watson et al., 1992; Watson, 1997).

National atlas surveys during 1968–72 and 1988–91 suggest that changes in the number of 10-km grid squares occupied by moorland raptors were generally less favourable in the Cairngorms than in the rest of Scotland (from Sharrock, 1976; Gibbons et al., 1993). Merlin, for example, showed a much smaller increase within the area now encompassed by Cairngorms National Park (+3%) than in Scotland as a whole (+28%). Similarly, Short-eared Owl showed a much larger *decrease* within Cairngorms National Park (-30%) than in Scotland as a whole (-17%). Note, however, that Short-eared Owl numbers tend to fluctuate markedly between years, reflecting changes in local vole densities. Moreover, these findings may have been influenced by differences in observer effort during the two atlas periods, or by chance events within the relatively small number of squares occupied in the Cairngorms. They may also reflect regional differences in the impact of organochlorine poisoning during the 1960s, which is likely to have been lower in the Cairngorms than in intensively farmed areas.

Table 18.5.   Status and recent trends in five moorland raptor species for which the Cairngorms area is considered nationally important (adapted from Thompson et al., 2003).

Species	UK or *GB* Population		Source[1]	As a % of European population[2]	Breeding pairs in Cairngorms SPAs[3]	As a % of pairs in all GB SPAs[4]	Trends in Europe[2]		Recent trend in Scotland[5]
							1970-90	1990-2000	
Hen Harrier	675–832[6]	territorial pairs	I	1–2%	30	13%	Decrease	Stable	Increase
Golden Eagle	422	occupied home ranges	II	4–5%	18	30%	Stable	Stable	Numerically stable
Merlin	1,305–1,320	pairs with nests	II	3–4%	33	8%	Stable	Stable	Increase
Peregrine	1,402	territorial pairs	III	6–12%	12	12%	Increase	Increase	Decrease
Short-eared Owl	*1,000–3,500*	'pairs'	II	c. 2%	20	15%	Decrease	Stable	Uncertain

[1]   **Source: I.** I. Sim, RSPB (2006). **II.** Greenwood et al. (2003). **III.** Scottish Raptor Monitoring Group (2003).

[2]   Including Russia. Estimates were taken from BirdLife International (2004b)

[3]   From Stroud et al. (2001). Includes SPAs that fall partly outside of the Cairngorms area.

[4]   From estimates provided by the JNCC at: www.jncc.gov.uk/

[5]   Over approximately the last 10 years.

[6]   Site-specific surveys indicate a decline over parts of eastern and southern Scotland.

Table 18.6. The main constraints on populations of five moorland raptor species.

Species	Main constraints
Hen Harrier	Wilful disturbance, nest destruction and the illegal killing of adults; habitat loss and deterioration (including the maturation of young plantations) (Etheridge *et al.*, 1997; Scottish Raptor Study Groups, 1998).
Golden Eagle	Wilful disturbance, illegal killing (Watson, 1997; Whitfield *et al.*, 2003).
Merlin	Habitat loss, especially through the conversion of heather moorland to grassland (Rebecca & Bainbridge, 1998).
Peregrine	Illegal killing; continued impacts of environmental pollutants; habitat deterioration through over-grazing; egg collectors; illegal supply of wild birds to the falconry trade (Scottish Raptor Study Groups, 1998; RSPB, 1999)
Short-eared Owl	Habitat deterioration, as young plantations mature (Glue, 1993).

National surveys of Merlin during 1983–84 and 1993–94 have shown that breeding numbers increased or remained stable in those areas for which comparable data were available (Rebecca & Bainbridge, 1998). They include north-east Scotland, which encompasses much of the Cairngorms area and held at least 70 breeding pairs during 1993–94. Since the 1980s, studies on lower Deeside and upper Donside have monitored abundance and breeding success annually in up to 4% of the British Merlin population (G. Rebecca, B. Cosnette & L.D. Steele, pers. comm.). Merlin numbers in Aberdeenshire remained fairly stable during the 1980s–90s, although with a slight decline evident in lower Deeside during the 1990s, and in territory occupancy overall. Abandonment of breeding territories was linked mainly to afforestation (in lower Deeside) and to excessive muirburn (in upper Donside) (Rebecca & Cosnette, 2003).

Following a population crash in the 1960s, the British Peregrine population has increased steadily, rising by 18% between the two most recent national surveys; in 1991 and 2002 (Figure 18.15). In contrast, the Scottish population showed a marked decline over this period (-13%). This trend was particularly pronounced in Highland Region (-30%), where it has been attributed to food shortages, possibly linked to a deterioration in moorland condition through over-grazing and muirburn (BTO, 2005). Persecution is also thought to explain the Peregrine's absence from many traditionally occupied sites, particularly in north-east and central Scotland. In Cairngorms National Park, which held 11% of the Scottish population in 2002, the number of pairs dropped by 19% during 1991–2002; a more marked decline than in Scotland as a whole.

Between 1998 and 2004 Scotland's Hen Harrier population rose by 45%, but declined by 38% within the Cairngorms area and by 81% within the National Park. The greatest decline occurred in the Ladder Hills, which held nine pairs in 1998 but none in 2004 (within the IBA). Persecution, particularly on grouse moors, has been identified as one of the main threats to this and other moorland raptor species

Photo: *M. Hamblin*

Figure 18.15. The number of Peregrine pairs counted during national surveys, expressed as an index, with a value of 1.0 in 1961–62.

Key: ● Britain   ◆ Scotland
     ▲ Cairngorms area   □ Cairngorms National Park.

The British Peregrine population has increased steadily since the 1970s, rising from 412 pairs in 1971 to 1,402 by 2002.

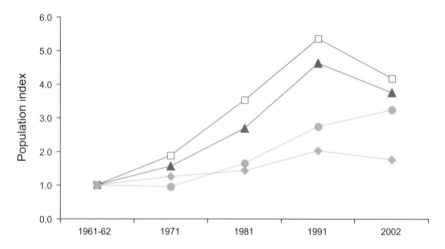

Source: S. Newson & H. Crick, BTO, pers. comm. (2005), based partly on data provided by Highland, North East Scotland and Tayside Raptor Study Groups.

During *c.* 1970–90 the Hen Harrier expanded its range by 32% within Cairngorms National Park, and by 26% in Scotland overall. More recently, it has declined in the Cairngorms while *increasing* in Scotland as a whole. The number of Hen Harrier pairs recorded during surveys in 1998 and 2004 rose by 45% in Scotland, but dropped by 38% in the Cairngorms area[8], and by 81% within the National Park (Sim *et al.*, 2001; I. Sim, pers. comm., 2005). The greatest change recorded in the Cairngorms area occurred within the 10-km square encompassing the Ladder Hills, which held 11 pairs in 1998; nine of these within the IBA. No pairs were recorded there during the 2004 survey (I. Sim, pers. comm., 2005).

The disparity between Cairngorms National Park and the rest of Scotland has been particularly marked in the case of trends in Golden Eagle numbers. During *c.* 1970–90 the number of occupied 10-km squares rose by 8% in Scotland but fell by 11% within the area now bounded by the National Park (from Sharrock, 1976; Gibbons *et al.*, 1993). A similar disparity was evident between 1992 and 2003, when the number of occupied territories increased by 3% in Scotland but fell by 15% within the National Park (D.P. Whitfield &

D.R.A. McLeod pers. comm., 2005). As a result, 54% of the National Park's Golden Eagle territories were unoccupied in 2003.

In conclusion, recent changes in the numbers Golden Eagle, Hen Harrier and Peregrine in Cairngorms National Park have been less favourable, or at variance with trends seen in Scotland as a whole (Figure 18.16). These disparities may be linked to the National Park's extensive areas of grouse moor, since raptor persecution has been shown to be more prevalent in areas maintained for grouse shooting than elsewhere (e.g. Whitfield *et al.*, 2003).

The ***Ring Ouzel*** is a widespread, migratory thrush, associated with heather moorland, particularly where it forms a mosaic with grassland on steep, broken ground, and with exposed rock. Most pairs nest at 230–730 m asl (Wotton *et al.*, 2002), although some reach 1,200 m or 1,300 m in the Cairngorms (Flegg & Glue, 1975; Nethersole-Thompson & Watson 1981; Dennis, 1995). In 1999, Scotland was thought to hold 4,341–5,503 pairs, accounting for about 73% of the UK total (Wotton *et al.*, 2002). Of these, a substantial proportion breeds in the Cairngorms area (Hill, 1993), notably in Glen Clunie and upper Glen Esk, each of which held at least 1% of the Scottish population during the late 1990s (Arthur & White, 2001; Rebecca, 2002). Ring Ouzels are also relatively common in glens Callater, Muick and Ey (I. Sim, pers. comm.), but are thought to be under-recorded generally (A. Watson, pers. comm.).

Britain's Ring Ouzel population has declined since the early 1900s, for reasons that are unclear. In Scotland, declines were noted during the 30 years up to the early 1950s (Baxter & Rintoul, 1953) and continued between the 1950s and 1980s (Thom, 1986). The scale of the decline has been estimated from national breeding atlases of 1968–72 and 1988–91, and through a more detailed survey in 1999 (Wotton *et al.*, 2002). These showed that the Ring Ouzel's breeding range in Britain contracted by 27% during *c.*1970–90, and by a further 39–43% during 1991–99, the latter accompanied by a 58% reduction in its population (Buchanan *et al.*, 2003).

The Ring Ouzel's decline has been attributed to a variety of factors, including afforestation (Tyler & Green, 1989), changes in agriculture (Cadbury, 1993), climate change (Tyler & Green, 1994) and increased predation (Thompson *et al.*, 1997). At Scottish sites surveyed during the 1990s declines were most evident at the extremes of the species' altitude range, in shallow-sloping areas and where improved pasture predominates (Buchanan *et al.*, 2003). Afforestation was also implicated.

---

[8] Derived from a sample of 10-km squares surveyed in both years (24 squares within the Cairngorms area; nine squares within the National Park boundary) containing respectively, 40 pairs and 21 pairs in 1998.

Figure 18.16. Changes in the geographic range and population size of Golden Eagle, Hen Harrier and Peregrine within the area now bounded by Cairngorms National Park, compared with Scotland as a whole. Range size changes were estimated from the number of 10-km squares occupied during atlas surveys carried out in *c.* 1970 and *c.* 1990 (from Sharrock, 1976; Gibbons *et al.*, 1993). Population estimates were derived from periodic national surveys, in the years indicated.

■ Scotland ■ Cairngorms National Park

Golden Eagle

Between 1992 and 2003 the number of occupied territories within Cairngorms National Park declined by 15% (from 33 to 28), while increasing by 3% in Scotland as a whole.

Sources: D.P. Whitfield & D.R.A. McLeod pers. comm., 2005.

Hen Harrier

The number of Hen Harrier pairs recorded during surveys in 1998 and 2004 rose by 45% in Scotland (from 436 to 633 territorial pairs), but declined by 38% in the Cairngorms area, and by 81% within the National Park.

Sources: Sim *et al.*, 2001; I. Sim, pers. comm., 2005

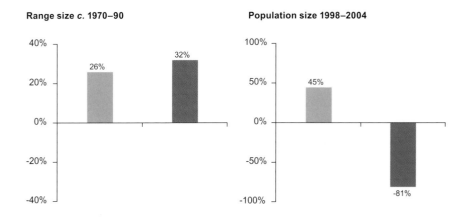

Peregrine

In Cairngorms National Park the number of Peregrine pairs declined during 1991–2002, from 74 to 60 pairs (-19%). A 13% decline was recorded in Scotland overall.

Sources: S. Newson & H. Crick, BTO, pers. comm. (2005), based on data provided by Highland, North East Scotland and Tayside Raptor Study Groups.

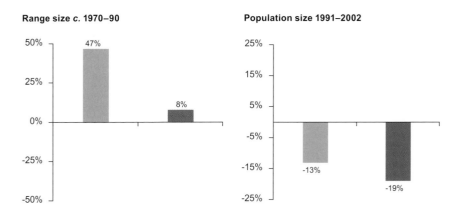

Declines in the Cairngorms' Ring Ouzel population during the 1980s and 1990s may have been less pronounced than elsewhere in Britain. Nonetheless, there is evidence of a recent substantial decline in its breeding range in upper Deeside and Donside, and in the number of pairs breeding at a study site in Glen Clunie.

Photo: *L. Campbell*

Figure 18.17. The number of territorial pairs of Ring Ouzel detected at a study site in Glen Clunie (from Sim *et al.,* 2005).

■ Territories occupied during the early part of the breeding season.
■ Additional territories occupied only in the later part of the breeding season.

During 1998-2000 the minimum number of territorial pairs detected at Glen Clunie varied between 37 and 39, but had dropped to just 17 by 2005 (Sim *et al.,* 2005).

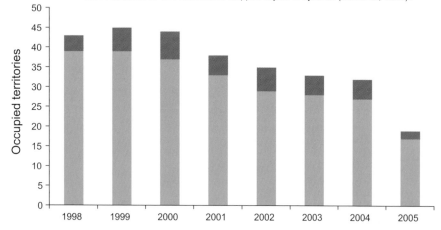

Source: Sim *et al.,* (2005); Sim pers. comm. (2005).

There is some evidence that declines in the Cairngorms in the 1980s and 1990s may have been less pronounced than elsewhere. During *c.*1970–90, for example, the species' range within the Cairngorms area contracted by 16%, in contrast to the 27% range contraction seen in Britain as a whole. Nonetheless, preliminary results from the breeding bird atlas of NE Scotland suggest that the Ring Ouzel's range in upper Deeside and Donside may have decreased by up to one-third between 1981–84 and 2002–04[9] (I. Francis pers. comm., 2005).

Detailed local studies have produced mixed results. Breeding numbers at one study site, in upper Glen Esk, showed little change during the 1990s (Arthur & White, 2001; Rebecca, 2002), while those at a site in Glen Clunie have declined steadily since the late 1990s (Sim *et al.,* 2005) (Figure 18.17). Since breeding output increased and return rates[10] declined over this period, it would appear that the population decline may have been linked to reduced survival between breeding seasons, rather than to poor breeding success. These results are provisional, however, and further work is required to identify the mechanisms underlying the Ring Ouzel's decline at this site.

Montane

Four breeding bird species – the Ptarmigan, Dotterel, Purple Sandpiper and Snow Bunting – are confined to the montane zone, and consequently are more abundant in the Cairngorms than in any other part of Britain.

The **Ptarmigan** has a circumpolar distribution, occupying Arctic-alpine habitats throughout much of western and southern Europe, Scandinavia, Russia, North America, Greenland and Iceland (Cramp & Simmons, 1983). In Britain, the species is confined to Scotland, breeding mainly at or above *c.* 760 m in the Cairngorms, reaching 1,265 m on Ben Macdui (Nethersole-Thompson & Watson, 1981). It breeds in dwarf shrub heath, high summit heaths and fell-fields, where it feeds mainly on the leaves and shoots of Crowberry *Empetrum nigrum,* Blaeberry, Heather and Dwarf Willow *Salix herbacea* (Watson, 1964; Moss & Watson 1984). Breeding pairs favour a fine-ground mixture of Blaeberry and Crowberry interspersed with boulders, which provide cover from predators and the elements, as well as song-posts for territorial males.

Britain's Ptarmigan population has been estimated at 10,000 pairs (Ratcliffe, 1990), but fluctuates considerably, and has never been systematically surveyed.

---

[9] Based on the number of atlas recording units from which Ring Ouzels were reported during the 1981-84 North-east Scotland breeding bird atlas (Buckland *et al.,* 1990), and a second breeding bird atlas project, begun in 2002. Note, however, that data from the second project span only three years' of fieldwork to date, and are therefore not directly comparable with the first (4-year) atlas period. Comparisons between the two breeding atlases may change once the second atlas project is complete (I. Francis pers. comm., 2005).

[10] The proportion of colour-ringed individuals re-sighted in successive years.

A. Watson (in McGowan *et al.*, 2003) has suggested that the population probably seldom falls below 10,000 birds in the spring, or exceeds 100,000 in the autumn. The Cairngorms' Ptarmigan population is thought to vary between 1,300 and 5,000 birds normally (Watson, 1965), but may occasionally reach about 13,000 birds in the autumn, and may have almost doubled this figure during the exceptional years of 1971–72 (Nethersole-Thompson & Watson, 1981).

Breeding densities in the Cairngorms are higher than those attained in many other countries, sometimes reaching 50 adults per km² on high quality areas (Watson & Rae, 1993). Densities tend to be lower in granite areas (about one pair per 3–4 ha) than on the schists of Cairnwell (one pair per 1.2–2.0 ha). The number of young raised per adult also tends to be lower on granite (typically <0.3 young per adult) than on schists (typically >0.7) (Nethersole-Thompson & Watson, 1981).

Since most female Ptarmigan lay in mid- to late May, their breeding success is strongly influenced by June weather, when the chicks are vulnerable to chilling (Watson *et al.*, 1998). In a study spanning more than 50 years, A. Watson and co-workers have demonstrated the impact of summer weather and other factors on the population dynamics of Ptarmigan in the Cairngorms (Watson *et al.*, 1998, 2000). At four Cairngorms sites (Derry Cairngorm, Beinn a' Bhuird, Lochnagar and Cairnwell), for the most part surveyed annually by A. Watson since 1943, Ptarmigan numbers tended to peak approximately once every 10 years, and were more erratic on the richer schists of the Cairnwell (Watson *et al.*, 1998; 2000). Counts at all four sites were low in the mid–1940s and late 1950s, and high in the mid–1960s, after which cyclical fluctuations became less synchronous between sites, and were more pronounced on (the less fertile) Derry Cairngorm than elsewhere (Watson *et al.*, 1998). The study showed that Ptarmigan cycles on the three granite sites were entrained by high June temperatures, which were associated with improved breeding performance and increased recruitment during the following 1–2 years (Watson *et al.*, 1998).

Factors affecting Ptarmigan numbers in some parts of the Cairngorms include over-grazing by Red Deer and sheep, which reduced Crowberry and Blaeberry cover, and the more localised impacts of skiing developments. On Cairn Gorm, collisions with skiing installations have raised adult mortality, while breeding success has declined significantly as a result of egg and chick predation by Carrion Crows *Corvus corrone*, attracted by food scraps left by skiers and others (Watson, 1996; Watson & Moss, 2004) (Chapter 22).

In the long-term, climate change (notably in relation to wind speed and temperature) is likely to have a more severe impact on the Ptarmigan in Britain. This will depend partly on whether the predicted level of warming encourages increased heather growth at higher altitudes, and a subsequent expansion in the altitudinal range of Red Grouse. The extent of any such change is impossible to predict, particularly since wind-blasting may continue to suppress heather growth on the high tops, perhaps enabling the Ptarmigan to persist there for some time to come. Notwithstanding these uncertainties, the range and population size of this endemic sub-species seem likely to decline significantly in the coming century.

The Cairngorms are a British stronghold for the **Dotterel**, an attractive upland wader whose disjunct global range stretches from western Europe to eastern Russia, from where it migrates south to winter in North Africa and the Middle East, respectively (Cramp & Simmons, 1983; Whitfield *et al.*, 1996). In Britain, Dotterel return to the high tops of the Cairngorms in late April or early May (Nethersole-Thompson, 1973), settling to breed on moss and lichen heaths or open *Juncus* fell-fields, on level summit plateaux at about 700 m

Female Dotterel are larger and more brightly coloured than their mates and, having laid a clutch of eggs, often seek additional partners elsewhere. Population estimates increased substantially between the early 1970s and late 1980s, but had declined by 1999.

Photo: *L. Campbell*

Figure 18.18. Estimates of the number of Dotterel breeding at six study sites in the Cairngorms during 1986–99. Gaps indicate a lack of data for the site and year in question.

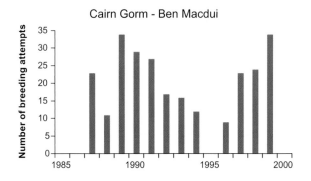

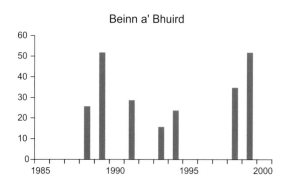

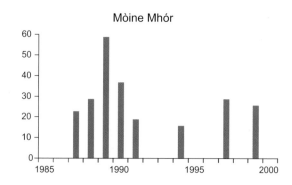

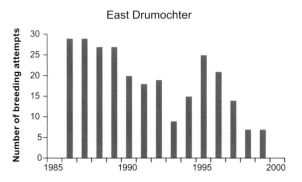

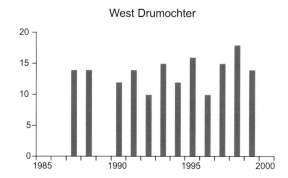

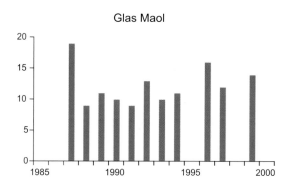

Source: SNH Mountain Plateau Ecology Project; Whitfield (2002)

or above (Thompson & Whitfield, 1993). The Dotterel is one of a very few British bird species to practise sex-role reversal; males performing most of the incubation and chick-rearing duties while their larger, brighter mates seek further breeding opportunities elsewhere (Cramp & Simmons, 1983; Owens *et al.*, 1994). Indeed, one female has been recorded pairing with five males in one summer (Holt *et al.*, 2002), and about 90% of females that lay in Scotland are thought to move as far afield as Norway in their search for additional mates (Whitfield, 2002).

Britain's Dotterel population, which represents about 3% of the European population (Stroud *et al.*, 2001), has evidently increased substantially since the 1950s (Galbraith *et al.*, 1993). However, part of this 'increase' may be due to a growing level of survey effort in the past 20 years. During 1970–90 its breeding range appeared to expand by as much as 115%, (Sharrock, 1976; Gibbons

et al., 1993), due mainly to gains made in the north and west Highlands (Thompson & Whitfield, 1993). This expansion has been more than matched by rising population estimates; from 100 pairs in 1968–72 (Sharrock, 1976) to at least 600 pairs in the mid-1980s (Watson & Rae, 1987), and over 840 pairs during a national survey in 1987–88 (Galbraith *et al.*, 1993). Whitfield (2002) has re-analysed data from this survey, and has suggested that the population at that time may have been even higher, with up to 980 males present. He estimated that the population had then declined to 630 males by 1999, when a second national survey was held. During each survey, East Highlands area (encompassing most of the Cairngorms) was thought to hold about 55–60% of males. Indeed, the Cairngorms' SPAs[11] alone were thought to hold 401 pairs during the mid-1990s, representing 48% of the British population, and about 86% of all Dotterel on British SPAs (Stroud *et al.*, 2001). By 1999, Cairngorms SPAs held at least 332 pairs of Dotterel (SNH data).

[11] Including Creag Meagaidh, which lies largely outwith the Cairngorms area.

Detailed studies at six sites in the Cairngorms, monitored as part of the SNH Mountain Plateau Ecology Project, yielded mixed trends during 1986–99. While Dotterel numbers at west Drumochter and Glas Maol showed little change (or a slight increase), those at three high altitude sites (Cairn Gorm–Ben Macdui, Beinn a' Bhuird and Mòine Mhór) fluctuated widely between some years (Figure 18.18). Only east Drumochter showed a marked decline, attributed mainly to localised Raven *Corvus corax* predation (Whitfield, 2002). Variation in Dotterel numbers and breeding success in these areas partly reflects differences in their bedrock (and hence, invertebrate prey numbers), the effects of predation pressure, trampling by deer and sheep, and severe weather in June–July.

The SNH Mountain Plateau Ecology Project has also examined the effects of human disturbance on Dotterel. While some trampling of nests by humans was noted, there was no strong evidence that birds avoided paths when selecting nest sites, and hatching success was unrelated to distance from paths (Whitfield *et al.*, in prep). Indeed, there was no evidence that broods avoided areas close to paths. Nonetheless, by attracting scavenging Carrion Crows, which predate eggs and chicks, visitors to Cairn Gorm have lowered Dotterel breeding success, as they have for Ptarmigan (see above) (Watson, 1996; Watson & Moss, 2004). Crows have become scarcer on this site since 1992, however, following increased trapping on nearby low ground by gamekeepers.

The reasons for the Dotterel's population increase up to the late 1980s, and its subsequent decline, are unclear. It has been suggested that cooler spring weather conditions during the 1960s and 1970s may have encouraged passage birds to settle in Britain rather than moving on to Norway (Galbraith *et al.*, 1993). Since there was no obvious deterioration in its Scottish breeding areas during the 1990s, it is possible that its subsequent decline could have been due to a redistribution of birds between Britain and Scandinavia (Whitfield, 2002) or a deterioration in the species' Moroccan wintering grounds (Whitfield *et al.*, 1996).

The **Purple Sandpiper** breeds mainly in the high Arctic, from north-east Canada east to the Taimyr Peninsula, Russia. Since 1978 its range has included the high tops of the Cairngorms, at which up to five pairs have been recorded breeding or attempting to breed, at up to three sites (Figure 18.19). Based on bill and egg measurements, this small population is thought to consist of birds originally from southern Norway (Smith & Summers, 2005), many of which winter on our coasts.

Figure 18.19. The maximum number of breeding pairs of Purple Sandpiper in Scotland, based on Smith & Summers (2005).

■ Data from Dennis (1983), Spencer & RBBP (1991), Ogilvie & RBBP (2002, 2003).
■ Smith & Summers (2005)

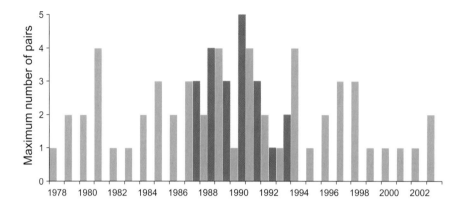

Although the survival and productivity of Scotland's breeding Purple Sandpipers may be sufficient to maintain the population, the number of pairs (1-5) appears to be tightly constrained by the small amount of breeding habitat available.

Photo: D. McGinn

In the Cairngorms, Purple Sandpipers nest mainly in Three-leaved Rush *Juncus trifidus*, Stiff Sedge *Carex bigelowii* and Woolly-fringe Moss *Racomitrium lanuginosum* heaths; habitats that in Britain are restricted to northern, montane areas (McVean & Ratcliffe, 1962). During 1987–93, 1–3 pairs nested within an area of 4 km² at one Scottish site, and were moderately successful. Although the median hatching date was late (27 June; 17 broods), pairs incubated through summer snowfalls that caused many Dotterel and Snow Bunting pairs in the vicinity to fail (Smith & Marquiss, 1994). Five clutches monitored (each of four eggs) had 90% hatching success, giving a mean brood size at hatching of 3.6 (Smith & Summers, 2005). An additional, failed clutch, with broken eggs, was found near a well-used footpath. Of 14 broods monitored, 12 were seen with chicks, and productivity was (conservatively) estimated at about 0.8–1.0 fledged young per pair.

The percentage of adults returning to breed between successive years (*c.* 65%) was fairly typical of north temperate waders, suggesting that the survival and productivity of Scottish Purple Sandpipers may be adequate to maintain the population. Having persisted in the Cairngorms for at least 26 years, with no substantial change in numbers, the population is probably constrained by the small amount of breeding habitat available (Smith & Summers, 2005), leaving it susceptible to chance events. Although breeding pairs are relatively tolerant of disturbance from hill walkers, their offspring are vulnerable to predation from gulls and crows. In the long-term, this small population is likely to be particularly susceptible to the effects of climate change on its montane habitat.

Britain lies on the extreme southern edge of the **Snow Bunting's** global range. Our small resident breeding population appears to have been derived mainly from Icelandic stock, and, although supplemented by flocks of wintering birds, its breeding productivity is probably sufficient to enable it to persist without significant immigration (Smith, 1994, 1996). During 1970–87, the Cairngorms held 49% of the known breeding sites for Snow Bunting in Britain, and 63% of sites known to have produced fledged young (from Watson & Smith, 1991).

In the Cairngorms, Snow Buntings typically breed at or above 980 m, laying mainly in late May to late July, depending partly on the pattern and extent of spring snowfall (Smith, 1994; Smith & Marquiss, 1994). Resident birds are often seen feeding around the edges of snow patches, leading Nethersole-Thompson (1966) to suggest that breeding numbers might also be influenced by the amount of late snow-lie. Milsom and Watson (1984)

later rejected this idea, however, finding no evidence of a correlation between snow cover and the number of cocks present in part of the central Cairngorms during 1971–77.

During a five-year study in the central and western Cairngorms Smith (1994) recorded high levels of breeding success, 92% of females rearing at least one brood in the course of a season. Perhaps not surprisingly – given their choice of breeding habitat – Snow Buntings showed remarkable resilience in the face of adverse weather, and even days of complete snow cover in June caused few desertions amongst incubating birds. Smith (1994) found that most first-year females reared a single brood, while most older females reared two broods per season. Some males wintered close to their breeding site, and were more likely to breed successfully in the following summer than those that had wintered elsewhere. A high percentage of marked adults (63%) were re-sighted between successive summers, indicating that the survival rate was relatively high (Smith, 1994).

In the 1970s there were thought to be around 50 breeding pairs of Snow Bunting in Scotland, rising to about 70–100 pairs in the early 1990s (Smith, 1994). This apparent increase reflected changes in the number of 10-km squares occupied during the atlas surveys of *c.* 1970 and *c.* 1990; which rose by 83% within the Cairngorms area (to 11 occupied squares), and by 200% in the UK as a whole (Sharrock, 1976; Gibbons *et al.*, 1993). Although this expansion may have been influenced by improvements in survey coverage, it is also thought to reflect a genuine increase in abundance over the 20-year period (Smith, 1993), and in comparison with previous decades. Supporting evidence is provided by Nethersole-Thompson (1966) who, during his classic study in 1929–66, encountered fewer territorial males each year in the entire Cairngorms massif than were recorded annually in the central Cairngorms in 1971–87 (Watson & Smith, 1991), and subsequently (Smith, 1994).

Recent trends in the Cairngorms Snow Bunting population have been monitored through the SNH Mountain Plateau Ecology Project (Smith, 1994) and by the RSPB (A. Amphlett, pers. comm., 2005). During 1987–91, the number of territorial males in a study area in the central Cairngorms (Cairn Gorm – Ben Macdui) rose from 15 to 25, but dropped to 14 in 1992[12]. In that year, the RSPB began an annual survey of part of the area, providing an index of the number of singing males present. This index suggests that the population increased during 1992–2002 and may have recovered by 2001 (Figure 18.20). Overall, the number of territorial males in the central Cairngorms appears to have fluctuated between about 14 and 25 during 1987–2002, and showed no clear trend.

[12] A similar initial increase was evident during 1988-91 at a study site in the western Cairngorms (Braeriach – Cairn Toul – Beinn Bhrotain) (Smith, 1994).

Trend summary

Twelve of the 26 bird species for which the Cairngorms are considered nationally important showed evidence of a decline during all or part of 1990–2005 (Table 18.7). Note, however, that these include species surveyed at only a handful of sites and whose apparent trends may reflect a change in distribution between surveyed and unsurveyed sites, rather than a genuine decline.

The 12 species thought to have declined do not include Capercaillie, which may have increased slightly during this period, but had declined to a far greater degree during the preceding 10–20 years. Among the remaining species, six have shown no clear evidence of a progressive change, and one, the Ptarmigan, tends to fluctuate cyclically, at least within the central parts of the Cairngorms massif. In four cases (Common Gull, Short-eared Owl, Scottish and Parrot Crossbill) trend data were lacking.

Several of the Cairngorms' nationally important bird species breed in such low numbers that their populations are likely to vary markedly as a result of chance events, as well as in response to changes in the quality of their breeding or wintering range. They include the Slavonian Grebe and Spotted Crake, which averaged just over 7 and 6 pairs, respectively, during the 1990s, but only 2–3 pairs each during 2000–05. The Cairngorms' tiny populations of Purple, Wood and Green Sandpiper are also particularly vulnerable to chance events, and hence tend to fluctuate relatively widely between consecutive years. Although Green Sandpiper was one of just two species showing a definite increase during 1990–2005 (from zero to two pairs), its population is, arguably, too small to show a meaningful 'trend'.

Perhaps of greater concern are those moderately common species whose populations appear to have declined substantially, or at least progressively, suggesting a deterioration in their environment. Declines in these species have been attributed to a variety of causes, reflecting the ecological diversity of the group. They include nest failure through natural causes (Slavonian Grebe); hunting pressure outside of the UK (Greylag Geese, in Iceland), a reduction in observer effort and nestbox availability (Goldeneye); habitat loss, low breeding success and mortality caused by deer-fence collisions (Capercaillie, Black Grouse); habitat deterioration through burning and over-grazing (Black Grouse); and persecution (Peregrine, Hen Harrier, Golden Eagle). The changing status of these last three species is of particular concern, since their declines in Cairngorms National Park have been more pronounced (Peregrine) or at variance with those

Figure 18.20. The number of male Snow Buntings detected annually in the central Cairngorms during the summers of 1987 – 2002.

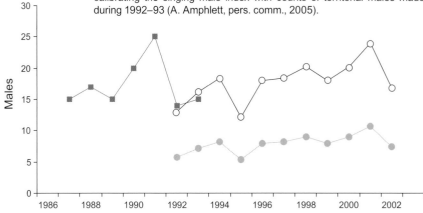

■ Territorial males detected during an intensive study spanning Cairn Gorm – Cairn Lochan – Ben Macdui (Smith, 1994).

● An index of the number of singing males present in part of this area (A. Amphlett, RSPB, pers. comm., 2005).

○ An estimate of the number of territorial males present, obtained by calibrating the singing male index with counts of territorial males made during 1992–93 (A. Amphlett, pers. comm., 2005).

Observations made during 2003–05 suggested that the number of males present had decreased slightly (A. Amphlett, pers. comm., 2005). This finding is consistent with a count of only nine territorial males during 2004 (Duncan, 2005), perhaps due in part to poor survey conditions in that year.

Cock Snow Buntings that winter close to their breeding area are more likely to breed successfully in the following year than those that move further afield. Productivity appears to be high enough to sustain Scotland's resident population, without the need for significant immigration.

Photo: *D. McGinn*

Table 18.7. A summary of changes in the populations of bird species for which the Cairngorms area is considered nationally important. The trend figures given cover different periods, reflecting differences in the timing of surveys for each species. Species have been grouped according to their apparent trend within the Cairngorms during all or part of 1990–2005.

Trend	Species	Measure	Period	Source	Summary
Evidence of a recent decline	Slavonian Grebe	Pairs	1990–2005	1	The Cairngorms area held a mean of 5.3 pairs of Slavonian Grebe during 1980–2005. Numbers increased during the 1980s and early 1990s, but have declined since, broadly reflecting the national trend.
	Whooper Swan	Winter counts	1992/93–2004/05	2	Peak winter counts at Insh Marshes – the main site for Whooper Swans in the Cairngorms area – have declined since 1992/93. Recent counts at lochs Garten, Davan and Kinord have also been relatively low, reflecting a general decline in Scottish winter counts since 1990/91.
	Pink-footed Goose	Winter counts	mid-1990s–2004/05	3	Peak winter counts of Pink-footed Goose in Scotland increased markedly during the 1980s, and showed signs of leveling out in the 1990s. Counts at several key sites in the Cairngorms area have also declined since the 1990s, indicating a population reduction or a dispersal away from count sites.
	Greylag Goose	Winter counts	1990s–2004/05	4	Peak winter counts of Greylag Goose in Scotland increased during the 1980s, but declined slightly after *c.* 1990. Winter counts of Greylag Goose have also declined at several key sites in the Cairngorms, suggesting that there may have been a general decline, or a dispersal away from count sites.
	Wigeon	Males/pairs	1990s–2000s	5	The UK breeding population of Wigeon is thought to have changed little during the 1970s–90s, comprising about 300 pairs. Although there are no population estimates for the Cairngorms area, the number of breeding pairs has declined at Insh Marshes (a key site) since the mid-1990s, and apparently also at Dinnet (since the 1980s).
	Goldeneye	Occupied nestboxes	1990–2004	6	The Goldeneye's breeding population in Strathspey appears to have declined since 1991. Elsewhere, small numbers have recently colonized Deeside, and the species has expanded into England and Wales.
	Hen Harrier	Pairs	1998–2004	7	The number of 10-km squares occupied by Hen Harrier increased within the Cairngorms during *c.* 1970–90. However, between 1998 and 2004 the number of pairs in the Cairngorms area fell by 38%, and by 81% within the National Park. These findings are at variance with results for Scotland as a whole, which saw a 45% increase over the same period.
	Golden Eagle	Occupied territories	1992–2003	8	The number of 10-km squares occupied by Golden Eagle decreased by 11% in Cairngorms National Park during *c.* 1970–90, but rose by 8% in Scotland as a whole. A similar disparity was evident during 1992–2003, when the number of occupied territories in Britain increased by 3%, but fell by 15% in the National Park.
	Peregrine	Pairs	1991–2002	9	During *c.* 1970–90, the number of 10-km squares occupied by Peregrine increased by 8% in Cairngorms National Park, and by 47% in Scotland as a whole. National surveys in 1991 and 2002 have revealed a 19% decline within the National Park, and a 13% decline in Scotland.
	Black Grouse	Lekking males	1990–2005	10	During *c.* 1970–90 the Black Grouse showed a 28% reduction in its British range, and a 6% reduction within the Cairngorms area. The number of lekking males in Scotland declined by 41–86% between 1991–92 and 1995–96, and by a further 29% by 2005. A 10% decline was recorded in a small sample of squares within Cairngorms National Park during 1995-2005.
	Spotted Crake	Singing males	1990–2005	11	Counts of singing males in Britain have increased since the 1980s, due in part to increased observer effort. The average number of singing males recorded at Insh Marshes and Dinnet together was 6.1 during the 1990s (5.2, if the 1999 national survey result is excluded), but only 2.3 during 2000–05. In 2003–05 only a single bird was detected at either site.
	Ring Ouzel	Abundance	1990s–2005	12	During *c.* 1970–90 the number of 10-km squares occupied by Ring Ouzel declined by 27% in Britain and by 16% in the Cairngorms area. Although its national population fell by 58% during 1991–99, numbers at one Cairngorms site showed little change during the 1990s. At a second site, the number of pairs declined steadily during 1998–2005.

Sources:

1. S. Benn, RSPB, pers. comm. (2005)
2. BTO in litt. (2004), C. Mitchell pers. comm. (2005)
3. WWT in litt. (2004), A. Leitch, pers. comm., (2005)
4. WWT in litt. (2004), A. Leitch, pers. comm., (2005)
5. Stroud *et al.* (2001), Duncan & Foster (1998), Buckland *et al.* (1990), Duncan *et al.* (1992), Duncan & Duncan, in litt., H. Scott pers. comm. (2005)
6. C. Mitchell, RSPB, pers. comm. (2005)
7. I. Sim, pers. comm. (2005)
8. D.P. Whitfield & D.R.A. McLeod pers. comm. (2005).
9. S. Newson & H. Crick, BTO, pers. comm., based on data provided by Scottish Raptor Study Groups.
10. Baines & Hudson (1995), Hancock *et al.* (1999), RSPB (2005), I. Sim, pers.comm.(2006).
11. Dennis (1995), Stroud in litt. (2004), I. Francis, pers. comm. (2005), C. Mitchell pers. comm. (2005)
12. Arthur & White (2001), Rebecca (2002), Buchanan *et al.* (2003), Sim *et al.* (2005)

Trend	Species	Measure	Period	Source	Summary
No clear trend	Merlin	Pairs	1980s–2000	13	During *c.* 1970–90, the Merlin's range increased by 26% in the Cairngorms area and by 28% in Scotland as a whole. National surveys in 1983–84 and 1993–94 showed that Merlin numbers in NE Scotland were fairly stable during the intervening decade. A study begun in the 1980s has shown that breeding numbers on Deeside and Donside were fairly stable over a 20-year period, albeit with a slight decline in lower Deeside in the 1990s.
	Dotterel	Pairs/males	1986–1999	14	National population estimates for Dotterel suggest a marked increase during the 1980s, followed by a decline during the 1990s. These changes are thought to partly reflect variation in survey effort. In combination, counts at six study sites in the Cairngorms together showed no evidence of a sustained decline during the 1990s.
	Purple Sandpiper	Pairs	1978–2003	15	Despite its small size, Britain's breeding population of Purple Sandpiper (confined to the Cairngorms) has varied little in absolute terms, fluctuating between 1 and 5 pairs in every year during 1978–2003.
	Wood Sandpiper	Pairs	1980s–2000s	16	Since breeding was first confirmed in 1968, small numbers of Wood Sandpiper have been recorded at up to four sites. The breeding numbers in the Cairngorms are perhaps too low to show a meaningful 'trend', although the national population appears to have shown a slight increase in recent years, perhaps reflecting variation in observer effort.
	Crested Tit	Range	1980s–90s	17	The Crested Tit's range in Britain increased by 11% during *c.* 1970–90, but showed no change within the Cairngorms area. Successive surveys have suggested an increase both in range and abundance, but these changes are thought to have been largely or wholly due to differences in observer effort and methods.
	Snow Bunting	Pairs/males	1987–2002	18	During *c.* 1970–90 the number of 10-km squares occupied by Snow Buntings in the Cairngorms area almost doubled, and trebled in the UK as a whole, at least partly reflecting improvements in survey coverage. Abundance in the central Cairngorms fluctuated markedly during 1987–2002, varying between about 14 and 25 males, but showed no clear trend.
Cyclical change	Ptarmigan	Individuals	1940s–2000s	19	Britain's Ptarmigan population has never been surveyed systematically. Several sites in the Cairngorms have been monitored annually since the 1940s. In the central Cairngorms massif numbers vary on a 10-year cycle, entrained by high June temperatures. The Cairngorms' population is thought to vary by a factor of 10 or 20 between exceptionally good and poor years.
Probable increase	Capercaillie	Abundance	1998/99–2005	20	During *c.* 1970–90 the Capercaillie's range contracted by 64% in Britain and by 39% within the Cairngorms area. Results from three national surveys since 1992 suggest that the national decline has been arrested, and possibly reversed. Annual counts at a large sample of leks during 2002–05 are consistent with the view that the species may have begun to recover.
Increase	Osprey	Pairs	1954–2005	21	The Osprey's Scottish population has increased rapidly, particularly since the mid-1980s, reaching 173 pairs in 2004. The number recorded in Badenoch & Strathspey, which accounts for the bulk of the Cairngorms' population, has also continued to increase, albeit very slowly during 1990–2005.
	Green Sandpiper	Pairs	1990s–2005	22	1–2 pairs were present or bred sporadically in the Cairngorms area during the mid- to late-1990s, and annually since 2000. Pairs or individuals have been recorded at up to four sites, but the numbers involved are too low to show a meaningful 'trend'.
No trend data available	Common Gull	Pairs	-	23	There are no reliable national trend data for Common Gull, the bulk of which nest inland in Scotland. Similarly, no trend data are available for the Cairngorms, which held about 11% of the UK population during 1998–2002.
	Short-eared Owl	Range	c. 1970–90	24	Trends in the abundance and distribution of the Short-eared Owl, which tends to show local, cyclical fluctuations, are poorly known. During *c.* 1970–90 the species' range contracted by 17% in Scotland and by 23% in the Cairngorms area. There have been no systematic surveys of Short-eared Owl in the Cairngorms area, or in Britain as a whole.
	Scottish Crossbill	-	-	25	Due to a lack of diagnostic physical characters, clearly visible in the field, there are no trend data available for Scottish Crossbill or for Parrot Crossbill.
	Parrot Crossbill	-	-	25	

13. Rebecca & Bainbridge (1998), Rebecca & Cosnette (2003)
14. Galbraith *et al.* (1993), Whitfield (2002)
15. Smith & Summers (2005).
16. K. Chisholm, RSPB, pers. comm. (2005)
17. Sharrock (1976), Cook (1982), Summers & Canham (2001)
18. Watson & Smith (1991), Smith (1993, 1994)

19. Watson *et al.* (1998), Watson *et al.* (2000)
20. Catt *et al.* (1998), Wilkinson *et al.* (2002), Kortland pers. comm. (2005)
21. R. Dennis pers. comm. (2005)
22. Ogilvie & RBBP (2004), RSPB pers. comm. (2005)
23. M. Parsons pers. comm., JNCC (2005).

24. Gibbons *et al.* (1993)
25. Marquiss & Rae (2002), Summers *et al.* (2002a), Summers *et al.* (2003)

seen in Scotland as a whole (Hen Harrier and Golden Eagle).

In conclusion, more than half of the 22 species for which survey information exists have shown an unfavourable trend in the Cairngorms during 1990–2005. Since the species concerned are ecologically diverse, they are, in combination, subject to a wide spectrum of environmental pressures. Most of the remaining species showed little evidence of a progressive change, and only 2–3 have increased over this period.

Important areas for birds

The Cairngorms encompass a wealth of areas of national or international importance for birds. Twenty-four such areas are identified here, using data from the Special Protection Area (SPA) review (Stroud *et al.*, 2001; JNCC, 2004) and the Important Bird Area (IBA) programme (Fisher *et al.*, 2000). Five areas lie mainly or entirely outside of the National Park (Figure 18.21).

Loch Gamhna and Loch an Eilein are part of the Cairngorms SPA: a rich matrix of woodland, montane and freshwater habitats supporting Golden Eagle, Merlin, Osprey, Peregrine, Capercaillie, Dotterel and Scottish Crossbill in internationally important numbers, as well as a high proportion of the UK's breeding Goldeneye and Crested Tits.

Photo: *L. Gill*

SPAs are areas designated under the EC Birds Directive[13] to help protect regularly occurring migratory species and rare or vulnerable species listed in Annex I of the Directive. Within SPAs, Member States are obliged to take steps necessary to avoid disturbance which could be significant to the species concerned, and the deterioration of natural habitats on which they depend. Selection criteria include: regular use of the area by at least 1% of the British population of Annex I species, or of the biogeographical population of a regularly occurring migratory species; and regular use by over 20,000 waterfowl. To identify 'most suitable territories', areas meeting one or more of these conditions are considered against a second set of criteria, relating to: population size and density, geographic coverage, breeding success, history of occupancy, the occurrence of other qualifying species, naturalness of the area, and its capacity to serve as a refuge in severe weather. SPAs that lie at least partly within the Cairngorms area are listed in Table 18.8, together with the species for which they were designated.

IBAs have been identified throughout Europe by BirdLife International partner agencies (Heath & Evans, 2000). They are areas that are particularly important for globally threatened species, migratory species that congregate in high numbers, species unique to a small region, or assemblages of birds that are highly representative of a major ecological community or 'biome' (Heath & Evans, 2000). Selection criteria for IBAs include the regular presence of species of global conservation concern, at least 1% of the biogeographical population of a waterbird species, at least 1% of the global population of a terrestrial species, or at least 20,000 waterbirds (Heath & Evans, 2000). IBAs also include sites that are nationally important for a species whose conservation status in Europe is considered to be Unfavourable, or whose European status is Favourable, but whose global population is concentrated mainly in Europe.

Most IBAs in the Cairngorms overlap extensively with SPAs. Indeed, data from a draft of the IBA inventory were used in the preparation of the SPA review (Stroud *et al.*, 2001). Differences between these two site series reflect differences in their selection criteria and selection periods (Stroud *et al.*, 2001). In the following accounts, the population estimates used during site selection date mainly from the 1990s or late 1980s, and may no longer be accurate in some cases. The areas described below are SPAs, except where indicated.

1. Cairngorms. Dominated by an extensive, high plateau, divided by deep glacial valleys, the Cairngorms SPA encompasses the largest contiguous area of montane habitats in Britain, much of it on acidic, base-poor granite, with

---

[13] Council Directive 79/409/EEC on the Conservation of Wild Birds; usually referred to as the Birds Directive.

extensive alpine communities, rock faces and occasional snow-beds. These give way on the lower slopes to heather, Blaeberry, grassland and, in the glens, to birch and pine woodlands, wet heaths, blanket mire and lochs. Not surprisingly, the area supports a substantial proportion of Britain's montane birds, particularly Dotterel (29% of the British population; Stroud *et al.*, 2001), Snow Bunting and Ptarmigan (Fisher *et al.*, 2000). A handful of other boreal or high Arctic species breed occasionally, or have attempted to do so. They include Purple Sandpiper, Lapland Bunting and Shore Lark. Snowy Owl, Long-tailed Skua and Sanderling have also been recorded during the summer (Table 18.2).

The Cairngorms SPA covers about 50,586 ha and, since it includes Rothiemurchus Forest, supports important populations of forest birds, including Capercaillie and Scottish Crossbill (Stroud *et al.*, 2001). Parrot Crossbill are also present (Summers *et al.*, 2002a), and may occur in nationally important numbers. Raptor species with significant populations include Golden Eagle, Merlin, Osprey and Peregrine (Stroud *et al.*, 2001). The area also supports a high proportion of the UK's breeding Goldeneye population.

2. River Spey – Insh Marshes. This area, which covers about 1,159 ha, includes Loch Insh, part of the River Spey and Insh Marshes. Stretching for 6 km along the floodplain of the Spey, between Kingussie and Kincraig, Insh Marshes encompass the largest contiguous area of flood-plain 'poor-fen' in Britain (Chapter 10). The area is designated as an SPA on account of its internationally important wintering populations of Whooper Swan (Figure 18.2) and Hen Harrier, although the latter have declined recently, from a high of 16 roosting bird in the 1990s (Figure 18.22). Breeding Ospreys, Wigeon and Spotted Crake are also designated SPA features, the latter accounting for 11% of the British breeding population in 1990–95 (Stroud *et al.*, 2001). Wood Sandpipers are occasionally present, but breed off-site (C. Mitchell, pers. comm.). Other notable species include Teal *Anas crecca* and Goldeneye (Fisher *et al.*, 2000).

3. Forest of Clunie. The Forest of Clunie comprises 19,348 ha of mainly upland moorland in Perthshire, extending north from the Dunkeld–Blairgowrie road to the southern slopes of Ben Vrackie in the north-west, and Spittal of Glenshee in the north-east. While the site lies entirely outwith the National Park, 7,445 ha (38%) lie within the Cairngorms area. It comprises heather moorland and rough grassland, with small, scattered stands of woodland, recent native pinewood plantations and several small lochs. The site is of international importance for its outstanding assemblage of breeding raptors, including Hen

Harrier, Osprey, Short-eared Owl and Merlin, and, in 1996, was thought to hold some 400 Black Grouse (Fisher *et al.*, 2000).

4. Glen Tanar. This area, covering 4,180 ha, is dominated by Britain's third largest semi-natural pinewood, which is currently regenerating naturally on adjacent heather moorland, improving the age structure of the forest (Stroud *et al.*, 2001). The area has been designated as an SPA on account of its Capercaillie population, its breeding Hen Harriers, Ospreys and Scottish Crossbill (Stroud *et al.*, 2001). Parrot Crossbill have been recorded (Summers *et al.*, 2002a), and Black Grouse occur in nationally important numbers (Fisher *et al.*, 2000).

5. Abernethy. This area encompasses the largest and most species-rich tract of Caledonian forest in Britain (Chapter 7), accounting for almost 14% of the global resource (Forestry Authority, 1994). It owes its richness to the diversity of its structure and topography, its scale, and to the variety of its habitats, which also include Heather-Bearberry heath, extensive Juniper *Juniperus communis*, lochs, pools and valley mires. As defined here, the area encompasses Abernethy Forest SPA (5,794 ha) and Craigmore Wood SPA (654 ha). Although Craigmore consists mainly of planted coniferous woodland less than 70 years old, it has supported woodland cover since the 18th century, and small pockets of Caledonian forest remain.

Abernethy is one of the most important areas in Britain for Capercaillie and

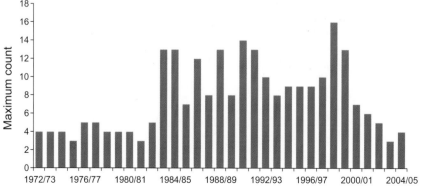

Figure 18.22. The maximum number of Hen Harriers counted each winter at roost sites at Insh Marshes.

Source: C. Mitchell, RSPB

Black Grouse. Counts at a sample of lek sites suggest that Abernethy Forest and Craigmore Wood together accounted for 3–7% of the British Capercaillie population in 2002–03, and for 1–3% of the British Blackcock population (RSPB, 1989–2003). The forest also holds significant numbers of crossbills, which breed mainly in low-density stands of Scots Pine (Summers *et al.,* 2002b). Although Scottish Crossbills breed here, they are currently much less abundant at Abernethy than had previously been thought, since many of the birds present are now known to be the larger-billed Parrot Crossbill (Summers, 2002). Abernethy's Parrot Crossbill population is of national importance, although very small alongside the species' vast Scandinavian population.

For similar reasons, the forest is of national (but not international) importance for its Crested Tits; a widespread species elsewhere in Europe. A winter survey of Abernethy Forest in 2001/02 suggests that it holds about 5–6% of the British population (Table 18.3).

The area's aquatic habitats, which include Loch Garten and Loch Mallachie, supported a mean of 1,240 wintering Greylag Geese during 1995/96–1999/2000 (Hearn & Mitchell, 2004), and a maximum of 226 Goosander in 1993/94 (WeBS, 1989–2000). Winter counts of both species have declined, however, with only 50–100 Goosander recorded in recent years (S. Taylor, pers. comm.). Loch Garten and Loch Mallachie are also important for their breeding Osprey and Goldeneye, although the latter have declined sharply,

from 27 pairs in 1994 (Fisher *et al.,* 2000) to only 3–8 pairs during 2000–04 (S. Taylor, pers. comm.).

6. Muir of Dinnet. This area spans approximately 158 ha, and comprises a mosaic of heaths, woodland, mire and open water habitats, including lochs Davan and Kinord. Also present are wet heath, swamp, carr woodland (of willow *Salix* spp. and Silver Birch *Betula pendula*) and pine forest. During the mid-1990s the two lochs supported a substantial wintering population of Greylag Geese, reaching 36,525 in 1995/96. Indeed, based on counts made the Dinnet lochs were considered the most important in Britain for wintering Greylag Geese in the late 1990s (Hearn & Mitchell, 2004). Peak winter counts have since dropped substantially, however, averaging 5,387 birds during 1998/99–2002/03 (Figure 18.23). The area also regularly supports an internationally important assemblage of waterfowl, with a peak mean count of 28,600 in the mid-1990s (Stroud *et al.,* 2001).

Spotted Crake were recorded regularly during the 1990s in a mosaic of wetland habitats associated mainly with lochs Davan and Kinord. As noted in the species account, singing male Spotted Crake were recorded annually during 1990–2000, with a maximum of six (8% of the national population) recorded during the national survey in 1999 (Stroud in litt., 2004) (Figure 18.5). Other notable species at Muir of Dinnet are Goldeneye (recently confirmed breeding), and Scottish Crossbill.

7. Kinveachy Forest straddles the River Dulnain, south-west of Carrbridge. Consisting mainly of remnant Caledonian pine forest and moorland, with some broadleaved woodland, Juniper scrub, wet heathland and fen, the area covers about 2,849 ha, and has been designated as an SPA on account of its breeding Capercaillie and Scottish Crossbill (Stroud *et al.,* 2001). Several measures have been undertaken recently to try to reverse a 60% decline in the Capercaillie population at Kinveachy between the mid-1970s and mid-1980s (Figure 18.8).

8. Ballochbuie. Situated to the east of Braemar and on the south side of the Dee, this area covers about 1,882 ha. It consists mainly of Caledonian pine forest, but includes Creag Clunie and the Lion's Face. In 1997 the area held important numbers of Capercaillie and Scottish Crossbill (Stroud *et al.,* 2001). Parrot Crossbills have also been recorded (Summers *et al.,* 2002a).

9. Caenlochan. Centred on Glas Maol, at the head of Caenlochan Glen, this

Figure 18.23. Peak counts of Greylag Goose at lochs Davan and Kinord during 1976/77 – 2002/03. (No data were available for 1981–82.)

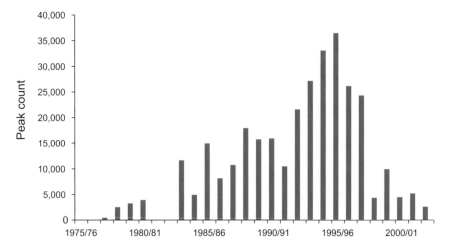

Source: WWT

area extends to 5,975 ha, and supports a diverse range of habitats, on both acidic and calcareous rocks. They include dwarf-shrub and bryophyte heath, mire, grassland, herb-rich communities, open-water, snow- bed communities and woodland. It is considered to be one of the most important areas in Europe for its montane/upland bird community, which included about 5% of the British Dotterel population in 1987-94 (Stroud *et al.*, 2001). Caenlochan is also used by Dotterel as a gathering ground during their onward spring migration to Scandinavia. Golden Eagle is an additional qualifying species on this SPA (Stroud *et al.*, 2001).

10. Drumochter Hills. Straddling the Drumochter Pass, this area covers almost 9,446 ha of bare, rounded hills (up to 900–950 m), divided by steep-sided gullies. Almost two-thirds of the area lies outside of the National Park, but within the wider Cairngorms. Above 750 m the vegetation is dominated by heather, montane heaths and grassland, with substantial areas of blanket mire and wet heath (Stroud *et al.*, 2001). The Drumochter Hills are particularly important for breeding Dotterel. Although there were thought to be 70 pairs in the mid-1990s (Stroud *et al.*, 2001), an average of only 29 breeding attempts were recorded during 1995–99 (SNH data). Drumochter is also important for breeding raptors, including Merlin (seven pairs in the mid-1990s; Stroud *et al.*, 2001).

11. Loch of Kinnordy. Situated near Kirriemuir, outside of the National Park, Loch of Kinnordy is a small (22 ha) eutrophic loch, fringed by basin mire, swamp and fen. During the 1980s–90s the area held important numbers of Icelandic Greylag Goose and Pink-footed Goose (Figure 18.24). Their numbers have declined substantially, however, averaging just 143 Greylag Geese during 1993/94–97/98 and 650 Pink-footed Geese during 1995/96–99/00 (the latest 5-yr periods for which counts are available). Indeed, since the mid-1990s neither species has roosted regularly at Loch of Kinnordy (A. Leitch, pers. comm., 2005), having apparently moved to Loch of Lintrathen, 10 km to the west (Mitchell & Hearn, 2004).

The loch has supported a nationally important breeding population of Black-necked Grebe, and notable populations of Gadwall *Anas strepera*, Shoveler *A. clypeata*, Pochard *Aythya ferina* (Fisher *et al.*, 2000) and Black-headed Gull *Larus ridibundus* (2,299 pairs in 2000; I. Mitchell, pers. comm., 2004). All have declined in recent years, however. In 1994, 11 pairs of Black-necked Grebe were recorded, representing 23% of the UK breeding population in that year (Fisher *et al.*, 2000). By 1999 this had dropped to a single pair, and successful breeding was last recorded in 1997. No Black-necked Grebes were

Figure 18.24. Peak counts of grey geese at Loch of Kinnordy.

Pink-footed Goose: 1985/86 to 1999/00

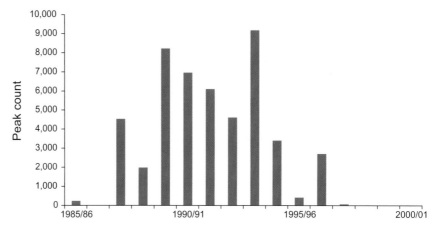

Greylag Goose: 1975/76 to 2002/03

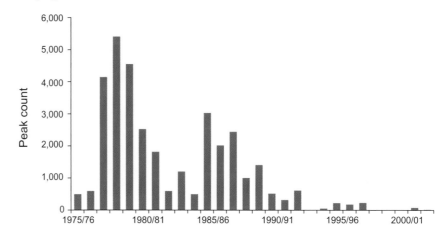

Source: WWT

present during 2002–05. Low breeding success of waterfowl, evident at most sites in the UK, has been attributed to predation by American Mink *Mustela vison*, and to fluctuating water levels (Ogilvie & RBBP, 2004).

During 2001–04 breeding Gadwall, Shoveler and Pochard each averaged fewer than five pairs, while Black-headed Gull numbers had dropped to 580 pairs (A. Leitch, pers. comm., 2005).

12. Loch Vaa, in Strathspey, is a small, spring-fed, oligotrophic loch, fringed by fen and bog communities, and largely surrounded by birch and Scots

Figure 18.21. Important areas for bird species. See text for details, and Table 18.8 for lists of nationally important species.

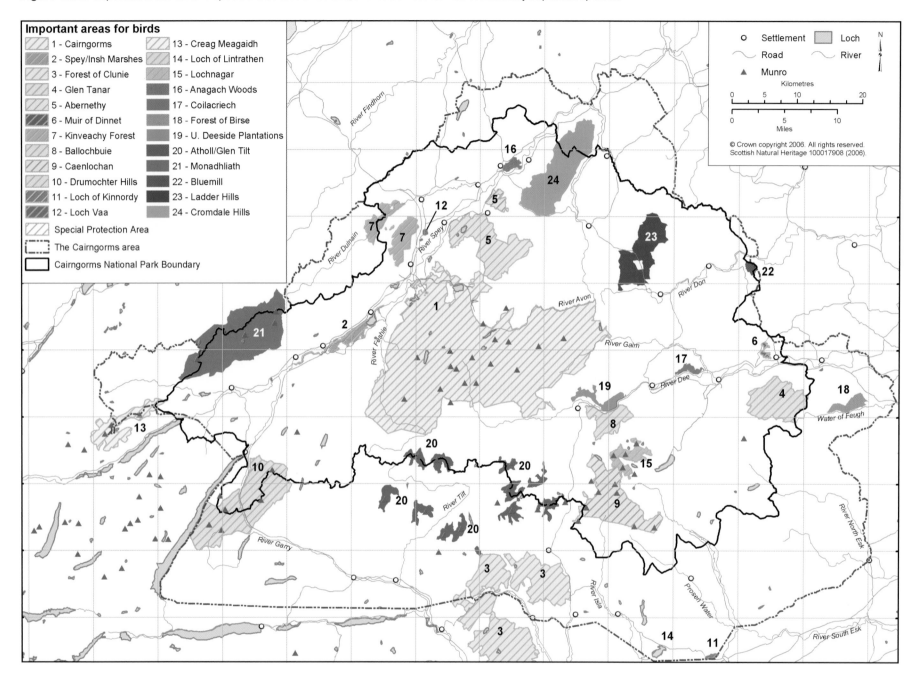

Important areas for birds

1 - Cairngorms
2 - Spey/Insh Marshes
3 - Forest of Clunie
4 - Glen Tanar
5 - Abernethy
6 - Muir of Dinnet
7 - Kinveachy Forest
8 - Ballochbuie
9 - Caenlochan
10 - Drumochter Hills
11 - Loch of Kinnordy
12 - Loch Vaa
13 - Creag Meagaidh
14 - Loch of Lintrathen
15 - Lochnagar
16 - Anagach Woods
17 - Coilacriech
18 - Forest of Birse
19 - U. Deeside Plantations
20 - Atholl/Glen Tilt
21 - Monadhliath
22 - Bluemill
23 - Ladder Hills
24 - Cromdale Hills

Special Protection Area
The Cairngorms area
Cairngorms National Park Boundary

Settlement
Road
Munro
Loch
River

Kilometres
0   5   10   20

Miles
0   5   10

© Crown copyright 2006. All rights reserved.
Scottish Natural Heritage 100017908 (2006).

Table 18.8. Important areas for birds in the Cairngorms, listed in descending order of the number of species with populations meeting SPA selection criteria (Stroud *et al.,* 2001), and additional species qualifying under IBA selection criteria (Fisher *et al.,* 2000). The areas listed are SPAs, except where indicated.

Percentage of site occurring within the Cairngorms area or Cairngorms National Park: *** >75%; ** 25–75%; * 10–24%; '-' <10%

Area	Species meeting SPA selection criteria	Species meeting IBA selection criteria only	% of site in: the Cairngorms area	% of site in: the National Park
1. Cairngorms	Golden Eagle, Merlin, Osprey, Peregrine, Capercaillie, Dotterel, Scottish Crossbill	Hen Harrier	***	***
2. River Spey – Insh Marshes	Whooper Swan, Wigeon, Hen Harrier, Osprey, Spotted Crake, Wood Sandpiper	Greylag Goose, Scottish Crossbill	***	***
3. Forest of Clunie	Hen Harrier, Merlin, Osprey, Short-eared Owl	Black Grouse	**	
4. Glen Tanar	Hen Harrier, Osprey, Capercaillie, Scottish Crossbill		***	***
5. Abernethy[1]	Osprey, Capercaillie, Scottish Crossbill	Greylag Goose, Black Grouse	***	***
6. Muir of Dinnet	Greylag Goose, wintering waterfowl assemblage	Scottish Crossbill	***	***
7. Kinveachy Forest	Capercaillie, Scottish Crossbill		***	***
8. Ballochbuie	Capercaillie, Scottish Crossbill		***	***
9. Caenlochan	Golden Eagle, Dotterel		***	***
10. Drumochter Hills	Merlin, Dotterel		***	**
11. Loch of Kinnordy[2]	Greylag Goose, Pink-footed Goose		***	
12. Loch Vaa	Slavonian Grebe	Scottish Crossbill	***	***
13. Creag Meagaidh	Dotterel		**	-
14. Loch of Lintrathen	Greylag Goose		***	
15. Lochnagar	Dotterel		***	***
16. Anagach Woods (pSPA)	Capercaillie	Scottish Crossbill	***	***
17. Coilacriech (IBA)		Scottish Crossbill	***	***
18. Forest of Birse (IBA)		Scottish Crossbill	***	-
19. Upper Deeside Plantations (IBA)		Scottish Crossbill	***	***
20. Atholl/Glen Tilt (IBA)		Dotterel	***	**
21. Monadhliath (IBA)		Dotterel	**	**
22. Bluemill (IBA)		Common Gull	***	***
23. Ladder Hills (IBA)		Assemblage of breeding moorland species	***	***
24. Cromdale Hills (IBA)		Assemblage of breeding waders and other upland species	***	**

[1] Includes Craigmore Wood SPA, on which Capercaille is a qualifying feature.
[2] Grey geese populations at Loch of Kinnordy have declined substantially since the mid-1990s.

Pine woodland. The area covers approximately 45 ha, and supports breeding waterbirds, including an average of five pairs of Slavonian Grebe during 1991–95 (7% of the British population; Stroud *et al.*, 2001). Few or no breeding pairs were recorded during 2000–05.

13. *Creag Meagaidh*. This area covers 2,873 ha, of which 28% lies within the Cairngorms area, but only 2% within the National Park. Extending from the shores of Loch Laggan to the summit massif of Creag Meagaidh itself, it includes one of the best examples of an uninterrupted transition from loch-side vegetation, through birch woodland, to bryophyte heath on the summit plateau. The latter is important for its assemblage of montane birds, particularly Dotterel, of which an average of 23 pairs were recorded during 1987–94, representing almost 3% of the British population (Stroud *et al.*, 2001).

14. *Loch of Lintrathen* is located north of Alyth in west Angus, and thus lies outside of the National Park. The area covers 186 ha and, like Loch of Kinnordy and Muir of Dinnet, is important for its wintering waterbirds. During 1996/97–2000/01 mean annual peaks of 3,938 Pink-footed Geese and 2,651 Greylag Geese were recorded. The latter figure represents about 3% of the species' Icelandic population (Stroud *et al.*, 2001), but was strongly influenced by a peak of 7,200 Greylag Geese during 1997/98 (Figure 18.25). Based on counts made during 1995/96–1999/2000, Loch of Lintrathen was the seventh most important site in Britain and Ireland for Greylag Goose, and

Figure 18.25. Peak counts of Greylag Goose at Loch of Lintrathen.

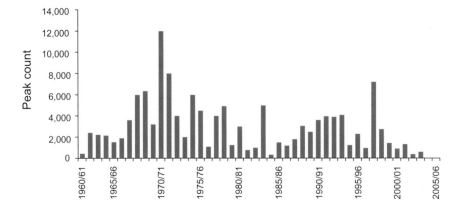

Source: WWT

the 26th most important for Pink-footed Goose (Hearn & Mitchell, 2004; Mitchell & Hearn, 2004).

15. *Lochnagar*. Situated south-east of Braemar and south of the Dee, this area covers 1,441 ha, encompassing an extensive montane plateau with rounded summits, large boulder fields, occasional snow beds, Dwarf Birch *Betula nana* scrub, and several lochs. The area supports a range of montane bird species, and is particularly important for its breeding Dotterel. During surveys in 1988 and 1996 it held a mean of 28 pairs, representing about 3% of the British population (Stroud *et al.*, 2001).

16. *Anagach Woods*. Lying adjacent to the town of Grantown-on-Spey, Anagach Woods consist mainly of (planted) Scots Pine and small areas of birch, with Juniper, heather and Blaeberry. The woods also encompass grassland, forest bog, mire and open water.

Anagach Woods are currently a proposed Special Protection Area (pSPA), qualifying under the EC Birds Directive by regularly supporting a Capercaillie population of European importance. During 2002–05, the 395 ha site held a mean of approximately 18 individuals, representing about 1.7% of the British population. The site is also part of Grantown-on-Spey IBA, which is noted for its Scottish Crossbill population.

17. *Coilacriech* (*IBA*). Situated by the Dee, to the west of Ballater, Coilacriech is a small (390 ha), wooded glen, consisting mainly of naturally regenerating coniferous forest, supporting Scottish Crossbill (Fisher *et al.*, 2000). This area used to hold high numbers of Capercaillie (A. Watson pers. comm.).

18. *Forest of Birse* (*IBA*) lies on lower Deeside, between Burnfoot and Turfgate, outside of the National Park but entirely within the Cairngorms area. Covering 850 ha, it comprises a mixture of broadleaved and native coniferous woodland, forestry plantation and heathland, supporting Scottish Crossbill and several raptor species (Fisher *et al.*, 2000).

19. *Upper Deeside Plantations* (*IBA*). This mixture of coniferous plantation and old Caledonian pinewood, with small amounts of broadleaved woodland, lies on the north side of the Dee, opposite Ballochbuie, and includes Craig Leek. The area extends to 1,010 ha, and holds Capercaillie, Black Grouse, Peregrine, breeding waders, Ring Ouzel and Scottish Crossbill (Fisher *et al.*, 2000).

20. *Atholl/Glen Tilt* (IBA). Encompassing 11 montane plateaux, from Beinn Dearg in the west to Carn a Gheoidh in the east, this area covers 6,166 ha, over two-thirds of which lies outside of the National Park but within the wider Cairngorms. Consisting mainly of grassland and heathland, the area is important for its breeding Dotterels (Fisher *et al.*, 2000).

21. *Monadhliath* (IBA). This extensive area, spanning approximately 10,700 ha of montane plateau, with steep-sided gullies, supports lichen-rich heaths and some late snow bed communities. It holds a range of breeding upland birds, including Dotterel (Fisher *et al.*, 2000).

22. *Bluemill* (IBA). A small (260 ha) area of moorland and acid grassland near to Strathdon, in 1998 Bluemill held the third largest breeding colony of Common Gull in Britain, supporting 2,436 – 4,328 pairs (about 5–9% of the British population; Mitchell & Thompson, 1998).

23. *Ladder Hills* (IBA). Located near to Strathdon, the Ladder Hills (4,420 ha) encompass extensive upland areas, dominated by heather moorland, and are recognised as an Important Bird Area on account of their rich assemblage of breeding moorland species (Fisher *et al.*, 2000). This site held nine pairs of Hen Harrier in 1998 (1.8% of the British population; Stroud *et al.*, 2001), but none in 2004. The site also has striking, extensive areas of lichen-rich moorland.

24. *Cromdale Hills* (IBA) (7,060 ha), near to Grantown-on-Spey, are extensive upland areas, dominated by heather moorland, and supporting a rich assemblage of breeding moorland species (Fisher *et al.*, 2000).

Conservation issues

Climate change. In the long-term, climate change represents the greatest potential threat to northern and montane bird species in the Cairngorms. Several of the species listed in Table 18.1 depend on upland or boreal habitats, which are likely to contract or deteriorate under the climatic conditions predicted for the 2050s and beyond (Chapter 20). However, predicting the impacts of climate change is complicated by uncertainties over the rate at which different aspects of the weather might change. For example, although northern, montane species such as the Ptarmigan, Dotterel, Purple Sandpiper and Snow Bunting seem likely to decline or disappear under the temperature

regimes predicted for the 2050s, there is some uncertainty over projected changes in average wind speed, which also influences the montane vegetation on which they depend. Moreover, if the insulation provided by snow cover is reduced, the effects of higher air temperatures may be partly mitigated by increased exposure to high winds, perhaps inhibiting the upward spread of heather moorland (Chapter 20).

Similarly, there are difficulties in predicting the impact of climate change on the Capercaillie population. Although Capercaillie broods may benefit from drier summer weather projected for the 2050s, this could be offset if heavier rain during the winter extends into the spring, reducing egg- or chick survival (Chapter 20). There are, therefore, too many uncertainties to be able to predict climate change impacts with confidence, beyond noting that upland, northern bird species are likely to be particularly vulnerable.

Wildlife crime in Scotland, involving the illegal use of poisons, traps and firearms, continues at a level that limits the distribution and abundance of several species (Moorland Working Group, 2002), and poses a serious threat to some of the Cairngorms' rarer bird species. The illegal poisoning of raptors is strongly associated with grouse shooting (Whitfield *et al.*, 2003), which is particularly widespread in Deeside and Perthshire.

Recent population trends in several raptor species have been markedly less favourable in the Cairngorms area than in Scotland as a whole (Figure 18.16). Of particular concern is the Hen Harrier, whose diet places it in direct competition with moorland grouse sporting interests, and which is a target species for illegal persecution. As noted above, substantial declines recorded in Hen Harrier numbers within the Cairngorms area during 1998–2004 were in marked contrast to the trend evident in Scotland as a whole.

Other species persecuted in the Cairngorms include Golden Eagle, Buzzard *Buteo buteo*, Peregrine Falcon and Short-eared Owl. As well as shooting, poisoning and the destruction of nests, persecution may take the form of deliberate disturbance through burning of moorland near to nests in early spring, forcing the adults to leave the nest, and causing their eggs to chill.

A recent review by CNPA examines wildlife crime in, and adjacent to, the National Park (to a distance of 10 km outside of the boundary) during 1988–2002. The review's findings are summarised below (P. Cosgrove, pers. comm.).

- Poisoning was the most commonly reported bird-related offence, with at least 60 confirmed cases recorded throughout and adjacent to the National Park.

- Direct persecution, other than by poison, was also common, with at least 30 confirmed cases.

- Reports of persecution appeared to be centred on moorland areas and along access routes through moorland.

- Incidents of crime relating to falconry appeared to be rare, but were widely scattered within the Park.

- Egg stealing appeared to be declining. Most cases reported within the National Park occurred in Badenoch & Strathspey, and related to Osprey, Slavonian Grebe and Dotterel. The introduction in 2002 of custodial sentences for egg stealing coincided with a reduction in reported incidents.

Were it not for illegal persecution some of the species targeted would be more common within the National Park. Through its effects on wildlife tourism, illegal persecution is likely to have an adverse impact on the local economy.

Native woodland expansion. Native woodland regeneration, proposed by the Cairngorms Working Party (1992) for Priority Forest Areas (PFAs) in Forest of Strathspey and Forest of Mar, is likely to occur at the expense of existing upland heather moorland. Within these PFAs, as elsewhere in the Cairngorms area, the encroachment of woodlands on heather moorland could lead to local declines in moorland bird species. To evaluate the likely impact of woodland regeneration on moorland birds, Tharme & Whitfield (1996) assessed the local importance of the two PFAs for 17 moorland bird species. They concluded that for most of these species regeneration will either be neutral, or have only a slightly detrimental or beneficial effect (Whitfield & Tharme, 1997). Only Red Grouse and, to a lesser degree, Golden Eagle, were considered likely to be adversely affected to a marked degree. Conversely, up to 40 species associated with woodland or scrub were considered likely to benefit from regeneration within the two PFAs. While native woodland regeneration is therefore likely to be of net ornithological benefit in these areas (Whitfield & Tharme, 1997) this must be balanced against adverse affects, particularly Natura species, such as Golden Eagle.

Wildlife tourism brings important economic benefits to communities in the Cairngorms. Birdwatching is especially popular, attracting a great many visitors to the Cairngorms area, particularly to the RSPB Osprey Centre at Loch Garten, and to other nature reserves. Recognising this demand, two wildlife tour companies have been established in Badenoch & Strathspey, and others regularly visit the area. Businesses offering accommodation also recognise the value of wildlife tourism, and market their services in wildlife magazines. By placing a cash value on these natural assets, communities and businesses are more likely to recognise the importance of protecting them in the long term.

Recreational disturbance. Disturbance caused, for example, by mountain bikers, walkers, climbers, skiers and birdwatchers, may be having some impacts on the breeding success of some of the Cairngorms' more vulnerable bird species. These include: Slavonian Grebe, which is potentially vulnerable to disturbance by anglers and watersports enthusiasts; scarce breeding waders, such as Green Sandpiper, Wood Sandpiper, Purple Sandpiper and Dotterel, which are vulnerable to wilful disturbance from birdwatchers; and the Ptarmigan, which has suffered increased mortality through collisions with ski tows and lifts, and reduced breeding success, as a result of increased egg and chick predation by Carrion Crows, attracted by food scraps left by visitors (Watson, 1996; Watson & Moss, 2004).

Recreational disturbance is potentially most critical to the Capercaillie, particularly during lekking and brood-rearing times. Higher levels of recreational activity cause greater disturbance, regardless of activity type, while irregular activity is thought to cause greater disturbance than regular activity patterns. Loose dogs allowed to range away from tracks are a threat at any time of year. However, the availability of good quality habitat can mitigate disturbance effects to some degree. To minimise disturbance at leks in Abernethy Forest the RSPB allows visitors to view Capercaillies lekking at one site near Loch Garten.

EC LIFE funding. The Cairngorms area encompasses one of the highest concentrations of SPAs in Britain. As well as providing direct protection for the habitats of qualifying bird species, these have helped secure funding through the EC 'Financial Instrument for the Environment' (LIFE) programme. Examples include the EC LIFE-Nature Capercaillie project and the EC LIFE-Nature Wet Woodlands restoration project.

Grazing and trampling by herbivores, particularly by Red Deer and sheep, inhibits the regeneration of natural forest cover (Chapter 21), and hence limits the abundance of several forest species for which the Cairngorms area is of at least national importance. As well as limiting the spread of woodland, grazing by Red Deer may have more subtle effects on forest habitats by, for example, reducing the abundance of lepidoptera larvae; an important food source for Capercaillie chicks (Baines & Sage, 1991; Baines *et al.*, 1994). Grazing and trampling also have direct, adverse effects on species such as Dotterel, whose nests and chicks in some locations have been trampled by high concentrations of deer.

Knowledge gaps

- Further research is required to understand the likely impact of climate change on bird species for which the Cairngorms area is nationally important.

- Research is also required on the effects of land use change in the Cairngorms. Examples include the expansion of woodlands, often at the expense of moorlands, and the effects of changes in the economics of farming in the uplands. Where species are dependent on more than one habitat, the impact of a change in the *proximity* of these habitats to each other is particularly difficult to quantify. For example, several bird species feed on farmland but nest in nearby woodland (e.g. Buzzard, Woodcock *Scolopax rusticola* and Mistle Thrush) or on moorland (e.g. Golden Plover).

- Abundance estimates used to identify important areas for birds in the Cairngorms have been derived mainly from surveys carried out during the 1990s (e.g. Fisher *et al.*, 2000; Stroud *et al.*, 2001). Further survey work is required to determine current population levels in many of these areas.

- Our knowledge of the importance of breeding farmland wader populations in the Cairngorms is improving, but we know little about their breeding productivity, whether they are self-sustaining, or of the likely impacts of recent changes in agricultural incentives.

- Opinion is divided over whether Goosander *Mergus merganser*, Red-breasted Merganser *M. serrator* and Cormorant *Phalacrocorax carbo* cause serious economic damage to Atlantic Salmon *Salmo salar* and Sea Trout *S. trutta* fisheries. Although they are shot under licence each spring to protect game fishing interests, further information is needed to understand predator-prey relationships between these species and juvenile fish. Specifically, more information is required on their population dynamics, breeding ecology and movements within and between the river catchments of the Cairngorms, to better determine the need to cull these species. Guidance is required from SEERAD on the evidence and circumstances that constitute 'serious damage' to salmonid fisheries by fish-eating birds.

- Further research is required on the status and population biology of raptor species in the Cairngorms, particularly Golden Eagle, Hen Harrier, Peregrine, Merlin, Buzzard and Short-eared Owl. As a priority, causes of the observed disparities between raptor population trends in the Cairngorms and in other parts of Scotland should be examined, to identify particular constraints operating within the Cairngorms area.

References

Arthur, D.S.C. & White, S.A. (2001). Numbers, distribution and breeding biology of Ring Ouzels in upper Glen Esk, 1992–98. *Scottish Birds* 22(1): 50–59.

Baines, D. & Hudson, P.J. (1995). The decline of Black Grouse in Scotland and northern England. *Bird Study* 42: 122–131.

Baines, D. & Sage, R. (1991). Capercaillie decline and caterpillar abundance in Highland pinewoods. *The Game Conservancy Review* 23: 104-105

Baines, D. & Summers, R.W. (1997). Assessment of bird collisions with deer fences in Scottish forests. *Journal of Applied Ecology* 34(4): 941–948.

Baines, D., Sage, R.B. & Baines, M.M. (1994). The implications of red deer grazing to ground vegetation and invertebrate communities of Scottish native pinewoods. *Journal of Applied Ecology* 31: 776–783.

Baker, H. (1991). *Habitat use by the crested tit* Parus cristatus *in Scottish Pinewoods*. PhD Thesis, University of Dundee.

Batten, L.A., Bibby, C.J., Clement, P., Elliott, G.D. & porter, R.F. (eds.) (1990). *Red Data Birds in Britain: action for rare, threatened and important species*. T. & A.D. Poyser: London

Baxter, E.V. & Rintoul, L.J. (1953). *The Birds of Scotland*. Oliver & Boyd: Edinburgh.

Beaumont, D.J., Amphlett, A. & Housden, S.D. (2005). Abernethy Forest RSPB Nature Reserve: managing birds, biodiversity and people. In: Thompson, D.B.A., Price, M.F. & Galbraith, C.A. (eds.) *Mountains of Northern Europe: Conservation, Management, People and Nature*. TSO Scotland: Edinburgh. pp. 239–250.

Benn, S. (2003). Conserving Scotland's Slavonian Grebes. *British Wildlife* October, 25–30.

BirdLife International (2000). *Threatened Birds of the World*. Barcelona & Cambridge: Lynx Edicions & BirdLife International: Barcelona & Cambridge.

BirdLife International (2004a). *Birds in the European Union: a status assessment*. BirdLife International: Cambridge.

BirdLife International (2004b). *Birds in Europe: Population Estimates, Trends and Conservation Status*. BirdLife International: Wageningen, The Netherlands.

Brown, P. & Waterston, G. (1962). *The Return of the Osprey*. Collins: London.

BTO (2005). *The National Peregrine Survey 2002*. http://www.bto.org/survey/complete/peregrine_results.htm

Buchanan, G.M., Pearce-Higgins, J.W., Wotton, S.R., Grant, M.C. & Whitfield, D.P. (2003). Correlates of the change in Ring Ouzel *Turdus torquatus* abundance in Scotland from 1988–91 to 1999. *Bird Study* 50(2): 97–105.

Buckland, S.T. & Knox, A.G. (1980). Brambling breeding in Scotland. *British Birds* 73: 360–361.

Buckland, S.T., Bell, M.V. & Picozzi, N. (eds.) (1990). *The Birds of North-East Scotland*. North-East Scotland Bird Club: Aberdeen.

Bucknall, R.H. (1983). Successful breeding of Brambling in Invernesshire. *Scottish Birds* 12(6): 191–193.

Butterfield, D. (2005). Area Reviews. *Birding Higfhland* 6: 5.

Cadbury, J. (1993). Grazing and other management of upland vegetation for birds in the UK. *RSPB Conservation Review* 7: 12–21.

Cairngorms Working Party (1992). *Common Sense and Sustainability: a Partnership for The Cairngorms*. The report of the Cairngorms Working Party to the Secretary of State for Scotland.

Calladine, J. (2005). *Site condition monitoring of the breeding aggregation of crested tits* (Parus cristatus) *on the North Rothiemurchus Pinewood SSSI*. Unpublished report by the British Trust for Ornithology. SNH: Perth.

Campbell, B., Watson, A. Snr, Watson, A. & Picozzi, N. (1974). Proof of breeding of Shore Larks. *British Birds* 67: 127.

Catt, D.C., Baines, D., Picozzi, N., Moss, R. & Summers, R.W. (1998). Abundance and distribution of capercaillie *Tetrao urogallus* in Scotland 1992–94. *Biological Conservation* 85: 257–267.

Cook, M.J.H. (1982). Breeding status of the Crested Tit. *Scottish Birds* 12(4): 97–106.

Cramp, S. & Simmons, K.E.L. (eds.) (1980). *Handbook of the Birds of Europe, the Middle East and North Africa: The Birds of the western Palearctic. Volume 2*. Oxford University Press: Oxford.

Cramp, S. & Simmons, K.E.L. (eds.) (1983). *Handbook of the Birds of Europe, the Middle East and North Africa: The Birds of the Western Palearctic. Volume 3: Waders to Gulls*. Oxford University Press: Oxford.

Cramp, S. & Perrins, C.M. (eds.) (1994). *Handbook of the Birds of Europe, the Middle East and North Africa: The Birds of the western Palearctic. Volume 8*. Oxford University Press: Oxford.

Cumming, I.G. (1979). Lapland Buntings breeding in Scotland. *British Birds* 72: 53–56.

Deadman, A.J. (1973). *A population study of the Coal Tit* (Parus ater) *and the Crested Tit* (Parus cristatus) *in a Scots Pine plantation*. Unpublished PhD Thesis, University of Aberdeen.

Dennis, R.H. (1983). Purple Sandpipers breeding in Scotland. *British Birds* 76:563–566.

Dennis, R. (1995). *Birds of Badenoch & Strathspey*. Colin Baxter Photography: Grantown-on-Spey.

Dennis, R. (2002). Birds and mammals. In: Gimingham, C.H. (ed.). *The ecology, land use and conservation of the Cairngorms*. Packard Publishing Limited: Chichester. pp. 43–53.

Denny, R.E. (1995). *Habitat requirements and nest site selection of the crested tit: implications for management*. MSc Thesis, University of Kent.

Denny, R.E. & Summers, R.W. (1996). Nest site selection, management and breeding success of crested tits *Parus cristatus* at Abernethy Forest, Strathspey. *Bird Study* 43(3): 371–379.

Duncan, K. (2005). *Report on Site Condition Monitoring of the 'breeding aggregation' of snow buntings in the Cairngorms SSSI, 2004*. Unpublished report. SNH: Perth.

Duncan, R & Foster, S. (1998). An unusually open Wigeon nest. *Scottish Birds* 19(3): 172.

Duncan, R., Cooper, J. & Leitch, A. (1992). Female natal philopatry in a Scottish Wigeon population. *Scottish Birds* 16(3): 222.

Etheridge, B., Summers, R.W. & Green, R.E. (1997). The effects of illegal killing and destruction of nests by humans on the population dynamics of the hen harrier *Circus cyaneus* in Scotland. *Journal of Applied Ecology* 34(4): 1081–1105.

Fisher, I., Gibbons, D., Thompson, G. & Pritchard, D. (2000). United Kingdom, the Channel Islands and the Isle of Man. In: Heath, M.F. & Evans, M.I. (eds.) *Important Bird Areas in Europe: Priority sites for conservation. 1: Northern Europe*. BirdLife International: Cambridge.

Flegg, J.J.M. & Glue, D.E. (1975). The Nesting of the Ring Ouzel. *Bird Study* 22: 1–8.

Forestry Authority (1994). *Caledonian Pinewood Inventory*. Forestry Commission: Edinburgh.

Galbraith, H., Murray, S., Rae, S., Whitfield D.P. & Thompson, D.B.A. (1993). Numbers and distribution of Dotterel *Charadrius morinellus* in Great Britain. *Bird Study* 40: 161–169.

Gibbons, D.W., Reid, J.B. & Chapman, R.A. (eds.) (1993). *The New Atlas of Breeding Birds in Britain and Ireland: 1988–1991*. T. & A.D. Poyser: London.

Glue, D.E. (1993). Short-eared Owl *Asio flammeus*. In: Gibbons, D.W., Reid, J.B. & Chapman, R.A. (eds.) *The New Atlas of Breeding Birds in Britain and Ireland: 1988–1991*. T. & A.D. Poyser: London. pp. 254–255.

Greenwood, J.J.D. (1968). Bluethroat breeding in Scotland. *British Birds* 61: 524–525.

Greenwood, J.J.D., Crick, H.Q.P. & Bainbridge, I.P. (2003). Numbers and international importance of raptors and owls in Britain and Ireland. In: Thompson, D.B.A, Redpath, S.M., Fielding, A.H., Marquiss, M. & Galbraith, C.A. (eds.), *Birds of Prey in a Changing Environment*. TSO Scotland: Edinburgh. pp. 25–49.

Gregory, R.D., Wilkinson, N.I., Noble, D.G., Robinson, J.A., Brown, A.F., Hughes, J., Procter, D., Gibbons, D.W. & Galbraith, C.A. (2002). The population status of birds in the United Kingdom, Channel Islands and Isle of Man: an analysis of conservation concern 2002–2007. *British Birds* 95(9): 410–448.

Hagemeijer, W.J.M. & Blair, M.J. (eds.) (1997). *The EBCC Atlas of European Breeding Birds: Their Distribution and Abundance*. T. & A.D. Poyser: London.

Hancock, M., Baines, D., Gibbons, D., Etheridge, B. & Shepherd, M. (1999). Status of male Black Grouse *Tetrao tetrix* in Britain in 1995–96. *Bird Study* 46, 1–15.

Hancock, M., Gibbons, D.W. & Thompson, P. (1997). Status of breeding Greenshank *Tringa nebularia* in the United Kingdom in 1995. *Bird Study* 44, 290–302.

Hancock, M., Summers, R. & Butcher, N. (2002). Predation of Slavonian Grebe nests by Otters. *British Birds* 95: 390–391.

Hartert, E. (1910). *Die Vögel der paläarktischen Fauna*. Friedlander & Sohn: Berlin.

Hearn, R.D. & Mitchell, C.R. (2004). *Greylag Goose* Anser anser *(Greenland/Iceland population) in Britain 1960/61 – 1999/2000*. Waterbird Review Series, The Wildfowl & Wetlands Trust/Joint Nature Conservation Committee: Slimbridge.

Heath, M.F. & Evans, M.I. (eds.) (2000). *Important Bird Areas in Europe: Priority sites for conservation*. BirdLife International: Cambridge.

Hill, D. (1993). Ring Ouzel *Turdus torquatus*. In: Gibbons, D.W., Reid, J.B. & Chapman, R.A. (eds.), *The New Atlas of Breeding Birds in Britain and Ireland: 1988–1991*. T. & A.D. Poyser: London. pp. 312–313.

Hill, D., Taylor, S., Thaxton, R., Amphlet, A. & Horn, W. (1990). Breeding bird communities of native pine forest, Scotland. *Bird Study* 37: 133–141.

Holt, S., Whitfield, D.P. & Gordon, J. (2002). Potential reproductive rates in the Eurasian Dotterel *Charadrius morinellus*. *Bird Study* 49(1): 87–88.

Hudson, P.J. (1986). *The Red Grouse: Biology and Management of a Wild Gamebird*. Game Conservancy, Fordingbridge.

Hudson, P.J. & Baines, D. (1993). Black Grouse *Tetrao tetrix*. In: Gibbons, D.W., Reid, J.B. & Chapman, R.A. (eds.) *The New Atlas of Breeding Birds in Britain and Ireland: 1988–1991*. T. & A.D. Poyser: London. pp. 130–131.

JNCC (2004). *Special Protection Areas (SPAs) in the UK*. http://www.jncc.gov.uk/ProtectedSites/spa/default.htm

Kershaw, M. & Cranswick, P.A. (2003). Numbers of wintering waterbirds in Great Britain, 1994/1995 – 1998/1999: I. Wildfowl and selected waterbirds. *Biological Conservation* 111: 91–104.

Knox, A.G. (1975). Crossbill Taxonomy. In: Nethersole-Thompson, D., *Pine Crossbills*. T. & A.D. Poyser: Berkhamsted. pp. 191–201.

Knox, A.G. (1976). The taxonomic status of the Scottish Crossbill *Loxia* sp. *Bulletin of the British Ornithologists' Club*. 96: 15–19.

Knox, A. (1983). The Crested Tit on Deeside. *Scottish Birds* 12(8): 255–258.

Kortland, K. (2000). Crisis time for Capercaillie. *Journal of the Scottish Landowners' Federation* September.

Koskimies, P. & Dvorak, M. (1997). Spotted Crake. In: Hagemeijer, W.J.M. & Blair, M.J. (eds.). *The EBCC Atlas of European Breeding Birds: Their Distribution and Abundance*. T. & A.D. Poyser: London.

Lens, L. & Dhondt, A.A. (1992). The effect of a severe storm on a population of Crested Tits *Parus cristatus* in Belgium. *Bird Study* 39: 31–33.

Marquiss, M. & Rae, R. (2002). Ecological differentiation in relation to bill size amongst sympatric, genetically undifferentiated crossbills *Loxia* spp. *Ibis* 144(3): 494–508.

Marquiss, M., Rae, R., Harvey, P. & Proctor, B. (1995). Scottish crossbill moves between Deeside and Strathspey. *Scottish Bird News* 37: 2–3.

Marquiss, M., Vickers, A.D. & Picozzi, N. (1997). *Baseline Survey of Pinewood Birds in Cairngorms proposed Special Protection Area, Glenmore Forest SSSI and Ballochbuie Forest*. Institute of Terrestrial Ecology report to SNH. Contract no. RASD/116/97 N2K. SNH: Perth.

McGowan, R.Y., Clugston, D.L. & Forrester, R.W. (2003). Scotland's endemic subspecies. *Scottish Birds* 24: 18–35.

McVean, D.N. & Ratcliffe, D.A. (1962). *Plant Communities of the Scottish Highlands*. Nature Conservancy Monograph No. 1. HMSO: London.

Milsom, T.P. & Watson, A. (1984). Numbers and spacing of summering snow buntings and snow cover in the Cairngorms. *Scottish Birds* 13(1): 19–23.

Mitchell, C.R. & Hearn, R.D. (2004). *Pink-footed Goose* Anser brachyrhynchus *(Greenland/Iceland population) in Britain 1960/61 – 1999/2000*. Waterbird Review Series, The Wildfowl & Wetlands Trust/Joint Nature Conservation Committee: Slimbridge.

Mitchell, P.I. & Thompson, K.R. (1989). Survey of breeding common gulls *Larus canus* in the Mortlach and Correen Hills, Grampian, 1998. Unpublished report to SNH. JNCC: Aberdeen.

Moorland Working Group (2002). *Scotland's Moorland: The Nature of Change*. SNH: Perth.

Moss, D. (1978). Diversity of woodland song-bird populations. *Journal of Animal Ecology* 47(2): 521–527.

Moss, R. (1986). Rain, breeding success and distribution of capercaillie *Tetrao urogallus* and black grouse *Tetrao tetrix* in Scotland. *Ibis* 128(1): 65–72.

Moss, R. (2001). Second extinction of the capercaillie (*Tetrao urogallus*) in Scotland? *Biological Conservation* 101: 255–257.

Moss, R. & Watson, A. (1984). Maternal nutrition, egg quality and breeding success of Scottish ptarmigan *Lagopus mutus*. *Ibis* 126(2): 212–220.

Moss, R. & Weir, D.N. (1987). Demography of Capercaillie *Tetrao urogallus* in north-east Scotland. III. Production and recruitment of young. *Ornis Scandinavica* 18: 141–145.

Moss, R., Oswald, J. & Baines, D. (2001). Climate change and breeding success: decline of the capercaillie in Scotland. *Journal of Animal Ecology* 70: 47–61.

Moss, R., Picozzi, N., Summers, R.W. & Baines, D. (2000). Capercaillie *Tetrao urogallus* in Scotland – demography of a declining population. *Ibis* 142: 259–267.

Murray, R.D. (1987). Bluethroats in Scotland during 1985. *Scottish Birds* 14: 168–174.

Nethersole-Thompson, D. (1966). *The Snow Bunting*. Oliver & Boyd: London & Edinburgh.

Nethersole-Thompson, D. (1973). *The Dotterel*. Collins: London.

Nethersole-Thompson, D. (1975). *Pine Crossbills*. T. & A.D. Poyser: Berkhamsted.

Nethersole-Thompson, D. & Nethersole-Thompson, M. (1979). *Greenshanks*. T. & A.D. Poyser: Berkhamsted.

Nethersole-Thompson, D. & Nethersole-Thompson, M. (1986). *Waders: their breeding haunts and watchers*. T. & A.D. Poyser: London.

Nethersole-Thompson, D. & Watson, A. (1981). *The Cairngorms: Their Natural History and Scenery*. Melven Press: Perth.

Ogilvie, M.A. & Rare Breeding Birds Panel (2002). Rare breeding birds in the United Kingdom in 2000. *British Birds* 95: 542–582.

Ogilvie, M.A. & Rare Breeding Birds Panel (2003). Rare breeding birds in the United Kingdom in 2001. *British Birds* 96: 476–519.

Ogilvie, M.A. & Rare Breeding Birds Panel (2004). Rare breeding birds in the United Kingdom in 2002. *British Birds* 97: 492–536.

Oliver, D.W. (1975). Long-tailed skua in central Grampians. *Scottish Birds* 8: 383–385.

Owens, I.P.F., Burke, T. & Thompson, D.B.A. (1994). Extraordinary sex roles in the Eurasian Dotterel: female mating arenas, female-female competition and female mate choice. *American Naturalist* 144: 76–100.

Payne, A.G. & Watson, A. (1990). Special bird communities. The high tops. In: Buckland, S.T., Bell, M.V. & Picozzi, N. (eds.), *The birds of north-east Scotland*. North-East Scotland Bird Club: Aberdeen. pp. 448–452.

Perkins, A.J., Hancock, M.H., Butcher, N. & Summers, R. (2005). Use of time-lapse video cameras to determine causes of nest failure of Slavonian Grebes *Podiceps auritus*. *Bird Study* 52: 159–165.

Prazák, J.P. (1897). Nachträgliche Bemerkungen. *Journal for Ornithologie* 45: 347–348.

Ratcliffe, D.A. (1990). *Bird life of mountain and upland*. Cambridge University Press: Cambridge.

Ratcliffe, D.A. & Thompson, D.B.A. (1988). The British uplands: their ecological character and international significance. In: Usher, M.B. & Thompson, D.B.A. (eds.), *Ecological Change in the Uplands*. Blackwell Scientific Publications: Oxford. pp. 9–36.

Rebecca, G.W. (2002). The contrasting status of the ring ouzel in 2 areas of upper Deeside, north east Scotland between 1991 and 1998. *Scottish Birds* 22(1): 9-19.

Rebecca, G.W. & Bainbridge, I.P. (1998). The breeding status of the Merlin *Falco columbarius* in Britain in 1993–94. *Bird Study* 45: 172–187.

Rebecca, G.W. & Cosnette, B.L. (2003). Long-term monitoring of breeding Merlin (*Falco columbarius*) in Aberdeenshire, North-East Scotland 1980–2000. In: Thompson, D.B.A, Redpath, S.M., Fielding, A.H., Marquiss, M. & Galbraith, C.A. (eds.), *Birds of Prey in a Changing Environment*. TSO Scotland: Edinburgh. pp. 183–199.

Rebecca, G.W., Weir, D.N. & Steele, L.D. (1987). Bluethroats killed by nesting Merlins in Scotland. *Scottish Birds* 14(3): 174–175.

Robinson, J.A., Colhoun, K., McElwaine, J.G. & Rees, E.C. (2004). *Whooper Swan Cygnus cygnus (Iceland population) in Britain and Ireland 1960/61 – 1999/2000*. Waterbird Review Series, The Wildfowl & Wetlands Trust/Joint Nature Conservation Committee: Slimbridge.

RSPB (1989–2003). *Abernethy Reserve*. Unpublished annual reports. RSPB: Forest Lodge, Abernethy.

RSPB (1999). *Persecution: A Review of Bird of Prey Persecution in Scotland in 1998*. RSPB: Edinburgh.

RSPB (2000). *Strathspey Breeding Farmland Wader Survey 2000*. RSPB: Edinburgh.

RSPB (2005). *Conservation action plan needed to help black grouse*. http://www.rspb.org.uk/scotland/action/blackgrouse.asp

Scottish Raptor Monitoring Group (2003). Population estimates for honey buzzard *Pernis apivorus*, red kite *Milvus milvus*, white-tailed eagle *Haliaeetus albicilla*, hobby *Falco subbuteo* and peregrine *Falco peregrinus*. SNH: Perth.

Scottish Raptor Study Groups (1998). *The illegal persecution of raptors in Scotland*. Scottish Office Central Research unit, Research findings No. 17. The Stationary Office: Edinburgh.

Sharrock, J.T.R (1976). *The Atlas of Breeding Birds in Britain and Ireland*. T. & A.D. Poyser: Berkhamsted.

Sim, I.M.W., Gibbons, D.W., Bainbridge, I.P. & Mattingley, W.A. (2001). Status of the Hen Harrier *Circus cyaneus* in the UK and the Isle of Man in 1998. *Bird Study* 48: 341–353.

Sim, I., Rebecca, G. & Wilkie, L. (2005). *Glen Clunie Ring Ouzel Breeding Ecology Project. Summary of Results 1998–2005.* Interim report of the Grampian Ringing Group/RSPB joint project on Ring Ouzel.

Smith, R. (1993). Snow Bunting *Plectrophenax nivalis*. In: Gibbons, D.W., Reid, J.B. & Chapman, R.A. (eds.) *The New Atlas of Breeding Birds in Britain and Ireland: 1988–1991.* T. & A.D. Poyser: London. pp. 430–431.

Smith, R.D. (1994). *Snow buntings breeding in the Cairngorms: population dynamics and the influence of recreation.* Scottish Natural Heritage Review No. 1. SNH: Edinburgh.

Smith, R.D. (1996). Racial composition of breeding and wintering snow buntings *Plectrophenax nivalis* in the north-east Scottish uplands. *Ringing and Migration* 17(2): 123–136.

Smith, R.D. & Marquiss, M. (1994). Breeding seasons and nesting success of snow buntings in northeast Scotland. *Scottish Birds* 17: 223–234.

Smith, R.D. & Summers, R.W. (2005). Population size, breeding biology and origins of Scottish Purple Sandpipers. *British Birds* 98: 579–588.

Spencer, R. & Rare Breeding Birds Panel. (1991). Rare breeding birds in the United Kingdom in 1989. *British Birds* 84: 349–370, 379–392.

Stattersfield, A.J., Crosby, M.J., Long, A.J. & Wege, D.C. (1998). *Endemic Bird Areas of the World. Priorities for Biodiversity Conservation.* BirdLife International: Cambridge.

Stroud, D.A., Chambers, D., Cook, S., Buxton, N., Fraser, B., Clement, P., Lewis, P., McLean, I., Baker, H. & Whithead, S. (2001). *The UK SPA network: its scope and content.* Joint Nature Conservation Committee: Peterborough.

Summers, R.W. (2002). Parrot Crossbills breeding in Abernethy Forest, Highland. *British Birds* 95:4–11.

Summers, R.W. (2004). Use of pine snags by birds in different stand types of Scots Pine *Pinus sylvestris*. *Bird Study* 51(3): 212–221.

Summers, R.W, & Canham, M. (2001). The distribution of Crested Tits in Scotland during the 1990s. *Scottish Birds* 22: 20–27.

Summers, R.W, & Ellis, J.A. (1994). *An assessment of the Scottish crossbill, capercaillie and crested tit populations and woodland habitat in Kinveachy Forest SSSI.* Unpublished report by RSPB: Contract no. SNH/075/94 BD. SNH: Perth.

Summers, R.W. & Mavor, R.A. (1995). Occupation patterns of lochs by Slavonian grebes in Scotland. *Scottish Birds* 18(2): 65–70.

Summers, R.W. & Mavor, R.A. (1999). Nest site selection and the time of breeding by Slavonian grebes *Podiceps auritus* in Scotland. *Wildfowl* 49: 219–227.

Summers, R.W. & Piertney, S.B. (2003). The Scottish Crossbill – what we know and what we don't. *British Birds* 96: 100–111.

Summers, R.W. & Proctor, R. (2002). *New transects at Abernethy Forest – report for 2001–2.* Internal report. RSPB: Inverness.

Summers R.W., Green R.E., Proctor R., Dugan D., Lambie D., Moncrieff R., Moss R. & Baines D. (2004). An experimental study of the effects of predation on the breeding productivity of capercaillie and black grouse. *Journal of Applied Ecology* 41(3): 513–525.

Summers, R.W., Humphreys, E., Newell, M. & Donald, C. (2002b). Nest-site selection by crossbills *Loxia* spp. in ancient native pinewoods at Abernethy Forest, Strathspey, Highland. *Bird Study* 49: 258–262.

Summers, R.W., Jardine, D.C. & Dawson, R.J.G. (2003). The distribution of the Scottish Crossbill, 1995–2003. *Scottish Birds* 24: 11–16.

Summers, R.W., Jardine, D.C., Marquiss, M. & Rae, R. (2002a). The distribution and habitats of crossbills *Loxia* spp. in Britain, with special reference to the Scottish Crossbill *Loxia scotica*. *Ibis.* 144(3): 393–410.

Summers, R.W., Mavor, R.A., Buckland, S.T. & MacLennan, A.M. (1999). Winter population size and habitat selection of Crested Tits *Parus cristatus* in Scotland. *Bird Study* 46: 230–242.

Tharme, A.P. & Whitfield, D.P. (1996). *Ornithological importance of moorland within the Forest of Strathspey and Forest of Mar Priority Forest Areas.* Unpublished RSPB Research Report. RSPB: Edinburgh.

Thom, V. (1986). *Birds in Scotland.* T. & A.D. Poyser: Calton.

Thompson, D.B.A & Whitfield, D.P. (1993). Dotterel *Charadrius morinellus*. In: Gibbons, D.W., Reid, J.B. & Chapman, R.A. (eds.) *The New Atlas of Breeding Birds in Britain and Ireland: 1988–1991.* T. & A.D. Poyser: London. pp. 166–167.

Thompson, D.B.A., Gillings, S.D., Galbraith, C.A., Redpath, S.M. & Drewitt, J. (1997). The contribution of game management to biodiversity: a review of the importance of grouse moors for upland birds. In: Fleming, L.V., Newton, A.C., Vickery, J.A. & Usher, M.B. (eds.). *Biodiversity in Scotland: Status, Trends and Initiatives.* The Stationary Office: Edinburgh. pp. 198–212.

Thompson, D.B.A., Shaw, P., Riley, H.T., Shewry, M.C., Mackey, E.C., Robertson, P. & Morton, K. (2003). An overview of land use change and implications for raptors. In: Thompson, D.B.A, Redpath, S.M., Fielding, A.H., Marquiss, M. & Galbraith, C.A. (eds.) *Birds of Prey in a Changing Environment.* The Stationery Office: Edinburgh. pp. 307–321.

Tyler, S.J. & Green, M. (1989). A preliminary Study of the Status and Breeding Performance of Ring Ouzels in Wales. RSPB unpublished report.

Tyler, S.J. & Green, M. (1994). The status and breeding ecology of Ring Ouzels *Turdus torquatus* in Wales with reference to soil acidity. *Welsh Bird Report* 7: 78–89.

Voous, K.H. (1978). The Scottish Crossbill: *Loxia scotica*. *British Birds* 71: 3–10.

Watson, A. (1964). The food of the Ptarmigan (*Lagopus mutus*) in Scotland. *Scottish Naturalist* 71: 60–66.

Watson, A. (1965). A population study of Ptarmigan (*Lagopus mutus*) in Scotland. *Journal of Animal Ecology* 34: 135–172.

Watson, A. (1996). Human induced increases of Carrion Crows and gulls on Cairngorms plateaux. *Scottish Birds* 18: 205–213.

Watson, A. & Moss, R. (2004). Impacts of ski-development on ptarmigan (*Lagopus mutus*) at Cairn Gorm, Scotland. *Biological Conservation* 116(2): 267–275.

Watson, A. & Rae, R. (1987). Dotterel numbers, habitat and breeding success in Scotland. *Scottish Birds* 14(4): 191–198.

Watson, A. & Rae, R. (1993). Ptarmigan *Lagopus mutus*. In: Gibbons, D.W., Reid, J.B. & Chapman, R.A. (eds.), *The New Atlas of Breeding Birds in Britain and Ireland: 1988–1991*. T. & A.D. Poyser: London. pp. 128–129.

Watson, A. & Smith, R. (1991). Scottish Snow Bunting numbers in summer 1970–87. *Scottish Birds* 16: 53–56.

Watson, A., Moss, R. & Rae, S. (1998). Population dynamics of Scottish rock ptarmigan cycles. *Ecology* 79(4): 1174–1192.

Watson, A., Moss, R. & Rotheray, P. (2000). Weather and synchrony in 10-year population cycles of rock ptarmigan and red grouse in Scotland. *Ecology* 81(8): 2126–2136.

Watson, A., Nethersole-Thompson, D., Duncan, K., Galbraith, H., Rae, S., Smith, R. & Thomas, C. (1988). Decline of shore waders at Loch Morlich. *Scottish Birds* 15(2): 91–92.

Watson, J. (1997). *The Golden Eagle*. T. & A.D. Poyser: London.

Watson, J., Rae, S.R. & Stillman, R. (1992). Nesting density and breeding success of Golden eagles *Aquila chrysaetos* in relation to food supply in Scotland. *Journal of Animal Ecology*. 61: 543–550.

WeBS (1989–2000). Wildfowl counts presented in annual Wetland Bird Survey reports. See: Pollitt, M., Hall, C., Holloway, S., Hearn, R., Marshall, P., Musgrove, A., Robinson, J. & Cranswick, P. (2003). *The Wetland Bird Survey 2000–01: Wildfowl and Wader Counts*. BTO/WWT/RSPB/JNCC: Slimbridge.

Whitfield, D.P. (2002). Status of breeding Dotterel *Charadrius morinellus* in Britain in 1999. *Bird Study* 49: 237–249.

Whitfield, D.P. & Tharme, A.P. (1997). *An evaluation of the effects of native pinewood regeneration on the birds of the Cairngorms*. Report to Research Advisory Services Directorate. SNH: Perth.

Whitfield, D.P., Duncan, K., Pullan, D. & Smith, R.D. (1996). Recoveries of Scottish-ringed Dotterel *Charadrius morinellus* in the non-breeding season: evidence for seasonal shifts in wintering distribution. *Ringing & Migration* 17: 105–110.

Whitfield, D.P., MacColl, A.D.C., Holt, S., Smith, R.D., Denny, R., Pullan, D., Gordon, J. & Stirling J. *The influence of human recreation on Eurasian dotterel* Charadrius morinellus *breeding in the Scottish Highlands. I. The effects of disturbance*. Unpublished report.

Whitfield, D.P., McLeod, D.R.A., Watson, J., Fielding, A.H. & Haworth, P.F. (2003). The association of grouse moor in Scotland with the illegal use of poisons to control predators. *Biological Conservation* 114(2): 157–163.

Wilkinson, N.I., Langston, R.H.W., Gregory, R.D., Gibbons, D.W. & Marquiss, M. (2002) Capercaillie *Tetrao urogallus* abundance and habitat use in Scotland, in winter 1998–99. *Bird Study* 49: 177–185.

Wotton, S.R., Langston, R.H.W. & Gregory, R.D. (2002). The breeding status of the Ring Ouzel *Turdus torquatus* in the UK in 1999. *Bird Study* 49(1): 26–34.

19. MAMMALS

Philip R. Ratcliffe, Robert Raynor and Mairi Cole

Introduction

Sixty-two terrestrial mammal species occur in the wild in Britain[1], of which 16 have been introduced. Britain's mammal fauna is thus relatively impoverished compared with that of many continental European countries. There are several reasons for this, including Britain's relatively high latitude and geographic isolation, which acts as a barrier to natural colonisation, other than by bat species. Thirty-seven mammal species have been recorded recently in the Cairngorms, of which 27 occur naturally in Britain.

A high proportion of Britain's native mammal species became extinct in post-glacial times. These include the Wolf *Canis lupus*, Lynx *Felis lynx*, Brown Bear *Ursus arctos*, Wild Boar *Sus scrofa*, Aurochs *Bos taurus*, Beaver *Castor fiber*, Elk *Alces alces* and Reindeer *Rangifer tarandus*. Introduced species include the Brown Hare[2], which is believed to have been brought to Britain by the Romans, and the Rabbit and Fallow Deer, which were introduced in Norman times. The Brown Rat colonised Britain in the 17th century, but its spread to the remoter parts of Scotland probably occurred much later. American Mink established feral populations after escaping or being released from fur farms in the 1950s and 1960s. Sika Deer and Grey Squirrels were introduced in the late 19th and early 20th centuries.

Although mammal recording has become more organised in recent years (see Harris *et al.*, 1995; Macdonald *et al.*, 1998), information on historic or recent changes in extant mammal populations in the Cairngorms is sparse.

Important species and habitats

All extant mammal species recorded recently in the Cairngorms are listed in Table 19.1. Of the 37 species listed, two are globally threatened: the Otter,

classed as Vulnerable, and the Red Squirrel, classed as near-threatened (IUCN, 2003). The Otter is also included in Annex II of the EC Habitats Directive, which lists species whose conservation requires the designation of Special Areas of Conservation (SACs), and in Annex IVa, which identifies species requiring strict protection. Also included in Annex IVa are all five bat species recorded in the Cairngorms area, and the Wildcat. The Pine Marten and Mountain Hare are both listed in Annex Va, which identifies species whose taking in the wild and exploitation may be subject to management measures. In addition, the Otter, Red Squirrel, Water Vole, Brown Hare and both the Common and Soprano Pipistrelle Bats are all UK Biodiversity Action Plan (BAP) Priority species.

Under the Wildlife and Countryside Act 1981, Pine Marten, Otter, Wildcat and Red Squirrel are afforded full protection, while the protection afforded to Water Voles is currently restricted to their place of shelter (and disturbance to the animals therein). In addition, there are restrictions on the methods used for the killing or taking of certain species (not otherwise fully protected), including Hedgehogs and all species of shrew. Badgers are afforded special protection under the Protection of Badgers Act 1992, while deer are the subject of special legislation under the Deer (Scotland) Act 1996 (see Chapter 21).

Of the 37 mammal species recorded recently in the Cairngorms, Red Squirrel and Water Vole are classified in the Review of British Mammals (Harris *et al.*, 1995) as 'Vulnerable' (Table 19.1). Indeed, the Water Vole is considered to be the most rapidly declining mammal in Britain (Barreto *et al.*, 1998; Strachan *et al.*, 1998; Strachan *et al.*, 2000).

Despite a recent recovery from low numbers during the early 1900s, the British Wildcat population is at risk from genetic introgression with domestic and feral cats. As a result, it is possibly the most threatened of British native mammals. Normally a difficult species to photograph, this individual was hand-reared.

Photo: *P. Cairns*

Ratcliffe, P.R., Raynor, R. & Cole, M. (2006). Mammals. In: Shaw, P. & Thompson, D.B.A. (eds.). *The Nature of the Cairngorms: Diversity in a changing environment*. The Stationery Office. pp. 341-351.

[1] This number varies between observers, depending upon the inclusion or exclusion of some of the rarer bats and shrews within the British fauna.
[2] Scientific names of extant species are given in Table 19.1.

Important areas for mammals

Areas supporting notable populations of species for which the Cairngorms are considered nationally important are described below. All are SACs, on which Otter is a qualifying species.

1. *Cairngorms SAC.* This site spans a wide range of habitats, including broadleaved woodlands, open mires, moorlands, montane heaths and major tracts of Caledonian forest; at Abernethy and Rothiemurchus. Together, they support a wide range of the Cairngorms' mammal species. At Rothiemurchus and Abernethy Forests, recent reductions in Red Deer numbers have resulted in much regeneration of tree seedlings, ultimately improving the forest structure and providing additional habitat for many species, including Pine Marten, Wildcat and Red Squirrel. Otters occupy the river and riparian areas, while the upper part of the River Feshie catchment is notable for Water Vole.

2. *Ballochbuie SAC.* This site supports one of the largest remaining continuous areas of Caledonian forest, situated on the slopes of the Dee valley below the

Forests in the Cairngorms represent an important national stronghold for the Red Squirrel, whose British population is declining as the Grey Squirrel's range expands. There is concern for the Red Squirrel elsewhere in Europe, and the species is now classed as globally 'near-threatened'.
Photo: *N. Mcintyre*

foothills of the Lochnagar massif. Much of the area is fenced to protect it from grazing Red Deer and, as a consequence, has a well-developed understorey, providing cover for Wildcats and many of their prey species. Red Squirrels are also present in the woodland, while Otters occupy the river and riparian areas.

3. *Glen Tanar SAC* is the third largest pinewood in Britain. Much of the forest consists of semi-natural pinewood with a wide age structure, and significant areas of Juniper *Juniperus communis*. By virtue of its size and varied structure, it supports significant numbers of Red Squirrel, while Otters occupy the river and riparian areas. Wildcats are also present.

4. *Muir of Dinnet SAC.* An area best known for its moorland species and glacial features, Muir of Dinnet includes lochs Davan and Kinord, whose proximity to the River Dee and varied freshwater habitats enable it to support significant numbers of Otter and several species of bat.

5. *River Dee SAC.* The River Dee also qualifies as an SAC on account of its internationally important Otter population. Otters occur throughout the Dee catchment, from its mouth to many of its high-altitude lochs. The river system contains extensive areas of habitat suitable for Otter, including watercourses with a high fish biomass, islands and marshy areas for resting in.

In addition, the headwaters of the Dee and several of its upper tributaries hold significant numbers of Water Voles. Although some sites, notably those in the upper parts of the catchment, do not yet appear to be occupied by Mink, they remain vulnerable as Mink are present in the general area. All populations in the remaining sites are threatened by Mink. The Dee valley also supports all five species of bat present in the Cairngorms.

6. *River Spey SAC.* This site supports an internationally important population of Otter, which depends on the river's reedbeds, islands and on their populations of important prey species. Other important habitats include alluvial Alder *Alnus glutinosa* woodland. The Spey Valley supports all five bat species present in the Cairngorms.

7. *Insh Marshes SAC.* An extensive complex of river, marsh and high quality oligotrophic mire, Insh Marshes is directly connected to the River Spey, and provides ideal feeding, resting and shelter areas for Otter; a primary reason for its selection as an SAC.

Recent research and survey findings

There have been few recent surveys of the distribution of mammals in the Cairngorms. They include a survey of Badgers in 1993 (Masson, 1993) and of Water Voles during 1998-2002 (Lambin *et al.*, 1998; WildCRU, 2004; Capreolus Wildlife Consultancy, 2005). The main findings of this work, much of it commissioned by SNH, are summarised below. In addition, SNH commissioned a survey of Otters in Scotland during 2003. This involved revisiting many sites in the Cairngorms that had been assessed during previous surveys. A report on this work is in preparation.

Badger. An objective of the 1993 Badger survey was to locate setts and to assess the species' occupancy in parts of Strathspey encompassing the low, relatively fertile areas between Abernethy Forest, Rothiemurchus and Inshriach (Masson, 1993). A secondary objective was to compare findings with those of a survey carried out in 1976-87 (Kruuk, 1989). During Kruuk's study, Badger numbers varied between 32 in 1978 and 26 in 1982, although the number of clans remained the same (eight). Masson's study showed no significant changes in overall numbers from 1987, although changes had occurred with respect to the dispersion of badgers and the occupancy of individual setts.

Masson (1993) expressed concern over the effects of disturbance and a deterioration in the food supply, and recommended greater care in tree planting, and sympathetic management of pastures and native woodlands aimed at maintaining earthworm populations. Further research was recommended on the impact of colonisation by the New Zealand Flatworm *Arthurdendyus triangulatus* (which predates earthworms). Masson (1993) also recommended a re-survey of land-uses, comparing them with Kruuk's study, and an expansion of the survey area in future.

Water vole. A survey of Water Voles in 1996 (Lambin *et al.*, 1996) reported a catastrophic decline in north-east Scotland, due largely to predation by Mink. A lack of earlier, comparable data, and the survey's limited geographic spread (covering the catchments of the Don and Ythan) make it difficult to determine the scale of the decline. Although a subsequent study of the catchments of the rivers Dee and Don (Lambin *et al.*, 1998) detected no Water Voles at 30 potential sites on the River Don, large populations were detected on two tributaries of the River Dee: River Muick and Feindallacher Burn. No Water Voles were detected at nine other tributaries where the species had previously been present.

Lambin *et al.* (1998) found that Water Voles were strongly associated with dense, bank-side vegetation of tall tussock-forming grasses, sedges, rushes and herbaceous plants, in close proximity to grasslands and in conjunction with vertical or undercut banks. Water Voles were widely distributed in the headwaters of the River Dee, where 67 sub-populations were detected over 37 km of watercourse. Their discontinuous distribution was thought to reflect the patchiness of suitable habitat and of areas free of Mink. Lambin *et al.* (1998) considered that the Water Vole will not persist in upland sites in Scotland unless the spread of Mink can be halted.

In a study of the catchments of the upper River Feshie, the River Tilt and Bruar Water, and the upper River Dee at Mar Lodge, surveys were conducted to detect indicators of the presence of Water Vole, Mink and Otter (WildCRU, 2004) (Figure 19.1). Evidence of Water Vole was found at 62 out of 123 sites assessed. Two sites had evidence of Mink and 10 had signs of Otter. During the study, an additional 15 sites with Water Voles were found.

Habitat deterioration and Mink predation have been implicated in the decline of the Water Vole in Britain. Scottish populations may be important for the species' national survival, particularly the Cairngorms' relatively isolated upland populations, which tend to be dark grey rather than brown.

Photo: *A. Ross*

Figure 19.1. Important areas for mammal species. Sites at which Water Voles have been located during recent surveys are also indicated. See text for further details.

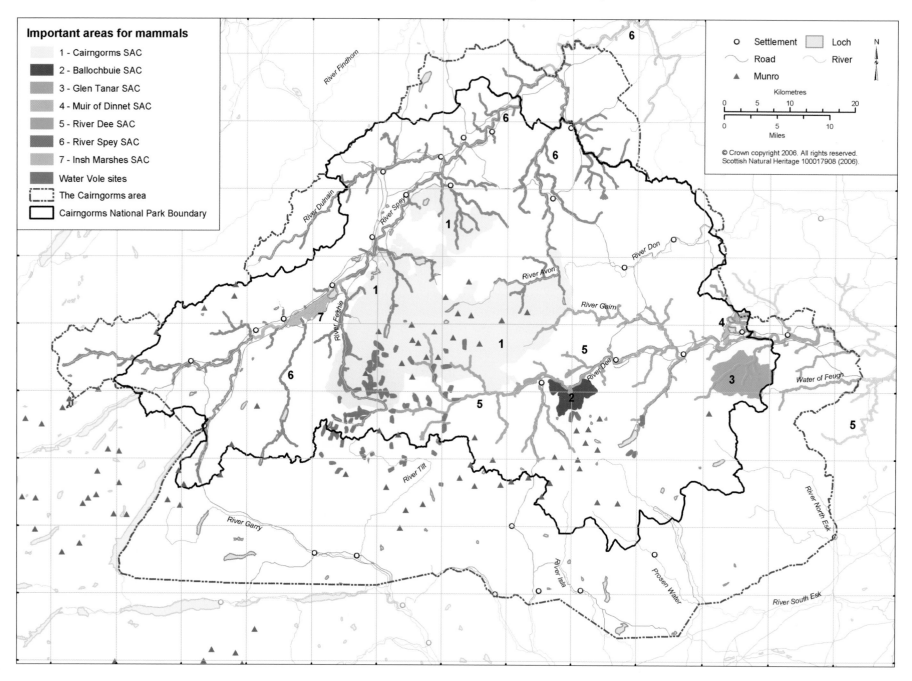

Important areas for mammals

- 1 - Cairngorms SAC
- 2 - Ballochbuie SAC
- 3 - Glen Tanar SAC
- 4 - Muir of Dinnet SAC
- 5 - River Dee SAC
- 6 - River Spey SAC
- 7 - Insh Marshes SAC
- Water Vole sites
- The Cairngorms area
- Cairngorms National Park Boundary

Settlement · Loch · Road · River · Munro

Kilometres
0 5 10 20

Miles
0 5 10

© Crown copyright 2006. All rights reserved.
Scottish Natural Heritage 100017908 (2006).

Table 19.1. The conservation status of mammal species occurring or recorded recently in the Cairngorms, ordered by main habitat.

Occurs naturally:	Y = occurs naturally in Britain; N = introduced to Britain.
Global:	IUCN global threat status: VU = Vulnerable; NT = Near Threatened.
National:	National threat status: V = Vulnerable; C = Common; LC = Locally Common (Harris *et al.,* 1995)[1].
BAP:	Biodiversity Action Plan Priority species.
WCA:	Protected under the Wildlife & Countryside Act 1981. Numbers indicate relevant Schedule in the Act: 5 = cannot be killed or injured; 6 = certain methods of killing are prohibited; 9 = release in the wild is prohibited.
SAC :	Qualifying species on at least one Special Area of Conservation.
Percentage of UK range:	The percentage of the species' UK range (in 10-km squares) occurring in the Cairngorms area: *** >75%; ** 25-75%; * 10-24%; '-' <10%.

Habitat General	Specific	Species	Occurs naturally	Global	National[1]	BAP	WCA	SAC	% of UK range
Aquatic habitats	Water courses and lochs	American Mink *Mustela vison*	N		C		9		-
	Water courses and lochs	Otter *Lutra lutra*	Y	VU	LC	Y	5,6	Y	-
	Banks of water courses and ponds	Water Shrew *Neomys fodiens*	Y		LC		6		-
	Banks of slow-moving water courses to 1,000 m	Water Vole *Arvicola terrestris*	Y		V	Y	5		-
Dense vegetation	Ubiquitous in dense vegetation. Occurs up to the high mountain plateaux	Common Shrew *Sorex araneus*	Y		C		6		-
	Ubiquitous in dense vegetation. Occurs up to the high mountain plateaux	Pygmy Shrew *Sorex minutus*	Y		C		6		-
Grassland	Arable, pasture and some semi-natural grasslands	Brown Hare *Lepus europaeus*	N		C	Y	-		-
	Well-drained and short grassland	Rabbit *Oryctolagus cuniculus*	N		C		-		-
	Ubiquitous in rich grasslands to 800 m where soils permit	Mole *Talpa europaea*	Y		C		-		-
Grassland/moorland	Grassland and moorland to 900 m	Field Vole *Microtus agrestis*	Y		C		-		-
Moorland	Rocky areas generally preferred.	Feral Goat *Capra hircus*	N		R		-		-
		Reindeer *Rangifer tarandus*	N		R		-		***
	Heather moorland	Mountain Hare *Lepus timidus*	Y		LC		-		**
Moorland/woodland		Badger *Meles meles*	Y		C		6		-
		Pine Marten *Martes martes*	Y		LC		5,6		-
		Red Deer *Cervus elaphus*	Y		LC		-		*
		Wildcat *Felis silvestris*	Y		LC		5,6		-
Woodland		Fallow Deer *Dama dama*	N		LC		-		-
		Roe Deer *Capreolus capreolus*	Y		C		-		-
		Sika Deer *Cervus nippon*	N		LC		-		-
	Woodlands, woodland edge and more open terrain up to 800 m	Bank Vole *Clethrionomys glareolus*	Y		C		-		-
	Grassland/deciduous woodland, scrub to 450 m	Hedgehog *Erinaceus europaeus*	Y		C		6		-
	Principally coniferous woodland up to *c.* 550 m	Red Squirrel *Sciurus vulgaris*	Y	NT	V	Y	5,6		*
		Grey Squirrel *Sciurus carolinensis*	N		C		9		-
	Open woodlands, usually close to water, generally below 400 m	Daubenton's Bat *Myotis daubentonii*	Y		LC		5,6		-
		Natterer's Bat *Myotis nattereri*	Y		LC		5,6		-

| Habitat | | | Species | Occurs naturally | Status | | | | | % of UK range |
General	Specific				Global	National[i]	BAP	WCA	SAC	
Woodland	Ubiquitous in various habitats usually close to woodland and/or water, generally below 400 m		Common Pipistrelle Bat *Pipistrellus pipistrellus*	Y		C	Y	5,6		-
	Ubiquitous in various habitats usually close to woodland and/or water, generally below 400 m		Soprano Pipistrelle Bat *Pipistrellus pygmaeus*	Y		C	Y	5,6		-
	A single record from upper Deeside in 1994.		Nathusius's Pipistrelle Bat *Pipistrellus nathusii*	Y				5,6		-
	Wooded areas generally below 400 m		Brown Long-eared Bat *Plecotus auritus*	Y		LC		5,6		-
Settlements	Ubiquitous around human habitation		Brown Rat *Rattus norvegicus*	N		C		-		-
	Around human habitation		House Mouse *Mus domesticus*	N		C		-		-
	Close to human habitation		Feral Cat *Felis catus*	N		C		-		-
Ubiquitous	All habitats and altitudes		Fox *Vulpes vulpes*	Y		C		-		-
	Farmland, woodland and moorland to mountain summits		Stoat *Mustela erminea*	Y		C		-		-
	Farmland, woodland and moorland to *c.* 600 m		Weasel *Mustela nivalis*	Y		C		-		-
	Various habitats up to 1,300 m		Wood Mouse *Apodemus sylvaticus*	Y		C		-		-

[i] These subjective assessments of national threat status were derived in 1995, and do not necessarily reflect current knowledge or opinion in every case. For example, the Wildcat is now regarded as possibly the most threatened native British mammal.

[ii] Population largely managed.

Three separate, robust populations were found on the River Feshie catchment: in the headwaters of the River Eidart and River Feshie, and along an 8.8 km section of the Allt na Leuma. Elsewhere, populations of only a few individuals each were encountered. This study proposed that defending key populations against incursions by Mink should be an essential action in the delivery of the Cairngorms Local Biodiversity Action Plan (LBAP) (WildCRU, 2004).

The number of occupied sites on the upper Dee at Mar Lodge Estate showed a 52% decline during the four years since the previous survey in 1997 (Lambin *et al.*, 1998). This large drop in numbers may have been exaggerated by natural cycles, but is nonetheless a cause for concern. The very small population sizes recorded during this study are considered to represent extremely fragile populations.

Capreolus Wildlife Consultancy (2005) compared Water Vole numbers on the Geldie and Bynack sub-catchments of the River Dee in 2002, with those detected during the 1997 survey (Lambin, 1998; Aars *et al.*, 2001). The proportion of burns supporting Water Voles declined from 73% to 9% in the Bynack and from 78% to 39% in the Geldie catchments between 1998 and 2001. Repeat surveys of these 11 burns in 2002 showed an increase from one to two burns occupied (probably representing fewer than five animals) in the Bynack catchment, and a further decline in the Geldie. In conclusion, Capreolus Wildlife Consultancy (2005) considered the species to be 'hovering on the brink of extinction' in these catchments.

An SNH survey (Ross, unpublished) recorded the decline in Water Voles at the Caenlochan NNR in 2003, following an invasion by Mink.

Mountain Hare. Ongoing research by the Game Conservancy Trust addresses aspects of the population biology of Mountain Hares, mainly with regard to their effects on the management of Red Grouse (Newey *et al.*, 2003). Recent research by S.J. Rao and her co-workers has described the impacts of Mountain Hares on woodland regeneration (Rao, 2001; Rao *et al.*, 2003a,b). This work does not specifically address issues relating to the Mountain Hare's status, trends or conservation in the Cairngorms.

Red Squirrel. In 1998, a study of the population size, distribution and habitat preferences of the Red Squirrel was conducted in the Glen Doll area of upper Glen Clova (Ross, 1998), about 15 km from a known population of Grey Squirrel. No data are currently available on population size, but a core area of activity has been identified in the existing stands of Norway Spruce *Picea abies* and Scots Pine *Pinus sylvestris* at Glen Doll. Recommendations are made for the extension of conifer woodlands to support a larger population of Red Squirrel, and to deter colonisation by Grey Squirrel.

Trends

While no recent trend data are available for mammal populations in the Cairngorms, other than those described above, the following historic trends have been recorded.

Red Squirrels declined to low numbers in the early 19th century, but apparently survived in Rothiemurchus. They subsequently spread from there and from a site near Dunkeld, where they had been reintroduced around 1790 (Harvie-Brown, 1880-81, cited in Nethersole-Thompson & Watson, 1974). The species is declining generally in the UK, although with some local gains in Scotland as a result of woodland expansion. The Cairngorms population is almost certainly of national significance (Leaper, 1997).

Grey Squirrels are increasing throughout the UK, although apparently less rapidly in Scotland, perhaps reflecting differences in woodland composition and management. The species is established on lower Deeside and Donside, and has been recorded occasionally from within the National Park. Grey Squirrels also occur in the south Angus Glens.

Pine Martens became extinct in the Spey and Avon valleys in the late 19th century (Nethersole-Thompson & Watson, 1974), but now occur throughout most of the Cairngorms area (Lockie, 1964; Leaper, 1997) including, most recently, upper Deeside. Surveys carried out in 1977-82 (Velander, 1983) and 1994 (Balharry *et al.*, 1996) suggest that the Pine Marten's range within the Cairngorms area expanded during the 1990s, particularly within Strathspey and upper Deeside.

Badgers have shown local reductions and extinctions in some parts of the UK since reaching a peak around 1960 (Neal & Cheeseman, 1991). In the Cairngorms there has been a reversal of local declines which, by about 1940, left only small populations in the lower Spey Valley and in Perthshire (Nethersole-Thompson & Watson, 1974). A recent study found little evidence of change in Badger numbers during the late 1980s (see above; Kruuk, 1989; Masson, 1993).

Otters declined dramatically during 1950-80 at most inland sites in the UK (Green & Green, 1980), with the possible exception of northern Scotland. The species now occurs over the whole of Scotland, with the Cairngorms area supporting a widespread and important population. The Otter's expansion is thought to have lead to a contraction in the Mink's range in some parts of Britain (Strachan & Jefferies, 1996), although perhaps not in Scotland (WildCRU, 2004).

Wildcats were extinct on Deeside by 1918, but survived in Speyside at Rothiemurchus, Glenmore and Abernethy (Nethersole-Thompson & Watson, 1974). Subsequently, there has been a recovery, at least in terms of range. This expansion may have resulted in an increased rate of introgression

Pine Martens became extinct in the Spey and Avon straths in the late 19th century, but now occur throughout most of the Cairngorms area, including, most recently, upper Deeside.
Photo: *M. Hamblin*

with domestic and feral cats, however, threatening the genetic integrity of the Wildcat population. Nonetheless, individuals conforming to our 'traditional' understanding of the species' characteristics – in terms of pelage markings, gut length, skull measurements and genetic markers – are still present, despite the possibility of 2,000 years of interbreeding (Macdonald *et al.*, 2004).

Mountain Hares have declined in the west of the Cairngorms during the last century, but remain at high densities in the south and east (Dennis, 2002). The Cairngorms area probably represents a significant part of the species' UK range. Since the 1940s a 1-4% annual decline in heather moorland, attributed to tree regeneration and over-grazing, has almost certainly had an adverse effect on the Mountain Hare population (Leaper, 1997).

Brown Hares have shown a decline in the UK since the 1960s (Harris *et al.*, 1995; Hutchings & Harris, 1996). Although common in parts of Glen Feshie in the early 1970s (Nethersole-Thompson & Watson, 1974), their current status in the Cairngorms is unknown.

The ***Water Vole*** declined throughout most of its range in the UK during the 1980s and 1990s. Loss and fragmentation of habitat, disturbance of riparian habitats, predation by Mink and pollution of watercourses are all implicated in its decline (UK BAP, 1995). Scottish populations may be important for the species' survival in the UK and, as noted above, the relatively isolated populations in the Cairngorms are considered to be of national importance (Leaper, 1997).

The status of the following species in the Cairngorms is unclear: Hedgehog[3], Mole, Common Shrew, Pygmy Shrew, Water Shrew, Natterer's Bat, Daubenton's bat, Common Pipistrelle[4], Soprano Pipistrelle, Brown Long-eared Bat, Bank Vole, Field Vole, Wood Mouse, Brown Rat, House Mouse, Fox, Stoat, Weasel, Mink, Feral Cat and Feral Goat. Trends in deer species are described in Chapter 21.

Conservation issues

The main conservation issues relating to mammal species in the Cairngorms are as follows.

Controlling Red Deer impacts. The impact of deer on semi-natural vegetation and its associated fauna is an important issue. Deer densities need to be managed in harmony with multiple objectives, but with due regard to nature conservation objectives.

The spread of Sika Deer on the Scottish mainland probably cannot be halted. Sika have adapted well to upland forestry plantations, where they pose an insidious threat to the existence of pure Red Deer through hybridisation. The main practical difficulty presented by such inter-breeding is that, like pure Sika, hybrids are more likely to occupy dense thickets than are pure Red Deer, thereby making them more difficult to cull. Efforts should be therefore made to limit colonisation of the Cairngorms. Deer management issues are discussed in Chapter 21.

The impact of Mink on Water Vole populations. The Water Vole is threatened throughout its British range, but has good (albeit small and fragmented) populations in the Cairngorms, considered to be of national importance. Poor riparian habitat management and the impact of Mink are the most important factors implicated in its decline. It is considered both important and urgent to address these issues. Evidence for the negative impacts of Mink on Water Voles is overwhelming, and there is a need to focus attention on the targeted control or local eradication of Mink.

Hybridisation in the Wildcat. The status of the Wildcat in the Cairngorms, especially with regard to hybridisation with domestic and Feral Cats, is poorly understood. There is, however, evidence that the Cairngorms support a high proportion of wild-living cats that conform to our current definition of a Wildcat. Macdonald *et al.* (2004) propose various measures to conserve the Wildcat, and each will need to be fully considered before an conservation strategy for this species can be implemented.

Control of Mountain Hares. Hares are controlled for three reasons: to protect growing trees; as quarry; and to reduce the incidence of louping ill in grouse. In the latter case, research suggests that the incidence of sheep ticks (the primary host for the louping ill virus) on grouse can be significantly reduced by heavily culling the local Mountain Hare population. This has been recommended (and applied) on some estates as a management objective. However, the Habitats Directive requires that the exploitation of Annex V species 'is compatible with them being maintained at a favourable conservation status'. In the absence of reliable population trend information, it is unwise to assume that favourable conservation status is being maintained while such heavy culls continue. Furthermore, long-term global climate change is likely to adversely influence the sub-Arctic/alpine habitats favoured by this species, possibly leading to increased population fragmentation.

---

[3] There is evidence of local declines in Hedgehog in some parts of the UK, although the trend in the Cairngorms is unknown.
[4] Data from the National Bat Monitoring Programme indicate that both Daubenton's Bat and Common Pipistrelle have shown significant population increases at the UK level since 1996. It is not known whether these trends are reflected locally in the Cairngorms. National trends in the Soprano Pipistrelle population are unclear.

Population monitoring. There is little objective information on the changing status of many important mammal species in the Cairngorms, including those of Brown Hare, Mountain Hare, Red Squirrel, Wildcat, Pine Marten and all five bat species (Table 19.1). The issue of mammal monitoring is being progressed at the UK level through the Tracking Mammals Partnership. This initiative aims to set up long-term monitoring schemes to detect overall population trends at the UK and country level. It is likely that additional targeted monitoring may be required in key areas, such as the Cairngorms, to detect more localised changes.

Red Squirrel. The increase in Grey Squirrels and concurrent decline in Red Squirrels is well documented, although the mechanism by which the former influence the Red Squirrel's distribution remains unresolved. Forests in the Cairngorms area represent an important national stronghold for the Red Squirrel. However, monitoring is required to assess changes in the range of Grey Squirrel populations within, or close to, the Cairngorms, and plans are required to prevent them from colonising woodlands and forests in the area.

Woodlands likely to provide the best opportunities for conserving Red Squirrel populations have been identified as part of the Priority Woodlands initiative (Poulsom *et al.*, 2005). Since Grey Squirrels are known to be able to cross substantial areas of non-wooded terrain, care should be taken to ensure that the development of Forest Habitat Networks[5] does not facilitate their spread into the Cairngorms' forests.

References

Aars, J., Lambin, X., Denny, R. & Griffin, A. (2001). Water vole in the Scottish Uplands: distribution patterns of disturbed and pristine populations ahead and behind the American mink invasion front. *Animal Conservation* 4: 187-194.

Balharry, E.A., McGowan, G.M., Kruuk, H. & Halliwell, E. (1996). Distribution of pine martens in Scotland as determined by field survey and questionnaire. *Scottish Natural Heritage Research, Survey and Monitoring Report.* No. 48. SNH: Perth.

Barreto, G.R., Macdonald, D.W. & Strachan, R. (1998). The tightrope hypothesis: an explanation of plummeting water vole numbers in the Thames catchment. In: R.G. Bailey, P.V. Jose & Sherwood, B.R. (eds.). *United Kingdom Floodplains.* Westbury Publishing, London. *Proceedings of the Linnean Society of London* 1: 311-327.

Capreolus Wildlife Consultancy (2005). *The ecology and conservation of water voles in upland habitats.* Scottish Natural Heritage Commissioned Report No. 99 (ROAME No. F99AC320). SNH: Perth.

Dennis, R. (2002). Birds and Mammals. In: Gimingham, C.H. (ed.). *The Ecology, Land Use and Conservation of the Cairngorms.* Packard: Chichester. pp. 43-53.

Green, R. & Green, J. (1980). *Otter Survey of Scotland 1977-79.* Vincent Wildlife Trust: London.

Harris, S., Morris, P., Wray, S. & Yalden, D. (1995). *A Review of British Mammals: Population Estimates and Conservation Status of British Mammals except Cetaceans.* JNCC: Peterborough.

Harvie-Brown, J.A. (1880-81). The history of the red squirrel in Great Britain. *Proceedings of the Royal Physiological Society.* 5: 343-348.

Hutchings, M. R. & Harris, S. (1996). *The current Status of the Brown Hare* (Lepus europaeus) *in Britain.* JNCC: Peterborough.

IUCN (2003). *IUCN Red List of Threatened Species. http://www.redlist.org/*

Kruuk, H. (1989). *The Social Badger.* Oxford University Press: Oxford.

Lambin, X., Telfer, S., Cosgrove, P. & Alexander, G. (1996). *Survey of water voles and mink on the rivers Don and Ythan.* SNH report. SNH: Perth.

Lambin, X., Fazey, I., Sansom, J., Dallas, J., Stewart, W., Piertney, S., Palmer, S.C.F., Bacon, P.J. & Webb, A. (1998). *Aberdeen water vole survey: the distribution of isolated water vole populations in the upper catchments of the Rivers Dee and Don.* Scottish Natural Heritage Research, Survey and Monitoring Report No. 118. SNH: Perth.

Leaper, G. (1997). *Biodiversity of the Cairngorm Partnership Area.* Cairngorms Partnership: Grantown-on-Spey.

Lockie, J. D. (1964). The distribution and fluctuations of the pine marten in Scotland. *Journal of Animal Ecology.* 33: 349-356.

Macdonald, D.W., Mace, G. & Rushton, S. (1998). *Proposals for Future Monitoring of British Mammals.* DETR: London.

Macdonald, D.W., Daniels, M.J., Driscoll, C., Kitchener, A. & Yamaguchi, N. (2004). The Scottish wildcat analyses for conservation and an action plan. WildCRU, Oxford.

Masson, S. (1993). *Badger survey (sett occupancy) Cairngorm sub-area.* Unpublished SNH report. SNH: Perth.

Neal, E.G., & Cheeseman, C.L. (1991). Badger. In: Corbet, G.B. & Harris, S. (eds.) *Handbook of British Mammals. 3rd edition.* Blackwell: Oxford. pp. 415-423.

Nethersole-Thompson, D. & Watson, A. (1974). *The Cairngorms: Their natural histroy and scenery.* Collins: London.

Newey, S., Bell, M., Enthoven, S. & Thirgood, S.J. (2003). Can distance sampling and dung plots be used to assess the density of mountain hares, *Lepus timidus? Wildlife Biology* 9: 185-192.

Poulsom, L., Griffiths, M., Broome, A. & Mayle, B. (2005). *Identification of priority woodlands for red squirrel conservation in North and Central Scotland: a preliminary analysis.* Scottish Natural Heritage Commissioned Report No. 89 (ROAME No. F02AC334). SNH: Perth.

[5] See: http://www.chm.org.uk/Library/ecosys/forest/for002i.htm

Rao, S.J. (2001). *The interaction between mountain hare feeding ecology and native woodlands.* Ph.D. Thesis, University of Aberdeen.

Rao, S.J., Iason, G.R., Hulbert, I.A.R., Daniels, M.J. & Racey, P.A. (2003a). Tree browsing by mountain hares (*Lepus timidus*) in young Scots pine (*Pinus silvestris*) and birch (*Betula pendula*) woodland. *Forest Ecology and Management* 176: 459-471.

Rao, S.J., Iason, G.R., Hulbert, I.A.R., Elston, D. A. & Racey, P.A. (2003b). The effect of sapling density, heather height and season on browsing by mountain hares on birch. *Journal of Applied Ecology* 40: 626-638.

Strachan, R. & Jefferies, D. J. (1996). *The Otter Survey of England 1991-1994.* The Vincent Wildlife Trust: London.

Strachan, C., Jefferies, D.J., Barreto, G.R., Macdonald, D.W. & Strachan, R. (1998). The rapid impact of resident American Mink on Water Voles: case studies in lowland England. In: Dunstone, N. & Gorman, M. (eds.). *Behaviour and Ecology of Riparian Mammals.* Cambridge University Press: Cambridge. pp. 339-357.

Strachan, C., Strachan, R. & Jefferies, D.J. (2000). *Preliminary Report on the changes in the Water Vole population of Britain as shown by the national surveys of 1989-90 and 1996-98.* The Vincent Wildlife Trust: London.

UK BAP (1995). *Biodiversity: the UK Steering Group Report Volume 2: Action Plans.* HMSO: London.

Velander, K.A. (1983). *Pine marten survey of Scotland, England and Wales 1980-1982.* Vincent Wildlife Trust: London.

WildCRU, Oxford University (2004). *Water vole surveys in Fife and Central Cairngorms.* Scottish Natural Heritage Commissioned Report No. 058 (ROAME No. F01AC316). SNH: Perth.

Ratcliffe, P.R. (2000). *Biodiversity in the Queen Elizabeth and Argyll Forest Parks: a Biodiversity Conservation Strategy.* Unpublished report to Forest Enterprise.

Spey Catchment Steering Group (2003). *River Spey. Catchment Management Plan.* Spey Catchment Steering Group: Aviemore.

Additional reading

Broome, A. (2004). *Conservation Strategy for the Cowal and Trossachs Forest District and the Identification of priority woodlands for red squirrel conservation in North and Central Scotland.* Unpublished Report. Forest Research: Edinburgh.

Bryce, J. & Balharry, D. (1995). Red squirrel *Sciurus vulgaris* conservation in Scotland: a position statement. *Scottish Natural Heritage Review* No.59. SNH: Perth.

Corbet, G.B. & Harris, S. (eds.) (1991). *Handbook of British Mammals. 3rd edition.* Blackwell: Oxford.

Easterbee, N., Hepburn, L.V. & Jefferies, D. J. (1991). *Survey of the Status and Distribution of the Wildcat in Scotland, 1983-1987.* Nature Conservancy Council for Scotland. NCCS: Edinburgh.

Holm, J. (1987). *Squirrels.* Whittet Books: London.

Morris, P.A. (1993). *A Red Data Book for British Mammals.* The Mammal Society: London.

20. CLIMATE CHANGE

Noranne Ellis and Geraldine McGowan

Introduction

The Cairngorm mountains experience a more continental climate than those further west, which bear the brunt of the prevailing westerly maritime air flow. As a consequence, their climate has traditionally been characterised by relatively severe winters and low rainfall, compared with other montane areas in the UK. Recently, however, Britain's climate has shown signs of progressive change, reflecting changes observed on a much wider scale. Globally, the mean annual temperature rose by 0.6°C during the 20th century and rainfall has increased, particularly in the winter months (Houghton *et al.*, 2001). In many montane areas in the Northern Hemisphere there has been a trend towards reduced snow depth, duration of snow cover, and a retreat of glaciers (Beniston & Tol, 1998; Brown, 1998; Hantel *et al.*, 2000). In contrast, parts of Russia have seen an increase in snowfall duration and snow depth (Ye, 2000).

In Scotland, a decrease in the duration of snowfall has been observed at 400–500 m asl, but with relatively small differences above 600 m, attributed to greater amounts of snowfall occurring during the winter months at these altitudes (Harrison *et al.*, 2001). It is believed that this is a result of a more persistent westerly influence on the Scottish winter climate (Mayes, 1996; Osborne *et al.*, 2000). So far, however, no systematic analysis of the latest alterations in climate across the Cairngorms area has been made, despite data being available from a number of weather stations, spanning a wide range of altitudes.

Due to the range and complexity of such changes it is unlikely that we will be able to fully understand and predict with certainty the likely effects of climate change on the natural heritage of the Cairngorms. However, an indication of what might occur within the range of climate scenarios for Scotland is given in this chapter. It should be noted that species mentioned here are those for which data concerning climate change impacts have been found, rather than those that are necessarily the most vulnerable to climate change. For a number of the species mentioned, this is a first attempt at interpreting the implications of potential changes in the distribution of species-specific climate for a local region. Note, however, that models calculating a redistribution of suitable climate for a species do not necessarily take account of all of the factors affecting the distribution and abundance of each species.

Recent climate

The following overview is based on data collected by the United Kingdom Meteorological Office, from a network of observation stations, including automatic weather stations positioned in the Allt a'Mharcaidh catchment (575 m, and at 750 m since 1999), Cairn Gorm (914 m), Cairnwell (933 m), Braemar (339 m) and Balmoral (283 m).

Temperature

The coldest months in Scotland are January and February (Meteorological Office, 1963). The lowest temperatures occur well inland, away from the moderating influences of the sea, and often in the glens. For example, the average January temperature in Braemar varied between 3.7°C and -2.5°C during 1931–60, with a mean of 0.6°C. During the winter, cold dense air occasionally accumulates in the straths, resulting in a temperature inversion (Brown & Clapperton, 2002). During one such episode, on 10 January 1982, the temperature in Braemar dropped to -27.2°C; the lowest temperature ever recorded in Britain and Ireland. The warmest months in Braemar are usually July or August, with average daily temperatures of 8.1°C to 17.6°C recorded during these months in 1931–61, and a mean of *c.* 12.9°C.

Looking south over the pines of Ballochbuie to Carn an t-Sagairt Mòr. Climate change scenarios suggest that winters in the Cairngorms may become wetter by the 2050s, with more of the precipitation falling as rain rather than snow. Summers may be drier, however, and annual precipitation may decline overall.
Photo: *L. Gill*

Ellis, N. & McGowan, G. (2006). Climate change. In: Shaw, P. & Thompson, D.B.A. (eds.). *The Nature of the Cairngorms: Diversity in a changing environment*. The Stationery Office. pp. 353-365.

In contrast, the lowest temperature recorded at the Cairn Gorm Chairlift (663 m asl) during 1980–98 was only -12.2°C (also in January 1982), while the mean minimum and maximum temperatures during this period were *c.* -2.1°C and 2.7°C, respectively (McGowan *et al.*, 2000). Here again, July and August were usually the warmest months (average minimum and maximum range from 8.1°C to 15°C), although the highest recorded temperature (27.1°C) was in June (1995).

Precipitation

The Cairngorms massif has a less oceanic climate than montane areas on the west coast, and produces a noticeable 'rain shadow', which reduces rainfall on the eastern side of the country. In the Cairngorms, annual precipitation varies greatly between years and in relation to topography. While annual precipitation usually exceeds 2,250 mm on the summits, Strathspey and Deeside normally receive less than 900 mm. Rainfall patterns differ slightly between the two straths, the driest month in Strathspey being February or March, while on Deeside it is July. Average annual rainfall at Glenmore Lodge (341 m asl) during 1961–79 (excluding 1964) was 1,059 mm, with a minimum of 749 mm (in 1971; McGowan *et al.*, 2000).

High summer temperatures can trigger convectional rainfall, more commonly to the west of the hills. These events can cause severe flooding as, for example in 1956 and during the 'Muckle Spate' of 1929, which devastated Moray (Brown & Clapperton, 2002).

Snow falls in the Cairngorms area when cold moist air is drawn from the north. Snow produced by weather systems originating in the north-west is 'wetter' than the powder snow that comes from the east, when temperatures are often very low (Brown & Clapperton, 2002). The average number of days with sleet or snow falling in Scotland each year ranges from 20 or less near the west coast to over 100 days on the summits of the Cairngorms. Here, snowfall can occur during any month, although only rarely in August. The average annual number of days with lying snow (at least 50% cover) has been estimated at 60 days on low ground in the Cairngorms and up to 200 days on the summits (e.g. Manley, 1971). The number of days with lying snow has declined since the late 1980s (see below).

Strong winds can scour snow from the Cairngorms plateaux and deposit it in hollows and corries, often forming cornices up to 15 m wide on corrie rims. Drifts in some shallower corries, such as Ciste Mhearaid (on Cairn

By the 2050s the Cairngorms area may be 1.5°C or 2°C warmer. Since the degree of warming in upland areas may greater than at lower altitudes, snow and ice cover are likely to be much reduced in upland coires and lochans, like this one on Braeriach.

Photo: *P. & A. Macdonald*

Gorm) and north-east of Ben Macdui, can be 20–30 m deep (Brown & Clapperton, 2002). Some snow patches, including that in Garbh Coire Mor (Braeriach), have become semi-permanent features, often persisting during poorer summers.

Overloading of slopes with snow means that avalanches are a common hazard. These can be caused by the collapse of cornices ('soft slab' release; Brown & Clapperton, 2002), the release of 'windslabs' on lee slopes, and as a result of melt-water lubricating the base of the snow-pack on rock slabs, as on the Great Slab (Coire an Lochain). Melting snow means that runoff exceeds precipitation in the Cairngorms during April and May (Ferguson, 1985; Brown & Clapperton, 2002). Rapid melting can lead to flooding, especially in Strathspey.

Wind

The prevailing winds in the Cairngorms, and in Scotland as a whole, are from the south-west. Gales are common on the plateau, with gusts of up to 177 and 275 km/hr recorded on Cairn Gorm during 1979–87. Local topography can have a significant effect on wind speed and direction, for example creating a wind funnel effect at Coire Cas. In spring and early summer, air over the snow fields cools and becomes heavier than the surrounding air, forming katabatic winds which flow down the lee side of the hills, sometimes producing blizzard conditions (Brown & Clapperton, 2002).

Cloud and sunshine

Cloud cover is greater in mountainous areas. Mean daily sunshine values peak in May or June, and are at their lowest in December. During 1931–60, Braemar enjoyed an average of 1,120 hrs, while the annual average throughout the Highlands was less than 1,100 hrs. In Braemar the sunniest month is normally May, with an average of 167 hrs of sunshine, while December and January average only 18 and 24 hrs respectively (Brown & Clapperton, 2002).

The growing season

The Cairngorms massif lies at a latitude of 57°N. As a result, summer and winter day lengths vary greatly, and there is a limited growing season, particularly at altitude.

The growing season for grassland species is commonly defined as the number of days when the mean daily soil temperature at a depth of 0.3 m exceeds 6°C.

While this is typically achieved on about 210 days in lowland arable areas, the growing season throughout most of the Cairngorms area is likely to be shorter than this. Mean air temperature declines by 0.6–1.0°C for each 100 m increase in altitude. For example, the average temperature difference between Braemar and the summit of Ben Macdui is 2.2°C per 300 m of altitude. Differences are more pronounced in the spring (April to June), due to the chilling effect of snow on the tops. The potential growing season thus falls off rapidly with altitude, and decreases by 11–20 days for every 100 m rise in altitude.

Frost heave

Frost heave occurs when air at sub-freezing temperatures overlays damp soil with a temperature above freezing (Mitchell, 1993), and can greatly affect soil structure. The increase in soil volume causes the formation of 'ice-lenses' in the soil, and has many important effects. These include damage to roads, displacement of foundations and the cracking of masonry and pipelines. Frost heave also reduces the likelihood of vegetation being restored successfully on disturbed ground at high altitudes (as, for example, around the infrastructure of ski resorts). A further effect of frost heave occurs during thawing, when water that has accumulated in the upper soil horizons is released. If the bottom layers are still frozen, the meltwater cannot drain through them. The soil then becomes saturated and loses most of its strength. When this happens to soils supporting roads, fence posts, foundations and other structures, the roads develop potholes and fence posts and foundations can often become skewed. Thawing areas on slopes are also susceptible to landslides.

Characterising local climatic conditions

Birse and Dry (1970) and Birse and Robertson (1970) have characterised local climatic conditions in Scotland, based on the following measures.

Accumulated Temperature: the integrated excess or deficiency of temperature, with reference to the approximate temperature at which plant growth commences, over an extended period of time (usually one year), expressed as 'day °C'.

Accumulated Frost: defined as the integrated deficiency of temperature relative to 0°C (at which level the plant cells suffer frost injury) over an extended period of time (usually one year), expressed as 'day °C'.

Potential Water Deficit (PWD): the excess of potential evapotranspiration over rainfall in the course of one year.

Table 20.1. Climatic zones within the Cairngorms area, based on Accumulated Temperature and Potential Water Deficit (PWD) (after Birse & Dry, 1970), and Exposure and Accumulated Frost (after Birse & Robertson, 1970).

Accumulated Temperature and Potential Water Deficit

Climatic zone	Example locations	Accumulated Temperature range (day °C)	PWD (mm)
Extremely cold wet mountain[1]	Ben Macdui, Braeriach, Cairn Gorm and Beinn a' Bhuird summits, Glas Maol, the summits south of Braemar	0–275	Rainfall exceeds evapotranspiration by at least 500 mm in all months.
Very cold and wet mountain and upland	Cairngorm Mountains, Glenfeshie Forest, Ben Dearg, summits in the Angus Glens, the Ladder Hills and parts of the Monadhliath Hills within the National Park	275–550	0
Cold wet upland	Parts of Glenfeshie Forest, lower-lying areas north and south of the Cairngorms and around the Spittal of Glenshee	550–825	0
Cold rather wet foothills and uplands	Glen Mark, Forest of Birse, Cock Bridge, the foothills of Morven between Ballater and Strathdon, and Abernethy Forest	550–825	0–25
Cool wet foothills and uplands	Dalwhinnie, foothills north of Dalwhinnie	275–550	25–50
Cool rather wet lowlands, foothills and uplands	Drumgask, Strath Avon, Strathdon, Strathspey and slopes north and south of Crathie and Ballater	825–1,100	0–25
Cool moist lowlands and foothills	Braemar, Crathie, Kirkton of Glenbuchat, Kingussie	825–1,100	25–50
Fairly warm moist lowlands and foothills	Grantown-on-Spey, Boat of Garton, Nethy Bridge, Aviemore, Inverdruie, Kincraig, Ballater, low ground in Glen Tanar	1,110–1,375	25–50

Exposure and Accumulated Frost

Climatic zone	Example locations	Accumulated frost (day °C)	Wind speed (m/s)
Extreme exposure and extremely severe winters	Cairn Gorm, Braeriach, Ben Macdui and Beinn a' Bhuird high summits	>470	>8.0
Extreme exposure conditions and very severe winters	Summits of the Ladder Hills, north of the Spittal of Glenshee, high mountains at the heads of the Angus Glens	270–470	>8.0
Very exposed, with very severe winter	Cairngorm massif, Glenfeshie Forest, uplands north of the Spittal of Glenshee, the head of the Angus Glens	230–470	6.2–8.0
Exposed with very severe winters	Forest of Mar, Spittal of Glenshee, Balmoral Forest, other foothill regions	230–470	4.4–6.2
Exposed with rather severe winters	Badenoch, Tomintoul, Strathdon	110–230	4.4–6.2
Moderately exposed with rather severe winters	Nethy Bridge, Abernethy Forest, Insh, Kingussie, Drumgask, Crathie, Braemar	110–230	2.6–4.4
Moderately sheltered	Lowland areas around Kincraig, Inverdruie, Ballater and Crathie	110–230	<2.6

[1] Physiographic conditions were defined as follows. Mountain: >800 m; Upland: 400–800 m; Foothill: 200–400m; Lowland: 0–200 m.

Exposure: the influence of air movement on the development and survival of living organisms, over an extended period of time. Exposure has been measured using wind speed data from 34 stations across Scotland, taking into account the effects of relative humidity and temperature at high altitude (Birse & Robertson, 1970). Since these stations provided inadequate spatial cover in some areas, the visible effects of exposure on vegetation has also been recorded at numerous sites. Heather *Calluna vulgaris* and broad-leaved trees growing singly were assessed and five exposure categories adopted, as follows.

Sheltered:	excellent tree growth
Moderately exposed:	moderate tree growth
Exposed:	poor tree growth
Very exposed:	very short heather
Extremely exposed:	zero or prostrate heather

Examples of locations in the Cairngorms that fall within climatic zones based on these measures are given in Table 20.1.

Current global climate changes

Periodic variations in climate have occurred throughout the lifetime of the planet, based on the orbital eccentricities of the Earth around the sun, the axis of the planet's spin, volcanic eruptions and changes in solar irradiance. Models simulating temperature changes from such natural causes alone fit historic climate data trends well (Houghton *et al.*, 2001). Yet these show a discrepancy from the current annual global mean surface temperature, unless the effects of greenhouse gas emissions (which cause warming) and sulphate aerosols (which cool the atmosphere) are taken into account (Houghton *et al.*, 2001). This has led the Intergovernmental Panel on Climate Change (IPCC) to conclude that most of the observed warming over the past 50 years is likely to have been due to the increase in greenhouse gas concentrations (Houghton *et al.*, 2001).

Using models that incorporate various scenarios of greenhouse gas emission rates (from low to high) with simulations of temperature changes from natural causes, allows projections of future climate to be described and likely impacts to be considered. Precipitation changes and other extreme events (such as storms) accompany this differential warming of the atmosphere, making the

Table 20.2. Dates of complete snow melt for two snow patches on the west side of the Cairngorms massif

Year	Allt a'Mharcaidh	Ciste Mhearad (Glen Feshie)
2001	20 June	6 August
2002	4 June	7 July
2003	9 April	1 June

Based on snow-lie information provided by D. Duncan (SNH).

term 'climate change' more correct than 'global warming'. Unfortunately, emissions of long-lived greenhouse gases have a lasting effect on climate, such that even if global emissions were to stabilise, changes in global climate would be expected to continue for many years.

Global trends in climate over the last century

Temperature
Over the last century, the global average surface temperature rose by around 0.6°C ±0.2°C (Houghton *et al.*, 2001). A spatially averaged increase of 0.4°C for Scotland has been recorded from the late 1960s (Harrison, 1997). For higher latitudes in the Northern hemisphere, minimum temperatures rose at a greater rate (0.2°C decade^{-1}) than maximum temperatures (0.1°C decade^{-1}) (Folland *et al.*, 2001). Equivalent data for specific areas such as the Cairngorms are not readily available.

Precipitation
A comparison between annual rainfall totals recorded during 1941–70 and 1961–90 indicates that over this time period there were alterations in seasonal rainfall, with a decrease of around 10–15% in the summer half-year and an increase of 5–10% in the winter half-year (Mayes, 1996).

Snow-lie
During the 1950s and 1960s there was some evidence that snow-lie decreased (Manley, 1971). Harrison (1997) also noted evidence of a decrease in the duration of snow cover between 1964 and 1993 at Braemar. In the western part of the Cairngorms massif some snow patches have melted progressively earlier each summer (Table 20.2). None survived in Scotland through the summer of 2003 (Watson *et al.*, 2004)

Potential future climates

Using models produced by the IPCC, the UK Climate Impact Programme (UKCIP) has published four alternative climate scenarios for the 30-year period centred around the 2020s (i.e. 2011–40) (Hulme *et al.*, 2002). The four climate scenarios are described according to the level of greenhouse gas emissions likely up to that time period, namely, 'Low', 'Medium-Low', 'Medium-High' and 'High'. Each scenario describes changes from the average conditions between 1961 and 1990, so that '1°C warmer' means 1°C above the mean (usually annual or seasonal) for the 1961–90 30-year block.

The four scenarios were repeated for the 30-year blocks centred on the 2050s and the 2080s. The resolution of the models was at the 50 km scale, with some adjustment made for altitude. Note that these climate change scenarios are being revised and may be altered when new revisions are published in 2007.

It is important to recognise that climate 'scenarios' enable us to consider the 'what if' situation, but are not predictions. They are based on extensive monitoring and scientific modelling of atmospheric chemistry and climate, and take into consideration the time-lag between changing atmospheric chemistry and its effects on climate. Therefore, although we can be certain that there will be climatic changes, the degree of change is dependent upon greenhouse gases already in the atmosphere and those emitted today. Whether the local effect of cooling (as a result of the North Atlantic Drift significantly slowing or turning off) might occur sooner rather than later, and whether such an affect might over-ride, negate, or influence the warming effect of the global phenomenon at all, is not known, because this depends upon the degree and timing of the affect. However, the UKCIP scenarios used here include the effect of a weakening of the North Atlantic Drift over the coming century.

Temperature
By the 2020s, the Cairngorms region may be around 1°C warmer, whichever emissions scenario is followed. This increase is expected to be distributed evenly across all seasons. By the 2050s, the scenarios suggest a potential warming of 1.5°C, or possibly of 2°C, for the two highest emission scenarios. An exploration of the regional climate models for Scotland indicated that the degree of warming in winter may increase with elevation (altitude). In other words, upland areas may experience a greater degree of warming beyond the standard projections, perhaps equivalent to an additional *c.* 0.1°C increase per 100 m of elevation. (This prediction is derived from only one study, which used an emissions scenario similar to the UKCIP Medium-High scenario produced in 1998 (Hulme *et al.*, 2001). Any projection of change must therefore be treated with caution.)

Precipitation
All four UKCIP climate scenarios suggest that, by the 2020s, winter precipitation in the Cairngorms area may increase by 10%, whilst summers may become drier by about 10%. Overall annual precipitation is expected to remain within the bounds of natural variability. By the 2050s, winters may be 10–15% wetter and summers 20% drier, with the overall annual precipitation possibly declining by 10%.

With an increasing proportion of winter precipitation falling as rain, as opposed to snow (particularly in mountainous areas), the flow regimes of rivers are expected to alter greatly. Flow regimes may show increased 'flashiness', a higher flow during the winter months, and very low flow during the summer, accentuated by little or no input from snowmelt.

Snow-lie
It is possible that heavier winter precipitation at higher altitudes may continue to fall as snow for the next few years, leading to the development of larger, more persistent snow patches, some of which may occasionally persist throughout the summer (S.J. Harrison *et al.*, 2001). However, warmer springs would accelerate melting, particularly at lower altitudes, with snowbeds below 800 m being unlikely to survive over most summer months (S.J. Harrison *et al.*, 2001).

Wind
Winds are a dominant feature of the climate over the Cairngorms, but are more difficult to predict than temperature or precipitation because fewer data on wind patterns exist. Therefore, any projection of change must be treated with greater caution. UKCIP models indicate that average winds are not expected to change much before the 2080s (Hulme *et al.*, 2002). Westerly airflows are expected to remain dominant. The number of gales may increase by no more than one per year with respect to the 1961–1990 average (Hulme *et al.*, 2002). However, this prediction may be a reflection of difficulties experienced in modelling gale data statistically, since historical data have not been collected using standard methods or definitions.

Table 20.3. Possible changes in the extent of suitable climate space for species in the Cairngorms area by the 2050s (P. Harrison *et al.*, 2001). These are based on the UKCIP climate change scenarios published in 1998 (Hulme & Jenkins, 1998), which vary in detail from those published in 2002. Note that the simulated distribution of suitable climate space for each species is not necessarily the same as the species' actual distribution, nor is a change in the distribution of suitable climate necessarily equivalent to a change in the species' distribution, which will depend, *inter alia*, upon its ability to respond to climatic shifts.

Suitable climate space in the Cairngorms area likely to:			
a. Contract	**b. Expand**	**c. Show no net loss**	**d. Remain ubiquitous across Britain and Ireland**
Variegated Horsetail *Equisetum variegatum*	Marsh Helleborine *Epipactis palustris*	Marsh Gentian *Gentiana pneumonanthe*	Hare's-tail Cotton Grass *Eriophorum vaginatum*
Common Stork's-bill *Erodium cicutarium*	Common Rock-rose *Helianthemum nummularium*	Stiff Sedge *Carex bigelowii*[2]	Bog Myrtle *Myrica gale*
Bog Rosemary *Andromeda polifolia*	Great Burnet *Sanguisorba officinalis*	Dwarf Willow *Salix herbacea*[2]	*Sphagnum papillosum*
Toothed Wintergreen *Orthilia secunda*	Large Heath butterfly *Coenonympha tullia*	Trailing Azalea *Loiseleuria procumbens*[2]	Sanicle *Sanicula europaea*
Red Squirrel *Sciurus vulgaris*[1]	Yew *Taxus baccata*	Wood Crane's-bill *Geranium sylvaticum*[2]	Hard Fern *Blechnum spicant*
Twinflower *Linnaea borealis*[2]	Hay-scented Buckler Fern *Dryopteris aemula*	Cloudberry *Rubus chamaemorus*[2]	
Capercaillie *Tetrao urogallus*	Large Skipper butterfly *Ochlodes venata*	Great-crested Newt *Triturus cristatus*	
Oystercatcher *Haematopus ostralegus*	Azure Damselfly *Coenagrion puella*		
Snow Bunting *Plectrophenax nivalis*	Willow Tit *Parus montanus*		
	Nuthatch *Sitta europaea*		
	Yellow Wagtail *Motacilla flava*		

[1] Suitable climate space in Britain is expected to expand
[2] Suitable climate space in Britain is expected to contract

Possible impacts on the natural heritage

General effects

A mean annual increase of 1°C is associated with an isotherm shift of about 200–275 m uphill and 250–400 km northwards. This may effectively raise the lower altitudinal limit for some mountain species, potentially reducing their range in Scotland. All other factors being equal, organisms inhabiting Arctic-alpine habitat above 600 m in 1960–91 would have to move to an altitude of 800–875 m to experience a similar climate. It is estimated that a 1°C increase may reduce the area of alpine/sub-alpine habitat by about 90% across the whole of Scotland. This amount of warming is indicated by all four UKCIP scenarios for the 2020s (Hulme *et al.*, 2002). However, it is possible that the capacity of species at these lower altitudinal limits to respond to climate change may be considerably slower than the rate at which warming occurs. Indeed, at altitudes of over 3,000 m in the Alps, montane plants at the lowest limits of their altitude range moved uphill at a rate of only about 4 m per decade in response to a 0.7°C rise during the 20th century (Grabherr *et al.*, 1994).

It should be noted that the studies used in this chapter have not included the ecosystem changes that might occur as a result of changing phenologies (for example earlier budburst or nesting activities), nor have such models included changes in whole ecosystems (such as the arrival in Arctic-alpine areas of more vigorous species from lower elevations), or changes in the physical structure of peatlands due to changing hydrological regimes. Our understanding of the potential impacts of climate change on ecosystem processes and biotic interactions is, unfortunately, still limited. The scenarios of change for climate space for individual species can therefore only provide a platform of understanding for what might occur.

Overall effects on species distributions

With the retreat of southerly limits of suitable climate for northern species, a number of species in the Cairngorms might respond by contracting in range or even disappearing from the area. Table 20.3a lists nine species for which suitable climate may contract across the Cairngorms area. Note that species-specific suitable climates do not necessarily match the actual distributions of these species, since habitat management and other factors also influence their distributions. For example, Bog Rosemary[1] does not currently occur in the Cairngorms, although the current climate should be suitable for this species.

As suitable climate for more southerly species begins to extend into the Cairngorms area, new species from the more mobile groups, such as birds, butterflies and damselflies, could colonise. However, less mobile species, such as plants like Marsh Helleborine, Common Rock-rose, Great Burnet and Yew might not colonise, unless aided physically, despite suitable climate becoming available (Table 20.3b).

Areas with a suitable climate may decline across Britain and Ireland for some species, with the Cairngorms providing a last stronghold. These include montane species such as Stiff Sedge, Dwarf Willow, Trailing Azalea and Cloudberry, as well as at least one woodland/hay meadow species: Wood Crane's-bill (Table 20.3c). However, whilst suitable climate space for Wood Crane's-bill might decline across the rest of Britain, the extent of such climate space in the Cairngorms in the 2050s is still likely to exceed the current distribution of the species in the area, indicating

Areas in which the climate is suitable for species such as Dwarf Willow may decline across Britain and Ireland, with the Cairngorms providing a last stronghold.

Photo: *L. Gill*

[1] For scientific names, see Table 20.3.

that some other factor (possibly grazing pressure and/or habitat availability) is restricting its current range there. Suitable climate space for a number of other species may remain widespread across Britain and Ireland (Table 20.3d).

Arctic-alpine habitats and species

Montane habitats of moss heaths and those with Arctic-alpine dwarf shrubs, such as Alpine Bearberry *Arctostaphylos alpinus* and the distinctive sub-species of Crowberry *Empetrum nigrum hermaphroditum*, are expected to undergo a severe decline in range size. Land at or above 600 m in Scotland covers an area of 4,780 km^2, whereas land at or above 900 m covers only 335 km^2. Therefore, a warming of 1°C would mean a shift uphill of about 200–275 m, potentially meaning a decline of 93% in Arctic-alpine habitat area. Most of the remaining Arctic-alpine habitat in Scotland would be concentrated in the Cairngorms.

Arctic-alpine lichens at the southern edge of their ranges, *Alectoria ochroleuca* and *Cladonia botrytes* (Hill *et al.*, 1999) for example, are especially threatened. The loss of two other such species from the Cairngorms in the last few decades (*Bellemerea alpina* and *Hypogymnia intestiniformis*) is believed to have resulted from increasing temperatures (Gilbert, 2004). Populations of Arctic and sub-arctic plants, such as Curved Woodrush *Luzula arcuata*, Tufted Saxifrage *Saxifraga cespitosa* and Drooping Saxifrage *S. cernua*, restricted to altitudes above 700 m, are thus expected to decline in extent. A predictive model also indicated declines in the area of suitable climate space for Stiff Sedge, Dwarf Willow and Trailing Azalea throughout the first half of this century, although not for the Cairngorms area itself, which may remain as a last stronghold (P. Harrison *et al.*, 2001).

Similar models, determining potential shifts in suitable climate space for various bird species (P. Harrison *et al.*, 2001), also indicate a complete loss from the Cairngorms of suitable climate for Snow Bunting, based on the UKCIP 2020s and 2050s 'High' scenarios. This may also be true for other bird species, such as Ptarmigan *Lagopus mutus* and Dotterel *Charadrius morinellus* (see Chapter 18), as well as for Mountain Hare *Lepus timidus*. Other factors will influence the rate at which these species decline, however, particularly the rate at which their habitats change in response to climatic change.

The complexity of the relationship between climate, habitat and species makes it difficult to determine the impacts of climate change on a species' status. For example, a reduction in the number and extent of snow patches will adversely affect nationally important bryophyte communities (Chapter 13) and associated alpine invertebrate species, the latter forming an important component of the diet of the Snow Bunting. However, it is possible that some snow beds at the highest altitudes may persist for several decades if precipitation levels continue to increase over the winter months, causing the formation of dense snow-packs capable of withstanding higher temperatures.

It is also possible that lower-level montane habitats may become increasingly representative of upland heathland, although they may contain plants that are wind-clipped, if windspeeds remain high (as seems likely). A number of Arctic-alpine plants may decline as a result of being shaded out by plant species extending their ranges uphill, however. Conversely, if snow cover is reduced in exposed areas, Arctic-alpine vegetation types may be exposed to greater extremes of temperature and humidity, due to the loss of insulation provided by the snow (A. Macdonald, pers. comm.).

Woodlands

Native pinewoods may be expected to continue to grow on the infertile, strongly leached podsolic soils of the Cairngorms, if other non-climatic factors are favourable. A forest succession model applied to a range of tree species, including oak, beech and spruce, showed that with increased temperatures alone (leading to drought), Scots Pine could be favoured (Prentice *et al.*, 1991). If this model is accurate, Scots Pine would be expected to spread further uphill, assuming that grazing intensity is also reduced. However, at lower altitudes on more fertile soil, birch and oak are likely to become more prevalent. There is no climatic reason why ground flora shrubs in native pinewoods (Heather, Blaeberry and Juniper) should alter, although the ground flora under deciduous woodlands (such as upland oakwoods and birchwoods) may be affected by an increased duration of canopy cover. However, the overall species composition of each of the woodland ecosystems is likely to change. Species of conservation importance that are likely to experience some adverse effects from climate change include the Capercaillie *Tetrao urogallus*, the spider *Clubiona subsultans*, Cousin German Moth *Paradiarsia sobrina*, Black Falsebolete *Boletopsis leucomelaena* (whose only two British sites both lie within the Cairngorms; Chapter 11) the European rarity Green Shield-moss *Buxbaumia viridus* (Chapter 13), Twinflower *Linnaea borealis* and Small Cow-wheat *Melampyrum sylvaticum* (Hill *et al.*, 1999). It is likely that the two forest grouse species – Black Grouse *Tetrao tetrix* and Capercaillie – would be adversely affected if there is an increase in heavy rain events in early summer (as has been the case) (Moss *et al.*, 2001). Alternatively, the early summer may become drier, improving conditions for these species. Details of the local weather patterns are thus important.

Higher temperatures may enable oak to become more prevalent in the Cairngorms straths, while Scots Pine may spread further uphill, assuming that grazing intensity on the hill permits their expansion.
Photo: *L. Gill*

In Scotland, suitable climate space for the Red Squirrel is expected to become tightly centralised on the Cairngorms area in the next 50–70 years, but is expected to expand over most of England and Wales during this time (P. Harrison *et al.*, 2001). These calculations do not, however, take account of any potential effects of climate change on the encroaching Grey Squirrel *Sciurus carolinensis* population. Suitable climate for Twinflower is also expected to become more tightly centralised on the Cairngorms area over the same time period but, unlike the Red Squirrel, the Twinflower is expected to lose suitable climate space across most of Britain. Since the current distribution of the Twinflower lies within the climate limits of scenarios for the 2050s, it is possible that impacts on this species may not be evident before then.

Theoretically, most of the above-mentioned species would be helped by encouraging the regeneration and expansion of native pinewoods. Controlling the ingression of oaks into historical pine strongholds would help maintain the Red Squirrel population by preventing colonisation by Grey Squirrel. Whilst some species may decline in extent it is likely that new, highly mobile species will colonise the area. Models indicate that the climate will become suitable for species such as the Willow Tit *Parus montanus* and Nuthatch *Sitta europaea* (P. Harrison *et al.*, 2001), although whether these species succeed in reaching and colonising the Cairngorms will depend on other factors.

Grasslands, heathlands and moorlands

Moorland shrubs such as Heather, Cross-leaved Heath *Erica tetralix* and Bell Heather *Erica cinerea* have a wide distribution, extending as far south as continental Europe, so are unlikely to be adversely affected by any of the climate scenarios outlined for the area. The warming effects of climate change may, however, encourage the extension of trees into open heaths and moors. Tree development would be dependant upon a low intensity or absence of grazing. Both heather and tree growth would be stunted or wind-clipped if wind speeds were to remain high.

Hay meadows might gain southern species, such as the Great Burnet *Sanguisorba officinalis*, if their dispersal capabilities enable them to keep pace with the northward extension of suitable climate space and other factors, such as soil, are suitable (P. Harrison *et al.*, 2001). Suitable climate space for Wood Crane's-bill, although expected to disappear from other parts of Britain, should remain within the Cairngorms area (P. Harrison *et al.*, 2001).

All of these habitats should expect to see a gain in the number of bird and winged invertebrate species from more southerly locations, because these mobile species are likely to be able to take advantage of the northward advancement of a warmer climate.

It is possible that drier summers will be less favourable for ticks, perhaps reducing the frequency of outbreaks of diseases such as louping ill in Red Grouse *Lagopus lagopus* and Lyme disease in people. Whilst drier summers might also reduce the prevalence of Heather Beetle *Lochmaea suturalis* outbreaks, which cause the greatest damage in relatively humid conditions, it is not clear what factors limit this pest. It might be that a reduced prevalence of very wet and cool summers is more significant than an increasing number of dry summers (A. Macdonald, pers. comm.). With the current altitudinal restriction of Heather Beetle being 300–400 m, it is likely that outbreaks will occur increasingly higher up the hill (A. Macdonald, pers. comm.).

Peatlands

Increases in annual temperature and annual precipitation would suggest a favourable future for peatland species. However, with drier summers and heavy rain events in autumn and winter, peatland habitats may suffer more extensive erosion. Nonetheless, models indicate that suitable climate space for species such as the Hare's-tail Cotton Grass *Eriophorum vaginatum*, Bog Myrtle *Myrica gale* and *Sphagnum papillosum* may remain more-or-less constant across Britain and Ireland. While suitable climate space for Bog Rosemary may contract in range, it is expected to remain in the Cairngorms area over the next 50–80 years (P. Harrison *et al.*, 2001). At present, Bog Rosemary and Marsh Gentian *Gentiana pneumonanthe* do not currently occur in the Cairngorms, although the current climate should be suitable. The Cairngorms may therefore be a key conservation area for these two species, if populations can be established through human intervention.

A key component of mountain bogs in Scotland is Cloudberry. By 2041–70, the range of suitable climate may have severely contracted across Britain, but is not expected to decline from the Cairngorms area. The Cairngorms area is therefore likely to remain a stronghold for this particular plant and the habitat it forms.

Freshwaters

With drier summers and a greater level of precipitation in the winter months, the extremes of stream flow are expected to magnify. With heavy rain events in the winter half year, more severe washouts of redds in the upper reaches of streams in north-west Scotland were observed during the late 1990s. Flooding along water-courses may become more common, as a result of heavy rain events and, perhaps, rapid snow melt in spring. Higher water temperatures, as observed in Deeside during December to May (Langan *et al.*, 2001), will have important implications for stream ecology, which have yet to be determined.

Discussion

Uncertainty over climate change impacts

This chapter has made use of models which outline potential changes in the distribution of species-specific climate space under different climate change scenarios (e.g. P. Harrison *et al.*, 2001) as well as studies that have used expert judgement to assess the likely effects of climate change on habitats and species (e.g. Hill *et al.*, 1999). These studies have considered only a limited number of habitats and species. The omission of a given habitat or species from this chapter should therefore not be taken to suggest that it will not necessarily be affected by climate change.

It is important to recognise that the appearance of suitable climate space is not necessarily indicative of the appearance of a species in the Cairngorms area. Most species, particularly vascular plants and trees, are limited in their dispersal capability and are unlikely to keep pace with advancing northern margins of suitable climate. Factors likely to limit their dispersal rate include slow reproductive strategies and the age to reproductive maturity. The same applies to the disappearance of climate space for a species; there are some species that may 'hang on', and until we know enough about extinction processes, we will not be able to predict which ones might.

Other factors likely to affect the Cairngorms area

Across the Cairngorms, atmospheric deposition of nitrogen oxides and nitrogen in the form of ammonia/ammonium are at a level[2] that can affect vegetative communities of low-nutrient status, such as montane and heath habitats (Fowler *et al.*, 2002). Effects include eutrophication and the acidification of lochs, especially montane lochans on base-poor geology. (Until the late-1980s, nitrogen was not recognised as an acidifying pollutant as was sulphur, but has been found to contribute significantly to acidification.) A further effect is the formation of ground-level ozone[3] from nitrogen oxides combining with volatile organic compounds during daylight. These have increased in concentration in the atmosphere as a result of combustion processes. Ground-level ozone can reduce the productivity of some plants. Although it is not yet certain as to how ozone affects ecosystems, it is known to be more persistent in rural areas.

Conclusions

Climate change is, on balance, expected to have a negative impact on the Cairngorms area, particularly in terms of the number and extent of Arctic-alpine species. It is likely that marked changes in species composition could be seen as early as 2010–20 if average temperatures continue to rise at the rate witnessed during the 1980s–90s.

Whilst a reduction in the extent of suitable climate space for a number of species is likely, how each species responds may also relate to the condition of its habitat and the way in which other biological, physical and chemical alterations arising from climate change influence habitat condition. Predicting what these might be, and selecting management likely to mitigate their effects, is likely to remain a challenge for a number of years. The establishment of an Environmental Change Network Site in the Allt a' Mharcaidh catchment is just one means by which this challenge can be tackled, with its simultaneous recording of climatic, pollutant and management trends alongside biological, physical and chemical responses. A comprehensive strategy to determine current climatic trends and natural heritage responses across the Cairngorms is required in order to identify relationships and trends upon which adaptive action may be based in the coming years.

References

Beniston, M. & Tol, R.S.J. (1998). Europe. In: Watson, R.T., Zinyowera. M.C. & Moss, R.H. (eds.), *The Regional Impact of Climate Change: An Assessment of Vulnerability.* Intergovernmental Panel on Climate Change, Working Group II. Cambridge University Press: Cambridge.

Birse, E.L. & Dry, F.T. (1970). *Assessment of climatic conditions in Scotland. 1. Based on Accumulated Temperature and Potential Water Deficit.* The Macaulay Institute for Soil Research: Aberdeen.

Birse, E.L. & Robertson, L. (1970). *Assessment of climatic conditions in Scotland. 2. Based on Exposure and accumulated frost.* The Macaulay Institute for Soil Research: Aberdeen.

---

[2] Currently *c.* 5-20 kg per ha per year (Fowler *et al.*, 2002).
[3] Ground-level ozone should not be confused with stratospheric ozone which occurs above the biosphere and sieves out harmful UV radiation.

Brown, I.M. & Clapperton, C.M. (2002). The Physical Geography. In: Gimingham, C.H. (ed.), *The Ecology, Land Use and Conservation of the Cairngorms*. Packard Publishing Limited: Chichester.

Brown, R.D. (1998). Spatial and temporal variability of Canadian monthly snow depths 1946–1996. *Atmosphere-Ocean* 36: 37–54.

Ferguson, R.I. (1985). High densities, water equivalent and melt rates of snow in the Cairngorms Mountains, Scotland. *Weather* 40: 272–276.

Folland, C.K., Karl, T.R., Christy, J.R., Clarke, R.A., Gruza, G.V., Jouzel, J., Mann, M.E., Oerlemans, J., Salinger, M.J. & Wang, S.-W. (2001). Observed Climate Variability and Change. In: Houghton, J.T., Ding, Y., Griggs, D.J., Noguer, M., van der Linden, P.J., Dai, X., Maskell, K. & Johnson, C.A. (eds.), *Climate Change 2001: The Scientific Basis. Contribution of Working Group I to the Third Assessment Report of the Intergovernmental Panel on Climate Change*. Cambridge University Press: Cambridge.

Fowler, D., Dragosits, U., Pitcairn, C., Sutton, M., Hall, J., Roy, D. & Weidemann, A. (2002). *Deposition of acidity and nitrogen and exposure of terrestrial surfaces to ozone in Scotland: mapping critical loads, critical levels and exceedances*. SNH Research, Survey and Monitoring Report No. 169. SNH: Perth.

Gilbert, O. (2004). *Lichens*. Naturally Scottish Series. SNH: Perth.

Grabherr, G., Gottfried, M. & Pauli, H. (1994). Climate effects on mountain plants. *Nature* 369: 448.

Hantel, M., Ehrendorfer, M. & Haslinger, A. (2000). Climate sensitivity of snow cover duration in Austria. *International Journal of Climatology* 20: 615–640.

Harrison, P., Berry, P.M & Dawson, T.E. (eds.) (2001). *Climate change and Nature Conservation in Britain and Ireland: MONARCH – Modelling Natural Resource Responses to Climate Change*. The UK Climate Impact Programme Technical Report: Oxford.

Harrison, S.J. (1997). Changes in Scottish climate. *Botanical Journal of Scotland* 49(2): 287–300.

Harrison, S.J., Winterbottom, S. & Johnson, R. (2001). *Climate Changes and Changing Snowfall Patterns in Scotland*. Scottish Executive Central Research Unit: Edinburgh.

Hill, M.O., Downing, T.E., Berry, P.M., Coppins. B.J., Hammond, P.S., Marquiss, M., Roy, D.B., Telfer, M.G. & Welch, D. (1999). *Climate Changes and Scotland's Natural Heritage: an Environmental Audit*. SNH Research, Survey and Monitoring Report No. 132. SNH: Perth.

Houghton, J.T., Ding, Y., Griggs, D.J., Noguer, M., van der Linden, P.J., Dai, X., Maskell, K. & Johnson, C.A. (eds.) (2001). *Climate Change 2001: The Scientific Basis*. Contribution of Working Group I to the Third Assessment Report of the Intergovernmental Panel on Climate Change. Cambridge University Press: Cambridge

Hulme, M. & Jenkins, G.J. (1998). *Climate Change Scenarios for the United Kingdom: Scientific Report*. UK Climate Impacts Programme Technical Report No. 1. Climatic Research Unit, University of East Anglia: Norwich.

Hulme, M., Crossley, J. & Lu, X. (2001). *An Exploration of Regional Climate Change Scenarios for Scotland*. The Scottish Executive Central Research Unit: Edinburgh.

Hulme, M., Jenkins, G.J., Lu, X., Turnpenny, J.R., Mitchell, T.D., Jones, R.G., Lowe, J., Murphy, J.M., Hassell, D., Boorman, P., McDonald, R. & Hill, S. (2002). *Climate Change Scenarios for the United Kingdom: The UKCIP02 Scientific Report*. Tyndall Centre for Climate Change Research, University of East Anglia: Norwich.

Langan, S., Johnston, L., Donaghy, M.J., Youngson, A.F., Hay, D.W. & Soulsby, C. (2001). Variation in river water temperatures in an upland stream over a 30-year period. *The Science of the Total Environment* 265: 199–211.

Manley, G. (1971). Scotland's semi-permanent snows. *Weather* 26: 458–471.

Mayes, J. (1996). Spatial and temporal fluctuations of monthly rainfall in British Isles and variations in the mid-latitude westerly circulation. *International Journal of Climatology* 16: 585–596.

McGowan, G.M., Truscott, A.M., French, D.D., Hall, R.L., Palmer, S.C.F. (2000). An assessment of the environmental impacts of naturally regenerating native pinewood, montane scrub and tree-lines on the northern slopes of Cairn Gorm. Report to Forest Enterprise.

Meteorological Office (1963). *Averages of temperature for Great Britain and Northern Ireland, 1931–1960*. HMSO: London.

Mitchell, J.K. (1993). *Fundamentals of soil behaviour*. John Wiley & Sons: New York.

Moss, R., Oswald, J. & Baines, D. (2001). Climate change and breeding success: decline of the capercaille in Scotland. *Journal of Animal Ecology* 70: 47-61.

Osborne, T.J., Hulme, M., Jones, P.D & Basnett, T.A. (2000). Observed trends in the daily intensity of UK precipitation. *International Journal of Climatology* 20: 347–364.

Prentice, I.C., Sykes, M.T. & Cramer, W. (1991). The possible dynamic response of northern forests to global warming. *Global Ecology and Biogeography Letters* 1(5): 129–135.

Watson, A., Pottie, J. & Duncan, D. (2004). No Scottish snow patches survive through the summer of 2003. *Weather* 59: 125–126.

Ye, H. (2000). Decadal variability of Russian winter snow accumulation and its associations with Atlantic sea-surface temperature anomalies. *International Journal of Climatology* 20: 1709–1728.

Additional reading

Alonso, I., Hartley S.E. & Thurlow M. (2001). Competition between heather and grasses on Scottish moorlands: interacting effects of nutrient enrichment and grazing regime. *Journal of Vegetation Science* 12: 249–260.

AQEG (2003). *Nitrogen dioxide in the United Kingdom*. Draft Report, Department for Environment, Food and Rural Affairs, Scottish Executive, Welsh Assembly Government and Department of the Environment in Northern Ireland: London.

Bobbink, R, Hornung, M. & Roelofs, J.G.M. (1996). Empirical nitrogen critical loads for natural and semi-natural ecosystems. In: *Manual on Methodologies and Criteria for Mapping Critical Levels and Geographical Areas Where They Are Exceeded*. UN ECE Convention on long-range trans-boundary air pollution, Federal Environmental Agency: Dessau.

Fangmeier, A., Hadwiger-Fangmeier A., Van der Eerden L.J.M. & Jager H.J. (1994). Effects of atmospheric ammonia on vegetation – a review. *Environmental Pollution* 86: 43–82.

Fowler, D., Cape, J.N., Leith, I.D., Choularton, T.W., Gay, M.J. & Jones, A. (1988). The influence of altitude on rainfall composition at Great Dun Fell. *Atmospheric Environment* 22: 1355–1362.

Haines-Young, R.H., Barr, C.J., Black, H.I.J., Briggs, D.J., Bunce, R.G.H., Clarke, R.T., Cooper, A., Dawson, F.H., Firbank, L.G., Fuller, R.M., Furse, M.T., Gillespie, M.K., Hill, R., Hornung, M., Howard, D.C., McCann, T., Morecroft, M.D., Petit, S., Sier, A. R.J., Smart, S.M., Smith, G.M., Stott, A.P., Stuart, R.C. & Watkins, J.W. (2000). *Accounting for nature: assessing habitats in the UK countryside*. Department of the Environment, Natural Environmental Research Council, Rotherham.

Hale, S.E., Quine, C.P. & Suarez, J.C. (1998). Climatic conditions associated with tree-lines of Scots pine and birch in Highland Scotland. *Scottish Forestry* 52: 70–76.

Hanson, P.J. & Lindberg, S.E. (1991). Dry deposition of reactive nitrogen compounds – a review of leaf, canopy and non-foliar measurements. *Atmospheric Environment Part A – General Topics* 25: 1615–1634.

Hartley, S.E. (1997). The effects of grazing and nutrient inputs on grass-heather competition. *Botanical Journal of Scotland* 49: 315–324.

Hornung, M., Sutton, M.A. & Wilson R.B. (eds.) (1995). *Mapping and modelling of critical loads for nitrogen – a workshop report*. Grange-over-Sands, Cumbria, UK. UN-ECE Convention on Long Range Transboundary Air Pollution, Working Group for Effects, 24–26 October 1994. Institute of Terrestrial Ecology: Edinburgh.

Kerr, A. & McLeod, A. (2001). *Potential Adaptation Strategies for Climate Change in Scotland*. Report to the Scottish Executive.

Milne, J.A. & Hartley, S.E. (2001). Upland plant communities – sensitivity to change. *Catena* 42(2–4): 333–343.

Quine, C.P. & White, I.M.S. (1993). *Revised windiness scores for the windthrow hazard classification: the revised scoring method*. Forestry Commission Research Information Note No. 230. Forestry Commision: Edinburgh.

Quine, C.P. & White, I.M.S. (1994). Using the relationship between rate of tatter and topographic variables to predict site windiness in upland Britain. *Forestry* 67: 245–256.

Sutton, M.A., Dragosits U., Tang Y.S., Fowler D. (2000). Ammonia emissions from nonagricultural sources in the UK. *Atmospheric Environment* 34 (6): 855–869.

Sutton, M.A., Fowler, D. & Moncrieff, J.B. (1993). The Exchange of Atmospheric Ammonia with Vegetated Surfaces .1. Unfertilized Vegetation. *Quarterly Journal of the Royal Meteorological Society* 119 (513): 1023–1045.

Thompson, D.B.A. & Baddeley, J. (1991). Some effects of acidic deposition on montane Racomitrium lanuginosum heaths. In: Woodin, S.J. & Farmer, A.M. (eds.), *The Effects of Acid Deposition on Nature Conservation in Great Britain*. NCC Focus on Nature Conservation Report 26. Nature Conservancy Council: Peterborough. pp. 17–28.

UKRGAR (1997). *Acid Deposition in the United Kingdom*. Fourth Report of the Review Group on Acid Rain. DETR: London.

21. DEER MANAGEMENT

John Thomson, Jenny Bryce, Ro Scott and David Horsfield

Introduction

Deer play many important roles in the Cairngorms. Red Deer, especially, are easily observed, enhance people's enjoyment of the hills and hence contribute to local tourism. As grazers, deer are also necessary for maintaining important habitats and, indirectly, species that depend on these habitats. As game on sporting estates, they make a significant input to the local economy. However, since deer numbers, patterns of range use and the management associated with deer can lead to negative impacts on the natural heritage, a careful balance is required. This chapter introduces the deer populations of the Cairngorms, describes efforts to monitor them and their impacts, and discusses the policy context and potential mechanisms for achieving this balance.

Deer populations

The Cairngorms area has two native, free-ranging deer species: the Red Deer *Cervus elaphus* and Roe Deer *Capreolus capreolus*. It also has a semi-domesticated herd of Reindeer *Rangifer tarandus* (which became extinct in Britain *c.* 8,200 years ago), and two introduced species: Fallow Deer *Dama dama* and Sika Deer *Cervus nippon*. Although there are thus five deer species present, this chapter will concentrate mainly on one – the Red Deer – as this species has the most significant impacts on the natural heritage and local economy, and is, accordingly, the focus of a great deal of management effort and resources.

Red Deer are the largest wild deer in the United Kingdom. They are essentially woodland animals that have adapted to the open hill. Although Red Deer in woodlands are generally more solitary, their open hill counterparts tend to congregate in single-sex groups which mix only during the annual rut or breeding season. On the open hill, male and female groups routinely establish separate patterns of movement influenced by weather conditions, the availability of grazing and patterns of disturbance; all of which can have both seasonal and diurnal influences. Red Deer are distributed throughout the Cairngorms area, utilising habitats at all altitudes, from the straths to the high tops. Range-use has a diurnal and seasonal pattern (Whitfield, 2001a), the highest ground being occupied only in the summer and particularly at night. Red Deer herding behaviour results in a concentration of grazing impacts caused by the movement of large numbers of heavy animals on fragile habitats. Hinds usually produce a single calf each year.

Roe Deer are essentially creatures of woodland and woodland edge, browsing on trees and associated ground flora. Increasingly, however, they can be found on agricultural and horticultural land, and on the open hill. They can have significant local impacts, particularly on woodland, but as both males and females are territorial, densities are largely self-regulating. Although active throughout the 24-hour period, their activity peaks around dawn and dusk. Twin kids are common in a healthy adult population.

In the Cairngorms, Roe Deer are widespread in woodlands and straths at low- to mid-altitudes, but do not routinely utilise the high tops. Due to their preference for wooded habitats, data on numbers and densities are not as readily available as they are for Red Deer. Being territorial, Roe Deer populations tend to be more evenly distributed than those of the more group-living Red Deer.

Both the Red and the Roe Deer have been recorded in every 10-km square in the Cairngorms area, and showed no substantial change in their gross distribution between 1993 and 2000; the most recent dates for which data are available (British Deer Society, 2002). There is, however, anecdotal evidence of a range expansion by Red Deer on the north and north-east periphery of the Cairngorms area (Thomson, pers. obs.).

Red Deer are essentially woodland animals that have adapted to the open hill. At times they tend to concentrate on lower open ground and in woodlands, where they may suppress natural regeneration through grazing and browsing.

Photo: *M. Hamblin*

Thomson, J., Bryce, J., Scott, R. & Horsfield, D. (2006). Deer management. In: Shaw, P. & Thompson, D.B.A. (eds.). *The Nature of the Cairngorms: Diversity in a changing environment*. The Stationery Office. pp. 367-379.

Roe Deer are creatures of woodlands, but can increasingly be found on agricultural and horticultural land, and on the open hill. In the Cairngorms they are widespread in woodlands and straths at low- to mid-altitudes, but do not routinely utilise the high tops.

Photo: *L. Campbell*

Sika Deer are now widespread throughout Scotland, following their introduction to deer parks in the 1860s. Their range largely overlaps that of Red Deer, both in terms of distribution and habitat use. Intermediate in size between Red and Roe, they are predominantly woodland animals, solitary in nature and are relatively uncommon on the open hill during daylight. Sika hybridise with Red Deer, particularly where Sika stags – the primary pioneers – are isolated from Sika hinds. Sika can have significant impacts on woodland, through grazing and bole scoring of commercial timber crops. Sika hinds produce a single calf annually.

Sika are now well-established north-west of the Spey, but are more sporadically distributed on both the northern and southern fringes of the Cairngorms. Sika extended their range between 1993 and 2000, when isolated occurrences were recorded for the first time in Deeside and Strath Avon (British Deer Society, 2002).

Fallow Deer in the Cairngorms are the result of small-scale introduction or inadvertent release, and have not colonised widely in the area. They are present around Blair Atholl and on the southern edge of the Cairngorms, where their range showed little change between 1993 and 2000. They are intermediate in size between Red and Roe Deer. Their social behaviour is significantly influenced by density and habitat. In predominantly woodland environments, single-sex groups are common, but on more open or agricultural ground large, mixed-sex groups can be seen year-round. A single calf is produced annually.

The introduced herd of *Reindeer* in the Glenmore area is managed on a semi-domesticated basis. They currently number about 50, and are hefted to the north-facing slopes of Cairn Gorm and Cairn Lochan, which they have occupied since the 1950s. (Cairngorm Reindeer Company, pers. comm.). A backup herd of approximately 100 is kept in Glenlivet.

Deer numbers

Because of their distribution throughout the Cairngorms, their large body size and herding behaviour, Red Deer are the most important deer species in terms of their influence on other natural heritage features. Historically, monitoring of Red Deer trends has concentrated mainly on counts rather than impacts. The Deer Commission for Scotland has previously undertaken a rolling programme of counts on the open hill. These data for Red Deer populations in the Cairngorms are available in the Annual Reports of the Deer Commission for Scotland (DCS) (e.g. Deer Commission for Scotland, 2000, 2001a, 2002). However, DCS is increasingly targeting its own resources on priority sites at which there is concern over impacts associated with deer. As a result, there is an increasing dependence on estates taking the lead on counting elsewhere, within clearly defined Count Areas. Seven of these Count Areas lie wholly or partly within the Cairngorms area (Figure 21.1), covering 87% of Cairngorms National Park and 85% of the Cairngorms area. The most recent data for these Count Areas are given in Table 21.1.

Deer Management Groups (DMGs), which are discussed in more detail later, exist in five of the Deer Commission for Scotland count areas (the exceptions being the Morven, Aberdeenshire, and Cabrach/Glenfiddich Count Areas), some of which span more than one DMG. The highest Red Deer densities recorded have been in East Grampian; specifically, in Glen Isla/Glen Shee DMG in 2000 (Table 21.2; Figure 21.2).

There have also been a number of studies of local Red Deer numbers. These include the SNH's Mountain Plateau Ecology Project, which gathered information on local summer deer densities at 10 high-altitude sites within the main Cairngorm massif, and at eight sites in the Drumochter Hills, between 1987 and 1999 (Whitfield, 2001b). Deer densities in the Cairngorms massif, expressed as the number of deer per day per km^2, were generally low. Exceptions were: Mòine Mhór, which attracted deer from both the Feshie and Mar Lodge sides (*c.* 2-98 per day per km^2); Ben Avon (up to *c.* 21); and Beinn a' Bhuird (up to *c.* 4).

In the Drumochter Hills Red Deer were found to be using montane bogs on the east side of the A9 during the day and the slopes between the plateau and the A9 at night. Counts there ranged from *c.* 11 to 93 per day per km^2. The highest densities were found in the South and Central Grampians on Sron Bhuirich (up to 330). Numbers in Glen Shee were very variable, being used rarely by large herds, peaking at 665 on Glas Maol in 1994. In the Monadhliaths, densities were low on Creag Meagaidh and Cam Liath (<0.5 per day per km^2), but higher to the south around Loch Ericht and Ben Alder (*c.* 8), the plateau of which was popular with calving hinds.

Forestry Commission Scotland has also carried out significant work within the Glen Feshie catchment, both in woodland and on the open hill, using dung counting techniques. The work was carried out on contract by Strath Caulaidh Limited in 2002, to inform deer cull targets in connection with a deer population control agreement between DCS, FCS and SNH. At the time of the survey Roe Deer occurred at an estimated mean density of 8 per km^2, while the equivalent figure for Red Deer was 16 per km^2. Red Deer density estimates varied substantially in different parts of the area: from 3 per km^2 on the highest hill ground to 35–45 per km^2 in open canopy semi-natural woodland.

Importantly, deer do not utilise all parts of their range evenly, so some areas are subject to much higher grazing pressure than others. In particular, numbers are concentrated on the lower open ground and in woodlands during bad weather and locally in the uplands on areas with richer soils. Counts inevitably provide a snapshot of deer numbers, and may not provide a representative picture of the normal distribution pattern. Hence, their ecological impact. Considerable caution therefore needs to be exercised in the use of count data as the basis for management. While analysis of deer numbers can be a useful tool by which to monitor population dynamics and

Deer information on display to visitors at Mar Lodge Estate.
Photo: *L. Gill*

Table 21.1. Red Deer population trends in Cairngorms Count Areas (from Deer Commission for Scotland Annual Reports, 1986–2003). Count areas that lie largely outwith the Cairngorms National Park are shown in *italics*. Note that counts, densities and trends are not directly comparable, due to differences in count periods.

Count Area		Year	Most recent count:				Gross[1] density (km^{-2})	Mean annual change	Period
			Stags	Hinds	Calves	Total			
19	*Monadhliaths*	1998	8,177	10,999	3,757	22,933	11.9	+2.0%	1987–1998
20	Cabrach/Glenfiddich	2000	465	895	203	1,563	3.1	-3.9%	1992–2000
21	Cairngorms/West Grampians	2001	12,502	16,442	5,316	34,260	13.3	+1.3%	1995–2001
22	East Grampians	1994	8,560	12,853	2,884	24,297	14.9	-0.6%	1986–1994
24	*Corrour/Ben Alder/Ardverikie*	1998	3,834	3,960	1,451	9,245	17.1	-0.4%	1986–1998
25	East Loch Ericht [2]	2003	2,181	4,096 [3]		6,277	17.8	[no change]	1996–2003
37	Morven (Aberdeenshire)	1995	145	37	12	194	1.0	[only 1 dataset]	

[1] Calculated by dividing the total number of deer by the total Count Area. The areas of lochs and other areas inaccessible to deer have not been subtracted. These figures therefore represent minimum average deer densities across the whole range. Winter densities will be considerably higher because only the lower-altitude parts of the range are used. Similarly, these figures give no indication of local variation in deer density.

[2] In East Loch Ericht Count Area only the (smaller) DMG area was counted in 2003. Deer numbers from the DMG area in 1996 were therefore used for comparison.

[3] Hinds and calves were not differentiated.

the effectiveness of management policies, where management objectives are primarily determined by nature conservation, deer management should be driven by habitat condition rather than by numbers of deer *per se*. Equally, in the analysis of apparent trends in deer numbers, it is desirable that comparisons should be 'like for like', taking account of timing, weather conditions and the nature of the ground. In count areas that have a mixture of open hill and accessible woodland, a comparable approach to recording woodland and open hill populations is essential, in order to maintain comprehensive records.

In the absence of natural predators such as the Wolf *Canus lupis*, deer are regulated by their food supply and by human intervention, in the form of culling and deer stalking. Deer control serves to avoid density-related impacts on herd physiology, and reduces damage to habitats within the deer range. Culling of Red Deer, especially of hinds, has, however, consistently lagged behind recruitment rates, and hence has generally failed to prevent an increase in overall numbers (Staines & Balharry, 2002) with consequences for grazing impacts on habitats. There are, however, several examples of local population reductions that have enabled trees and scrub to regenerate well. Red Deer numbers fell in the Northern Corries in the 1940s and 1950s (Watson, 1997), before starting to increase again in the late 1980s. During this period scrubby trees and shrubs regenerated from the woodland

edge at around 500 m, up to and beyond *c.* 650 m (Miller & Cummins, 1982). Other examples of habitat improvements brought about by reducing deer numbers include the natural regeneration of trees and shrubs at the RSPB Abernethy Reserve and SNH holdings at Creag Meagaidh and Invereshie.

Impacts

Wild deer populations can have a significant impact on their habitat. Their grazing and browsing can substantially modify the species composition and structure of vegetation, and strongly influence ecological processes, particularly woodland regeneration (Kirby *et al.*, 1994). The physical impact of trampling can also adversely affect fragile vegetation, exacerbating the effects of climate, and can destroy the nests and eggs of ground-nesting birds (Whitfield, 2001b). In addition, human activities associated with deer management can impact on natural heritage features. Examples include the use of all-terrain vehicles and the imposition of fencing on wild land. They may also affect people's ability to enjoy the natural heritage through, for example, uncertainties over access during the stalking season or physical impediments to access through deer fencing. Grazing and trampling impacts associated with fencing are examined in more detail below.

Table 21.2. Gross Red Deer population density in each Deer Management Group or sub-Group (calculated from digitised data supplied by the Deer Commission for Scotland). Count areas that lie largely outwith Cairngorms National Park are shown in *italics*.

Deer Management (sub-) Group	Year	Total deer	Gross density (km⁻²)
Monadhliaths[1]	1998	22,879	13.0
West Grampian: Cairngorm/Speyside	2001	8,358	7.8
East Grampian: Upper Deeside	2001	7,088	11.6
East Grampian: Deeside	1994	6,355	12.2
Mid West Association: Ardverikie/BA	1998	9,245	16.2
East Grampian: Glen Dye	1994	1,542	9.6
East Grampian: Angus Glens	1994	10,313	11.5
West Grampian: Tayside	2001	17,860	22.2
East Loch Ericht	2003	6,277	17.8
East Grampian: Glen Isla/Glen Shee	2000	5,037	31.0

[1] Although this DMG has the same name as a Count Area in Table 21.1, the DMG covers a smaller area. Some of the deer counted were outwith the DMG boundary. Therefore, although based on the same 1998 count data, the number of deer appears lower and the density higher than in Table 21.1.

Grazing and trampling by Red Deer

It is difficult to separate the effects of grazing by deer and sheep. Impacts from both are therefore considered together in this section. Long-term effects of grazing by both deer and sheep in the uplands include the prevention of woodland and scrub regeneration and the restriction of species sensitive to grazing, including tall-herbs and many trees and shrubs, to localities inaccessible to grazing animals (see Chapter 14). Grazing effects include the suppression of growth and flowering and, where persistently heavy, the death of plants, such as Heather *Calluna vulgaris* and Blaeberry *Vaccinium myrtillus*. High concentrations of Red Deer and sheep can also cause changes in the plant composition of communities, and damage to soils by trampling, dunging and urination.

In Scandinavia, where man-induced burning and grazing is less intense, an extensive zone of subalpine and alpine scrub occurs both above and below the treeline. In the Cairngorms, grazing by both Red Deer and/or sheep, probably combined with burning, has resulted in the loss of virtually all such scrub between about 500 and 800 m. Remnants of scrub communities can be found mainly on rock ledges and only very locally in the open. Juniper *Juniperus communis* scrub, which is more resistant to grazing than other species, is locally abundant at high altitude. Montane willow scrub is now almost wholly confined to inaccessible localities by grazing pressures, as are tall-herb communities. Current grazing levels in the Cairngorms are generally too high to allow either community to prosper.

Blanket bog is particularly susceptible to trampling, which causes localised loss of *Sphagnum* cover and contributes to erosion. The characteristic Woolly-fringe Moss *Racomitrium lanuginosum* heaths of summits and plateaux tend to show increasing cover of grasses and reductions in Woolly-fringe Moss in areas with high Red Deer or sheep numbers. This may be attributed to nutrient input in the form of dunging and urination, particularly in areas used for shelter.

There is evidence of recent significant loss of heather cover in a number of glens, due to browsing by Red Deer and sheep. In Glen Clunie, Watson (1989) reported a shift from heather to grass-dominated swards during the 1970s to 1989, observing that sheep numbers had changed little in the area while deer numbers had increased. Evidence was also given by Staines *et al.* (1995) for a loss of heather cover, due to Red Deer browsing, in Glen Feshie (since 1970) and Glen Lui, on Mar Lodge Estate (since 1946). Scott *et al.* (1999) examined levels of heather offtake in Glen Geldie in squares that had previously been assigned to different classes of grazing impact, including heavily impacted short heather. They found a significant, positive correlation between the grazing impact and the occurrence of 'drumstick' shaped heather clumps, and a negative correlation between heather height and the number of shoots observable in the autumn. Grazing pressure has also been implicated in the loss of heather from much of Caenlochan Glen, but the relationship in this area was less clear; since the soil type will tend to favour graminoids, heather may be more marginal in this Glen. However, the loss of heather in Caenlochan has been accompanied by tracking and soil erosion in alpine calcareous grasslands and flushes confirming that there are heavy herbivore impacts associated with these sensitive habitats (Hewison *et al.*, 2000).

Recent field surveys (Rae, 1995, 1996, 1997; Gill & Scott, 1996; Nolan *et al.*, 1996; Pearce, 1997; Gill *et al.*, 1998; Stolte *et al.*, 1998a,b) have assessed grazing and trampling impacts on upland habitats. Heavy impacts were found mainly in glen bottoms and in sheltered or base-rich ground at high altitudes. Concentrations of heavy impact on dwarf-shrubs, causing loss of heather cover, were found in Glen Feshie, to the south of Glen Geldie and in Glen Dee on Mar Lodge Estate, on Craig Leek in Deeside, in glens Clunie, Callater, Gairn, Gleann Beag, and in the Gaick Forest. Heavily impacted blanket bog was observed in Glen Geldie, Gleann Einich, Glen Clunie, Caenlochan Glen and south of Glen Shee. Montane moss-heaths were impacted heavily enough to show a loss of moss, while replacement by grasses occurred around Mòine Mhór to Clach a' Bhlair. It is difficult to make generalisations about the extent and severity of impacts, as these can be localised or specific to certain habitats. Figure 21.3 illustrates the summary impact assessments for the four Deer Management Groups Areas within Cairngorms National Park. Detailed analysis of the impact maps produced from these surveys is required to gauge the extent and distribution of moderate and heavy impacts on the full range of habitats – which differ in sensitivity – and to incorporate these findings into deer management plans.

Although high densities of Red Deer and sheep can be damaging to upland vegetation, moderate grazing helps to maintain a diversity of open ground habitats, and the biodiversity of individual patches of vegetation. Moderate grazing is especially important in maintaining the biodiversity of open ground

A pine seedling protected from browsing by traditional deer fencing.
Photo: *N. Benvie*

habitats such as species-rich grasslands. These occur especially on Tulach Hill in Glen Tilt and other areas on Beinn a' Ghlo, Inchrory and on Caenlochan. Hence, large herbivores are essential for maintaining large- and small-scale habitat diversity in both woodland and upland ecosystems.

Impacts associated with deer fencing

Fencing has commonly been used to deliver divergent management objectives in close physical proximity to each other; allowing significant variations in grazing pressure within and outwith exclosures. In woodlands especially, fencing has in the past been a standard prescription used to secure establishment, either through planting or natural regeneration. More recently, there has been an increased recognition of the negative impacts of fencing in terms of impediment to access, influence on the landscape, and nature conservation impacts.

In the absence of compensatory culling, fencing can serve to exacerbate impacts outside of the fenced area, increasing deer density and preventing access to shelter and grazing. This can further result in tracking and erosion damage adjacent to the fence, and can sometimes channel deer onto roads, with implications for public safety. Exclusion of deer reduces grazing within the fenced area to artificially low levels and can result in a loss of biodiversity, enabling those plants best able to respond quickly to low grazing pressure to establish dominance. Management prescriptions must therefore recognise the pivotal role of herbivores in a balanced upland/woodland ecosystem.

There is a general recognition that collisions with fencing can have significant effects on populations of woodland grouse, particularly the Capercaillie (Catt *et al.,* 1994). Whilst by no means the only factor contributing to population declines, additional losses due to fencing are not sustainable at current population levels (Chapter 18).

Survey methods and findings

Full herbivore impact assessments have been carried out by four Deer Management Groups (Figure 21.3), covering 36% of the National Park and 48% of the Cairngorms area. These assessments include impacts by domestic livestock and other wild herbivores, such as Mountain Hares. Because habitats differ in their sensitivity to herbivore impacts, impact levels need to be considered in context. For example, in dwarf-shrub heaths, the level of grazing impact above which heather may begin to decline falls within the 'Moderate' impact class (see

Macdonald *et al.*, 1998). However, some of the more sensitive habitat types, such as flushes, tall-herb communities and blanket bog, may be adversely affected by all impacts exceeding those assessed as 'Light'. In very general terms, there are many places within the Cairngorms where herbivore impacts are higher than would be substainable for both woodland and open ground habitats and their associated species. For example, Hewison *et al.* (2000) suggested that Red Deer had, and were, causing damage to 10 habitat types within Caenlochan Glen. Similarly, Whitfield (2001b) considered that locally high Red Deer densities during the summer (up to 98 individuals per km² per day) may be having a detrimental effect on montane vegetation at Mòine Mhór, Ben Avon and the east Drumochter Hills. In the same survey, up to 25% of Dotterel nests were found to have been trampled by Red Deer on Mòine Mhór.

Comprehensive herbivore impact surveys carried out by MLURI for the Cairngorm/Speyside and Angus Glens DMG sub-Groups have been used to derive a rapid habitat assessment methodology (based on a sampling regime), which has subsequently been used in the other DMG areas (Brewer *et al.*, 2004; Stolte *et al.*, in press).

Results from other surveys are as follows.

• Research by the RSPB at Abernethy (Parlane, 1998) and the NTS at Mar Lodge (Luxmoore, 2001) has concentrated on analysing the effects of deer population reductions on the vegetation and on the deer themselves. Several count methods have indicated a drop in hind numbers on Abernethy since the reserve was acquired in 1988, although density estimates have varied between <2 per km² to *c.* 30 per km² depending on the method, the habitat (moorland, woodland edge, glades) and season. Fluctuations in numbers suggest that deer move between Abernethy and neighbouring estates, hence necessitating an integrated management plan. Luxmoore (2001) suggests that although deer numbers on Mar Lodge Estate have not declined as rapidly as might have been predicted by population models (and explores possible reasons for errors in these predictions), the population is nevertheless declining.

• Scott *et al.* (1996) analysed data from woodland regeneration transects at sites in the Cairngorms and Monadhliaths. Their study collates the

Figure 21.1. The mean annual percentage change in the population density of Red Deer, between the two most recent counts in each Count Area (from Deer Commission for Scotland Annual Reports, 1986-2003) (see Table 21.1 for details).

Figure 21.2. The Red Deer population density in each Deer Management Group area, derived from the most recent counts available (calculated from digitised data supplied by the Deer Commission for Scotland) (see Table 21.2 for details).

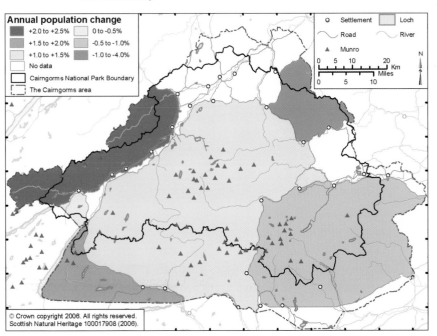

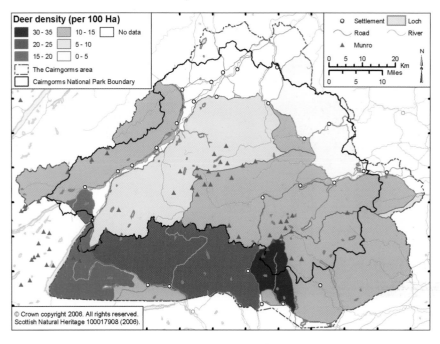

Figure 21.3. The impact of foraging herbivores in four Deer Management Group areas. Figures show the percentage of each DMG area within each impact class.

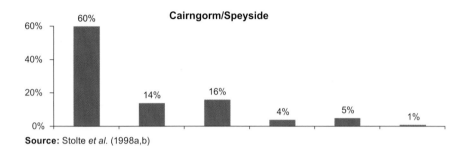

Cairngorm/Speyside

Source: Stolte *et al.* (1998a,b)

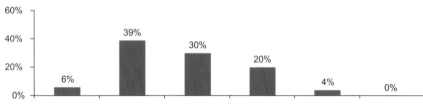

East Grampian: Angus Glens

Source: Stolte *et al.* (2000)

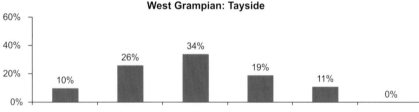

West Grampian: Tayside

Source: Nolan *et al.* (2002)

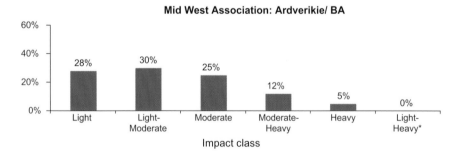

Mid West Association: Ardverikie/ BA

* Applies to wind-clipped summit heaths, where moderate impacts cannot be differentiated.

Source: Waterhouse *et al.* (2003)

results of monitoring across sites, but did not produce strong relationships between deer dung counts and levels of regeneration that could be used in a predictive way.

- Palmer and Truscott (2003) attempted to model relationships between deer occupancy and pine regeneration at sites which included Glen Tanar and Inshriach. Winter browsing of saplings increased with indices of Red Deer use (based on dung counts) but not Roe Deer use, while in summer browsing was associated with increased use by Roe Deer, but not Red Deer. The pattern of browsing was influenced by the surrounding vegetation and the history of browsing. However, the severity of browsing of shoots was found to have little effect on basal diameter increment.

- MLURI has carried out some radio-tracking of stag movements using GPS collars. These studies provided detailed data on the movements of individual stags from different herds around Mar Lodge Estate in different seasons. The tracking also examined the influence of deer management and recreational activities on Red Deer movements, the results of which have still to be published (Sibbald, 2001).

- DCS and its predecessor, the Red Deer Commission, have led a programme of calf tagging since 1963 (Daniels & McClean, 2003). This provided information on movement patterns, suggesting that hinds were unlikely to move more than 3 km from their birthplace and stags slightly further, up to 5 km, with some exceptions, during the rut. Movement behaviour has obvious implications for collaborative deer management.

Policy context

National and local perspectives

The Deer (Scotland) Act 1996 is the main legal instrument governing the management of wild deer. The Nature Conservation Act 2004, the Scottish Biodiversity Strategy (Scottish Executive, 2004) and the Land Reform Act 2003 also have implications for their management. The Deer Act empowers DCS to enter into voluntary control agreements where deer are causing, or are likely to cause, damage to woodland, crops, to the natural heritage, or become a potential danger to public safety. Where deer have caused and are causing damage, and control agreements have not been achieved, or prove unsuccessful, the Act makes provision for DCS to undertake the necessary control at the owner's expense. DCS are also empowered to carry out control measures, where natural heritage interests are affected by a significantly higher than normal presence of deer. The Act also gives DCS powers to assist in the pursuance of a control agreement.

Extensive tracts of the Cairngorms area are designated as *Natura 2000* sites (Chapter 1). These are Special Protection Areas (SPAs) or Special Areas of Conservation (SACs), under the EC Birds Directive and the Habitats Directive, respectively. SNH and other competent authorities have a duty to avoid the deterioration of the qualifying interests on these sites, under the provisions of The Conservation (Natural Habitats, &c) Regulations 1994. Additionally, public bodies have a duty to further the conservation of biodiversity (Nature Conservation Act, 2004). In the context of deer, the lead competent authority is the DCS.

Deer Commission Scotland (2001b) *Wild Deer in Scotland – A Long-term Vision* provided the early framework for much of the policy development in relation to deer management. The aspiration is for sustainably managed populations, based on robust principles, which are managed locally through collaboration and are integrated with other land use objectives, whilst adhering to high standards of welfare and public safety.

Joint agency working over the past two years has produced significant advances in procedures for addressing natural heritage concerns relating to deer. Principally, there has been broad recognition of the need for a joint-working approach between the agencies and deer managers. In March 2004 DCS, FCS, SEERAD and SNH signed up to an agreement on using incentives and regulations to secure the effective management of deer and other herbivores[1], and in June 2004 the same agencies agreed on a *Joint Agency Statement & Guidance On Deer Fencing*. Both are to be supplemented with technical guidance.

SNH's general deer policy, presented in *Red Deer and the Natural Heritage* (SNH, 1994), has recently been updated with a policy summary complementing the above joint working approaches.

At a more local level, SNH has produced, in consultation, a series of *Natural Heritage Futures* documents, which set a contemporary context for deer management policy. Put simply, these reflect a vision in which deer populations are in balance with the habitats on which they depend and are consistent with sport shooting objectives.

The Cairngorms Partnership identified the following objectives for deer populations in its Management Strategy (Cairngorms Partnership, 1997):

- to manage deer populations at levels and densities which will allow for the conservation and enhancement of woodland and moorland habitats, and significantly reduce economic loss to timber production and agriculture;

- to reduce and avoid the use of deer fencing; and

- to maintain a viable deer economy in the remoter glens.

Joint working

DCS, SNH, FCS and SEERAD have different grant-giving and regulatory powers that can be used to support the sustainable management of grazing animals. Under joint working arrangements, SNH will be carrying out an audit of all designated sites as the basis for identifying where there are concerns about the impacts of wild deer on their own or in combination with other herbivores. The results of Site Condition Monitoring (SCM) assessments will be used as the starting point for this process. Following on from this initial audit, a range of other factors such as the nature of evidence and an assessment of the relative urgency of action will be considered in developing a programme of work for securing natural heritage interests for designated sites. Further surveys may be needed to confirm that designated interests are at risk. Once identified as a site for priority action, the agencies will discuss with owners and managers the options associated with this, including the possibility that the site could be a priority for public support. The sites in the work programme will continue to be updated thereafter, as progress is made and further survey is carried out. Sites that are already the subject of joint agency working will automatically form part of this work programme.

In the East Grampians and Cairngorms/West Grampians Deer Count Areas, five voluntary Deer Control Agreements are currently[2] in place, under the Deer (Scotland) Act 1996, with the aim of preventing deer damage to agriculture, woodlands or the natural heritage over a total area of 77,400 ha (Deer Commission for Scotland, 2003). SNH and the DCS are also actively engaged with regard to referrals on Creag Meagaidh and Monadhliath SSSIs. Two *Natura 2000* sites are also the subject of third-party referrals to DCS.

Natural Care

Natural Care is the collective name given to positive management schemes which aim to bring about natural heritage benefits on SSSIs and Natura sites.

---

[1] See http://www.snh.org.uk/strategy/deer/wild_deer.asp

These are complemented by Scottish Forestry Grant Schemes on woodland sites. New approaches are being developed by the statutory agencies through joint working arrangements to avoid pre-judging whether deer impacts will be addressed through regulation or through incentives. The agencies, owners and managers may wish to seek 'enhancement', i.e. improvementsover and above what might be considered as the minimum standard, without first having to demonstrate that damage has occurred or is likely to occur. Incentives and regulation are regarded as complementary tools; incentives being designed to support the 'enhancement' of habitats, with regulation providing the back-up to ensure that damage does not occur or continue. Where 'enhancement' is the objective, habitat improvements are expected to form the baseline for future habitat condition assessments. Initiatives piloting these joint-working approaches are underway at Kinveachy and under the Forest of Clunie Natural Care programme. Natural care agreements may in turn be superseded by land management contracts.

The large area of woodland and moorland owned by NTS and the RSPB at Mar Lodge and Abernethy, respectively, together with public ownership at Invereshie (SNH) and land managed by FCS, ensures that natural heritage objectives receive the highest priority within these areas. This is facilitated directly in the case of the publicly owned lands and is assisted by grant aid and management agreements within the NGO estates.

Management Issues

Deer Management Groups
Deer movements are such that management issues do not fall within single units of ownership. Deer Management Groups therefore aim to co-ordinate deer management at the level of the sub-population across land holdings. Such collaboration is important, as the same individual deer occupy different parts of their range on a diurnal and seasonal basis. DMGs are voluntary, do not hold a statutory mandate, and operate by consensus. Since membership consists mainly of representatives of deer management interests, cull targets have tended to focus on achieving sporting objectives, rather than natural heritage objectives. However, within the DMGs there is increasing recognition of the benefits of including a wider range of interest groups. The DMGs' umbrella organisation, the Association of Deer Management Groups (ADMG), has been progressive in encouraging engagement with the agencies, notably SNH and DCS, particularly through a collaborative

In the absence of natural predators Red Deer are regulated by their food supply and by human intervention, in the form of culling. The protection of natural heritage interests may at times require the use of non-traditional cull logistics and extraction techniques to complement stalking activities, as here at Mar Lodge Estate.

Photo: *N. Benvie*

[2] As at December 2005.

statement on joint-working (ADMG, DCS, FCS & SNH, 2003). Owing to the diversity of management objectives it can at times be difficult for DMGs to reach consensus, and this significantly influences policy direction and speed of implementation. DCS and SNH attend most DMG meetings, by invitation.

DMGs cover 74% of Cairngorms National Park and 76% of the wider Cairngorms area. Those within the National Park have agreed to form a co-ordination group.

Deer management can be addressed at a hierarchy of scales, from DMG areas, through DMG sub-Groups, to individual estates and beats within estates. Two of the DMG sub-Groups in the Cairngorms (West Grampian: Cairngorm/Speyside; East Grampian: the Angus Glens) have Deer Management Plans, covering 35% of the National Park area and 30% of the Cairngorms area. These Plans were drafted by Deer Commission staff as part of a pilot project (Deer Commission for Scotland, 1999, 2000). The Glen Shee/Glen Isla sub-group of East Grampian has produced its own Plan, in 2002. Whilst all three include targets to maintain their respective areas in a stable or improving condition, they lack the specific prescriptions necessary to bring this about. Deer Management Groups are increasingly recognising this, and a number are active in developing new plans which address this need. The Cairngorm/Speyside DMP is currently under review (December 2005) and will be circulated for wider consultation for the first time.

Recreation

Staines & Scott (1992) reported on estate workers' perceptions of the disturbance caused to stalks by hillwalkers. The authors considered that the most legitimate concerns raised were those relating to the impact of hillwalkers on estate management and sporting activities, rather than to perceived impacts on deer population performance. Deer Management Groups are active in providing information on the interaction between stalking and other recreational activities and, for the most part, it seems that there is an increasing acceptance of the need for accommodation on all parts.

SNH and the Mountaineering Council of Scotland (MCofS) set up the Hillphones Scheme in 1996 to facilitate the management of public access during the stag stalking season. In 2003 and 2004 Hill Phones were in operation on estates covering 19% of the Cairngorms area and 20% of the National Park.

Deer Fencing

Deer fencing can impact significantly on access. Examining impacts on access and identifying possible means of mitigation will therefore form part of the process for assessing future fencing proposals, as agreed in the joint agency statement (June 2004). Technical guidance will also be developed, which will form the basis of the DCS Best Practice Guidance on fencing. One developing area of policy guidance is in relation to the impacts of fencing on wild land. Equally, tracks and footpaths maintained primarily for deer and other sporting purposes are used extensively by other access groups. The Scottish Outdoor Access Code (2004) sets parameters for providing responsible access, which will require constructive approaches both from deer managers and recreational users.

References

Association of Deer Management Groups, Deer Commission for Scotland, Forestry Commission Scotland & Scottish Natural Heritage (2003). *Joint working agreement between ADMG, DCS, FCS and SNH.* Press Release.

Brewer, M.J., Elston, D.E., Hodgson, M.E.A., Stolte, A.M., Nolan, A.J. & Henderson, D.J. (2004). A spatial model with ordinal responses for grazing impact data. *Statistical Modelling* 4(2): 127-143.

British Deer Society (2002). Scottish Deer Distribution Survey 2000. *Deer* 12(2): 106–109.

Cairngorms Partnership (1997). *Managing the Cairngorms – The Cairngorms Partnership Management Strategy.* The Cairngorms Partnership: Grantown-on-Spey.

Catt, D.C., Dugan, D., Green, R.E., Moncrieff, R., Moss, R., Picozzi, N., Summers, R.W. & Tyler, G.A. (1994). Collisions against fences by woodland grouse in Scotland. *Forestry* 67: 105–118.

Daniels, M. J. & McClean, C. (2003). Red deer calf tagging programmes in Scotland – an analysis. *Deer* 12: 420–423.

Deer Commission for Scotland (1999). *Cairngorms/Speyside Deer Management Group Deer Management Plan.* DCS: Inverness.

Deer Commission for Scotland (2000). *East Grampian Deer Management Group sub–Area IV (Angus Glens) Deer Management Plan.* DCS: Inverness.

Deer Commission for Scotland (2001a). *Annual Report 2000–2001.* DCS: Inverness.

Deer Commission for Scotland (2001b). *Long Term Strategy. Wild deer in Scotland – Long Term Vision.* DCS: Inverness.

Deer Commission for Scotland (2002). *Annual Report 2001–2002*. DCS: Inverness.

Deer Commission for Scotland (2003). *Annual Report 2002–2003*. DCS: Inverness.

Gill, J.P. & Scott, L. (1996). *Cairngorms Project Moorland and Montane Habitat Condition Assessment Final Report to SNH*. Unpublished report. Contract RASD/063/96 CNG. SNH: Perth.

Gill, J.P., Sales, D. & Horsfield, D. (1998). *Cairngorms Montane and Moorland Habitat Survey and Impact Assessment ESS Report to SNH*. Unpublished report. SNH: Perth.

Hewison, R.L., Nolan, A.J. & Alfaro, P. (2000). *Assessment of Grazing and Trampling impacts Caenlochan Glen, Angus*. Unpublished report to DCS by Macaulay Research and Consultancy Services Ltd.

Kirby, K.J., Mitchell, F.J. & Hester, A.J. (1994). A role for large herbivores (deer and domestic stock) in nature conservation management in British semi-natural woods. *Arboricultural Journal* 18: 381–399.

Luxmoore, R. (2001). *Deer Management at Mar Lodge Estate. Preliminary analysis of data derived from culls and counts*. NTS: Mar Lodge.

Macdonald, A., Stevens, P., Armstrong, H., Immirizi, P & Reynolds, P. (1998). *A Guide to Upland Habitats: Surveying Land Management Impacts*. Scottish Natural Heritage: Perth.

Miller, G.R. & Cummins, R.P. (1982). Regeneration of Scots pine *Pinus sylvestris* at a natural tree-line in the Cairngorm mountains, Scotland. *Holarctic Ecology* 5: 27–34.

Nolan, A.J., Gillick, T.H., Sellers, J.E., Malcolm, A. & Milne, J.A. (1996). *Invercauld Estate: Habitat Assessment and Options for Future Management*. Macaulay Land Use Research Institute: Aberdeen.

Nolan, A.J., Waterhouse, E.C., Dalziel, A.J.I. & Malcolm, A. (2002). *Rapid Assessment of Grazing and Trampling Impacts on Upland Habitats for the West Grampian Deer Management Group Area*. MLURI: Aberdeen.

Palmer, S.C.F. & Truscott, A.M. (2003). Browsing by deer on naturally regenerating Scots pine (*Pinus sylvestris* L.) and its effects on sapling growth. *Forest Ecology and Management* 182: 31–47.

Parlane, S. (1998). *Analysis of red and roe deer data collected at Abernethy Forest Reserve, 1988–1998*. RSPB: Edinburgh.

Pearce, I.S.K. (1997). *Moorland and Montane Habitat Condition Assessment: Cairngorms*. Unpublished report. Scottish Natural Heritage: Perth.

Rae, S. (1995). *Cairngorms Moorland and Montane Habitat Survey and Condition Assessment Carn Dearg, Geldie and Braemar Survey Areas*. Unpublished report. Contract RASD/063/96 CNG. SNH: Perth.

Rae, S. (1996). *Cairngorms Project: Continuation of Moorland and Montane Habitat Survey and Condition Assessment South Geldie Area*. Unpublished report. Contract RASD/091/97 CNG. SNH: Perth.

Rae, S. (1997). *Cairngorms Project: Montane and Moorland Habitat Survey and Condition Assessment Inchrory Area*. Unpublished report. Contract RASD HT/97/98/52. SNH: Perth.

Scott, D., Hirst, D., Staines, B.W. & Elston, D. (1996). *Red Deer and Tree Regeneration in the Cairngorms and Monadhliaths*. SNH contract RASD/019/95 UPB. SNH: Perth.

Scott, D., Welch, D. & Gornall, J. (1999). *Calibration and status assessments of heather habitat condition classes in Glen Geldie*. Report to Scottish Natural Heritage. SNH: Perth.

Scottish Executive (2004). *Scotland's Biodiversity: It's in your hands*. Scottish Executive: Edinburgh.

Sibbald, A. (2001). Using GPS to track wild red deer stags. *Deer* 11(10): 524–529.

SNH (1994). *Red Deer and the Natural Heritage. SNH Policy Paper*. SNH: Perth.

Staines, B.W. & Balharry, R. (2002). Red Deer and their management in the Cairngorms. In: C.H. Gimingham (ed.), *The Ecology, Land Use and Conservation of the Cairngorms*. Packard Publishing Limited: Chichester.

Staines, B.W. & Scott, D. (1992). *Recreation and Red Deer: a preliminary review of the issues*. Scottish Natural Heritage Review No 31. SNH: Perth.

Staines, B.W., Balharry, R. & Welch, D. (1995). The impacts of red deer and their management on the natural heritage in the uplands. In: Thompson, D.B., Hester, A.J. & Usher, M.B. (eds.), *Heaths and Moorlands: Cultural Landscapes*. HMSO: Edinburgh.

Stolte, A.M., Henderson, D.J. & Nolan, A.J. (1998a). *Assessment of Impacts on Upland Habitats for North-East and South-West sections of Cairngorm/Speyside Deer Management Group Area*. MLURI: Aberdeen.

Stolte, A.M., Nolan, A.J., Henderson, D.J. & Horsfield, D. (1998b). *Overall impact of grazing and trampling, Cairngorm/Speyside Deer Management Group Area*. MLURI: Aberdeen.

Stolte, A.M., Alfaro, P., Henderson, D.J., Nolan, A.J. & Connolly, H. (2000). *Rapid assessment of grazing and trampling impacts on upland habitats for East Grampian Deer Management Group sub-Area 4: Angus Glens*. MLURI: Aberdeen.

Stolte, A.M., Nolan, A.J., Brewer, M.J., Duff, E.I., Elston, D.A. & Henderson, D.J. (in press). Rapid assessment of grazing and trampling impacts over large areas of rangeland: a sampling approach. *Biological Conservation*.

Waterhouse, E.C., Alexander, J., Malcolm, A. & Nolan, A.J. (2003). *Rapid assessment of grazing and trampling impacts on upland habitats for the Mid-west Association Deer Management Group Area*. MLURI: Aberdeen.

Watson, A. (1989). Land use, reduction of heather and natural tree regeneration on open upland. In: *ITE Annual Report 1988*. HMSO: London. p.p. 25–27.

Watson, A. (1997). Human-induced changes in numbers of Red deer in the Cairn Gorm area. *Deer* 10: 278–281.

Whitfield, D.P. (2001a) *Temporal trends in the density of grazing mammals on montane sites in the Highlands of Scotland.* SNH Commissioned Research Report No. F99AC402b. SNH: Perth.

Whitfield, D.P. (2001b). *Geographical variation in the density of grazing mammals on montane sites in the Highlands of Scotland.* SNH Commissioned Research Report No. F99AC402a. SNH: Perth.

22. RECREATION

Graham Neville, Keith Duncan and Alex Mackay

Introduction

The Cairngorms area is recognised nationally and internationally for its great environmental and scenic value. Its diverse landscape provides opportunities for participation in a wide range of outdoor recreational pursuits, including walking, climbing, cycling, watersports, airsports, ski-touring, downhill skiing, wildlife watching and photography. From the high massif and its wild land areas to the lower slopes and straths, people are consistently attracted by the quality of the natural environment. The Cairngorms area is a year-round recreational centre, with three downhill skiing areas and an international reputation for good quality winter mountaineering. Hillwalkers from the rest of the UK and throughout the world are drawn to the Cairngorms massif, which has the largest area of high ground in the UK, containing some 50 Munros[1].

International events such as the World Mountain Bike Championships (held at Rothiemurchus in the early 1990s) and long-established facilities such as the national centre for mountain training at Glenmore Lodge, confirm the area's importance for organised recreational activities. Just as important is the variety of other opportunities available for informal outdoor recreation, all of which add to the very important role played by recreation within the local economy. This recreational value depends highly, even critically, on the maintenance of environmental values of wildness or naturalness in the Cairngorms (Mackay, 2002).

In this chapter, which is based largely on responses to visitor surveys, automatic people-counter data and other survey reports, we describe the recreational importance of the area, in terms of its natural features and local economic benefits, from the perspective of local people and visitors alike. We also discuss some of the key issues relating to the management of recreation in the Cairngorms.

Data sources

Visitor surveys

Several visitor surveys have been carried out in the Cairngorms, or within wider areas of which the Cairngorms are a part (Table 22.1). These surveys all share the aim of assessing participation in outdoor recreational activities. Most aim to describe patterns in recreational use and the characteristics and attitudes of visitors to the Cairngorms area. In each case, information was collected using self-completion questionnaires and face-to-face interviews, although some also used direct observation of patterns of use.

The Scottish Recreation Survey (first conducted in 2003) indicates levels of participation in outdoor recreation across Scotland, and shows how many of those participating in leisure activities outdoors in Scotland do so within a National Park (TNS, 2004). Nationally, of all respondents making visits to the outdoors within a four-week recall period, around 6% visited a National Park (TNS, 2004). The Scottish Recreation Survey also gives some information on where people come from and go to, in pursuit of leisure activities. For example, it demonstrates that Aberdeenshire and Highland areas, both of which overlap substantially with the Cairngorms National Park, each had the highest proportion of visits, accounting for 9% of the total number of visits to any Local Authority area (TNS, 2004). The Highlands of Scotland Visitor Survey (2002–03) covers the whole of the Highlands and Islands Enterprise area, and is also available for Moray, Badenoch and Strathspey (George Street Research, 2003b) or as an activity-specific report (George Street Research, 2003c).

There have also been several surveys relating specifically to the Cairngorms area. The Cairngorms Mountain Recreation Survey, carried out in 1997–98, collected comprehensive baseline information on visitor characteristics, patterns of activity and attitudes among visitors to the mountainous regions of

---

A line of walkers make their way along Coire an t-Sneachda ridge on a pristine winter's day.
Photo: *N. Mcintyre*

[1] Mountains exceeding 3,000 feet (914.4 m).

Neville, G., Duncan, K. & Mackay, A. (2006). Recreation. In: Shaw, P. & Thompson, D.B.A. (eds.). *The Nature of the Cairngorms: Diversity in a changing environment*. The Stationery Office. pp. 381-393.

Table 22.1   Recent recreational surveys carried out wholly or partly in the Cairngorms.

Survey	Period	Undertaken by	Purpose	Respondents	Reference
Scottish Recreation Survey[1]	2003	Scottish Natural Heritage and the Forestry Commission	Ongoing project to monitor participation in outdoor recreation in Scotland.	12,000 per year	TNS (2004)
Cairngorms National Park Visitor Survey	2002	Cairngorms National Park Authority	To collect information on the volume of use, visitor profile and visitor behaviour. Sought to guide management of the Cairngorms National Park.	1,536	Lowland Market Research (2003)
National Nature Reserve Visitor Survey.	2002	Scottish Natural Heritage	To establish a profile of visitors to NNRs and to identify their reasons for visiting and related aspirations.	60: Abernethy/Dell Wood NNR 240: Muir of Dinnet NNR 124: Creag Meagaidh NNR	NFO (2003a,b,c)
Highlands Visitor Survey[1]	2002	Highlands and Islands Enterprise et al.	To supply information and guide future tourism policy.	4,750	George Street Research (2003a)
Rothiemurchus and Glenmore Recreation Survey	1998–99	Scottish Natural Heritage	To collect comprehensive baseline information on visitor characteristics, patterns of activity in the Rothiemurchus and Glenmore area, and to inform management strategy.	1,762	Mather (2000)
Cairngorms Mountain Recreation Survey	1997–98	Scottish Natural Heritage	To collect comprehensive baseline information on visitor characteristics, patterns of activity in the core Cairngorms massif, and to inform management strategy.	2,915	Taylor & MacGregor (1999)
East Grampians and Lochnagar	1995	Scottish Natural Heritage	To collect comprehensive baseline information on visitor characteristics, patterns of activity in the eastern Grampian and Lochnagar area, and to inform management strategy.	2,842	Mather (1998)

[1] Covers a wider geographical area, which includes part of the Cairngorms.

the Cairngorms (Taylor & MacGregor, 1999). A complementary study, the Rothiemurchus and Glenmore Recreation Survey, collected similar information at lower levels (Mather, 2000). Recreation surveys have also been carried out in the East Grampians and Lochnagar, in 1995 (Mather, 1998), and on National Nature Reserves in the Cairngorms area in 2003 (NFO, 2003a,b,c). All of these surveys aim to assess the recreational use of the area, to record the activities undertaken and reasons for visiting, and to inform the management of the area. For example, the East Grampian & Lochnagar Survey has led, in part, to the establishment of the Upper Deeside Access Trust to manage high- and low-level access routes in the area. Visitor surveys have led to a similar initiative in Badenoch and Strathspey.

People-counters
SNH holds data from 14 people-counters placed at selected sites around Cairngorms National Park. In some years, data from some of these counters have been adjusted to take account of conditions likely to reduce their accuracy, for example where snow cover or freezing conditions render pressure mats ineffective. The severity and longevity of winter conditions thus affects annual counts, and individual counters will be affected by the winter conditions to varying degrees, depending on the year, altitude and location. Data have also been adjusted to remove spurious counts, for example from counter malfunctions or passes by deer. Extrapolated evidence from people-counters is thought to give a reasonably accurate picture of the popularity of different routes and locations across the area, but is, of course, less reliable where fewer days of data have been received. Calibration factors are applied where there is evidence that counters are over- or under-counting, and this is used to reduce the margin of error of the counts. As a result of these and other factors, whilst much useful data are available, it has been difficult to establish long-term aggregated trends from automatic people-counter data in the Cairngorms.

Table 22.2 Reasons for visiting the survey area, given by respondents to the Rothiemurchus and Glenmore Recreation Survey (Mather, 2000).

Reason given for visiting	Percentage of respondents
Walk	25%
Brochure/leaflet/map/book	15%
Regular Visitor	9%
Love it/like the area	6%
Cycle	5%
Weather	4%
Just passing/touring/sightseeing	4%
Specific attraction	4%
Sledging/skiing/wintersports	3%
Scenery	3%
Stay in Aviemore	2%
Birds/wildlife	1%
Shops/cafes	1%
Watersports	1%
Other	9%

Table 22.3 Main reasons for visiting the survey area, given by respondents to the Cairngorm Mountain Recreation Survey (Taylor & MacGregor, 1999).

Reason given for visiting	Percentage of respondents
Been to the Cairngorms before	17%
Near home/easily accessed	16%
In holiday/near holiday base	15%
Beautiful/quiet/clean place	15%
Weather	11%
Munro/Corbett bagging	10%
Seasonal conditions	7%
Exercise/activity	7%
Visit specific location/feature	7%
Good walking country	5%
Visit new places	5%
Other	31%

Note that more than one reason may have been given by respondents to this question.

Reasons for visiting

Many survey respondents have identified the Cairngorms' scenery and natural beauty as the area's main attractions. Of those responding to the Rothiemurchus and Glenmore Recreation Survey, 97% agreed with the statement that they thought the area was 'special' in some way, while 40% also agreed that the scenery or natural beauty of the area were what made it so. Tables 22.2 and 22.3 demonstrate the variety of reasons given for visiting the area, cited by respondents to the Cairngorms Mountain Recreation Survey (1997–98) and the Rothiemurchus and Glenmore Recreation Survey (1998–99). A quarter of all respondents to the Rothiemurchus and Glenmore Recreation Survey cited opportunities for walking as their main reason for visiting (Table 22.2). It is apparent that a substantial proportion of visitors make repeat visits to the Cairngorms area (Table 22.3).

Accessibility was important for respondents to the Cairngorms Mountain Recreation Survey, perhaps because of the diversity of recreational pursuits possible in the area. When asked to rank the importance of various factors influencing their decision to visit the area, almost all (98%) of the respondents to the Rothiemurchus and Glenmore Recreation Survey considered the scenery or natural beauty to be 'important' or 'very important'. A similarly high proportion (90%) of respondents stated that the opportunities for walking or cycling in the forest were either 'important' or 'very important' (Table 22.4).

Features relating to the infrastructure (accessibility, variety of sites and activities, visitor facilities) were considered less important. Other reasons mentioned for visiting the area were 'wildness', and the fact that it was 'unspoilt' or 'preserved' and contained a combination of mountains, lochs and trees. Respondents appeared able to appreciate these features, despite the numbers of visitors to the area, estimated at 375,000–500,000 during 1998–99 (Mather, 2000).

Respondents to the Highlands Visitor Survey showed that 16% of visitors to the Moray, Badenoch & Strathspey Enterprise area were attracted by its scenery and views, 19% because they had visited before and 12% because of a specific natural attraction (George Street Research, 2003b). These included Loch Morlich, Rothiemurchus Estate, Loch an Eilein, the RSPB Loch Garten

Walkers decending the Mount Keen path leading south, to the Water of Mark. Walking is by far the main activity of visitors to the Cairngorms.

Photo: *L. Gill*

Table 22.4 The relative importance of the Cairngorms' attractions to 560 respondents participating in the Rothiemurchus and Glenmore Recreation Survey (Mather, 2000)

Factor	Very Important	Important	Not important	No response
Scenery/natural beauty	87%	11%	1%	2%
Opportunities for walking/ cycling in the forest	71%	19%	5%	5%
Caledonian Pinewoods	46%	35%	10%	10%
Opportunities for hillwalking/ climbing above the forest	45%	18%	23%	14%
Accessibility of the area	32%	43%	15%	10%
Variety of sites and activities	18%	35%	35%	14%
Facilities for visitors	18%	38%	32%	13%
Personal recommendations	16%	18%	48%	18%
Well signposted from A9	11%	23%	50%	16%
Recommendation from book, leaflet, magazine or TV	6%	16%	59%	20%

visitor centre and Glenmore Forest Park. Overall, 26% of respondents stated that their visit to the Badenoch and Strathspey area had exceeded expectations due, in part, to its scenery and natural beauty.

It is clear from these studies that the natural heritage of the Cairngorms area, and the opportunities it provides for walking and for enjoying its scenery, are key attractions. An important part of its attraction is its extensive areas of land remote from disturbance (Figure 22.1), sometimes termed 'wild land'. Definitions of 'wild land' take account of recreational as well as of natural heritage elements, and include areas where remoteness and aesthetics give rise to opportunities for 'physical and spiritual refreshment' (Price *et al.*, 2002). Wild land has been defined in National Planning Policy Guideline 14 as 'uninhabited and often relatively inaccessible countryside where the influence of human activity on the character and quality of the environment has been minimal' (Scottish Office Development Department, 1999).

SNH, in its Policy Statement (SNH, 2002), has identified criteria for determining wild land, some of which are met in parts of the Cairngorms. These are areas that are relatively inaccessible, have few visible signs of human interaction with the environment, and provide a feeling of solitude, or of sanctuary (see Chapter 4). This is not a new concept, and was recognised by the Cairngorms Working Party, which recommended a zoned approach to management, with minimum intervention and a strong presumption against development in the 'core' (Cairngorms Working Party, 1992). This principle has since been reiterated in the *Natural Heritage Futures* prospectus for the Cairngorms Massif (Scottish Natural Heritage, 2002b). Recently, national recognition of Scotland's wild land resource has lead to the central Cairngorms massif being outlined as an 'area of search' for wild land (Scottish Natural Heritage, 2002a).

In remote areas, footpath erosion, bulldozed tracks, telecommunications masts and skiing developments can have a negative impact, detracting from their 'wild land' quality. Ski developments, in particular, detract from the quality of wild land through, for example, improved accessibility created by new roads and ski lifts. In a recent questionnaire survey carried out in the Cairngorms, 55% of respondents said that ski facilities detracted from their enjoyment of the area.

Figure 22.1   Remote areas in the Cairngorms, in terms of their distance from public and private roads and tracks.

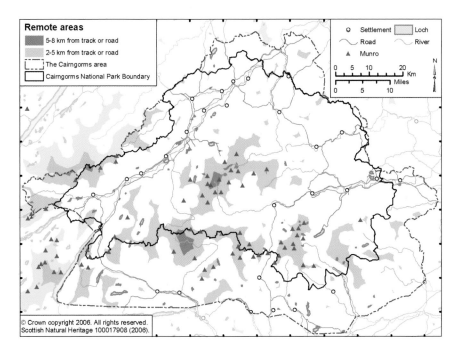

Recreational Activities

Walking is the most popular activity for the majority of people taking part in active outdoor recreation in Scotland. The Scottish Recreation Survey (TNS, 2004) shows that for the first six months of the survey (July–December 2003), 53% of respondents had walked as their main activity. In the Cairngorms the percentage is much higher, 83% of respondents to the Cairngorms Mountain Recreation Survey (1997–98) stating that walking was their main activity (Taylor & MacGregor, 1999) (Table 22.5).

Not surprisingly, the type of setting in which people choose to walk differs between Scotland as a whole and the Cairngorms area specifically. While only 3% of those responding to the Scottish Recreation Survey had walked in mountains, 49% of respondents to the Cairngorms Mountain Recreation Survey walked to the mountain summits. Other activities accounted for just 10% of the respondents' main activities (Table 22.5).

Similarly, the majority of respondents to the Rothiemurchus and Glenmore Recreation Survey (1998–1999), stated that walking in some form was their main activity (Table 22.6) (Mather, 2000), as did most of those responding to the East Grampians and Lochnagar Visitor Survey (1995) (Mather, 1998). In the latter survey, the main activities identified were hill walking, other walking, rock or ice climbing, mountain biking, cross-country skiing and wildlife observation.

In contrast, respondents to the Highlands Visitor Survey in Moray, Badenoch and Strathspey Enterprise Area identified general sightseeing as their main activity (49%), with only 19% of respondents stating that they would go for a walk (of any distance or on any terrain) as their main activity (George Street Research, 2003b). This difference could reflect the wider scope of the Highlands Visitor Survey, which surveyed all visitors, rather than focussing on open-air recreation.

Skiing impacts

Downhill skiing itself can have relatively little impact on the natural heritage during periods of complete snow cover. However, associated developments, such as the construction of skiing infrastructure, new access tracks, footpaths, snow fences and bulldozing of ski pistes during the establishment of downhill ski centres in the 1960s and 1970s, have had substantial adverse environmental

Downhill skiing

Downhill ski centres are well-established recreational attractions, which provide local income and employment on a seasonal basis. Three of the five Scottish ski centres are located in the Cairngorms area: on Cairn Gorm, established in 1960, with a capacity of 5–6,000 skiers over an area of 844 ha; at Glen Shee, established in 1962, with a capacity of 6,000 skiers over 790 ha; and at the Lecht, established in 1977, with a capacity of 2,500 skiers, over an area of 210 ha. All three ski areas lie partly in, or adjacent to, SSSIs and SACs. In addition, two lie partly within SPAs, and two lie within or adjacent to National Scenic Areas.

Trends in visitor numbers

The number of skiing visitors to sites in the Cairngorms has declined substantially since the late 1980s, when a mean of 491,393 skiing visits was recorded during the winters of 1986–91. In contrast, the mean number of skiing visits recorded per annum during 1995–99 was 265,058, dropping to 205,165 in 2000–03 (Figure 22.A).

Factors influencing this downturn include a series of consecutive winters with unreliable snow cover, the increased ease of access to Continental and North American ski centres, and domestic demographic patterns (a decline in the Scottish population and in the number of young people taking up the sport). Unfavourable winter weather, particularly in the past ten years, may be due to climate change (Chapter 20), which is thought likely to make downhill skiing in Scotland unviable within the next 20–50 years.

As a result of these declines the skiing industry in Scotland is under immense pressure to diversify or restructure. Diversification into non-skiing activities by the ski areas in the Cairngorms has included the Cairn Gorm funicular railway, a visitor centre, go-kart and quad bike hire, and a golf course (en route to Glen Shee).

At Cairngorm, the opening of the funicular railway in 2002 led to a dramatic increase in the number of non-skiing visitors (Figure 22.B) which, during each of the first three years of operation, has exceeded the number of skiing visitors (Cairngorms Mountain Ltd., pers. comm.). In accordance with the Visitor Management Plan for the development, non-skiing visitors using the funicular are not permitted to leave the top station to access the plateau itself. This measure is aimed at limiting disturbance to ground-nesting birds and to fragile plateau habitats, which qualify for designation under European Conservation Directives. Since walkers must now walk up to the plateau themselves, their numbers on Cairn Gorm and on the wider plateau have been greatly reduced.

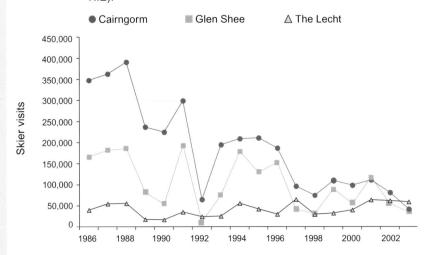

Figure 22.A Changes in the number of visits made by skiers to each of the Cairngorms ski centres during 1986-2003 (from figures provided by HIE).

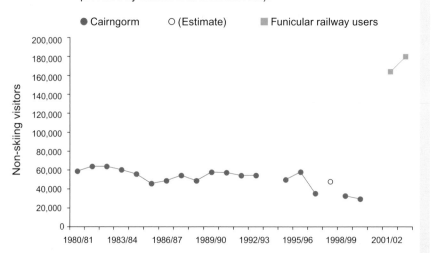

Figure 22.B The number of non-skiing visitors to Cairn Gorm using the chairlift (1980/81-2002/03) or the funicular railway (since 2002) (from figures provided by CairnGorm Mountain Ltd).

Table 22.5 The main activity identified by respondents to the Cairngorm Mountain Recreation Survey 1997–98 (Taylor & MacGregor, 1999).

Main activity	Percentage of respondents
Walking to mountain summits	49%
Walking in the glens (>3 hours)	21%
Walking in the glens (1–3 hours)	13%
Winter climbing	3%
Mountain biking	3%
Ski tour/mountaineering	2%
Wildlife observation	2%

Table 22.6 Main activities identified by respondents to the Rothiemurchus and Glenmore Recreation Survey 1998–99 (Mather, 2000).

Main activity	Percentage of respondents
Walking (1–3 hours)	33%
Walking (>3 hours)	21%
Walking (<1 hour)	11%
Cycling	10%
Resting/taking breaks/stretching legs	7%
Visiting an attraction	4%
Shopping	2%
Watersports	2%
Wildlife observation	2%
Sunbathing/relaxing	2%

impacts on upland habitats, species and landscape interests in their vicinity. Persistent habitat damage can be caused by the use of equipment for creating pistes, and by continued skiing over insufficient snow.

Damage to habitats as a result of the construction of ski areas in the Cairngorms has long been documented (e.g. Bayfield, 1974, 1979; Watson, 1985; Hindley, 1988). Much work has been carried out on reinstating damaged ground in ski areas, including grass seeding on bulldozed ski pistes (Bayfield, 1980, 1996). Modern construction methods have improved since the 1960s and 1970s, reducing their environmental impact. During the construction of the Cairngorm funicular railway, for example, new techniques and equipment applied during the development phase resulted in reduced impacts to habitats (Duncan & Robinson, 2002). As noted in Chapter 18, skiing infrastructure can also result in adverse impacts on bird species. For example, during 1967–96, skiing activities adversely affected the numbers and breeding success of Ptarmigan *Lagopus mutus* at Cairn Gorm ski area and on adjacent ground. These changes were attributed to collisions with overhead cables on tows and lifts, and to an influx of Carrion Crows *Corvus corone*, which predate Ptarmigan eggs and are attracted by the availability of food scraps left both by non-skiing and skiing visitors (Watson, 1996; Watson & Moss, 2004).

The facilities and infrastructure associated with downhill skiing can therefore also have indirect effects on habitats and species, by attracting non-skiing visitors into the area. Easier access to ski areas and adjacent upland habitats via lifts and

Road providing access to the Lecht sking area, Aberdeenshire.
Photo: *L. Gill*

Collisions with snow fences and other skiing infrastructure on Cairn Gorm have raised adult mortality in the Ptarmigan population. Breeding success has also declined significantly, as a result of egg and chick predation by Carrion Crows, attracted onto the hill by food scraps left by visitors.

Photo: *N. Benvie*

constructed tracks and paths has contributed to an increase in visitor numbers (Watson, 1991), which in turn has contributed to an increase in the number and width of informal footpaths, both within ski areas and on adjacent land (Lance *et al.,* 1989, 1991; Watson, 1991; Taylor & MacGregor, 1999). Furthermore, these trampling impacts have spread away from footpaths (Watson, 1985). Such changes cannot be wholly attributed to ski areas, however, as there has been a general increase in the popularity of hillwalking over the same period.

Damage to habitats as a result of skiing has been examined at three Scottish ski centres, two of which lie within the Cairngorms. Changes in the proportion of bare ground, from whatever cause, were compared on skied and non-skied areas alike. The results showed a small difference at Cairngorm (c. +3% in skied areas, which may not be statistically significant), but the difference at the Lecht was significantly greater (*c.* +17%) (Ross, 2001). The damage at this site is a product of the comparatively low altitude, deep peat and heather-dominated vegetation, and has been caused by the use of piste machines and skiing when there is inadequate snow cover.

For these reasons, management of ski areas includes ongoing habitat reinstatement. For example, annual inspections take place after each ski season on Cairn Gorm and Glen Shee to identify and reinstate any damaged areas. Footpaths are actively managed in order to avoid new paths from developing and to reduce trampling effects. Users are advised on ways of reducing their impact on habitats close to and well away from footpaths. Management of some ski areas involves actively pursuing the removal of redundant ski infrastructure, one notable example being the removal of snow fencing from Coire an t'Sneachda in 2001.

Visitor numbers

Results from visitor surveys indicate that the more popular parts of the Cairngorms receive several hundred thousand visitors annually. For example, it has been estimated that around 150,000 people used the East Grampians and Lochnagar survey area for recreation during 1995 (Mather, 1998), that 123,000 mountain users visited the Cairngorms massif over a twelve-month period in 1997–98 (Taylor & MacGregor, 1999), and that around 450,000 recreational visits were made to the Rothiemurchus and Glenmore area during a twelve-month period in 1998–99 (Mather, 2000). In addition, automatic people-counters sited on popular paths and routes around the Cairngorms give some information about patterns of use along the most popular routes. In general, counter data show that the routes with the highest visitor numbers are close to popular access points, such as the Cairn Gorm car park and the Linn of Dee. Counters located further from these points, even if they are on popular hillwalking routes, may only have 2,000–8,000 passes per year.

Figure 22.2 demonstrates the popularity of the Northern Corries route (which leads away from the Cairngorm Ski Area car park) and compares counts from this route with those from other parts of the Cairngorms. The dip in visitor passes during 1998–2000 may reflect the construction period of the funicular railway, when fewer visitors were using the Cairngorm car park. The recent increase in numbers probably reflects the changed visitor management arrangements in this area, which accompanied the opening of the funicular railway.

Seasonal variation

Seasonal variation in the number and age profile, time spent and activities of visitors to the Cairngorms has been noted both from surveys and people-counter data. In 2003, the number of visitors detected by seven people-counters peaked in August, with smaller peaks evident in February and April. Similar patterns have been demonstrated by Gardiner (2000) for the period 1996–1999. These findings demonstrate the seasonal shift in patterns of recreational use of land in the Cairngorms, where use of particular routes reflects change in the demand for hillwalking, ice climbing or winter mountaineering. Summer is the most popular season for visitors to most of the sites where people-counters are installed, reflecting the wider appeal of outdoor recreation in good weather. In contrast, counters installed on popular winter climbing or walking routes have recorded peaks in late winter or early spring, although the volume of visitors in these periods is much lower than the summer peaks.

In East Grampian, July–September is the busiest period in the mountains, with visitor numbers exceeding 25,000 in August (Mather, 1998). Note, however, that visitors who did not leave their cars, or ventured only short distances, were not counted. Hence, the true number of visitors will have been higher than indicated here. For example, about 12% of visitors to East Grampian were thought to have spent less than one hour in the area. The number of such visitors recorded during the summer months was some 2–3 times that recorded in other seasons.

Visitor profiles can also vary according to season. This was particularly marked in the Cairngorms Mountain Recreation Survey, where young, male winter climbers had significantly different attitudes towards many of

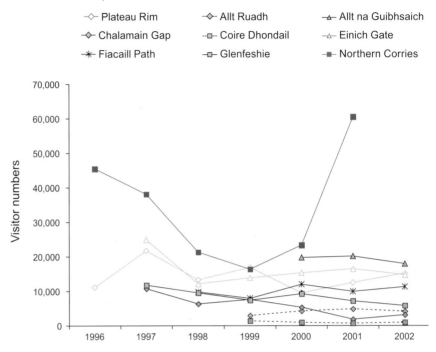

Figure 22.2 Visitor numbers recorded from nine people-counters in the Cairngorms (1996–2002), showing the relative popularity of the Northern Corries compared to other routes.

the questions asked, and also represented a very different visitor profile from other mountain users. Age profiles also represented a difference, for example in the Rothiemurchus and Glenmore Recreation Survey, the percentage of respondents under 35 years of age was higher during the summer and winter months than at other times of the year. This age category accounted for 24% of respondents in the autumn, rising to 38% in the winter, suggesting that winter sports (skiing, snow boarding and ice climbing) or winter weather may have attracted relatively high numbers of this age category. Conversely, the number of respondents over 35 years of age peaked in the spring and autumn.

Duration of visits

Nationally, the mean duration of leisure visits as shown by the Scottish Recreation Survey was 4.3 hours (TNS, 2004). In the Cairngorms, survey responses have shown a wide variation in the average duration of leisure visits. In the Cairngorms Mountain Recreation Survey the mean trip length was 5.4 hours (Taylor & MacGregor, 1999), whereas the mean duration of visits to

Figure 22.3 Three indices of growth in mountain recreation in Scotland during 1945–99.

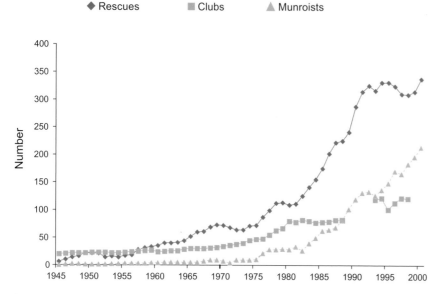

Sources: Data supplied by R. Aitken, after Aitken (1977). Derived from annual listings of mountain rescues and Munro completions in the *Scottish Mountaineering Club Journal*, and from records of the Mountaineering Council of Scotland.

the Rothiemurchus and Glenmore area was of *c.* 90 minutes, but varied widely (Mather, 2000). Substantial numbers of respondents visited for less than 30 minutes, and fewer than 20% of visits lasted more than 3 hours. However, trip lengths were much longer for those undertaking hillwalking or rock or ice climbing. Amongst respondents to the East Grampians and Lochnagar Visitor Survey (1995), mountain users had a significantly longer stay in the hills, often of around 5–7 hours in length (Mather, 1998). This would also explain the longer average visits by respondents to the Cairngorms Mountain Recreation Survey, a higher percentage of whom were hillwalking.

Data from people-counters show marked diurnal variation, some counters having distinct peaks in the morning (for example, at around 10 am at Derry Lodge or White Bridge), while higher altitude counters on Cairngorm summit show peaks in the middle of the day (Gardiner, 2000). The lower altitude counters also show a late afternoon peak. This contrasts with counters at 'honeypot' sites such as Glen Muick, which demonstrate no such distinct pattern, indicating that there are a large number of short visits to this area at all times of the day.

Recreation trends

Evidence suggests that participation in informal outdoor recreation in the Cairngorms has increased markedly in the last 50 years. For example, national data show an increase in the number of hill walkers completing all of the Munros (although this of course will exclude hillwalkers who do not complete the Munros), the number of mountain rescues made and the number of hill-walking/mountaineering clubs established, although trends since the 1990s have been more variable (Figure 22.3) (Scottish Natural Heritage, 2002b). The longest run of comparable data on visitor numbers in any mountain area in Scotland has been collected on the Cairn Gorm plateau (Watson, 1991). Spot counts taken in the summer over the period 1941–88 indicate that visitor numbers were low but fluctuating during 1947–55, and that there were slightly higher numbers during 1956–61. Following the construction of the Cairngorm ski area in 1960–61, there was a big increase in summer visitor numbers on the plateau in 1962, and numbers continued to rise until the mid-1970s. Thereafter, numbers fluctuated throughout the late 1970s and 1980s.

Although people-counter data has been collected for over 10 years, it has been difficult to establish trends from these. This is due partly to the reliability problems of the counters and the fact that for certain counters no long-term data are available. For the majority of counters, however, count records were more or less stable over the period 1996–2002 (Figure 22.2).

Key issues and future management

As has been demonstrated above, participation in outdoor recreation in the Cairngorms has increased over the past century. Many more people are now accessing the area, and participating in a wider range of activities than was the case 40–50 years ago. New opportunities afforded by the commencement of a general right of responsible access under the Land Reform (Scotland) Act 2003, alongside other initiatives to encourage participation in outdoor recreation, are likely to continue to stimulate growth in recreational use of the area, particularly on lower altitude path networks. This trend helps to support many jobs in the local and national economy, and is beneficial for the maintenance of a viable rural community and for public health, but can also have a negative impact on the area's natural heritage.

Overcrowding. Loss of habitat, disturbance of birds or other species, trampling of vegetation (see Legg, 2000), erosion of footpaths, litter and the wider impacts of unsustainable forms of transport, can all detract from the area's quality. This is particularly the case at 'honeypot' sites, such as Loch Morlich and the Linn of Dee, where the cumulative impacts of large numbers of visitors require on-going management. Perceptions of the natural environment can also be affected when the area's recreational 'carrying capacity' is exceeded, either through visual impacts or through overcrowding.

Trampling. In upland environments, sensitive moss and lichen communities are easily damaged by trampling (Bayfield *et al.*, 1981), and the resulting bare soil is much more susceptible to wind and other erosion. Development of an infrastructure for recreation can lead to a loss of habitat, and can alter drainage patterns locally. All of these negative impacts can affect the wild qualities that underpin these activities (Scottish Natural Heritage, 2002b).

Footpath erosion. Specific problems identified in the Cairngorms relating to recreational land use include a growing concern over the condition of footpaths, as severe erosion on upland paths leads to widening of paths, loss of habitat, and erosion. These effects are now often countered to some degree by sensitive path restoration. Examples include footpath work carried out on the HIE Cairngorms Estate, on Lochnagar by the Upper Deeside Access Trust, and in particular where there is some evidence of an increasing wild land resource (sometimes termed 'rewilding'), as on the Mar Lodge Estate, where bulldozed tracks are being restored to footpaths by the National Trust for Scotland (Mackay, 2002).

Impacts on land management. There are concerns that recreational use disturbs other land management practices traditionally undertaken in the Cairngorms, such as deer stalking. Latterly, this concern has been addressed with the promotion of the 'Hillphones' programme by SNH and the Mountaineering Council of Scotland, where estates can leave messages on dedicated telephone numbers advising walkers where stalking is taking place, and of alternative routes available. The Scottish Outdoor Access Code, with its key message of mutual respect and detailed guidance for both 'recreation takers' and land managers, should also help to minimise disturbance.

Downhill skiing. A decline in the number of skiers, and an increased reliance on income generated from non-skiing visitors, may in future lead to greater pressure for further diversification at ski centres. Also, as winter conditions change, new skiing uplift methods may be considered as parts of existing ski areas become unsuitable for skiing. The latter may lead to some skiing infrastructure becoming redundant and subsequently removed. Further research is required into reliable methods for reinstating damaged habitats in a variety of montane conditions.

The National Planning Policy Guideline (NPPG) 12 (Scottish Office Development Department, 1997), on Skiing Developments, calls for caution regarding the establishment of new ski centres, while encouraging further growth at existing centres. In particular, specific guidance is provided for all of the ski centres in the Cairngorms area, providing guidance on identifying preferred areas for expansion, areas where expansion is inappropriate, and for work required to maintain and enhance existing infrastructure. The main objectives of the guidelines are to ensure that environmental considerations are addressed, and that future expansion can be achieved in a sustainable manner.

Integrated access. As the profile of much of the Cairngorms area is raised through National Park status, it is inevitable that changes will occur in the volume of visitors, and perhaps also in their recreational preferences. New developments for recreation, such as the cycle route from Aviemore to Glenmore, may alter patterns of recreational use to some extent. The implementation of the right of responsible access, and the increasing development of new outdoor sports, may also introduce new visitor impacts. One possibility is an increase in water-based recreation. Awareness of these changes will help ensure that a good understanding of visitor use of the area is maintained, so that visitors and their impacts on the natural heritage can be managed suitably in the future.

National Park status in the Cairngorms offers an unprecedented opportunity for the integrated management of recreation with all other land uses and conservation interests in the area. One example of such an initiative is the Eastern Cairngorms Access Project, which aims to develop sensitively path and other access infrastructure in the Eastern Cairngorms. In partnership with other initiatives (perhaps rural development or wider nature conservation projects), there is much scope for future use of the National Park as a demonstration area for best practice recreational management, or to pilot innovative recreational management practices.

This chapter has detailed the activities that people can participate in when visiting the Cairngorms area, and outlined some of the reasons why people visit this particular area of Scotland. It is important to remember the key

Erosion, associated with run-off, can seriously damage well-used footpaths in the hills.
Photo: *L. Gill*

A footpath with repaired edges, Ben Vrackie.
Photo: *L. Gill*

factors that attract visitors to the Cairngorms: peace and quiet, wildness and beautiful scenery. However, it must be recognised that one of the key issues for the Cairngorms area is how to manage this existing recreational resource and to recognise new opportunities in the area, whilst ensuring that the quality of the natural heritage is not compromised. It is crucial that recreation is managed appropriately, ensuring that provisions for recreation enhance the visitor's experience, and do not damage the natural heritage attributes that are so important to the visitor.

References

Aitken, R. (1977). *Wilderness Areas in Scotland.* PhD thesis, University of Aberdeen.

Bayfield, N.G. (1974). Burial of vegetation by erosion debris near ski lifts on Cairngorm, Scotland. *Biological Conservation* 6: 246–251.

Bayfield, N.G. (1979). Recovery of four montane heath communities on Cairngorm, Scotland, from disturbance by trampling. *Biological Conservation* 15: 165–179.

Bayfield, N.G. (1980). Replacement of vegetation on disturbed ground near ski lifts in the Cairngorm Mountains, Scotland. *Journal of Biogeography* 7: 249–260.

Bayfield, N.G. (1996). Long term changes in colonization of bulldozed ski pistes at Cairn Gorm, Scotland. *Journal of Applied Ecology* 33: 1359–1365.

Bayfield, N.G., Urquhart, U.H. & Cooper, S.M. (1981). Susceptibility of four species of *Cladonia* to disturbance by trampling in the Cairngorm Mountains, Scotland. *Journal of Applied Ecology* 18: 303–310.

Cairngorms Working Party (1992). *Common sense and sustainability: a partnership for the Cairngorms.* The Report of the Cairngorms Working Party to the Secretary of State for Scotland. The Scottish Office: Edinburgh

Duncan, K. & Robinson, B. (2002). The Cairn Gorm funicular railway – Minimising the impact, 2002. *Enact* 10(3): 13–16.

Gardiner, J. (2000). *Analysis of data from automatic people-counters in the Cairngorms.* Scottish Natural Heritage Commissioned Report F99AA615. SNH: Perth.

George Street Research (2003a). *Highlands Visitor Survey Full year report.* Highlands of Scotland Tourist Board, Highland Council, Scottish Natural Heritage, Highlands and Islands Enterprise, VisitScotland and Forest Enterprise. HOST: Strathpeffer.

George Street Research (2003b). *Highlands Visitor Survey— Moray, Badenoch and Strathspey Area Report.* Highlands of Scotland Tourist Board, Highland Council, Scottish Natural Heritage, Highlands and Islands Enterprise, VisitScotland and Forest Enterprise. HOST: Strathpeffer.

George Street Research (2003c). *Highlands Visitor Survey — Walking Wild Report.* Highlands of Scotland Tourist Board, Highland Council, Scottish Natural Heritage, Highlands and Islands Enterprise, VisitScotland and Forest Enterprise. HOST: Strathpeffer.

Hindley, J. (1988). *Visitor impact on the distribution of montane invertebrates and vegetation in Coire Cas, Cairngorms: some management implications.* MSc Thesis, University of Edinburgh.

Lance, A., Baugh, I.D., & Love. J.A. (1989). Continued footpath widening in the Cairngorm Mountains, Scotland. *Biological Conservation* 49: 210–214.

Lance, A., Thaxton, R. & Watson, A. (1991). Recent changes in footpath width in the Cairngorms. *Scottish Geographical Magazine* 7(2): 106–109.

Legg, C. (2000). *Review of published work in relation to monitoring of trampling impacts and change in montane vegetation.* Scottish Natural Heritage, Review No. 131. SNH: Edinburgh.

Lowland Market Research (2003). *Cairngorms National Park Visitor Survey — Interim Report.* Unpublished Report. Cairngorms National Park Authority: Grantown-on-Spey.

Mackay, J.W. (2002). Open air recreation in the Cairngorms. In: Gimingham, C.H. (ed.), *The Ecology, Land Use and Conservation of the Cairngorms.* Packard: Chichester.

Mather, A.S. (1998). *East Grampians and Lochnagar User Survey 1995.* Scottish Natural Heritage Research Survey and Monitoring Report No. 104. SNH: Perth.

Mather, A.S. (2000). *Rothiemurchus & Glenmore Recreation Survey 1998–99.* Scottish Natural Heritage Research Survey and Monitoring Report No. 166. SNH: Perth.

NFO (2003a). *Abernethy/Dell Wood National Nature Reserve Visitor Survey.* Unpublished Report. SNH: Perth.

NFO (2003b). *Muir of Dinnet National Nature Reserve Visitor Survey.* Unpublished Report. SNH: Perth.

NFO (2003c). *Creag Meagaidh National Nature Reserve Visitor Survey.* Unpublished Report. SNH: Perth.

Price, M.F., Dixon, B.J., Warren, C.R. & Macpherson, A.R. (2002). *Scotland's Mountains: Key issues for their future management.* SNH: Perth.

Ross, A. (2001). A comparison of the impacts of skiing at three ski resorts in Scotland. Unpublished thesis, University of Aberdeen.

Scottish Natural Heritage (2002a). *Wildness in Scotland's countryside – a policy statement.* SNH: Perth.

Scottish Natural Heritage (2002b). *Natural Heritage Futures: Cairngorms Massif.* SNH: Perth.

Scottish Office Development Department (1997). *NPPG 12, Skiing Developments.* The Scottish Office: Edinburgh.

Scottish Office Development Department (1999). *NPPG 14, Natural Heritage.* The Scottish Office: Edinburgh.

SNH (2002). Wildness in Scotland's Countryside. *Scottish Natural Heritage Policy Statement No. 02/03.* SNH: Perth.

Taylor, J. & MacGregor, C. (1999). *Cairngorms Mountain Recreation Survey 1997–1998.* Scottish Natural Heritage Research Survey and Monitoring Report No. 162. SNH: Perth.

TNS (2004). Scottish Recreation Survey: Interim Report (July–December 2003). Unpublished report. SNH: Perth.

Watson, A. (1984). Paths and People in the Cairngorms. *Scottish Geographical Magazine* 100: 151–160.

Watson, A. (1985). Soil erosion and vegetation damage near ski lifts at Cairn Gorm, Scotland. *Biological Conservation* 33: 363–381.

Watson, A. (1991). Increase of people on the Cairn Gorm Plateau following easier access. *Scottish Geographical Magazine* 107(2): 99–105.

Watson, A. (1996). Human induced increases of carrion crows and gulls on Cairngorms Plateaux. *Scottish Birds* 18(4): 205–213.

Watson, A. & Moss, R. (2004). Impacts of ski-development on ptarmigan (*Lagopus mutus*) at Cairn Gorm, Scotland. *Biological Conservation* 116(2): 267–275.

Additional reading

Sidaway, R. (2001). The effects of recreation on the natural heritage: the need to focus on improving management practice. In: Usher, M.B. (ed.), *Enjoyment and Understanding of the Natural Heritage.* The Stationery Office: Edinburgh.

Smith, G. (2004). New buzz on the slopes as karts cash in at ski centres. *The Herald* 30 August 2004.

23. PATTERNS OF SPECIES DIVERSITY IN THE CAIRNGORMS

Philip Shaw and Des B.A. Thompson

Summary

1. This concluding chapter explores patterns of variation in species diversity and richness in the Cairngorms, focussing on those species for which the area is considered to be nationally or internationally important.

2. A total of 1,153 such species have been identified in the Cairngorms area. Of these, 32% are invertebrates, 28% lichens, 20% fungi, 9% bryophytes and 7% vascular plants. Only 2% are birds, and fewer than 0.5% are fish or mammals.

3. These nationally important species are associated mainly with woodlands (39% of species), rock (20%) and montane habitats (15%). Two of the most extensive habitats in the Cairngorms, moorland and grassland, each support only about 3% of the area's important species. The number of nationally important species associated mainly with woodlands in the Cairngorms is thus more than ten times greater than that associated mainly with moorland or grassland.

4. Habitat associations of 223 species largely or entirely restricted to the Cairngorms show a broadly similar pattern, 45% being associated mainly with woodlands, 20% with montane habitats and 15% with rocky habitats. The Cairngorms' woodlands are therefore more than twice as rich in nationally important and restricted-range species as its montane habitats.

5. Fungi, lichens, bryophytes and vascular plants differ markedly in their habitat associations. While the majority of important fungi species occur mainly in woodlands, important lichens and vascular plants are more strongly associated with rocky habitats, and bryophytes with montane habitats.

6. The four largest invertebrate groups (diptera, coleoptera, lepidoptera and hymenoptera) were more consistent in their preference for wooded habitats, but differed in their dependence on wetland and freshwater habitats (important for coleoptera and diptera), and on grassland and moorland habitats (more important for lepidoptera and hymenoptera).

7. The three richest areas identified are Strathspey forests: at Abernethy, Rothiemurchus, and Craigellachie to Coylumbridge. Abernethy Forest alone holds one fifth of the Cairngorms' nationally important species, and almost one third of its restricted-range species.

8. Strathspey appears to be much richer in nationally important species than Deeside, although such differences may in part reflect variation in survey effort. In the hills and mountains, the central and eastern Cairngorms, and the Glas Maol – Lochnagar complex support the richest assemblages of nationally important and restricted-range montane species.

9. We highlight some likely biases due to variation in sampling effort, and the pace with which species distribution data are changing. We note that several recent finds have been made in the Cairngorms, of species new to Britain or new to science; some discovered during the preparation of this book. Estimates of the number of important species in the Cairngorms will therefore doubtless change, as species distribution data are improved.

10. We discuss the importance of developing a more comprehensive knowledge-base of the distribution and ecological needs of nationally important species. Effective management and conservation calls for a better understanding of the diverse and changing nature of the Cairngorms.

The high tops and, especially, the native pine forests of the Cairngorms support a wealth of nationally important species. The remnant pinewoods of Glen Quoich (opposite) have rich assemblages of scarce fungi and lichens, while nearby Beinn a' Bhuird and Ben Avon are important for lichens, bryophytes and vascular plants, some of which occur nowhere else in Britain.

Photo: L. Gill

Shaw, P. & Thompson, D.B.A. (2006). Patterns of species diversity in the Cairngorms. In: Shaw, P. & Thompson, D.B.A. (eds.). *The Nature of the Cairngorms: Diversity in a changing environment.* The Stationery Office. pp. 395-411.

Introduction

The landforms, habitats and mix of species in the Cairngorms are more Arctic-alpine in nature than those of any other part of Britain. The area's boreal forest and mountain ecosystems are unique in terms of their composition, scale and quality, and especially important as a western outpost of Europe's mountain ranges. This largely accounts for the Cairngorms' abiding appeal for naturalists, walkers, scientists, photographers and many others, detailed by Nethersole-Thompson and Watson (1981), Cosgrove (2002), Gimingham (2002) and others. It also accounts for the area's many national and international conservation designations; indeed, some workers have argued that the Cairngorms area is the most important in Britain for nature conservation (Ratcliffe, 1977).

In this book we have sought to describe the nature of the Cairngorms in a British context rather than a local one, highlighting features for which the area is nationally important. This is more easily accomplished for discrete physical or natural features than it is for the area's more aesthetic elements. It is, for example, less easy to evaluate the special appeal of the Cairngorms' landscape, or the spiritual value of its 'wild land', the qualities of which are – in every sense – beyond measure.

Instead, we have assessed the area's value in terms of tangible biological attributes: its rare and threatened species. This approach was borne partly out of a need to identify and list what appear to be 'priority' species, rather than attempt to compile full species lists, which would, in any case, include many taxa more widespread or abundant elsewhere in Britain. Moreover, the Cairngorms' relatively modest species totals would only tend to confirm a general rule of biogeography: that cool, mountainous areas at high latitudes usually support fewer species than warm, lowland, southerly ones (e.g. Fischer, 1960; Rapoport, 1982; Stevens, 1989; Nagy et al., 2003).

Throughout, we have used the term 'important species' to mean species whose range or population in the Cairngorms area is considered to be nationally important, either by virtue of its size (relative to the rest of the Britain), or because the species is nationally rare or threatened. Here, we compare the number of important species associated with each of the Cairngorms' main habitat types, and show how this varies throughout the area, identifying localities particularly rich in such species. However we recognise the limitations inherent in applying a single yardstick to the area, and are aware that alternative measures, based perhaps on geodiversity, landscape, habitats or recreational use, would highlight quite different aspects of the area's natural wealth. Nevertheless, we hope that this approach can be developed for other, comparable parts of Europe.

How many species have nationally important populations in Cairngorms?

By virtue of their size, rarity or appeal, some of the Cairngorms' important species have a much higher public profile than others. Familiar groups such as the birds and mammals include prominent conservation 'flagship' species like the Osprey *Pandion haliaetus*, Capercaillie *Tetrao urogallus* and Red Squirrel *Sciurus vulgaris*; species which, by definition, receive much greater public attention than those from less 'celebrated' groups. Yet it is the latter – particularly the fungi, lichens, bryophytes and insects – that make up the bulk of the area's nationally important species.

Based on lists presented in Chapters 11–19, the Cairngorms area is nationally important for 1,153[1] species, of which 90% are fungi, lichens, bryophytes or invertebrates (Figure 23.1; see Box 23.1). In contrast, birds account for only about 2% of the area's important species, and mammals and fish for less than 0.5% each. Among the invertebrates, the 'true flies' and beetles dominate, accounting for about 45% and 25%, respectively, of important invertebrates, and thus greatly out-numbering the area's important dragonfly, butterfly and moth species. Indeed, flies alone make up about 15% of the Cairngorms' important species.

Disparities between the main taxonomic groups, in terms of the number of nationally important species they contain, are therefore striking. However, gaps in our knowledge of status and distribution have introduced two main areas of uncertainty into the analysis, as follows. First, the identification of many fungi, lichens, bryophytes and invertebrate species often requires specialist skills that are themselves scarce. As a result, the national rarity of some of the species in these groups may have been overstated. Indeed, as noted in Chapter 12, almost two-thirds of British lichen taxa are either 'nationally rare' or 'nationally scarce', limiting the usefulness of these categories. Whilst it is possible that many of the taxa in these groups are genuinely less widespread than most higher plants and vertebrates, it seems likely that their small known ranges are also due to under-recording, given that there is a dearth of experienced mycologists, bryologists, lichenologists, coleopterists and other such specialists.

[1] Including a small number of species whose occurrence in the Cairngorms is in doubt, and requires confirmation. These figures will doubtless change, as species distribution data are improved.

Second, much of the Cairngorms area has not been surveyed adequately for fungi, lichens, bryophytes or invertebrates. As a result, important populations of rare species might have been overlooked, in which case the figures presented in Figure 23.1 could instead prove conservative.

While most species were selected on the basis of range or distribution, the criteria used for identifying important bird species differed slightly from those applied to other groups. Most bird species identified as 'important' (Chapter 18) were selected partly because the Cairngorms encompass a high proportion of their UK *breeding* range. If wintering range had also been taken into account the Cairngorms area would appear far less significant for migratory species such as Purple Sandpiper *Calidris maritima*, Green Sandpiper *Tringa ochropus*, Wood Sandpiper *T. glareola*, Snow Bunting *Plectrophenax nivalis* and Wigeon *Anas penelope*. Since no distinction was made between breeding range and general occurrence for other species, most of which are sedentary, the effect of this will have been to raise very slightly the number of 'important' bird species in comparison with other groups.

Noting these matters, it is clear that invertebrate species for which the Cairngorms are nationally important greatly out-number vertebrates; by a factor of 11:1. Similarly, nationally important fungi, lichens and bryophytes together out-number important vascular plants by about 8:1. Even assuming that our knowledge of species distributions improves significantly over time, enabling us to distinguish the genuinely rare from the under-recorded, important species in the Cairngorms will continue to be dominated numerically by lichens, fungi, bryophytes and invertebrates: groups whose ecological requirements tend to be least understood, and with which most land managers and conservationists are unfamiliar.

Species largely restricted to the Cairngorms

In Chapter 15, Rotheray and Horsfield list 92 invertebrate species which, in Britain, are currently known only from Cairngorms National Park. These include 52 'true flies', 20 beetles and two spider species, one of which (the wolf spider *Pardosa lugubris*) has thus far been recorded in Britain only from Abernethy Forest. The fungi, lichens and bryophytes include many similar examples; of species found

Figure 23.1. The number of species for which the Cairngorms area is considered nationally important. Taxonomic groups have been arranged in descending order of the number of nationally important species in the Cairngorms. Box 23.1 gives details of the selection criteria and methods used.

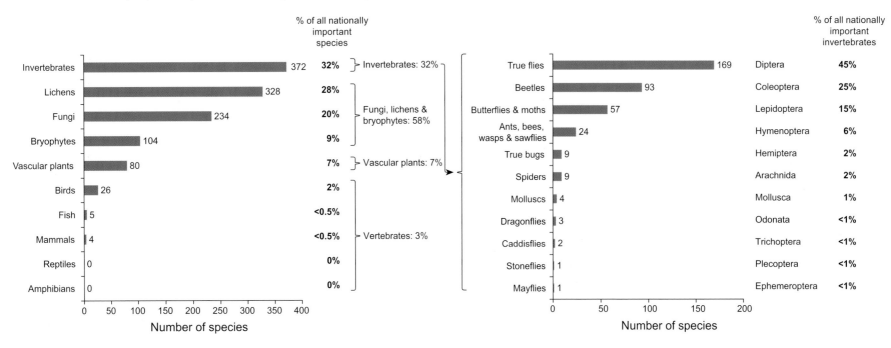

Sources: Species lists presented in Chapters 11–19.

in the Cairngorms at one or only a few sites, and nowhere else in Britain.

Altogether, 223 species have been found to be largely or entirely restricted, in Britain, to the Cairngorms area. These account for 23% of the Cairngorms' important bryophytes, but for only 11% of its (better surveyed) vascular plants. Similarly, 26% of the area's important invertebrate species are largely restricted to the Cairngorms, but only 9% of its vertebrates.

Habitat requirements of important species in the Cairngorms

Perhaps the most notable physical characteristics of the Cairngorms area are its broad 'whaleback' mountains and extensive high plateaux, exceptional in Britain in terms of their scale and sub-Arctic climate (see Ratcliffe & Thompson, 1988). Although their extent might suggest that montane specialists are likely to predominate among the Cairngorms' important species, a much higher number of such species are associated with woodlands

than with montane habitats. Indeed, woodlands support about 39% of the area's important species, while only 15% are associated mainly with montane habitats and 20% with rocky habitats (Figure 23.2a). Wetlands and freshwaters, in combination, support a further 13% of important species. These figures should be treated with caution, however, given the level of uncertainty that exists over the distributions of many fungi, lichens, bryophytes and invertebrate species, and, in some cases, their habitat associations. Variation in survey effort probably also partly accounts for disparities between habitats, woodlands being more accessible than the more exposed, montane habitats. Moreover, differences between habitats may also reflect the way in which species have been apportioned between them. Rocky habitats, for example, occur within a range of settings, from straths to hillsides to high tops, and some of the species they support might well depend on being in close proximity to woodland, moorland, grassland or montane habitats. Indeed, a number of moorland and grassland species have retreated to rock crevices or ledges, in the face of intense grazing pressure within their 'preferred' habitats. As a result, some of the species

Figure 23.2.   Habitat categories with which the Cairngorms' important species are mainly associated. Each species was assigned to one habitat only.

a. Species for which the Cairngorms area is nationally important (1,153 species)

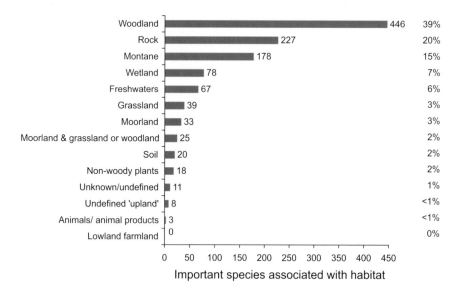

b. Species largely or entirely restricted to the Cairngorms area (223 species)[1]

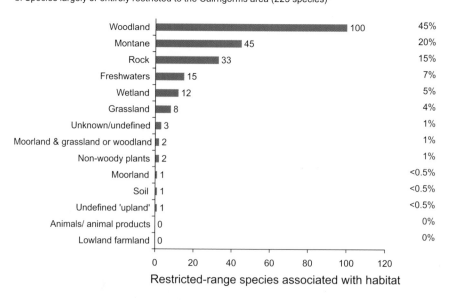

[1] Species whose range or population in the Cairngorms area is thought to account for >75% of their British range or population (or 25% in the case of BAP Priority species).

Sources: Species lists in Chapters 11–19.

assigned here to rocky habitats may naturally have closer affinities with moorland or grassland.

Clearly, some of the area's habitats support much greater numbers of rare and threatened species than others. Figure 23.2a shows that wooded habitats in the Cairngorms are about 13 times richer than heather moorland and 11 times richer than grassland, in terms of nationally important species. These disparities are even more pronounced when the extent of each habitat is considered. Despite being the main habitat for some 39% of important species, woodlands cover only about 17% of the land area of the Cairngorms (Chapter 7). In contrast, moorland appears to support only 3% of the Cairngorms' important species, but covers some 42% of its area (Chapter 5)[2]. This finding probably reflects the fact that although well-managed heather moorland can be species-rich, most of its species are widespread and abundant throughout much of upland Britain.

Wooded habitats were found to support an even greater proportion of those species largely confined, in Britain, to the Cairngorms. Of 223 such species, 100 (45%) are associated mainly with woodlands or trees (Figure 23.2b). Montane habitats were also relatively more important for these restricted-range species than for nationally important species *per se*. Conversely, moorlands hold proportionately fewer restricted-range species, being the main habitat of just one such species: the fungus Northern Bilberry Redleaf *Exobasidium expansum*, recorded in Britain just once, on a lower flank of Cairn Gorm (Chapter 11).

The area's woodlands support more than twice as many nationally important and restricted-range species as its montane habitats. However, this disparity stems mainly from the habitat affinities of the two largest species groups examined: invertebrates and fungi. About 43% of important invertebrate species and 70% of fungi were associated mainly with woodland habitats. Although many lichens were also dependent on woodlands, more were associated with rocky habitats, which were also favoured by vascular plant species (Figure 23.3). In contrast, more of the area's important bryophyte species were dependent on montane habitats than on rock or woodlands, where they are likely to be out-competed by vascular plants.

The four largest invertebrate groups were more consistent in their preference for wooded habitats (Figure 23.4). Between 37% and 55% of the area's important 'true fly' species (diptera), beetles (coleoptera), butterflies and moths (lepidoptera) and ants, bees, wasps and sawflies (hymenoptera) were associated mainly with woodlands, the most woodland-dependent being the beetles.

Figure 23.3. Habitats with which the Cairngorms' nationally important fungi, lichens and plant species are mainly associated.

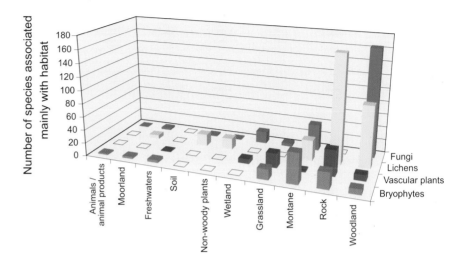

Natural regeneration of native pinewoods should benefit the many forest species for which the Cairngorms area is nationally important, particularly its fungi, lichens and invertebrates, some of which are found nowhere else in Britain.

Photo: *N. Benvie*

[2] Land cover estimates presented in Chapter 5 were derived from the Land Cover Map 2000 (Fuller *et al.*, 2002), and should be treated with caution, particularly estimates of the extent of heather moorland, grassland and bog. For this reason, the woodland cover estimate used here (17%) was derived from the Scottish Semi-Natural Woodland Inventory (Chapter 7), which is considered more accurate.

Figure 23.4. Habitats with which the Cairngorms' nationally important diptera (true flies), coleoptera (beetles), lepidoptera (butterflies and moths) and hymenoptera (ants, bees, wasps and sawflies) are mainly associated.

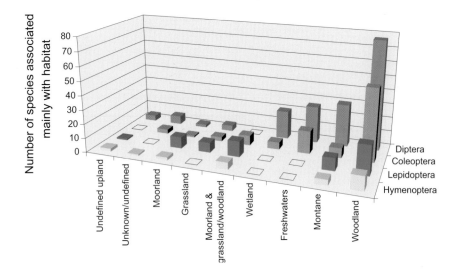

In contrast, relatively few important beetle species were associated mainly with montane habitats, which supported 16-18% of important species from each the other three groups. While 22% of the area's important beetles and 27% of its true flies were associated mainly with wetland or freshwater habitats, none of its important butterfly, moth, ant, bee, wasp or sawfly species were. Instead, the latter were more dependent on grassland and moorland habitats, sometimes in combination with woodlands (Figure 23.4).

The forests, woods, scrub and scattered trees of the Cairngorms thus support some 446 important species, of which 74% are either fungi or invertebrates. Not surprisingly – given the composition of the Cairngorms' woodlands – both groups are associated more with coniferous than with broad-leaved trees. Among the area's 164 important fungi species, almost two-thirds are associated mainly with semi-natural pine, with most of the remainder occurring in birchwoods, and only 5% occurring mainly in oakwoods (Figure 23.5a). Similarly, the majority of the Cairngorms' important woodland invertebrates were associated mainly with conifers, while many of those dependent on broad-leaved woodlands were associated mainly with birch or Aspen (Figure 23.5b).

Many of the area's important invertebrate and fungi species are dependent on dead timber, which tends to be scarce in 'well-managed' forests. As a result, wood-decomposing fungi are generally under-represented in Scottish pine

forests compared with those in continental Europe (Chapter 11). The practice of removing or burning fallen timber thus poses a significant threat to both of these major groups.

Management implications

Figure 23.2 highlights the relative importance of the Cairngorms' woodlands and, to a lesser degree, its montane and rock habitats. One interpretation of these findings is that native woodland expansion is likely to yield net benefits in terms of species diversity. This is partly because larger areas of woodland tend to be more species-rich, supporting a greater diversity of woodland specialists, such as the tooth fungi (Chapter 11). They also provide a more secure refuge for such species, reducing the risk of chance extinctions. In addition, woodland expansion could bring less obvious benefits. In Scandinavia and the Alps, for example, shrubs such as Net-leaved Willow *Salix reticulata* are rich hosts for ectomycorrhizal fungi (Chapter 11). An expansion of the montane scrub zone in the Cairngorms could therefore raise the area's fungal diversity, as well as its vascular plant and landscape diversity.

As elsewhere in Scotland, changes in woodland cover in the Cairngorms have tended to mirror the expansion and contraction of moorland and grassland areas, these changes having been well documented for the 1940s-1980s (Figure 5.3). Given the marked disparity in species richness between woodlands, moorland and grassland, it seems likely that an expansion of the former at the expense of the latter would generally yield net gains in species diversity, and a local improvement in the status of threatened and restricted-range species. But whether it does so will depend on local circumstances. In an evaluation of the likely impact of woodland expansion in the Forests of Strathspey and Mar, Whitfield & Tharme (1997) concluded that native woodland regeneration is likely to yield a net ornithological benefit in these areas (Chapter 18). Nonetheless, care will be needed to minimise any local, adverse impacts on *Natura* species, such as Golden Eagle *Aquila chrysaetos*. Also, afforestation and natural tree regeneration can impact on the area's geodiversity, by damaging or obscuring geological and geomorphological features (Chapter 2), and by changing the acidity and organic content of the soil (Chapter 3). Furthermore, heather moorland is economically and culturally important in the Highlands, and is regarded by some as almost an iconic component of its landscape (Chapters 1 & 4).

Woodland regeneration could also adversely affect sites rich in grassland fungi, as at Lui and Inverey Flats. Where regeneration does occur, care is required to ensure that conditions remain favourable for fungi, lichens and bryophytes. As noted in Chapter 11, reduced grazing pressure within woodlands, and the consequent development of a more luxuriant ground flora, may suppress the fruiting of mycorrhizal species, adversely affecting important populations of woodland specialists, such as the tooth fungi. Non-wooded habitats within woodlands may also require management attention, since these sometimes prove more species-rich than the woodland itself. Areas of old, semi-improved grassland in Abernethy Forest support an impressive suite of grassland fungi, including 29 *Hygrocybe* species, but could become unsuitable for fungal fruiting unless appropriate grazing levels are maintained (Chapter 11). In the case of bryophytes, open areas of scree, low crags and small areas of mire can support a more diverse flora than the surrounding woodland, and should be kept open where possible. As G. Rothero notes in Chapter 13, "in the enthusiasm for regeneration of woodland cover it is possible that the value of such small features may be overlooked".

Semi-improved grasslands can also be important for common species that are exceptionally abundant in parts of the Cairngorms, but whose populations nonetheless fall short of the criteria applied here. The grasslands of Strathspey, for example, support some of the highest densities of breeding waders in mainland Britain (Chapter 8), although none of the species concerned is thought to have more than 10% of its population within the Cairngorms area.

In conclusion, the large number of important and restricted-range species associated with wooded habitats in the Cairngorms (Figure 23.2) would seem to support arguments in favour of the expansion of native woodlands, at the expense of species-poor habitats. However, as noted in Chapter 14, woodland expansion should proceed in a sensitive manner, pursuing an appropriate spatial balance with more open habitats, to maximise the biodiversity and landscape values of the area.

Geographical patterns of diversity

"The crags, screes, associated flushes and snow-beds at the upper end of Caenlochan Glen form the richest single area for rare bryophytes in the Cairngorms" (Chapter 13). Similar statements are made in other parts of this book, often identifying small, discrete locations holding an unrivalled diversity of rare or threatened species. Lui Flats at Mar Lodge, for example, are outstanding for their grassland fungi, while Inverey Wood is an "extraordinarily rich area

Figure 23.5. Woodland types with which the Cairngorms' important fungal and invertebrate species are mainly associated.

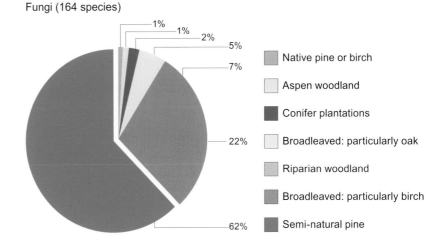

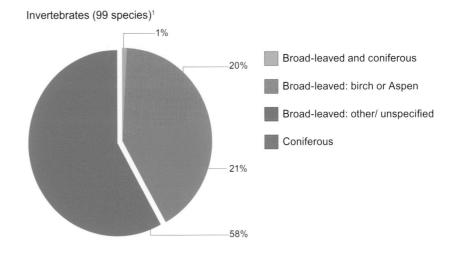

[1] Excluding 67 invertebrate species for which woodland type was not specified.

for nationally threatened pinewood fungi" (Chapter 11). Abernethy Forest is the richest of any eastern forest in terms of native pinewood indicator lichens, and the third richest area in the UK (Chapter 12). Glen Doll, Caenlochan Glen and Canness Glen are exceptionally rich for vascular plants (Chapter 14), while over 100 important invertebrate species have been recorded in the small area stretching from Craigellachie to Coylumbridge (Chapter 15). The Cairngorms clearly encompass a number of exceptional sites for scarce plant

Box 23.1. Methods and criteria used to identify species-rich habitats and areas

Identifying important species

This chapter identifies habitats and areas rich in species for which the Cairngorms are considered nationally important, based on information presented in Chapters 11-19. The species selection criteria used varied between taxonomic groups, reflecting differences in the type and quality of status information available. Distribution data for most fungi, lichen, bryophyte and invertebrate species, for example, tend to be much less comprehensive or reliable than for most bird species, whose national threat assessments often incorporate measures of abundance, trends and breeding success, as well as range size. Despite these differences, the lists of nationally important species compiled for each species group have focussed on

Table 23.A. Selection criteria used to identify species for which the Cairngorms area is nationally important.

Groups	Criteria applied
Fungi, lichens, plants and invertebrates	• At least 10% of the species' UK range occurs within the Cairngorms area; or • species classed as Nationally Rare (occurring in <16 10-km squares in the UK); or • species classed as nationally threatened; or • the species' population in the Cairngorms is considered to be of international importance.
Fish	• A qualifying species on an SAC (four species) or an SSSI (one species).
Amphibians	[No amphibian species were thought to have nationally important populations in the Cairngorms.]

Birds	• A qualifying species on an SPA or IBA in the Cairngorms area; or
	• At least 25% of UK range or population occurs in the Cairngorms area; or
	• 10-24% of UK range or population occurs in the Cairngorms area and at least one of the following applies:
	  – small UK breeding range (recorded breeding in <16 10 km squares); or
	  – small population (1-300 pairs); or
	  – Red Listed; or
	  – a BAP Priority species; or
	  – has a nationally important population on at least one IBA or SPA; or
	  – is an endemic taxon.

Mammals	• A qualifying species on an SAC in the Cairngorms area; or • At least 10% of UK range or population occurs in the Cairngorms area; or • A BAP Priority species with at least 10% of UK range likely to occur within the Cairngorms area; or • A globally threatened or near-threatened species.

similar measures: of rarity, threat status and distribution. For the purposes of this analysis, we have applied more consistent criteria to those groups for which the quality of the distribution and status data are broadly similar: the fungi, lichens, plants and invertebrates (Table 23.A).

Despite the inclusion of threat status and rarity as selection criteria, the majority of species selected (97%) qualify on the basis that the Cairngorms area encompasses at least 10% of their UK range or population. The remaining 3% were selected on the basis of their rarity within Britain or Europe, or their threat status, or because they have shown a recent decline.

Assigning species to habitat categories

Chapters 11-19 identify habitats with which the Cairngorms' important species are associated. The habitat types identified vary between chapters, largely reflecting the affinities of each group. In Chapters 12-14 (lichens, bryophytes and vascular plants) for example, types of rocky habitat are more narrowly defined than in other chapters, while in Chapter 11 (fungi) woodland types are more narrowly defined. To determine species-habitat associations consistently across all groups, the habitats listed were each assigned to an appropriate broad habitat category (Table 23.B). The number of important species associated with each broad habitat category was then summed for all species groups. In a small number of cases, where a species appears to be associated equally with two habitat categories, it has been assigned instead to a habitat combination, e.g. 'moorland and grassland' or 'moorland and woodland'.

Identifying areas rich in 'restricted-range' species

The term 'restricted-range' is commonly applied to species whose geographical range falls below a given threshold area (e.g. Stattersfield, 1998). However in this analysis we have used the word 'restricted' in the sense of being largely confined to a particular location. Restricted-range species were defined here as species whose range within the Cairngorms represents at least 75% of their British range; or 25% in the case of BAP Priority species. The latter accounted for 19% of the species considered.

Areas rich in restricted-range species were identified by counting the number of such species listed in each 'important area' defined in Chapters 11-19. Since large areas are likely to encompass greater numbers of restricted-range species the number present was divided by the area's size, yielding an average figure for the area. Areas containing restricted-range species from each taxonomic group were overlaid, producing a composite map in which colour intensity indicates the density of restricted-range species from one or more groups.

Table 23.B. Habitat categories to which habitats listed in Chapters 11-19 were assigned.

Habitat category	Component habitats	Chapter(s)
Animals/ animal products	Horn Carrion, Dung	11: Fungi 13: Bryophytes
Freshwaters	Burns: acid, calcareous, meltwater Standing water Water bodies Lochs, Rivers & streams Lochs/ farmland, Lochs/ rivers Aquatic habitats	13: Bryophytes 14: Vascular plants 15: Invertebrates 16: Fish 18: Birds 19: Mammals
Grassland	Acid/neutral grassland, Calcareous grassland Above treeline: base-poor grassland, base-rich grassland Below treeline: grassland Grassland	11: Fungi 14: Vascular plants 15: Invertebrates
Lowland farmland	Arable	14: Vascular plants
Montane	Montane Alpine heath, Late snow-lie, Montane heath Calcareous montane rocks, Snowbed Base-poor summits	11: Fungi; 15: Invertebrates; 18: Birds 12: Lichens 13: Bryophytes 14: Vascular plants
Moorland	Upland heath Heathland, Damp heath Heath, Hepatic heath Heaths Moorland	11: Fungi 12: Lichens 13: Bryophytes 15: Invertebrates 18: Birds; 19: Mammals
Moorland & grassland/ woodland	Moorland & woodland Grassland & moorland, Woodland & moorland Woodland/ moorland	14: Vascular plants 15: Invertebrates 19: Mammals
Non-woody plants	Moss cushions on limestone boulders Algae, Bryicolous, Lichenicolous, *Sphagnum*	11: Fungi 12: Lichens
Rock	Base-rich rock, Siliceous rock, Non-siliceous rock, Rock Acid rocks, Base-rich rocks, Block scree, Limestone crags Serpentine rocks Base-poor rock - cliffs and ledges, Base-rich rock - grasslands on cliffs and ledges, rock crevices, scree, serpentine or ultramafic fell-field, rocky outcrops	12: Lichens 13: Bryophytes 14: Vascular plants
Soil or peat	Peat, soil Acidic soil, Base-rich soil, Soil	11: Fungi 12: Lichens
Undefined uplands	Uplands	15: Invertebrates
Unknown/undefined	Other, unknown	15: Invertebrates
Wetlands	Bog Acid flushes, Calcareous flush, Mires Blanket bog, soligenous mires and flushes (base-poor), soligenous mires and flushes (base-rich), mires Peatland, wetland Wetland	11: Fungi 13: Bryophytes 14: Vascular plants 15: Invertebrates 18. Birds
Woodland	Aspen woodland, Broad-leaved woodland, particularly birch or oak, Conifer plantations, Native pine or birch, Riparian woodland, Semi-natural pine woodland Coniferous trees, Deciduous trees, Trees, Wood Decaying wood, Trees Upper montane scrub, base-rich woodland Pine forest, Pine forest edge/ scrub Woodland	11: Fungi 12. Lichens 13: Bryophytes 14: Vascular plants 18: Birds 14. Vascular plants; 15. Invertebrates; 19. Mammals

and animal species. Here, we identify the richest areas for species whose British range is largely restricted to the Cairngorms. The distribution of such areas is shown for fungi, lichens, bryophytes and vascular plants (Figure 23.6) and for all species groups combined (Figure 23.7).

Most of the areas notable for species largely restricted to the Cairngorms are clustered in Strathspey, the central and eastern Cairngorm mountains, on upper Deeside, the upper Angus Glens, between Glas Maol and Lochnagar, and around Blair Atholl (Figures 23.6, 23.7). In the straths, several of these areas are extensive and relatively well-surveyed, consisting mainly of pinewoods, as at Abernethy, Rothiemurchus and, to a lesser degree, Glen Tanar. Species-rich areas in the hills or on the high tops tend to coincide with base-rich rocks, as at Coire Kander, Glen Callater, Caenlochan and Glen Doll, or with small patches of late snow-lie, as at Ciste Mhearad, Coire Domhain, Feith Buidhe and Garbh Uisge Mor. Indeed, the Cairngorm mountains have a greater abundance of snow-bed lichens than any other part of Britain (Chapter 12), and more bryophyte-dominated snow-beds than, for example, Ben Nevis, Ben Alder and Creag Meagaidh combined (Chapter 13).

Strathspey

Despite its wealth of montane species, the three richest areas in the Cairngorms are forests in Strathspey. At least 180 important species have been recorded from Rothiemurchus and 241 from Abernethy Forest, of which 65 are largely confined to the Cairngorms area. While these pinewoods are among the largest native forests in Britain, the Cairngorms' third richest woodland, at Craigellachie, is relatively small. At least 123 important species and 39 restricted-range species have been recorded from an area encompassing Craigellachie and stretching to Coylumbridge (Figure 23.7). These high figures doubtless partly reflect the area's easy accessibility for visiting entomologists and other specialists, by way of rail links to Aviemore, established at the end of the 19th century.

Strathspey contains many other small areas rich in important species. Of particular note is Curr Wood, near Dulnain Bridge, a relatively small (c. 100 ha) area of mature pine plantation from which at least 34 important species have been recorded, including five fungi largely restricted to the Cairngorms. The BAP priority hoverfly *Blera fallax* also occurs here, at one of its two known British sites – the other being at nearby Grantown-on-Spey. Further south, a small area of mixed habitats at Kinrara, near Alvie, supports 12 important species, comprising 10 fungi (three restricted-range)

Only recently have we begun to fully appreciate the biodiversity value of Aspen in the Highlands, most of which occurs in stands of only a few hectares, mainly in the Cairngorms area.

Photo: *L. Gill*

and two bryophytes (both restricted-range). Together these occupy a diverse range of habitats, including pine forest, Aspen and willows, the latter providing a recent record of the fungus Scarlet Splash *Cytidia salicina*, previously recorded here in 1900, and known from only three other British sites (Chapter 11).

Joining the Spey just north of Loch Insh, the River Feshie and surrounding land has rich assemblages of fungi, bryophytes, vascular plants and invertebrates, the latter accounting for 40% of the 66 nationally important species recorded from the glen. Sixteen of these are largely restricted to the Cairngorms. While Glen Feshie's important fungi occur mainly in its remnant pinewoods, most of its other important plant species occur on limestone crags, ravines and scree (bryophytes and vascular plants), or in its base-rich grasslands and flushes (vascular plants only). In contrast, the glen's important invertebrate species are associated mainly with sand, shingle and vegetated areas along the margins of the Feshie itself. The apparent absence of nationally important lichens from Glen Feshie almost certainly reflects a lack of systematic survey work in this area (Chapter 12).

Continuing south-west along the Spey, at least 54 nationally important species have been recorded from Insh Marshes, 10 of which are largely restricted to the Cairngorms. While most of the Insh Marshes' important vascular plants are associated with wetland habitats, several of its fungi and invertebrate species are dependent on stands of Aspen or willow, particularly dead limbs or fallen trees. Insh Marshes also support the fungus Scarlet Splash, and is one of two Scottish sites for *Phellinus punctatus* (the other being Kinrara) and *Russula font-queri* (the other being Dunachton) (see Chapter 11).

At nearby Newtonmore, three important invertebrate species occur, two of them in sand and shingle along the Calder and Spey. South-west of Newtonmore are the unremarkable looking crags and birchwoods of Creag Dhubh, where at least 10 important species have been recorded, including two restricted-range bryophytes and one lichen.

Deeside
In marked contrast to Strathspey, Deeside appears to have few large areas supporting assemblages of important or restricted-range species, reflecting to some degree its less extensive semi-natural pine forests. As a result, several of Deeside's important areas are relatively small, discrete sites, encompassing a mix of mainly non-wooded habitats. Of particular note is the cluster of sites

around Braemar, which include very rich limestone crags, grasslands and birchwoods. To the east of Braemar, Craig Leek, Creag Clunie and the Lion's Face together hold at least 38 important lichens and 17 important fungi; including the fungus White Stalkball *Tulostoma niveum*, recorded from just two sites in Scotland, the new lichen *Rimularia globulosa* and, in 1999, the first British record of *Ionaspis obtecta*. Craig Leek is also an extremely important site for bryophytes, supporting one of only two UK populations of the thalloid liverwort *Athalamia hyalina*, and the largest of two UK populations of Alpine Pottia *Tortula leucostoma* (the other being at Glen Shee; Chapter 13). Together, these sites support at least 14 fungi, lichen or bryophyte species largely restricted to the Cairngorms.

West of Braemar, 46 important fungi and 10 important vascular plants have been recorded in a mosaic of limestone crags, mires, flushes, grassland and ancient birchwood at Morrone. The rich flora of this small site includes at least four species largely confined to the Cairngorms. One of these – the fungus *Amanita flavescens* – has been recorded nowhere else in Britain (Chapter 11).

Two sites adjacent to the Dee (Corriemulzie and Inverey Flats) and one next to the Water of Lui (Lui Flats) are of outstanding importance for their grassland fungi, between them supporting 26 species for which the Cairngorms are nationally important. Inverey Woods, nearby, is one of the richest areas for nationally important pine-associated fungi. This exceptional 11 ha site supports 50 important fungi species, including 11 species largely restricted to the Cairngorms area, and three species new to Britain in 1999 (Chapter 11).

Across the Dee, in Mar Lodge Estate, remnant pinewoods and their associated grasslands and crags in Glen Quoich and Lui support 34 fungi and 18 lichens for which the Cairngorms are nationally important. Indeed, these forests are considered the sixth most important in the UK for their lichen mycobiota, and have recently provided the first British records of two lichen species (Chapter 12).

Deeside's invertebrate fauna includes at least 92 nationally important species, of which 29 are restricted largely to the Cairngorms area. Most have been recorded between the Linn of Dee and Aboyne, mainly in pine or birch woodland at Mar and Glen Tanar (Chapter 15). Impressive as these figures are, they fall short of species totals recorded from the much smaller area of Craigellachie to Coylumbridge in Strathspey, suggesting either that the Dee's invertebrate fauna is relatively poor or, as seems likely, the area has received less attention from entomologists and other specialists to date.

Figure 23.6. Areas supporting notable assemblages of fungi, bryophytes, lichens or vascular plants which, in Britain, are largely restricted to the Cairngorms area. Index values are positively related to the number of such species present in each area (See Box 23.1 for details).

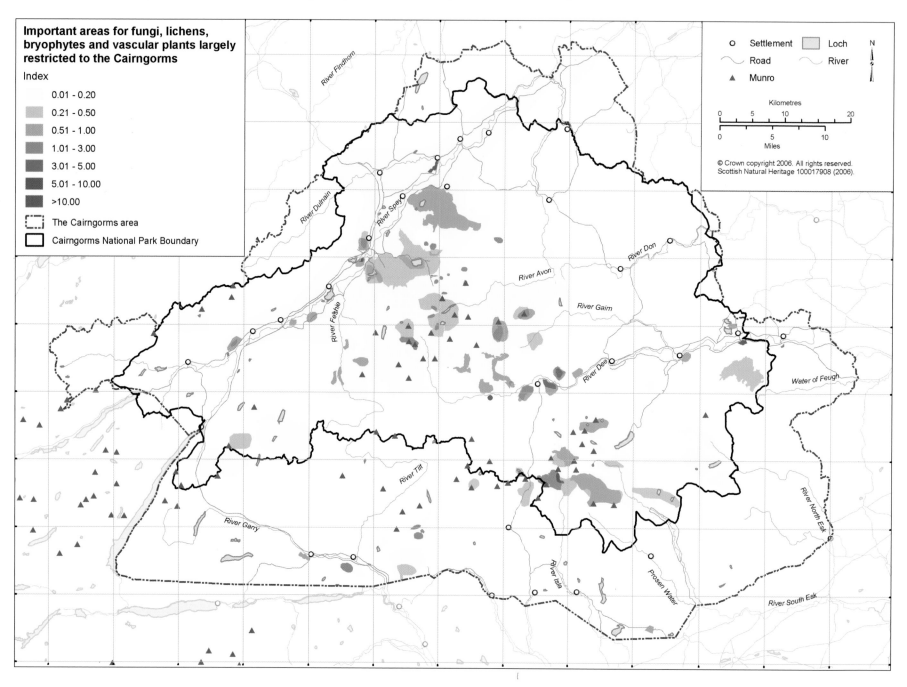

Figure 23.7. Areas supporting notable assemblages of fungi, lichens, plants or animals which, in Britain, are largely restricted to the Cairngorms area. Index values are positively related to the number of such taxa present in each area (See Box 23.1 for details).

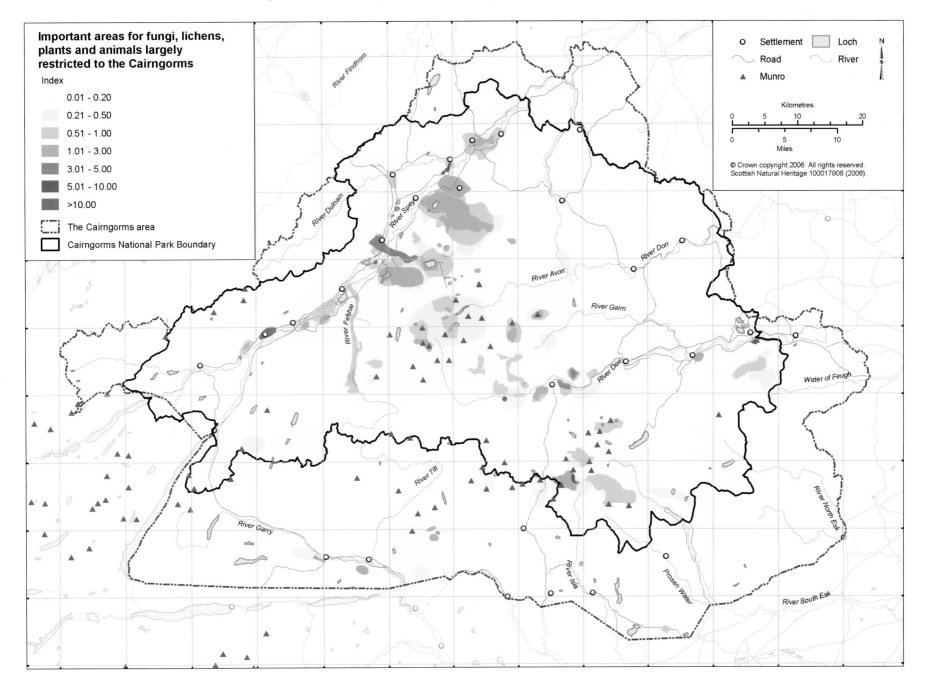

Deeside's bryophyte flora would also appear to be under-recorded, compared with that of Strathspey. East of Craig Leek, only two sites have been identified for nationally important bryophyte species: near Ballater, where the European rarity Green Shield-moss *Buxbaumia viridis* has recently been found; and at Dinnet, where the UK's largest known population of Aspen Bristle-moss *Orthotrichum gymnostomum* occurs on Aspen, near Loch Kinord (Chapter 13). The Dinnet area (including Dinnet oakwood) also has important fungi, lichens, birds and mammals; totalling 42 important species, eight of which are largely restricted to the Cairngorms. These include the fungus Aspen Bracket *Phellinus tremulae*, also recorded on Aspen at Loch Kinord, and new to Britain in 2000.

South of Dinnet, 46 important species have been recorded from the extensive semi-natural pinewoods of Glen Tanar, eight of them largely confined to the Cairngorms. Curiously, although Glen Tanar has 32 important fungi species, including Gilded Bolete *Aureoboletus gentilis* (at one of its two Scottish sites) and three BAP tooth fungi, it is not noted for its lichen or bryophyte flora (Chapters 12 & 13). Also, Rothiemurchus, which has a similar area of native pinewood (Leaper, 1999), has more than four times as many important fungi and almost six times as many important invertebrate species as Glen Tanar, perhaps reflecting differences in survey effort in these two forests.

The hills and mountains

The high ground of the Cairngorms may be divided into five main ranges: the central and eastern Cairngorm mountains; Cairnwell – Glas Maol – Lochnagar and the upper Angus Glens; Blair Atholl – Glen Tilt – Beinn a' Ghlo (including Tulach Hill and Ben Vrackie); the Drumochter Hills; and the Monadhliaths, of which only a small part lies within the Cairngorms area. The central and eastern Cairngorms, and the Glas Maol – Lochnagar complex support rich assemblages of important and restricted-range species, many of which are largely confined to the Cairngorms. In contrast, relatively few important or restricted-range species have been recorded in the Drumochter Hills, Glen Tilt – Beinn a' Ghlo, or in the Monadhliaths (Figures 23.6, 23.7).

To some degree these differences may reflect variation in survey effort. For example, no important invertebrate assemblages are described for the eastern Cairngorm mountains (Beinn a' Bhuird – Ben Avon), or for Glas Maol – Lochnagar, although these botanically rich areas seem very likely to hold important montane invertebrates also. This suggests that these areas may have been relatively neglected by entomologists, in which case there could be much

more to discover there. The central Cairngorm mountains therefore appear to hold by far the richest assemblage of invertebrate taxa for which the Cairngorms are important. Of its 54 important species, six are largely restricted to the Cairngorms, and nine have been recorded nowhere else in Britain. Twenty-two of a group of 24 species of montane Higher Diptera occur here.

Mycologically, the central and eastern Cairngorms, and the Glas Maol – Lochnagar area, are less species-rich than many much smaller areas down in the straths, particularly those containing woodlands. Together, they hold 42 important species, including 16 out of the 21 slime mould 'snow-line specialists' recorded in Britain (Chapter 11). These require at least three months of continuous snow cover in order to become established, and hence may be particularly vulnerable to climate change.

The area encompassing the Cairnwell, Glas Maol, Lochnagar and the upper Angus Glens contains more nationally important lichen, bryophyte and vascular plant species than are found in any other montane area in the Cairngorms. Together, 188 important species have been recorded from these three groups; almost 50% more than in the central and eastern Cairngorms, and almost three times as many as in Blair Atholl – Glen Tilt – Beinn a' Ghlo. The richest single site is Caenlochan, supporting 101 important species from these groups, of which 13 are largely restricted to the Cairngorms. In Britain and Ireland, Caenlochan is also the only known site for the three lichens *Rinodina parasitica*, *Rhizocarpon caeruleoalbum* and *R. chioneum*, and shares a number of taxa with just one other British site: Ben Lawers. These include the lichens *Acarospora badiofusca* and *Halecania rhypodiza* (a British endemic), four bryophytes (Hair Silk-moss *Plagiothecium piliferum*, Haller's Feather-moss *Campylophyllum halleri*, Alpine Hump-moss *Plagiobryum demissum* and Ambiguous Thyme-moss *Mnium ambiguum*), and Alpine Gentian *Gentiana nivalis*.

Species-poor or under-surveyed?

Despite many recent discoveries, our knowledge of species distributions in the Cairngorms, particularly of its invertebrates, fungi, lichens and bryophytes, is still strongly influenced by patterns of survey effort, which tends to be concentrated in the more accessible areas. Many areas that appear to be species-poor may yet provide exciting new finds, and have much to offer the experienced botanist or entomologist. Indeed, in our view, the potential for discovering species new to Britain, or to science, is higher in the Cairngorms than in any other part of the UK. The pace with which important new finds are being made (Table 23.1) gives an indication of how much remains to be discovered. Many new finds have resulted from targeted survey work undertaken as part of the UK Biodiversity Action Plan, or though SNH's Site Condition Monitoring programme. These initiatives have helped us to better appreciate the value of sites long-suspected of holding important assemblages of lichens, bryophytes or fungi, heightening the apparent contrast between surveyed and unsurveyed ('species-poor') areas.

Some of these apparent disparities are evident in the maps presented here. Why, for example, are there so few important areas for lichens, bryophytes or vascular plants in Deeside, compared with Strathspey (Figure 23.6)? Are individual woodlands in Strathspey genuinely richer in important invertebrates than the whole of Deeside, west of Aboyne? And why does the botanically rich Glas Maol – Lochnagar area appear to lack assemblages of important montane invertebrates?

Gaps in survey coverage have been highlighted in Chapters 11–15. For fungi enthusiasts seeking new discoveries, areas likely to prove rewarding range from the high mountain plateaux, where large tracts are under-surveyed, to the semi-improved grasslands of Abernethy, Craig Leek, Glen Clunie, Glen Tanar, Dinnet, Mar Lodge and Dunachton. Much of Deeside's deciduous woodlands would benefit from greater attention from lichen specialists, as would Glen Feshie, the Angus Hills, and calcareous outcrops at Inchrory, Creag an Dail Bheag and Craig Leek. The bryologically rich areas of Garbh Choire on Braeriach, and at the head of Glen Einich, also deserve greater attention, as would less obviously attractive sites like Glen Esk, which has probably had no more than one or two visits by bryologists in the last 50 years (Chapter 13). While sites rich in vascular plants are often comparatively well-visited, less accessible areas like Ben Avon might benefit from greater attention. Here, four rare vascular plant species have been 'absent' since the 19th century, and a further three species have not been recorded for more than 20 years.

The invertebrate fauna of much of the Cairngorms also remains under-recorded, and there is a strong bias both towards well-known, accessible sites and towards the more 'popular' groups, including the butterflies, dragonflies and bumble-bees. In contrast, our knowledge of species from groups such as the parasitoids (Hymenoptera), cecidomyiids (Diptera) and staphylinids (Coleoptera) is poor. While parts of the Cairngorms appear to be particularly under-recorded for invertebrates, including the hills south of the Feshie and the Geldie Burn, several areas considered important for invertebrates have been identified partly from records more than 50 years old. They include

Craigellachie and Coylumbridge, Deeside from Linn of Dee to Aboyne, Abernethy, Grantown-on-Spey and Loch an Eilein to Rothiemurchus. All would benefit from an up-to-date re-assessment of their invertebrate fauna.

The Cairngorms' vertebrates are comparatively few in number and, consequently, rather better known. Nonetheless, our knowledge of their distributions and – especially – their population trends, is surprisingly limited in some cases. This applies particularly to the amphibians, reptiles, and to some mammal species.

Final remarks

While the Cairngorms provide a British stronghold for many iconic bird, mammal and vascular plant species, the majority of taxa for which the area is important belong to groups with which most land managers are unfamiliar, and whose ecological requirements are generally poorly known. Effective management of the area's important species, particularly of its 'silent majority' of fungi, lichens, bryophytes and invertebrates, calls for a greater understanding of their distribution and habitat requirements and, we feel, a wider appreciation of their significance.

Recent conservation initiatives, many of them supported directly by SNH, have led to a number of important new discoveries. The pace with which these have been made conveys an impression of the rate at which our knowledge-base is changing – and is likely to continue to change in the near future. The sheer volume of recent 'new' finds in the Cairngorms suggests that, with sufficient time and attention from specialists, almost any fragment of semi-natural forest, fen, crag or shingle bank, might offer up species rarely recorded elsewhere, gradually transforming our understanding of species diversity in the area.

These advances have enabled us to better appreciate the relative importance of the Cairngorms' wooded habitats, which appear to support in excess of ten times more nationally important species than are found in more open habitats, such as heather moorland and grassland. Most of these important woodland species are associated mainly with native conifers and birch, supporting the view that native woodland expansion is likely to substantially boost species diversity in the Cairngorms. However, care will be needed to avoid damaging

Table 23.1 Examples of recent discoveries in the Cairngorms, illustrating the pace with which our knowledge of species distributions is changing.

Species group	Recent discoveries
Fungi	Craig Leek and Mar Lodge, 1998 and 2001: White Stalkball and Black Falsebolete *Boletopsis leucomelaena* discovered; BAP species each previously known from just one location.
	Species new to Britain include Aspen Bracket (2000), *Russula font-queri* (Strathspey) and *R. fusconigra* (Curr Wood; 2001), *Cortinarius phaeopygmaeus* (Cairngorm plateau; 2002), *Mycena viridimarginata, Tubulicrinis propinquus* and *Russula vinosobrunnea* (Mar Lodge Estate; 2003).
	Kinrara, 2002: Scarlet Splash discovered at possibly the same location from which it was last recorded in 1900, and previously in 1879.
	Insh Marshes, 2005: first Scottish record of BAP species Marsh Honey Fungus *Armillaria ectypa*.
Lichens	Creag Clunie and the Lion's Face SSSI, 1999: *Rimularia globulosa* discovered (new to science); first British record of *Ionaspis obtecta*. On nearby Creag Choinnich, *Rhizocarpon ridescens* (first British record) and *Pleopsidium chlorophana* (second British record) have since been discovered.
	Mar Lodge Estate Pinewoods, since 2000: several important new lichens discovered, including the first British records of *Acrocordia subglobosa* and *Rhizocarpon amphibium*, and the third British record of *Hypocenomyce anthrocophila*.
	Beinn a' Bhuird, 2005: a substantial population of the critically endangered *Brodoa intestiniformis* discovered (previously recorded there once in the 1960s), plus *Arctoparmelia centrifuga* (new to Britain).
	In addition, a recent survey of the Aspen woods of Strathspey has revealed four lichens new to Britain: *Arthonia patellulata, Caloplaca ahtii, Candelariella superdistans* and *Rinodina laevigata*. Two extremely rare Red Data Book lichens were also discovered: *Caloplaca flavorubescens* and *Schismatomma graphidioides*.
Bryophytes	Insh, Kinrara and Grantown-on-Spey, 1999 onwards: several stands of Blunt-leaved Bristle-moss *Orthotrichum obtusifolium* discovered; a moss previously known from one extant site in the UK.
	Craig Leek SSSI and Creag Clunie and the Lion's Face SSSI, 1999: first UK record of *Athalamia hyalina* and the first Scottish record for many years of Many-fruited Dog-tooth *Cynodontium polycarpon*.
	Ben Vrackie, 2002: Elegant Feather-moss *Eurhynchium pulchellum* discovered; its third extant site in Britain.
	Kinrara and Loch Kinord, 2003 onwards: Aspen Bristle-moss discovered; once thought to be extinct in the UK.
	Other recent finds include the first Scottish record of Welsh Notchwort *Gymnocolea acutiloba* (Abernethy Forest), and an increase in the number of known sites for Long-leaved Fork-moss *Paraleucobryum longifolium*, once thought extinct in Britain but now known from at least eight sites in Scotland; five in the Cairngorms.
Invertebrates	Struan Wood, 1998: first British record of the lance fly *Lonchaea ragnari*.
	Creag Dhubh, 1999: *Creagdhubhia mallochorum* discovered; a saproxylic fungus-gnat new to science.
	Abernethy, 2005: first British record of the wolf-spider *Pardosa lugubris*.
	In addition, a recent survey of saproxylic Diptera discovered *Ectaetia christii* (new to science) and *Mycetobia gemella* (new to Britain). Both appear to be confined to Cairngorms National Park.

important landforms, geological features and exceptionally rich moorland or grassland sites. To help plan for changes in habitat cover we need to better understand the distributions and ecological needs of the Cairngorms' nationally important species. This is a special challenge, as much for naturalists as for conservation agencies, the National Park Authority, Local Authorities, land owners and others concerned with managing the diverse and changing nature of the Cairngorms.

Acknowledgements

We are grateful to the authors of the 'species' and 'habitats' chapters in this book for providing much of the material analysed here. We applaud the exceptional efforts of specialists working in the Cairngorms, many of whom are committed naturalists, working in their free time, and who have contributed so much to our knowledge and understanding of the nature of the Cairngorms.

References

Cosgrove, P. (2002). *The Cairngorms Local Biodiversity Action Plan.* Cairngorms Partnership: Grantown-on-Spey.

Fischer, A.G. (1960). Latitudinal variations in organic diversity. *Evolution* 14: 64-81.

Fuller, R.M, Smith, G.M., Sanderson, R.A., Hill, R.A., Thomson. A.G., Cox, R., Brown, N.J., Clarke, R.T., Rothery, P. & Gerard, F.F. (2002). *Land Cover Map 2000. Final Report.* Centre for Ecology and Hydrology: Monks Wood.

Gimingham, C. (ed.) (2002). *The Ecology, Land Use and Conservation of the Cairngorms.* Packard Publishing Limited: Chichester.

Leaper, G. (1999). *Biodiversity of the Cairngorms: an assessment of priority habitats and species.* Cairngorms Partnership: Grantown-on-Spey.

Nagy, L., Grabher, G., Koerner, K. & Thompson, D.B.A. (eds.) (2003). *Alpine Biodiversity in Europe.* Springer: Berlin.

Nethersole-Thompson, D. & Watson, A. (1981). *The Cairngorms: Their Natural History and Scenery.* Melven Press: Perth.

Rapoport, E.H. (1982). *Areography. Geographical Strategies of Species.* Oxford: Pergamon Press.

Ratcliffe, D.A. (ed.) (1977). *A Nature Conservation Review.* Vols. 1 and 2. Cambridge University Press: Cambridge.

Ratcliffe, D.A. & Thompson, D.B.A. (1988). The British Uplands: their ecological character and international significance. In: Usher, M.B. & Thompson, D.B.A. (eds.), *Ecological change in the Uplands.* Blackwell Scientific Publications: Oxford. pp. 9-36.

Stattersfield, A.J., Crosby, M.J., Long, A.J. & Wege, D.C. (1998). *Endemic Bird Areas of the World: Priorities for biodiversity conservation.* Cambridge: BirdLife International.

Stevens, G.C. (1989). The latitudinal gradient in geographical range: how so many species coexist in the tropics. *American Naturalist* 133: 240-256.

Whitfield, D.P. & Tharme, A.P. (1997). *An evaluation of the effects of native pinewood regeneration on the birds of the Cairngorms.* Report to Research Advisory Services Directorate. SNH: Perth.

GLOSSARY

Acidophilous 'Acid loving'. A term applied to organisms that grow best in acidic habitats, e.g. in a bog or marsh. Also called acidophilic.

Algal bloom Rapid growth of algae caused by the addition of nutrients to water.

Alluvial soil Immature soil forming on recent freshwater, estuarine or marine alluvial deposits.

Alluvium Material such as clay, silt, sand and gravel deposited by rivers (adj. alluvial).

Ammocoete Lamprey larvae.

Anadromous Species that spawn in freshwater and migrate to sea as juveniles, before returning to spawn as adults.

Anuran Tailless amphibian with long hind legs for jumping (e.g. frog).

Apomictic Plants that set seed without the normal fertilisation process. Such plants are effectively clones of the mother plant.

ASL Above Sea Level.

Autecology The ecology of individual species, as opposed to whole communities.

Baltica Continent that contained Scandinavian Europe before continental drift finally closed the Iapetus Ocean around 425 million years ago.

Base-rich Rocks or soils rich in alkaline minerals (having a pH greater than 7).

Basidiomycete A fungus of the Basidiomycota group, commonly called 'club fungi'.

Basin fens A fen within a depression.

Basin peat Organic soil representing the accumulation of partly or completely decomposed plant residues deposited in distinct depressions.

Basiphilous 'Base-loving'. A plant that tends to be restricted to basic (i.e. alkaline) soils.

Bathymetry Underwater topography.

Biodiversity Biological diversity.

Biome A division of the world's vegetation, corresponding to a particular climate and characterized by certain plants and animals, forming a major ecological community.

Blanket bog or mire An ombrotrophic wetland that receives more than c. 1,000 mm of rainfall per annum, in oceanic climates, resulting in build-up of deep peat on level- to moderately-sloping ground.

Blanket peat Peat formed under cool, wet climatic conditions, which, in combination with high acidity and nutrient deficiency, depress microbiological activity.

Blockfield An accumulation of boulders of local rocks, often frost-shattered, found on mountain tops or plateaux.

Boreal Pertaining to the northern and/or mountainous areas of the New or Old World.

Brachycera The 'short-horned' Diptera, including all Diptera that have short antennae. More usually used to refer to one of the three sub-orders of flies, including the Robber Flies and Horse Flies (or 'cleg').

Brittle fault A fault (fracture within a body of rock along which observable relative displacement has occurred) exhibiting no component of ductile stretching prior to brittle failure.

Brown earth soil A freely draining, deep and fertile soil type highly valued for agricultural use.

Calaminarian grassland Generally short, open vegetation of fine-leaved grasses, flowers, mosses and lichens, on spoil and gravel from mineral extraction, or associated with metal-rich ultrabasic exposures.

Calcareous Containing calcium carbonate.

Calcicole A term applied to plants that prefer calcareous soil or rocks, or water of high calcium status.

Caledonian Orogeny A mountain-building event which resulted from continental collisions between 480 and 425 million years ago.

Cecidomyidae Gall Midges.

Chasmophytic Plant species and communities that colonise the cracks and fissures of rock faces.

Chionophilous 'Snow loving'. A term applied to plants associated mainly with snow-beds.

Coire See 'Corrie'.

Coleoptera Beetles: an order of insects.

Congeners Two species belonging to the same genus.

Corbet A mountain exceeding 2,500 ft (762 m). See also 'Munro'.

Corrie A semicircular mountain basin with a steep headwall and a more gently sloping floor, formed by a small mountain glacier.

Corticolous Growing on or in tree bark.

Crustose Crust-like. A form of lichen lacking a lower cortex (outermost layer) and hyphae, and having their main bodies in contact with the substratum.

Cryptogam A plant that reproduces by spores or gametes, rather than by seeds.

Cumecs Cubic metres per second.

Cyclorrapha One of three sub-orders of Diptera, strictly Brachycera - Cyclorrapha. These have short antenna and emerge from the pupa by a circular slit. Includes the House Flies and Blue Bottles.

Dalradian (Supergroup) A sequence of sedimentary rocks, originally sandy and muddy sediments deposited on the floor of an ancient ocean basin 600-700 million years ago, which now form much of the Scottish Highlands south of the Great Glen.

Debris cone A fan or cone-shaped accumulation of sediment built up by repeated debris flows, and usually consisting of coarse material.

Debris flow A rapid downslope flow of poorly sorted debris (mud, soil and rock fragments) mixed with water.

Deeside Lineament The line of what is thought to be an ancient fault associated with the opening of the Iapetus Ocean 600-700 million years ago, which runs along the Dee Valley.

Deflation surface An area of ground where the vegetation and soil have been stripped by wind erosion, often leaving a stony surface.

Designated interest A habitat, species, species assemblage or earth science feature for which a Site of Special Scientific Interest has been designated.

Devonian period A geological period, 416-359 million years ago.

Diatom A unicellular plant: microscopic algae with cell walls made of silica.

Diorite A coarse-grained rock formed from cooled magma containing up to 10% of quartz, white crystals of the mineral feldspar and dark crystals of magnesium- and iron-rich minerals, giving the rock a mottled black-and-white appearance.

Diptera An order of insects known as the 'true flies' (two-winged).

Disjunct Term applied to a population of a species widely separated geographically or ecologically from other populations of the same species.

Diurnal Active during daylight.

Drift mantle A layer of glacial drift covering the ground surface.

Drosophila A genus of Fruit Flies.

Dystrophic Water high in humic substances and plant degradation products. Brown in colour and associated with peat-based catchments.

Earth's curst The thin outermost solid layer of the Earth which varies in thickness between approximately 5 km beneath the oceans to 60 km beneath mountains.

Eastern Avalonia Continent that contained England before continental drift finally closed the Iapetus Ocean around 425 million years ago.

Ecophysiology The study of the interrelationship between an organism and its physical and abiotic environment.

Ecotone A zone of transition between two well-defined vegetation types, e.g. scrub and tall herbs between forest and grassland.

Ectomycorrhizal A type of mycorrhiza in which the fungal hyphae do not penetrate the cells of the root, but cover the root and grow between the root cells.

Endemic Native to, and restricted to, a particular location.

Epigaeic Growing above ground.

Epilithic Growing on the surface of a rock or stone.

Epiphytic Growing on the surface of a plant.

Erratic Stone or boulder transported some distance from its source by a glacier.

Esker A long, narrow, sinuous ridge formed of sand and gravel deposited in an ice-walled tunnel by glacial meltwaters.

Euryhaline Type of fish capable of living in waters with a wide range of salinity.

Eutrophic Term applied to water or soil enriched with excessive amounts of plant nutrients, such as nitrates and phosphates.

Evapotranspiration The combined action of evaporation (a physical process that converts liquid water to a gas) and transpiration (the loss of water vapour from plants).

Fell-field Frost-shattered stony debris occurring on gentle summits and other high ground in the mountains. The vegetation cover is scattered, usually occupying less than half of the ground.

Fennoscandia Finland and the Scandinavian peninsula.

Ferox form (of Brown Trout) A large fish-eating form of Brown Trout that may be genetically distinct from other forms.

Ferro-magnesian base rock Rocks that are rich in iron and magnesium.

Floodplain fen or mire Occupying permanently saturated floodplains.

Fluvial Relating to rivers.

Frost heave The upward expansion of ground caused by the freezing of water in the soil.

Gelifluction The slow, downslope movement of the soil, resulting from the melting of ice lenses in areas of frozen ground.

Geodiversity The variety of rocks, minerals, fossils, landforms, sediments and soils, together with the natural processes which form and alter them.

Geological fault A fracture in the Earth's rocky crust, or in any body of rock.

Geomorphology The study of the landforms on the Earth's surface and the processes that have fashioned them.

Glacial drift A general term for rock material deposited by glaciers and in glacier-associated streams and lakes.

Glacial troughs Deep valleys or glens carved by glaciers.

Glacifluvial (outwash terraces) Relating to glacier meltwater streams and the landforms and deposits produced by them.

Gley Soil which develops under conditions of intermittent or permanent waterlogging.

Graminoid Grass or grass-like plants, such as sedges and rushes.

Grampian Orogeny A deformation and mountain building event around 480-465 million years ago. It was the first phase of the Caledonian Orogeny and occurred as closure of the Iapetus Ocean caused a chain of volcanic islands to collide with Laurentia (an ancient continent containing Scotland).

Granitic 'Granite-like'; usually referring to a silica-rich composition similar to that of granite.

Granitoid A term used to encompass granite and other similar rock types, including granodiorite (with less quartz than granite) and tonolite (with more sodium-rich feldspar than granite).

Great Glen The glen which run across Scotland between Inverness and Fort William.

Grilse Atlantic Salmon that have returned to freshwaters to spawn after spending only one winter at sea.

Hepatic Applies to liverworts; non-flowering plants in the botanical class Hepaticae, closely related to mosses.

Herpetofauna Amphibian or reptile species.

Herptile An amphibian or reptile species.

Hibernaculum The place where an organism or organisms (e.g. bats) spend the winter or cold season.

Holarctic Biogeographical region including the northern parts of the New and the Old World; the Nearctic and the Palearctic regions combined.

Holocene The present interval of geological time, beginning at the end of the last glaciation, 11,500 years ago.

Humic Of, or containing humus.

Humus Well-decomposed organic material.

Hydrophilic Water-loving.

Hydroseeded Hydroseeding involves mixing lime, fertilizer, seed and mulch, and then mechanically blowing this mixture onto the soil surface.

Hydroseral A plant succession originating in water.

Hydrothermal fluid Hot water with dissolved mineral components.

Hydrothermally altered rock Rock altered by interaction with circulating hydrothermal fluid.

Hymenoptera An insect order which includes the ants, bees, wasps and sawflies.

Hyporheic (zone) The saturated zone under a river or stream.

Iapetus Ocean Ancient ocean which separated the three continents Laurentia (containing Scotland), Eastern Avalonia (containing England) and Baltica (Scandinavia) from around 600 to 425 million years ago.

Ice lenses Lenses of ice formed in the ground as growing ice crystals attract water from the surrounding soil.

Ice-dammed lake deposit A deposit in a lake dammed by a glacier blocking a valley mouth.

Igneous rock Rock that has solidified from molten rock material (magma).

Interglacial Warm interval between two glacial periods.

Interstices Pore spaces in soil or rock.

Isotherm A line on a map connecting points having the same measured or average temperature.

Isotope Atom of a single element that has the same number of protons but a different number of neutrons.

Joint A discrete brittle fracture in a rock, along which there has been little or no movement parallel to the plane of fracture, but slight movement at right angles to it (opening of the crack).

Kame A mound composed chiefly of stratified sand and gravel formed by glacial meltwater at, or near, to the snout of a glacier.

Katabatic wind A generic term for wind that occurs when cold, dense air moves downslope gravitationally beneath warmer, less dense air.

Kernel The inner part of a plant seed, containing the embryo.

Kettle hole A depression in an area of glacial drift, produced by the melting of a mass of buried ice.

Lacustrine Relating to lakes.

Lateral moraine A linear accumulation of rock debris formed along the margins of a glacier and left as a ridge when the glacier retreats.

Laurentia Ancient continent containing the landmass which eventually formed Scotland.

Lek (lekking) An area in which display territories are held and defended against rivals, for the purpose of attracting a mate. Lekking species include Capercaillie and Black Grouse.

Lepidoptera An order of insects which includes the butterflies and moths.

Lineament A linear topographical feature thought to reflect crustal structure.

Lithosol A very shallow soil with continuous, coherent hard rock within 10 cm of the ground surface.

Littoral An interface region between the land and a loch or sea.

Macrolichen A large, scaled, shrub-like or leaf-like lichen.

Macrophyte A large or macroscopic plant that is easily seen without the aid of a microscope.

Magnesian soil Soils with a high magnesium content and with a surface horizon often high in organic matter content and dark in colour. Parent materials are wholly or partly from ultrabasic rocks.

Meltwater channel A channel formed by a glacial meltwater river.

Meristem The growth zone (of a plant).

Mesotrophic A body of water with a moderate nutrient content.

Metamorphic rock Rock formed by recrystallisation of pre-existing rocks (sedimentary, igneous or metamorphic) in response to a change in the temperature, pressure or content of volatiles such as water.

Mica-schist A rock containing the platy, sheet-silicate mineral, mica, and with a strongly layered fabric (known as 'schistosity').

Microbe A microscopic organism, such as a bacterium, fungus, protozoan or virus.

Minerotrophic Receiving nutrients from groundwater containing dissolved minerals.

Mire A general term for a wetland area and its associated ecosystem, applied most often to peat-forming ecosystems.

Mites Arachnids, of the order Acarina.

Moine (Supergroup) A sequence of sedimentary rocks, originally sandy and muddy sediments on the floor of an ancient sea 1,000-870 million years ago, which now form much of the Scottish Highlands north of the Great Glen and east of the Moine Thrust (a fault running roughly from Loch Eriboll to the south of Skye).

Montane Of, or inhabiting mountainous regions.

Moraine An accumulation of unsorted rock material transported and deposited by a glacier.

Morph A distinct form, e.g. of a species. See also 'Polymorphism'.

MSW fish Multi-sea winter fish (e.g. Atlantic Salmon that have spent more than one year at sea before returning to their natal river to spawn).

Munro A mountain exceeding 3,000 ft (914.4 m) (after Sir Hugh Munro, 1856–1919).

Nematode Member of a phylum (Nematoda or Nemata) of elongated cylindrical worms parasitic in animals or plants, or free-living in soil or water.

Nivation Processes associated with persistent snow beds.

Notified interest A habitat, species, species assemblage or earth science feature for which a Site of Special Scientific Interest has been designated.

Oligotrophic Describes a body of water with a low level of plant nutrients.

Ombrotrophic Applied to a mire system fed by rainwater.

Organochlorine A synthetic chemical substance. A hydrocarbon compound containing chlorine.

Orogeny see 'Caledonian Orogeny'.

Osmoregulation Regulation of the pressure differential that exists between two solutions . Associated with fish that display an anadromous life history pattern.

Outwash fan or terrace Stratified sands and gravels deposited by glacial meltwater rivers in the form of a fan or terrace, at or near to an ice margin.

Oviparous Producing eggs (as opposed to live young).

Ovo-viviparous Producing live young from eggs retained within the mother's body.

Palaeolimnology The study of the history and development of freshwater ecosystems, especially lochs.

Palearctic The region that includes Europe, Asia north of the Himalayan-Tibetan border, North Africa, and Arabia.

Paleochannels River channels formed at some point in the historical or geological past.

Panmictic Random mating within a population.

Passerine Members of the bird order Passeriformes, usually referred to as songbirds or perching birds.

Pedogenesis The process of soil development and soil evolution.

Periglacial Relating to the landforms and geomorphological processes in cold, non-glacial environments.

Petrology The mineralogy, texture, origin, distribution, structure and history of rocks and the study of these.

Phenocryst A crystal significantly larger than crystals of surrounding minerals.

Phenology The study of the timing of biological events, e.g. of budburst, the arrival of migrant birds or egg-laying.

Piciform A member of the order Piciformes, which includes the woodpeckers and wrynecks.

Piscivorous Fish-eating.

Planform The outline or shape of a body of water, as determined by the stillwater line.

Ploughing boulder A boulder that moves downslope through the surrounding soil, in which it is partly embedded, leaving a vegetated furrow behind and forming a turf-covered rampart in front.

Pluton A mass of igneous rock of any shape, size or composition, which has cooled and solidified underground.

Podzol An acidic soil with organic surface horizons underlain by a leached, ashen-grey layer and a more brightly reddish-coloured zone in which iron and aluminium materials accumulate. From the Russian *pod* (under) and *zola* (ash).

Policy, policies Open parkland on Scottish estates.

Polymorphism The characteristic of having two or more distinct physical forms of a single species. Lochs containing Arctic Charr, for example, can host up to four 'morphotypes' of this one species.

Precocious parr Young Atlantic Salmon that have not yet gone to sea, but have become sexually mature as parr while in freshwater.

Protalus rampart A ridge formed by the accumulation of rockfall debris at the base of a semi-permanent snowbed below a rock face.

Quaternary The period of geological time that includes the last 2.6 million years, and is synonomous with the 'Ice Age'.

Raised bog A bog lying above groundwater level, which develops on former lake sediments, uniform clay substrates and sometimes on valley bog surfaces.

Ramsar site A site designated under the Convention on Wetlands, signed in Ramsar, Iran, in 1971.

Ranker soil A poorly developed soil, with a surface organic layer more than 10 cm deep, resting directly on hard, non-calcareous rock.

Readvance The advance of a glacier or glaciers following a period of retreat. Towards the end of the last glaciation, following the melting of the last ice sheet, glaciers readvanced in the Highlands. This event is known as the Loch Lomond Readvance after the area in which it was first identified.

Recessional moraine An end moraine deposited during a temporary halt in the retreat of a glacier.

Redd A gravelly spawning bed or nest in branches of rivers, made by Atlantic Salmon. Similar 'nests' can be made by lamprey species.

Regosol A thin soil that rests directly on unconsolidated material. Generally formed on parent material of windblown sand.

Relevé In phytosociology, the basic field unit recorded, e.g. a sample of the plant community.

Rendzina A shallow calcareous soil with an organic horizon more than 10 cm deep that develops over limestone-derived parental material.

Riparian Of, or pertaining to river banks.

Roche moutonné A glaciated bedrock knoll or small hill which has an asymmetric shape, with a steeper slope facing in the down-ice direction of ice flow.

Saprotroph Any organism that absorbs soluble organic nutrients from inanimate sources.

Saproxylic A species dependent at some stage in its life cycle on dead wood, such as fallen trees or branches.

Saxicolous Term applied to a (lichen) species which grows on rocks .

Serpentine See 'Serpentinite'.

Serpentinite Rock formed by alteration of ultrabasic rock by low temperature and water interaction, and composed almost completely of one or more of a group of silica-poor, magnesium-rich minerals known as 'serpentine-group minerals'.

Sessile Lacking a stalk.

Shear zone A region, narrow compared to its length, within which rocks have undergone intense deformation.

Siliceous Containing abundant silica.

Slide An alternative name for a shear zone; largely obsolete but still retained in the formal names of some shear zones (e.g. 'Grampian Slide', Fort William Slide').

Smolt The stage in the life of Atlantic Salmon or Sea Trout in which the pre-adult acquires a silvery colour and migrates downstream to begin its adult life in the sea.

Solifluction The slow, downslope movement of soil, resulting from seasonal freezing and thawing. Solifluction comprises gelifluction (q.v.) and frost creep (downslope movement of the soil due to expansion and contraction as the soil freezes and thaws).

Soligenous flush A flush dependant on an inflow of drainage water.

sp. Species (singular).

spp. Species (plural).

ssp. Sub-species.

Stadial A very cold period during a glaciation.

Stenothermic Fish capable of living or growing only within a narrow range of temperatures.

Stillstand A temporary halt in glacier retreat.

Strath A wide, flat river valley.

Subglacial meltwater channels Channels eroded by glacial meltwater rivers flowing beneath a glacier.

Submontane The zone of upland vegetation above the forest, but below the potential tree-line (sub-alpine).

Substrate With reference to plants or animals: any object or material on which an organism grows, or to which an organism is attached.

Sward A measure of the thickness or leafiness of a grass crop.

Sympatry Term applied to organisms occurring together in the same geographic area. Such organisms have a 'sympatric' distribution.

Talus An accumulation of scree.

Tephra (horizons) Dust, ash, and pumice ejected by the eruption of a volcano, and carried downwind before settling to earth.

Terrace A level or gently sloping feature running across a hillside or along the sides or floor of a valley.

Terricolous Living on or in the ground.

Therevidae Stilleto Flies; small, predatory long-legged flies.

Tor Tower-like masses of locally more resistant rock, standing above the surrounding area on mountain summits or ridges.

Transition mire Vegetation that in floristic composition and general ecological characteristics is transitional between acid bog and alkaline fen.

Truncated spur A spur that formerly projected into a valley and was completely or partially cut back through erosion by glaciers.

Tufa A sedimentary rock of calcium carbonate, precipitated by evaporation.

Tungsten-molybdenum mineralisation Occurrence of a concentration of minerals containing tungsten and molybdenum.

Ultrabasic rock An igneous rock that has a very low silica content, no quartz, and consists almost entirely of magnesium- and iron-rich minerals.

Ultramafic rock See 'ultrabasic rock'.

Urodel Tailed amphibian (e.g. newt).

Vascular plants Flowering plants or ferns.

Acronyms and legislation

ADMG Association of Deer Management Groups

APEM Aquatic Consultancy

AWI Ancient Woodland Inventory

BAP Biodiversity Action Plan

BGS British Geological Survey

Birds Directive EC Directive 79/409/EEC on the Conservation of Wild Birds

BLS British Lichen Society

BMS British Mycological Society

BTO British Trust for Ornithology

CAP Common Agricultural Policy

CEFAS Centre for Environment, Fisheries & Aquaculture Centre

CNPA Cairngorms National Park Authority

CPI Caledonian Pinewood Inventory

CPS Countryside Premium Scheme

CS2000 Countryside Survey 2000

DCS Deer Commission for Scotland

DMG Deer Management Group

EC European Commission

ECCB European Committee for Conservation of Bryophytes

EMERGE European Mountain Lake Ecosystems: Regionalisation, Diagnostic and Socio-economic Evaluation

ERA Ecological Research Associates

ESA Environmentally Sensitive Area

FCS Forestry Commission Scotland

FWAG Farming & Wildlife Advisory Group

GCR Geological Conservation Review

GCT Game Conservancy Trust

GIS Geographic Information System

GLORIA Global Observation Research Initiative in Alpine Environments

GPS Global Positioning System

Habitats Directive EC Directive 92/43/EEC on the Conservation of natural habitats and of wild fauna and flora

HBR Highland Bird Report

Hectad A 10 km x 10 km grid square

HIE Highlands & Islands Enterprise

HLA Historic land-use assessment

HLCA Hill Livestock Compensatory Allowances

HS Historic Scotland

IBA Important Bird Area

ICES International Council for the Exploration of the Sea

ICP International Cooperative Programmes

IPCC Intergovernmental Panel on Climate Change

IUCN The World Conservation Union: International Union for Conservation of Nature and Natural Resources

JNCC Joint Nature Conservation Committee

LBAP Local Biodiversity Action Plan

LCA Landscape Character Assessment

LCS88 Land Cover of Scotland 1988

LFA Less Favoured Area

LFASS Less Favoured Area Support Scheme

LMC Land Management Contract

MCofS Mountaineering Council of Scotland

MLURI Macaulay Land Use Research Institute

MOLAR Mountain Lakes Research & Monitoring Projects

MTR Mid-term Review (of the Common Agricultural Policy)

Natura 2000 A European network of sites protected under the EC Birds Directive or Habitats Directive. These represent areas of the highest value for natural habitats and species that are rare, endangered or vulnerable in the European Community.

Natural Heritage Futures A Scottish Natural Heritage initiative promoting integrated management of the natural heritage.

NC Nature Conservancy

NCC Nature Conservancy Council

NCMS National Countryside Monitoring Scheme

NCR Nature Conservation Review

NESBReC North East of Scotland Biological Records Centre

NNR National Nature Reserve

NP National Park

NPPG National Planning & Policy Guideline

NSA National Scenic Area

NTS National Trust for Scotland

NVC National Vegetation Classification

NWM Native Woodland Model

OAS Organic Aid Scheme

OS Ordnance Survey

PBRL Provisional British Red Data List

PERL Provisional European Red Data List

PWD Potential Water Deficit

RBGE Royal Botanic Gardens Edinburgh

RCAHMS Royal Commission on the Ancient and Historical Monuments of Scotland

RDB Red Data Book: a list of species threatened with extinction

Red List See RDB

RIEC Revised Index of Ecological Continuity

RSPB Royal Society for the Protection of Birds

RSS Rural Stewardship Scheme

SAC Special Area of Conservation (see Habitats Directive)

SAP Species Action Plan (under the UK Biodiversity Action Plan)

SCM Site Condition Monitoring: a monitoring programme carried out by SNH on SSSIs and Natura sites, to common standards agreed between JNCC and the statutory agencies

SEERAD Scottish Executive Environment & Rural Affairs Department

SEPA Scottish Environment Protection Agency

SFCC Scottish Fisheries Co-ordination Centre

SIRI Scottish Insects Records Index

SOAFD Scottish Office Agriculture and Fisheries Department

SPA Special Protection Area (see Birds Directive)

SSNWI Scottish Semi-Natural Woodland Inventory

SSSI Site of Special Scientific Interest

UKAWMN UK Acid Waters Monitoring Network

UKCIP UK Climate Impact Programme

UNECE United Nations Economic Commission for Europe

WCA Wildlife & Countryside (Scotland) Act 1981

WEWS Water Environment & Water Services (Scotland) Act 2003

In conjunction with the list opposite, this map may help identify the relevant 5-km square for a given location. Because of space constraints, only a small proportion of place names are shown. Therefore, to pin-point a location more precisely, refer to the OS 1:50,000 scale map series.

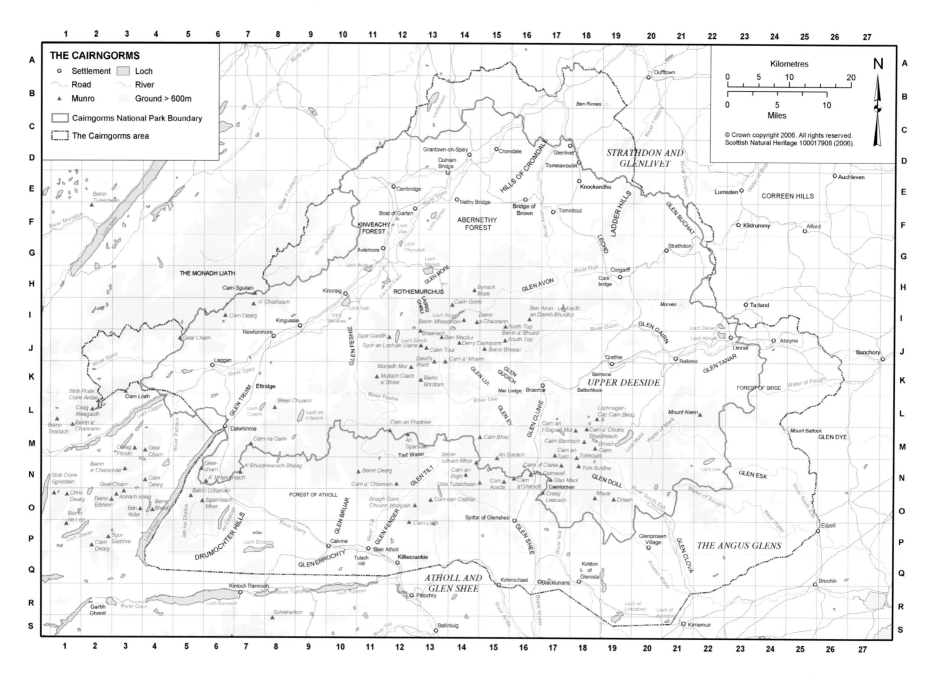

GAZETTEER

Place names mentioned in the text are listed here in alphabetical order. Two map references are given for each location. The first (e.g. 'N7') identifies the relevant 5-km square on the map opposite. The second reference (e.g. 'NN6575') identifies the bottom left corner of the equivalent 5-km square on an Ordnance Survey (OS) map. For instructions on how to interpret national grid coordinates, refer to the OS 1:50,000 scale map series. Principal areas are shown on the map opposite. Spellings of place names below follow the OS map series.

To minimise space requirements only one 5-km square has been identified per feature, although some features, e.g. rivers, may span several squares.

Location	Map reference	OS Reference	Location	Map reference	OS Reference	Location	Map reference	OS Reference
A' Bhuidheanach Bheag	N7	NN6575	Atholl	O11	NN8570	Ben Avon	I16	NJ1000
A' Chailleach	I7	NH6500	Auchleven	E26	NJ6020	Ben Macdui	J13	NN9595
A' Chioch	J15	NO0595	Aviemore	G11	NH8510	Ben Rinnes	B19	NJ2535
A' Mharconaich	N6	NN6075	Badan Mosach	K10	NN8090	Ben Vrackie	Q13	NN9560
A' Mharconaich	M8	NN7080	Baddoch	M16	NO1080	Ben Vuirich	O13	NN9570
Abernethy Forest	F13	NH9515	Badenoch	K8	NN7090	Bhrodainn	M8	NN7080
Aboyne	J24	NO5095	Ballater	J21	NO3595	Black Burn	A15	NJ0738
Airgiod-meall	H13	NN9505	Ballindalloch Castle	B17	NJ1535	Blackhall	J27	NO6595
Aldclunie	Q12	NN9060	Balloch Moss	R21	NO3555	Blacklunans	Q16	NO1060
Alford	F25	NJ5515	Ballochbuie	K18	NO2090	Blair Atholl	P11	NN8565
Allt a' Ghlinne Bhig	O16	NO1070	Balmoral	K19	NO2590	Blargie Craig	J5	NN5595
Allt a' Mharcaidh	I11	NH8500	Balnacraig	I23	NJ4500	Bluemill	G22	NJ4010
Allt Bhran	L10	NN8085	Balnascriten	J10	NN8095	Boat of Garten	F12	NH9015
Allt Cuaich	L7	NN6585	Balneden	E16	NJ1020	Bochel Wood	E18	NJ2020
Allt Dubhaig	O6	NN6070	Banchory	J28	NO7095	Bogieshiel Lodge	J25	NO5595
Allt Mór	E14	NJ0020	Barns of Bynack	H14	NJ0005	Braemar	K17	NO1590
Allt na Glaise	P5	NN5565	Beachan Wood	D14	NJ0025	Braeriach	J13	NN9595
Allt na Leuma	J11	NN8595	Beinn a' Ghlo	O13	NN9570	Braigh Coire Chruinn-bhaigain	O12	NN9070
Allt na-giubhsaich	L19	NO2585	Beinn a' Bhuird (North Top)	I15	NJ0500	Brechin	Q25	NO5560
Allt Ruadh	J11	NN8595	Beinn a' Bhuird (South Top)	J15	NO0595	Brerachan Meadows	Q14	NO0060
Alltcailleach Forest	K18	NO2090	Beinn a' Chalachair	N3	NN4575	Bridge of Brown	E16	NJ1020
Alvie	H11	NH8505	Beinn a' Chaorainn	I14	NJ0000	Broad Cairn	M18	NO2080
An Cearcall	O6	NN6070	Beinn Bheoil	O4	NN5070	Brown Cow Hill	I18	NJ2000
An Garbh Choire	J13	NN9595	Beinn Bhreac	J15	NO0595	Bruar Water	O10	NN8070
An Lochan Uaine	J14	NO0095	Beinn Bhrotain	K13	NN9590	Bynack Burn	L13	NN9585
An Sgarsoch	M12	NN9080	Beinn Dearg	N11	NN8575	Bynack More	H14	NJ0005
An Socach	N15	NO0575	Beinn Eibhinn	O2	NN4070	Cabrach	D21	NJ3525
An Suidhe	H10	NH8005	Beinn Mheadhoin	I14	NJ0000	Caenlochan Glen	N17	NO1575
Anagach	D14	NJ0025	Beinn na Lap	P1	NN3565	Cairn Bannoch	M18	NO2080
Angel's Peak	J13	NN9595	Beinn Teallach	L2	NN4085	Cairn Gorm	I14	NJ0000
Aonach Beag	O3	NN4570	Beinn Udlamain	O5	NN5570	Cairn Leuchan	K21	NO3590
Ardverikie	L4	NN5085	Ben Alder	O3	NN4570	Cairn Lochan	I13	NH9500

Location	Map reference	OS Reference	Location	Map reference	OS Reference	Location	Map reference	OS Reference
Cairn of Claise	N17	NO1575	Coire an t-Sneachda	I13	NH9500	Creag Fhiaclach	H11	NH8505
Cairn Toul	J13	NN9595	Coire Bhachdaidh	O5	NN5570	Creag Leacach	O17	NO1570
Cairnwell	N16	NO1075	Coire Cas	I13	NH9500	Creag Meagaidh	L2	NN4085
Calvine	P10	NN8065	Coire Chais	M7	NN6580	Creag nam Ban	K19	NO2590
Cambus O'May	J22	NO4095	Coire Chuirn	N6	NN6075	Creag nan Gamhainn	F17	NJ1515
Candacraig House	G20	NJ3010	Coire Dhondail	J12	NN9095	Creag Pitridh	M3	NN4580
Canness Glen	N18	NO2075	Coire Domhain	I13	NH9500	Cromdale	D15	NJ0525
Carlochy	M22	NO4080	Coire Garbhlach	K11	NN8590	Crossbog Pinewood	Q21	NO3560
Carn a' Chlamain	N12	NN9075	Coire Kander	M17	NO1580	Culblean Hill	I21	NJ3500
Carn a' Choire Bhoidheach	M18	NO2080	Coire na Laogh	I6	NH6000	Curr Wood	E13	NH9520
Carn a' Gheoidh	N16	NO1075	Coire Raibeirt	I14	NJ0000	Dalwhinnie	M6	NN6080
Carn a' Mhaim	K13	NN9590	Conglass Water	F17	NJ1515	Dell Lodge	F14	NJ0015
Carn an Fhidhleir	M12	NN9080	Corgarff	H19	NJ2505	Dell Wood	F14	NJ0015
Carn an Righ	N14	NO0075	Corrie Fee	N18	NO2075	Den of Ogil	Q22	NO4060
Carn an t-Sagairt Mòr	M18	NO2080	Corrie Sharroch	O19	NO2570	Derry Burn	J14	NO0095
Carn an Tuirc	M17	NO1580	Corriebreck	G20	NJ3010	Derry Cairngorm	J14	NO0095
Carn Aosda	N15	NO0575	Corriemulzie	L16	NO1085	Deskry Water	G22	NJ4010
Carn Bhac	M15	NO0580	Corrieyairack	J2	NN4095	Devil's Point	K13	NN9590
Carn Dearg	I6	NH6000	Corrour	J13	NN9595	Dinnet	J23	NO4595
Carn Dearg	P2	NN4065	Coyles of Muick	K20	NO3090	Dinnet Oakwood	J23	NO4595
Carn Dearg	N4	NN5075	Coylumbridge	G12	NH9010	Dorback Burn	B13	NH9535
Carn Liath	K3	NN4590	Cragganmore	B17	NJ1535	Driesh	O19	NO2570
Carn Liath	P12	NN9065	Craig Bhuilg	H17	NJ1505	Drumgask	K6	NN6090
Carn na Cairn	M7	NN6580	Craig Leek	K17	NO1590	Drumochter Hills	N6	NN6075
Carn nan Gabhar	O13	NN9570	Craig Meagaidh	L2	NN4085	Drumore Loch	Q17	NO1560
Carn Sgulain	H7	NH4505	Craig Rennet	N19	NO2575	Dubh Ghleann	J15	NO0595
Carrbridge	E12	NH9020	Craigellachie	G11	NH8510	Dubh Loch	I6	NH6000
Castle Grant	C14	NJ0030	Craigendarroch	J21	NO3595	Dubh Loch	S14	NO0050
Cat Law	Q20	NO3060	Craigendinnie	J24	NO5095	Dulicht	D14	NJ0025
Chalamain Gap	H13	NH9505	Craigmore Wood	E14	NJ0020	Dulsie Bridge	A12	NH9040
Chama Choire	N7	NN6575	Crathie	K19	NO2590	Dunachton	I10	NH8000
Chno Dearg	O1	NN3570	Crathie Wood	K5	NN5590	Edzell	P26	NO6065
Ciste Mhearad	I14	NJ0000	Creag a' Chalamain	H13	NH9505	Einich Cairn	J12	NN9095
Clach a' Bhlair	K11	NN8590	Creag an Dail Bheag	J16	NO1095	Ernan Water	G19	NJ2510
Clachan Yell	K22	NO4090	Creag an Diuchd	K15	NO0590	Errochty Water	Q9	NN7560
Clais Fhearnaig	K15	NO0590	Creag Choinnich	K17	NO1590	Ey Burn	L15	NO0585
Clunie	L16	NO1085	Creag Clunie and the Lion's Face	K17	NO1590	Fafernie	M18	NO2080
Cock Bridge	H19	NJ2505	Creag Dhubh	J7	NN6595	Farleitter Crag (Creag Far-leitire)	I10	NH8000
Coilacriech	J20	NO3095	Creag Ealraich	C12	NH9030	Farr	I10	NH8000
Coire an Lochain	I13	NH9500	Creag Far-leitire (Farleitter Crag)	I10	NH8000	Fealar	N14	NO0075

Location	Map reference	OS Reference	Location	Map reference	OS Reference	Location	Map reference	OS Reference
Feindallacher Burn	L18	NO2085	Glen Ey	L15	NO0585	Killiecrankie	Q12	NN9060
Feith Buidhe	I13	NH9500	Glen Fender	P12	NN9065	Kincraig	H10	NH8005
Feshiebridge	I11	NH8500	Glen Feshie	J10	NN8095	Kindrogan	Q15	NO0560
Fiacaill Path	I13	NH9500	Glen Geldie	L13	NN9585	Kingussie	I9	NH7500
Fodderletter	E16	NJ1020	Glen Geusachan	K13	NN9590	Kinloch Rannoch	R7	NN6555
Forbridge Hill	G21	NJ3510	Glen Isla	P17	NO1565	Kinlochlaggan	L4	NN5085
Forest Lodge (Glen Tilt)	O12	NN9070	Glen Lee	M21	NO3580	Kinrara	H11	NH8505
Forest of Birse	K24	NO5090	Glen Lui	K15	NO0590	Kinveachy Forest	F11	NH8515
Gaick	M8	NN7080	Glen Mark	M22	NO4080	Kirkmichael	R15	NO0555
Gaick Forest	M8	NN7080	Glen Prosen	P20	NO3065	Kirkton of Glenbuchat	F21	NJ3515
Gairn	J21	NO3595	Glen Quoich	K15	NO0590	Kirkton of Glenisla	Q18	NO2060
Gairnshiel	I19	NJ2500	Glen Shee	P16	NO1065	Kirriemuir	S21	NO3550
Gairnshiel Bridge	I19	NJ2500	Glen Tanar	K23	NO4590	Knockandhu	E18	NJ2020
Garbh Choire	J13	NN9595	Glen Tilt	N13	NN9575	Kymah Burn	E19	NJ2520
Garbh Uisge Mor	I13	NH9500	Glen Tromie	J9	NN7595	Ladder Hills	F19	NJ2515
Garva Bridge	K4	NN5090	Glen Truim	L7	NN6585	Laggan	K6	NN6090
Geal Charn	O3	NN4570	Glencarvie	H20	NJ3005	Lairig an Laoigh	I14	NJ0000
Geal Charn	M4	NN5080	Glenfiddich	A20	NJ3040	Lairig Ghru	I13	NH9500
Geal Charn	J5	NN5595	Glenlivet	D17	NJ1525	Lechd	G18	NJ2010
Geal-charn Mòr	N5	NN5575	Glenmore	H13	NH9505	Lecht Mine	F18	NJ2015
Geldie Burn	L13	NN9585	Glenmullie	F17	NJ1515	Leslie	E25	NJ5520
Gilbert's Bridge	O11	NN8570	Glenogil	Q22	NO4060	Linn of Dee	L15	NO0585
Girnock Burn	K20	NO3090	Grantown-on-Spey	D14	NJ0025	Linn of Muick	L20	NO3085
Glas Maol	N17	NO1575	Green Hill of Strathdon	G20	NJ3010	Lion's Face	K17	NO1590
Glas Tulaichean	N15	NO0575	Hill of Dalnapot	B17	NJ1535	Loch an Duin	N8	NN7075
Gleann Beag	O16	NO1070	Inchrory	H17	NJ1505	Loch an Eilein	H11	NH8505
Gleann Einich	I12	NH9000	Insh Marshes	I10	NH8000	Loch an t-Seilich	I12	NH9000
Glen Avon	H16	NJ1005	Inshriach	I10	NH8000	Loch an t-Seilich	L9	NN7585
Glen Banchor	J7	NN6595	Inver	K18	NO2090	Loch Avon	I14	NJ0000
Glen Beg	D14	NJ0025	Inveravon	B17	NJ1535	Loch Brandy	N20	NO3075
Glen Bruar	P10	NN8065	Invercauld Bridge	K17	NO1590	Loch Builg	I17	NJ1500
Glen Buchat	F21	NJ3515	Inverdruie	G12	NH9010	Loch Callater	M17	NO1580
Glen Builg	H17	NJ1505	Invereshie	I10	NH8000	Loch Con	P7	NN6565
Glen Clova	P21	NO3565	Inverey	L15	NO0585	Loch Crunachdan	K4	NN5090
Glen Clunie	L16	NO1085	Inverey Flats	L15	NO0585	Loch Cuaich	L7	NN6585
Glen Derry	J14	NO0095	Inverey Wood	L15	NO0585	Loch Davan	I22	NJ4000
Glen Doll	N19	NO2575	Inverton	J8	NN7095	Loch Einich	J12	NN9095
Glen Dye	M26	NO6080	Invervack Meadow	Q12	NN9060	Loch Ericht	O5	NN5570
Glen Effock	N22	NO4075	Juanjorge	N19	NO2575	Loch Errochty	P7	NN6565
Glen Esk	N23	NO4575	Kildrummy	F23	NJ4515	Loch Etchachan	I14	NJ0000

Location	Map reference	OS Reference	Location	Map reference	OS Reference	Location	Map reference	OS Reference
Loch Etteridge	K7	NN6590	Meall Odhar Mòr	M7	NN6580	River Eidart	K12	NN9090
Loch Gamhna	H11	NH8505	Meall Reamhar	Q9	NN7560	River Einich	I12	NH9000
Loch Garry	O6	NN6070	Meikle Kilrannoch	N18	NO2075	River Gairn	I19	NJ2500
Loch Garten	F13	NH9515	Moidach More	A14	NJ0040	River Garry	P8	NN7065
Loch Insh	I10	NH8000	Mòine Mhór	J11	NN8595	River Isla	P17	NO1565
Loch Kander	M17	NO1580	Monadh Mor	K12	NN9090	River Livet	D18	NJ2025
Loch Kinord	J22	NO4095	Monadhliath	H5	NH5505	River Mashie	K5	NN5590
Loch Lee	N22	NO4075	Morinsh Wood	D18	NJ2025	River Nethy	F14	NJ0015
Loch Loch	O13	NN9570	Morrone	K16	NO1090	River North Esk	O25	NO5570
Loch Mallachie	F13	NH9515	Morven	I21	NJ3500	River Pattack	M4	NN5080
Loch Moraig	P12	NN9065	Mount Battock	M24	NO5080	River South Esk	O20	NO3070
Loch Morlich	H13	NH9505	Mount Keen	L22	NO4085	River Tilt	P11	NN8565
Loch Muick	M19	NO2580	Muckle Fergie Burn	G17	NJ1510	River Tromie	J9	NN7595
Loch nan Eun	N15	NO0575	Muir of Dinnet	J22	NO4095	River Truim	K7	NN6590
Loch of Kinnordy	S21	NO3550	Mullach Clach a' Bhlair	K11	NN8590	Rothiemurchus	H12	NH9005
Loch of Lintrathen	S19	NO2550	Mullachdubh	H21	NJ3505	Ruthven Barracks	J9	NN7595
Loch Ossian	P1	NN3565	Nethy Bridge	E14	NJ0020	Rynettin	G14	NJ0010
Loch Pityoulish	G12	NH9010	New Kinord	J22	NO4095	Schiehallion	S8	NN7050
Loch Rannoch	R6	NN6055	Newtonmore	J8	NN7095	Sgairneach Mhor	O5	NN5570
Loch Tarff	H2	NH4005	North Rothiemurchus Pinewood	G13	NH9510	Sgor an Lochain Uaine	J13	NN9595
Loch Tummel	R10	NN8055	Northern Corries	I13	NH9500	Sgor Gaibhre	P2	NN4065
Loch Vaa	F12	NH9015	Old Struan	P10	NN8065	Sgor Gaoith	J12	NN9095
Loch Vrotachan	N16	NO1075	Pannanich Hill	K21	NO3590	Shannel	J26	NO6095
Lochan na Leathain	Q10	NN8060	Pass of Killiecrankie	Q12	NN9060	Skye of Curr	E13	NH9520
Lochindorb	B13	NH9535	Pass of Ryvoan	G14	NJ0010	Slochd Beag	K10	NN8090
Lochnagar	L18	NO2085	Pitlochry Dam	R12	NN9055	Sluggan	E11	NH8520
Logie Coldstone	I22	NJ4000	Pollagach Burn	K22	NO4090	Sow of Atholl	O6	NN6070
Lower Strathavon Woods	D17	NJ1525	Pools of Dee	I13	NH9500	Spey Dam	K5	NN5590
Lui Bridge	K14	NO0090	Prosen Water	Q20	NO3060	Speybank	H10	NH8005
Lui Flats	K14	NO0090	Quithel Wood	J25	NO5595	Spittal of Glenshee	P16	NO1065
Luibeg	K14	NO0090	Quoich Bridge	K16	NO1090	Sron Bhuirich	J2	NN4095
Luibeg Burn	K14	NO0090	Quoich Water	K16	NO1090	Stob Coire Sgriodain	O1	NN3570
Lumsden	E23	NJ4520	Quoich Water Fan	K16	NO1090	Stob Poite Coire Ardair	L2	NN4085
Lutharn Mhor	N14	NO0075	Raitts Burn	I9	NH7500	Straloch Moraines	Q14	NO0060
Lynchat	I9	NH7500	Red Craig	N19	NO2575	Strath Nethy	H14	NJ0005
Mar Estate Pinewoods	K15	NO0590	River Ailnack	G16	NJ1010	Strathavon Woods	C17	NJ1530
Mayar	O18	NO2070	River Avon	H16	NJ1005	Strathdon	G21	NJ3510
Meall Chuaich	L8	NN7085	River Calder	J7	NN6595	Struan	P10	NN8065
Meall Dail-chealach	P8	NN7065	River Deveron	E21	NJ3520	Struan Wood	P10	NN8065
Meall Gruaim	P11	NN8565	River Dulnain	E13	NH9520	Tarland	I23	NJ4500

Location	Map reference	OS Reference
The Bruach	H16	NJ1005
The Burn	O25	NO5570
The Ca	H19	NJ2505
The Cairnwell	N16	NO1075
The Maim	J19	NO2595
Tillypronie	H22	NJ4005
Tolmount	N18	NO2075
Tom Breac	J18	NO2095
Tom Buidhe	N18	NO2075
Tomintoul	F17	NJ1515
Tomnagowhan (Tom a' ghobhainn)	F13	NH9515
Tomvaich	C15	NJ0530
Towanreef	E23	NJ4520
Tulach Hill	Q11	NN8560
Tulloch	F13	NH9515
Uath Lochan	I10	NH8000
Water of Ailnack	G16	NJ1010
Water of Buchat	F21	NJ3515
Water of Caiplich	G15	NJ0510
Water of Feugh	K25	NO5590
Water of Mark	M20	NO3080
Water of Nochty	F20	NJ3015
Water of Saughs	O22	NO4070
Water of Unich	N21	NO3575
West Water	O24	NO5070
White Mounth	M18	NO2080

SUBJECT INDEX

Note: Page numbers in *italics* indicate captions to illustrations and maps; there are frequently textual references on the same page. Page numbers in **bold** indicate chapters. Specific names of flora and fauna can be found in the *Species Index*

SPECIES INDEX

Note
1 *Italicised* page numbers indicate captions to illustrations. There may also be textual references on these pages.
2. Footnotes are indicated by *n*
3. *Passim* indicates non-continuous references on consecutive pages.